NATIONAL GEOGRAPHIC SOCIETY
Research Reports

Adult male and female rhesus monkeys, Abraham and Deborah, at Pashupati, Kathmandu (see p. 619). Photograph courtesy of Jane Teas.

NATIONAL GEOGRAPHIC SOCIETY

Research Reports

VOLUME 14

On research and exploration projects
supported by the National Geographic Society,
the initial grant for which
was made in the year

1973

Compiled and edited by
Paul H. Oehser, John S. Lea, and Nancy Link Powars
under the direction of the
Committee for Research and Exploration

NATIONAL GEOGRAPHIC SOCIETY

WASHINGTON, D. C.

Statement by the Chairman

The National Geographic Society was founded in 1888 by a group, composed largely of Washington scientists, to increase and diffuse geographic
knowledge and to promote research and exploration. The Society's activities
toward achieving its second objective date from 1890, when the society sponsored a geographic and geologic expedition to study the Mount St. Elias
Range of Alaska. Since then it has made more than 2,350 grants in support of
approximately 1,800 projects in research and exploration. The work has encompassed the broad scope of geography, including such scientific disciplines
as geology, paleontology, astronomy, geophysics, oceanography, biology, anthropology, archeology, ethnology, and geographic exploration. The research
program has increased as the Society has grown, until today the budget of the
Society provides $2,500,000 annually in support of the program.

To assist in the task of selecting from among the hundreds of applicants
those best qualified to continue the high standards of accomplishment set by
recipients of grants during the past nine decades, the Society has assembled
the panel of distinguished scientists and scholars listed above.

This is the fourteenth in a series of volumes presenting summary reports
on the results of all the research and exploration projects sponsored by the Society since it was established. These are being published volume by volume, as
rapidly as the material can be assembled. The present volume contains 84 ac-

v

counts covering work for which the initial grant was made in 1973. In instances when a continuing research program has been supported by grants over a number of years, and a breakdown of results by year is impracticable, it has seemed best to report on the subsequent grants in one résumé, with cross references to the main account inserted in other volumes as appropriate. The volumes now in print, and the grant years covered in them, are listed in the Editor's Note that follows.

In presenting the reports, no attempt has been made to standardize the style and specific approach of the investigator, other than to confine each account to reasonable space limitations. In many cases fuller but scattered reports on the work have been, or will be, published elsewhere—in technical and scientific journals, occasionally in the *National Geographic,* or in book form. Published accounts emanating from the research projects are included in the literature references, which each author has been encouraged to supply.

Although the editors of these Reports make every reasonable effort to obtain a timely report from every grantee, so that the results of all projects supported in a given year will be accounted for in one volume, circumstances occasionally interfere. In these instances the delayed report will be published in a later volume. Grantees generally have been most cooperative in this publication project: the Committee for Research and Exploration takes this opportunity to thank them for their support, and we solicit their continued help.

Experience with the preceding volumes of this series has convinced us that the presentation of research findings as given in these books is of significant value to the scientific community. Scholars the world over find this record of the accumulating results of National Geographic Society research grants of real assistance in their own investigations and in the preparation of scientific publications. The general reader also gains new and important knowledge about the current state of research related to geography from each of these volumes.

MELVIN M. PAYNE

Editor's Note

The accounts in this volume are arranged alphabetically under the name of the principal investigator, who is not necessarily the senior author named in the Contents (p. xi). A full list of the 1973 grants on which these are based is to be found in the Appendix (p. 511) of *National Geographic Society Research Reports*, vol. 9 *(1968 Projects)*, published in 1976.

The following accounts published in *National Geographic Society Research Reports*, vol. 11 *(1970 Projects)*, vol. 12 *(1971 Projects)*, and vol. 13 *(1971 and 1972 Projects)* deal with research that continued into 1973 and was supported by grants in that year. Since these accounts cover this 1973 research, no further treatment of it is required here.

"Prehistoric and Historic Settlement Patterns in Western Cyprus," by *J. M. Adovasio, G. F. Fry, J. D. Gunn,* and *R. F. Maslowski,* vol. 13, pp. 53-67.

"Studies of Pre-Columbian American Diseases, 1971-1976," by *Marvin J. Allison,* vol. 12, pp. 1-11.

"The Thermal Significance of the Nest of the Sociable Weaver," by *Fred N. White, George A. Bartholomew,* and *Thomas R. Howell,* vol. 13, pp. 107-115.

"Behavior of Vertebrate Populations on Abandoned Strip-mine Areas," by *Fred J. Brenner,* vol. 12, pp. 67-74.

"Biology of the Franciscana Dolphin *(Pontoporia blainvillei)* in Uruguayan Waters," by *Robert L. Brownell, Jr.,* vol. 13, pp. 129-140.

"Photographic Record in Color of Live Deep-sea Cephalopods," by *P. Noel Dilly,* in vol. 12, pp. 145-147.

"The 'Acropolis' of Aphrodisias in Caria: Investigations and Excavations of the Theater and the Prehistoric Mounds, 1971-1977," by *Kenan T. Erim,* vol. 12, pp. 185-204.

"Mountain Gorilla Research, 1971-1972," by *Dian Fossey,* vol. 12, pp. 237-255.

"Wild Orangutan Studies at Tanjung Puting Reserve, Central Indonesian Borneo, 1971-1977," by *Biruté M. F. Galdikas,* vol. 13, pp. 1-10.

"Papyrus and the Ecology of Lake Naivasha," by *John J. Gaudet,* vol. 12, pp. 267-272.

"Collections, Observations, and Illustrations of the Flora of Tierra del Fuego, 1971-1973," by *Rae Natalie Prosser Goodall,* vol. 12, pp. 275-281.

"Fossil Amphibians and Reptiles of Nebraska and Kansas," by *J. Alan Holman,* vol. 13, pp. 253-262.

"Investigation of Cave Deposits of Quaternary and Holocene Origin: The Muleta Expedition, 1971-1973," by *William H. Waldren,* vol. 12, pp. 731-732.

"Vision and Orientation in Aquatic Animals," by *Talbot H. Waterman,* vol. 11, pp. 547-566.

"National Geographic Society-Cave Research Foundation Salts Cave Archeological Project, 1971-1975," by *Patty Jo Watson,* vol. 11, pp. 567-573.

"The Late-Postglacial Vegetational History of the Argolid Peninsula, Greece," by *Mark C. Sheehan* and *Donald R. Whitehead,* vol. 13, pp. 693-708.

"Expedition to the Center City," by *William H. Whyte,* vol. 13, pp. 709-715.

Reports on the following grants made in 1973 or earlier (as noted) were not available at the time this volume went to press. They will appear in later volumes as they are received.

889:70, 999:71, 1223: To Dr. Gilbert L. Voss, School of Marine and Atmospheric Sciences, University of Miami, Miami, Florida, for a study of biology and distribution of deep sea fauna of the tropical Atlantic.

1159: To Mr. Pedro Galindo, Gorgas Memorial Institute of Preventive Medicine, Inc., for ecological investigations in the canopy of a semideciduous tropical forest.

1182: To Dr. Peter Michael Kranz, The University of Chicago, Chicago, Illinois, for a study of biological destruction of animal hard parts in the marine environment.

1187: To Miss Rosemary Cramp, University of Durham, Durham, England, for an archeological investigation of the seventh-century monastery at Jarrow, England.

1193: To R. J. Englemann, United National Environment Programme, Nairobi, Kenya, in support of Project da Vinci—Trans-America Manned Scientific Balloon Flights.

1224: To Dr. Stuart Struever, Northwestern University, Evanston, Illinois, for testing a model for post-Hopewellian subsistence change.

1255: To Dr. Robert M. King, Catonsville Community College, Catonsville, Maryland, in support of biosystematic studies of South American Asteraceae.

1256: To Dr. Thomas N. Taylor, Ohio State University, Columbus, Ohio, for a study of living and fossil Araucarian cones from Argentina.

1272: To Dr. Paul Leyhausen, Max-Planck Institut für Verhaltensphysiologie, Boettinger, West Germany, for study of the ecology and conservation of the Iriomote cat.

1275: To Dr. Gerald Collier, San Diego State University, San Diego, California, for a study of ecological relations, reproduction, and distribution of the Andalusian hemipode *Turnix sylvatica.*

Libraries and institutions regularly receiving copies of these reports will note that this one bears the volume number 14 and that this practice of numbering is now being used to identify volumes. For their convenience, the earlier ones may be considered to bear numbers (shown in parentheses) as follows:

Vol. No.	Covering grant years	Date Issued
(1)	1890-1954	1975
(2)	1955-1960	1972
(3)	1961-1962	1970
(4)	1963	1968
(5)	1964	1969
(6)	1965	1971
(7)	1966	1973
(8)	1967	1974
(9)	1968	1976
(10)	1969	1978
(11)	1970	1979
12	1971	1980
13	1971, 1972	1981

To aid researchers, the Society's grants made from 1966 onward are listed numerically in the Appendix of *Research Reports* volumes as indicated below:

Grants (year made)		In volume	(project year)
550 - 600	(1966)	(4)	1963
601 - 670	(1967)	(5)	1964
671 - 743	(1968)	(5)	1964
744 - 822	(1969)	(6)	1965
823 - 917	(1970)	(6)	1965
918 - 1036	(1971)	(7)	1966
1037 - 1136	(1972)	(8)	1967
1137 - 1285	(1973)	(9)	1968
1286 - 1421	(1974)	(10)	1969
1422 - 1568	(1975)	(11)	1970
1569 - 1701	(1976)	(11)	1970
1702 - 1844	(1977)	12	(1971)
1845 - 1974	(1978)	12	(1971)
1975 - 2130	(1979)	13	(1971, 1972)
2131 - 2287	(1980)	14	(1973)

Contents

xiv

The Shabakites of Northern Iraq

Principal Investigator: Sami Saïd Ahmed, University of California, Los Angeles, California.

Grant No. 1174: To study the Shabakites, an esoteric ethnic group in northern Iraq.

The Shabakites form a community of about 15,000 inhabiting some 50 villages in the Mosul area in northern Iraq. They were originally Sufis, and their regard for Ali, son of Abi Talib (fourth successor of Prophet Mohammed), led them to extremist ideas. Ali is known to them by such names as the Creator, God, Mohammed, and Justice. Shabakites believe the element of divinity descended from Ali to his wife Fatima, to her two sons, Hasan and Husain, and to nine of the latter's descendants.

Various theories have been advanced on the origin of the Shabakites. Some followers say that they originally came from southern Iran and claim to have distant relatives still living there. However, they do not know when or why this migration occurred. Another theory is that they are remnants of the Turks who came to Iraq with Sultan Tughral in 1055 and lived in villages near. Mosul. However, the language of these Turks was the Azarya dialect of Turkish, very unlike the language of the Shabakites, so this may rule out this hypothesis. The name *Shanbekyyah* (very similar to Shabakyyah or Shabakite) has come down to us as the name of an old Kurdish tribe no longer in existence. Again this theory is difficult to accept because of the dissimilarity of Shabakite and Kurdish languages. Others assert the Shabakites to be Turks of the Black Sheep (Qara Qiunlu) tribe who established the Barani State and ruled from 1411 to 1470, or of the Aq Qiunlu (White Sheep) tribe, founders of the Bandiri State and ruled from 1470 to 1507. Since very little is known of the dialects spoken by these two Turkish tribes, no true conclusions may be drawn. Another postulation is that the Shabakites were Turks who were settled in this region by Sultan Murad IV around 1637. And another view is that they are Turks who settled in their present location during the time of the Safavids and were probably originally followers of the Sufi way of al-Khawajeh Ahmed Ya savi (d. 1166). There is also the possibility the Shabakites migrated from Azarbaijan in northwest Iran from the area around Ardabil in the 17th century during Safavid rule. Their order was probably established by Safyy al-Din (d. ca. 1334), the sixth successor of Shah Ismail, founder of the Safavid Dynasty.

1

The Shabakites are tall, fair-skinned, sometimes bearded and usually mustached. Their mustaches are not to be cut, trimmed, or one hair removed, for such is believed to be committing mortal sin.

They are peace-loving and do not steal, plunder, or cut off highways. Formerly they were persecuted for their extremist views on the sanctity of Ali. All consume wine, even during prayer. They are moderate and live simple, highly conservative lives as farmers and keepers of herds. Rarely is a person of low morals found among them; they refrain from debauchery and corruption; in fact, a corrupt person would not be accepted in their society. They are hospitable and honest, and obviously the Sufi principles attributed to Safyy al-Din have influenced them greatly. Shabakites respect the descendants of Prophet Mohammed (and name children after him) and view the presence of those among them as a blessing.

The percentage of illiteracy is high in Shabakite society but is diminishing as a result of governmental efforts imposing compulsory education. Most are not well acquainted with the precepts of their own faith, and they have no scholars or theologians among them. Many still practice old methods of healing, seek the Pir's blessing, and go to certain holy places for recovery from disease.

The Shabakite tongue is a strange mixture of Persian, Kurdish, Turkish, and Arabic but is mostly inclined toward Turkish. Some words have no relationship with any of these languages or to Aramaic or Assyrian, which are also known in the area. The Shabakites call their language *Bor Abor* or *Shabaki*, meaning "the barbarian" or "entwined tongue."

The majority of names of Shabakite villages have meanings in one of the four languages known in the area (Arabic, Kurdish, Turkish, and Aramaic): For example, Abu Jarbu' (Arabic, father of the jerboa); Orta Kharab (Turkish, the middle ruin); Bashbitha (Aramaic, the plundered village); Barda Resh (Kurdish, village of the black captive); Khorsabad (Kurdish-Persian, city of Khisru).

Shabakite houses ordinarily are one- or two-room huts in a yard surrounded by a wall. Both huts and walls are made of lumps of mud mixed with straw or are of sun-dried bricks. Most yards contain a well near which is usually an L-shaped trough of dried mud for watering animals, and the area is strongly permeated by the smell of animal dung.

Prayer and fasting are part of Shabakite religious practice, but it is estimated that perhaps only one or two followers in every thousand actually perform such duties. Most Shabakites explain this by saying, "We do not pray because Ali was killed while praying, and we do not fast because Ali was killed during Ramadan" (the Muslim month of fasting).

The Shabakites may believe in a trinity consisting of God (Allah), Mohammed, and Ali, for they repeat the letters A *(alef,* the first letter of the word Allah), M (beginning letter of Mohammed's name), and 'ain (the first letter of Ali's name). The last prayer of the initiation rite to the Shabakite order clearly states, "Ali is God and Mohammed." However, it seems they assign to each a separate individuality.

Shabakite practice of prayer differs from that of Muslims. They pray but once a week, on Friday eve (Thursday night). The prayer meeting is held at the home of the Pir (elder); at least 12 persons must be present, and they sit in a circle. The Pir begins the service by reciting passages from their prayerbook, the Gulbang. After this recitation the Rahbar (leader) might quote passages from the same book. Then the Pir asks all present to prostrate themselves as he recites more prayers. During the service all attending must drink wine. Male children may not attend until age 7. When a boy reaches this age his parents take him to the Pir and the boy must kiss his Pir's hands seven times. The Pir then ties a belt of seven folds around the child's waist. Three days later the parents and boy return to the Pir to whom the child now must give 40 dirhams (about 6 dollars) and 40 eggs, which symbolize the substitutes (disciples). The Pir reads sections from the Gulbang to the child now and thereafter he is eligible to attend all religious services.

Shabakite prayers contain their belief in the divinity of Ali, and it seems their fear that this confession may be overheard by Muslims, or that the neighboring Yazidis (a nearby esoteric group revering Satan) might hear them curse Yazid and bring disastrous consequences to the entire community as it did in former times, has led the Shabakites to construct hidden subterranean chambers for worship services. One such place is to be found at the Shrine of Ali Musa al-Rida near Tis Kharab on the road from Mosul to Bashiqa.

The lion's share of a Shabakite's income is given to the Pirs, Rahbars, and to certain inhabitants of their villages thought to be descendants of Ali and Fatima. This latter amount is called the "ancestor's fifth."

To become a pilgrim a Shabakite is required to visit the shrine of Husain, son of Ali, in Karbala, Iraq, seven times. The initiation rite is equated with 30 pilgrimage performances.

Every Shabakite must confess and seek forgiveness for his sins from his Pir. This may explain the great influence of the Pirs on Shabakite society. There is a special Gulbang dealing with confession, and the believer may go to his Pir at any time for confession.

When Shabakites assemble for worship at the Pir's home for Friday-eve prayer, on the Night of Forgiveness and at the New Year gathering, each is required to bring bread, wine, and perhaps also a cock. A butcher is present to slaughter the cocks with a holy knife permanently in his possession, and he is the only person who may perform this task. The cocks are roasted and all present eat the meat with bread and wine amid the sounds of tambourines and the recitation of poetry in singing tones.

Numbers hold special significance in Shabakite meetings and prayers: No. 40 refers to the 40 disciples headed by Ali. Many stories are told of these 40 wherein they are termed "Men of God," "Soldiers of God," and "Men of the Unknown World." No. 14 signifies Prophet Mohammed, his daughter Fatima, and the 12 Imams. No. 12 refers to the 12 Imams. No. 7 is symbolic of the 7 degrees of the Sufi order: *The Associates,* those who are not yet members of the order but who have expressed interest. *The Seekers,* those who have passed a training period of isolation, self-blame, prayer, and fasting; the Seeker is usually a young man who is trained by a Dervish guide in obedience and restraint of all self-desires. *The Dervish,* one who has completed a probation period, served in the small convent, behaved well morally, and is known for his piety, righteousness, and to have deserted all worldly desires. *The Guide,* the Convent Master, grand chief of all the dervishes; he leads the circles of remembrance prayer on Friday eve, at funerals, and the mourning gatherings held during the first 10 days of the first Muslim month (Muharram). *Qalander* (Wanderer), described by the dervishes as one liberated from all life's desires, hopes, bonds, and responsibilities. *Rind* (Sagacious, Sufi), higher than the Qalander but usually known for a reckless and carefree manner, for which he is often criticized, but possessing a pure heart. *The Pole (Qutb),* one who is called "The Star of Wisdom" and whose authority is acknowledged by all members of the order. No. 5 refers to Mohammed, Ali, Fatima, Hasan and Husain, who are known as "people of garments." No. 3 signifies God, Mohammed, and Ali.

Feasts and Holy Days include: *New Year's Eve,* celebrated on the first of December. *March 21,* which Shabakites celebrate as the day Ali ascended to the Caliphate. *Night of Forgiveness,* when quarreling parties meet on this night to mend their differences; special ceremonies are headed by the Pir and his 12 assistants, and this is regarded as one of the most sacred of religious meetings. *Night of Confession,* wherein confession of all sins is made to the Pir. On this occasion the Pir ordinarily recites the Gulbang of confession and sometimes the Rahbar joins him in the singing. This Gulbang is in the form of a dialogue between Pir and confessor.

For enrollment of a new member into the order, and before initiation, every prospective Shabakite must seek out a married couple belonging to the order and enter into friendship with them. The man and his wife must actually dwell with the Shabakite couple for 40 or 70 days to become one. At the end of the assigned period the four go to the Pir taking with them a ram and 40 or more bottles of wine. The Pir then invites 40 Shabakite couples to the ceremony. The initiate arranges for a bull to be slaughtered, the meat of which is distributed to all Shabakites in the village.

During the first 10 days of Muharram corteges of Shabakites assemble to mourn the murder of Husain, son of Ali, which event occurred in Karbala on the 10th of October, 680. Members of the corteges ordinarily dress in black and chant and beat their hands on their chests as they walk. The Pir stands among them shouting expressions of mourning and the assembly responds by repeating his words.

On the eve of and during the day of the 10th of Muharram followers gather at the Shrine of Ali Resh in the Shabakite village of Ali Resh. Those who cannot for some reason be present at this shrine are required to go at that time to the shrine nearest their village.

No official gathering such as the New Year celebration, Night of Forgiveness, etc., can be considered legally valid unless the following 12 "attendants" are present: *The Pir* (Elder, Papa), who is the master (shaikh), or head authority. *The Rahbar* (leader), who assists the Pir in performing religious functions. *The Light Bearer*. *The Butcher,* who is keeper of the holy knife; slaughters cocks at meetings. *The Sweeper Bearer,* who is responsible for sweeping and cleaning the Pir's home in preparation for meetings. *The Water Bearer,* who carries a water jar and a glass among those assembled for meetings. *First Servant,* who receives the bread, wine, and cocks brought to the meetings. *Second Servant,* who removes the covers or containers of the bread and wine. *Third Servant,* who breaks the bread into small pieces. *Fourth Servant,* who returns the empty containers and coverings to the rightful owners. *First Butler,* who guards the door to the Pir's house day and night during ceremonies to examine all who enter in order to ascertain no outsider has infiltrated. *Second Butler,* who stands at the door of the room where the ceremony takes place.

To the Shabakite, his Pir is everything. He performs marriage ceremonies, divorce, blesses newborn infants, reads to them from the Gulbang, and accepts confessions.

When a child is 7 days old he is taken by his parents to the Pir along with bread, wine, and a ram. The butcher slaughters the animal in the presence of the child's family, relatives, and friends. The Pir reads from the Gulbang, prays for the child's good fortune, then all assembled eat, drink, and dance the debka.

Male children are circumcised, but there is no set age when this must take place; it can be performed any time between the ages of one year and 13. It must be done in the presence of the Pir who holds the child on his lap during the operation. The family of the child ordinarily gives a party at their home on this occasion, at which time they distribute food and sing and recite poems accompanied by flutes.

Married people are respected among the Shabakites, but single women have a more difficult role. The unmarried woman usually wears a special shawl (*malfa'*) covering neck and chest. She lives under strict conditions; sometimes she is not permitted to stand in the doorway of the house, talk with men, or joke with other women in public. Married women have all these privileges.

Marriage arrangements are conducted by the girl's father or, if he is deceased, by an elder brother. A young man's parents usually begin looking for a suitable wife for him when he reaches the age of manhood (16-22). The help of the Pir is often sought in selecting the right girl for their son. When the girl is chosen, the suitor's father and a few of his friends who know the girl's father go to her home. If her father consents to the marriage the first important step is completed. However, if the request is refused, the boy might seek assistance from his Pir in convincing the girl's father, and in most cases this intervention by the Pir will gain acceptance of the boy.

After acceptance, the suitor's parents, relatives and friends, led by the Pir, go to the home of the girl, taking with them food for lunch. After the meal candy is distributed and the boy's father gives a sack of money to one of the men present and asks him to count it. The man counts it, informs the boy's father of the exact sum, and hands it back to him. Then the father of the girl receives this dowry money from the boy's father. He recounts the money, takes a good part of it for himself, and returns the remainder to the boy's father. The Pir no doubt takes a share from both sides. The marriage ceremony is conducted by the Pir, and two witnesses are needed for the marriage contract. Following the ceremony there is a similar party but the Pir cannot attend. The wedding party continues for 3 and sometimes 7 days and includes all relatives and friends. Sheep are slaughtered for banquets; there is dancing to drums and flutes, and some amuse themselves with a duel combat game played with long sticks. The length and expense of the party depend upon the status of the groom.

Shabakites are polygamists and may marry as often as they wish, but it seems they will have four or possibly five wives at most. Many, however, have but one wife. The Shabakite who marries a woman descendant of Ali and Fatima must himself be a descendant of Mohammed, as they think it evil for a nondescendant to wed a descendant.

Divorce is difficult under all circumstances in Shabakite society. If a man insists on divorce, his religion requires him to sell all he owns and give eleven-twelfths of the proceeds to the Pir. Then he must journey to the city of Karbala (southwest of Baghdad) accompanied by two witnesses, and there in the courtyard of Husain's Shrine he utters the divorce formula. Upon arrival back at his own village the man must buy 40 bottles of white wine and take his two witnesses and other Shabakite men to the home either of the Pir or the Rahbar. There a fire is lit and allowed to burn to ashes. The one seeking divorce must then stand in the ashes and the Rahbar hangs two stones symbolic of punishment around his neck. The Pir asks the assembly, "Are you satisfied with this slave?" And they respond, "If the notables are satisfied with him, we are also." The Pir replies, "The notables [literally 'reachers'] are men of hospitality." Thus, the divorce is final.

When a Shabakite dies the Pir comes to the home of the deceased and reads passages from the Gulbang over the body and washes and shrouds the corpse for burial. Burial is usually near the village, after which the family of the deceased gives food to the poor. On special occasions such as feast days, the family visits the gravesite and distributes food to the poor as charity for his soul.

Most Shabakite villages contain shrines of men who to the believers have had distinguished careers, either real or legendary. Among these is the shrine of Sultan Abdulla, son of Omar, a person of whom we know nothing, but his tomb is in the village of Manara Shabak. In the same village another shrine marks the spot believed to have been the residence of Ali Ibn Ali Talib. Other shrines include the following: *Shrine of Ali al-Rida at Tis Kharab,* which reportedly is the tomb of Ali al-Rida; however, there is no shadow of doubt that Ali al-Rida died and was buried in Khurasan in northeast Iran and his tomb is still today visited by Shii pilgrims. *Shrine of Abbas,* located in the village of Abbasyyah on the Khosar River near Mosul. Abbas was Ali's son and his actual tomb is in Karbala, but the Shabakites claim it to be here. *Tomb of Hasan al-Firdawsi,* near the village of Darawish in the Mosul vicinity. The tomb attracts visitors every Friday and is especially popular in spring. *Shrine of Ali Resh,* in the village of Ali Resh near Hamdanyyah not far from Mosul. This is the most important Shabakite shrine. Ali Resh (Ali the Black), according to Shabakite belief, is Ali Zain al-Abidin, son of Husain, whose actual tomb is in Medina, Saudi Arabia.

The Shabakite holy book of scriptures is the Buyruq (sometimes called the Burkh). It is written in the form of a dialogue between Shaikh Sadr al-Din and Shaikh Safyy al-Din (d. 1334) on the principles of the order. The Buyruq contains a description of the way of life to be followed by the guide and seekers, the meaning of prostration, the seeker's obedience, his submission, the degrees of saints and traits of saints, avoidance of enemies of the order, secrecy of the sect, the manner in which the seeker should administer the affairs of his family, necessity of trusteeship, stipulations of the Caliphate, its meaning, and the appointment of Ali by Prophet Mohammed as his executor. It is difficult to say who actually wrote the Buyruq; perhaps it was Shaikh Sadr al-Din or Shaikh Safyy al-Din.

The Shabakite prayerbook is called the Gulbang (Sound of the Rose) and is a collection of prayers to be recited on prescribed occasions.

Many Shabakites do not know (or possibly pretend ignorance) of the names of their holy scriptures. In their shrines one sees books describing and eulogizing the battle of Karbala, the miracles and narratives of Ali and Husain and some of their descendants.

SAMI SAÏD AHMED

Corpus of the Mosaics of Tunisia: Thuburbo Majus, 1974-1976

Principal Investigator: Margaret A. Alexander, Department of Classics, University of Iowa, Iowa City, Iowa.

Grant Nos. 1238   In support of a *Corpus* of the ancient mosaics of Tunisia.
and 1570.

In 1974 the Tunisian–American team of the Corpus of the Mosaics of Tunisia (CMT) began research at Thuburbo Majus, a Roman site about 75 kilometers south of Carthage. Fieldwork, financed in part by National Geographic grants 1238 and 1570,[1] was finished in 1976; the preparation of the four fascicles of the *Corpus* continues.

The project is part of an international endeavor, instigated in 1963 by AIEMA (Association Internationale pour l'Etude des Mosaïques Antiques), to publish all the mosaics of the Roman world. Mosaics are important in themselves and as integral parts of buildings. They are the richest documentation we have for the history of Roman painting. By virtue of their subject matter, inscriptions, and materials, they provide a great deal of information on social, intellectual, religious, and economic history. Yet in many countries once part of the Roman Empire, much of the basic data are still not readily available.

For Tunisia, the only general catalogue was published by Gauckler and Merlin in 1910, with a supplement in 1915. Since then hundreds of mosaics have been found and though the literature is growing it consists mainly of articles and a few books on individual sites or monuments (Ennaïfer, 1976; Charles-Picard, 1977; and Mahjoubi, 1978). Aware of the need for an up-to-date corpus, the Institut National d'Archéologie et d'Art (INAA) readily agreed in 1969 to a collaborative project sponsored also by the American Academy in Rome, the Dumbarton Oaks Center for Byzantine Studies in Washington, the University of Iowa, and the Institute of Fine Arts, New York University. The project is co-directed by Dr. Margaret A. Alexander, Department of Classics, University of Iowa, and Dr. Mongi Ennaïfer, Conservator, Musée du Bardo, and Secretary-General of the Commission for Mu-

---

[1] Major funding was provided by the Foreign Currency Program of the Smithsonian Institution, supplemented by grants from the National Endowment for the Humanities, Dumbarton Oaks, and the University of Iowa.

seums, Tunis. Professors Frank E. Brown of the American Academy, Ernst Kitzinger of Harvard University, and Irving Lavin of the Institute for Advanced Study, Princeton, serve as the American Steering Committee.

The project is organized by geographical regions as established in the *Atlas Archéologique de la Tunisie* (1893-1913). Our first site was Utica (1969-71); the results were published in 1974-76 as volume I of the *Corpus*. The second site was El Jem (1972-73); publication is momentarily postponed.

Thuburbo Majus is the third and largest site undertaken by the CMT. Originally it covered about 40 hectares, approximately a fifth of which was excavated by the French Direction des Antiquités (1912-37) under Alfred Merlin and his successor Louis Poinssot.[2] Sporadic digging continued into the 1950's, when the amphitheater was discovered, then ceased altogether. Many of the buildings and most of the mosaics are unpublished. We are indebted to M. Azzedine Beschaouch, director, and to the Commission for Research of INAA for permission to work at Thuburbo and to publish the results.

The general layout of the city is clear (fig. 1). See also Lezine, 1968. The civic center to the NW comprises the Forum (F) and Capitolium (T1) around which are grouped the Temple of Mercury (T2), the Market (Ma1-3) and adjacent Baths of the Labyrinth (Th1), exedrae (Ex1-6), the Curia (Cu), and a few houses (fig. 2). To the SE, sprawling over a sizable residential quarter, are the Summer and Winter Baths (Th3 and 4), the Peristyle of the Petronii (Pe), and the Temples of Caelestis (T4) and Baalat (T5). In the largely unexcavated area beyond are the Temple of the Cereres (T6), later converted into a church, and the Temple of Saturn (T9), the amphitheater (A), and reservoir (R). The essentially residential sectors to NW, NE, and SW include a few temples (T3,7,8,10), two small baths (Th2 and 5), oil presses, dyeing establishments, and shops.

For purposes of the fieldwork, we divided the site into three areas, each corresponding to a season's campaign. Area I comprises the region around the Forum and the blocks immediately NW and SW. Area II covers the zone of the Great Thermae and the Temple-Church. These two areas constitute Fascicles 1 and 2, respectively. Area III was divided into two parts. Area IIIb, comprising the houses to the SW of the Summer Baths and near the W gate (Po3), will be published in Fascicle 3. Area IIIa, NE of the Forum and including the East Temple (T8), will form part of Fascicle 4.

---

[2] Reports in Bulletin archéologique du Comité des Travaux historiques et scientifiques and Comptes Rendus de l'Académie des Inscriptions et Belles Lettres. See also Drappier, 1920, and Merlin, 1922.

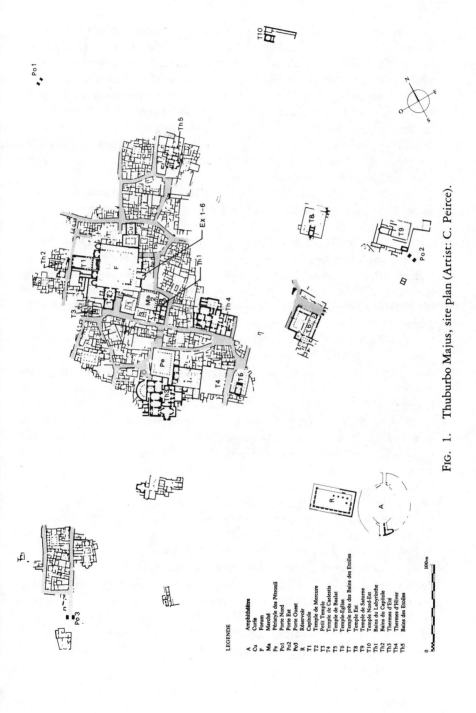

FIG. 1.   Thuburbo Majus, site plan (Artist: C. Peirce).

LEGENDE

A	Amphithéâtre
Cu	Curie
F	Forum
Ma	Marché
Pe	Péristyle des Pétronii
Po1	Porte Nord
Po2	Porte Est
Po3	Porte Ouest
R	Réservoir
T1	Capitole
T2	Temple de Mercure
T3	Petit Temple
T4	Temple de Caelestis
T5	Temple de Baalat
T6	Temple-Eglise
T7	Temple près des Bains des Etoiles
T8	Temple Est
T9	Temple de Saturne
T10	Temple Nord-Est
Th1	Bains du Labyrinthe
Th2	Bains du Capitole
Th3	Thermes d'Eté
Th4	Thermes d'Hiver
Th5	Bains des Etoiles

0   100m

The fieldwork consists of three major activities which reflect the purpose of the project: To publish a definitive catalogue of the mosaics and to present them in their archeological and architectural contexts. Documentation of the mosaics was directed by Dr. Alexander and by the American assistant director, Dr. Marie Spiro, University of Maryland. The initial recording was done by American and Tunisian students, Mme. Saïda Besrour-Ben Mansour, and Dr. Spiro. The information, recorded on special forms devised by the CMT to insure completeness and consistency, includes all technical data (dimensions, materials, foundations, condition), relationship of mosaics to each other and to the architecture, and detailed descriptions.

Technical studies have confirmed that the mosaics and sectile floors are made of local stone. The limestone and sub-marble used for most of the tesserae, as well as the variegated marble and travertine of the sectile pavements, came from nearby Jbel Klab, Jbel Rouass, Jbel Azeiz, and Jbel Oust; the ancient quarries are still visible. With sources of good stone of a wide color range close at hand, the mosaicists of Thuburbo did not need to bring the colorful Numidian marble from far-off Chemtou for special effects and for the nuances of figural representation. Only the white marble, used in many of the backgrounds, seems to have been imported.

The classification of colors of stone is difficult. The Munsell color system, even as adapted for geological purposes, proving unsatisfactory, we made our own cards using actual tesserae. In order to standardize and simplify the recording, each card contains the accepted range to which a single color designation is given. A complete chart will be assembled for publication in Fascicle 4.

The study of the composition of foundations has led to few conclusions. Types of foundations seem to be remarkably consistent over rather long periods of time; slight variations may be simply the result of a different day's pour. Marked differences in a single floor, however, are useful in pinpointing later additions or repairs.

On completion of the fieldwork, the mosaic records are revised in catalogue form, comparisons are made with similar mosaics in Thuburbo and elsewhere in Tunisia, and dates are proposed, based on all our various researches. In describing the geometric compositions and motifs, we adopted the terminology proposed by the Association Internationale pour l'Etude des Mosaïques Antiques (AIEMA, 1973). Since a similar repertoire does not exist for floral motifs, we are compiling our own. Tables of basic compositions and foliate designs will be published in Fascicle 4. Of approximately 350 mosaics recorded at Thuburbo, most are geometric and floral. Only about 6 percent contain figural compositions or representations of fauna or inanimate objects. Marble

FIG. 2.   Area I, balloon photo (Photographer: W. A. Graham).

floors are limited to temples, the Forum exedrae, and the Curia, and to the dining-room of the House of Neptune (fig. 3).

Archeological investigations were conducted by the American field director, Dr. David Soren, University of Missouri, Columbia, in collaboration

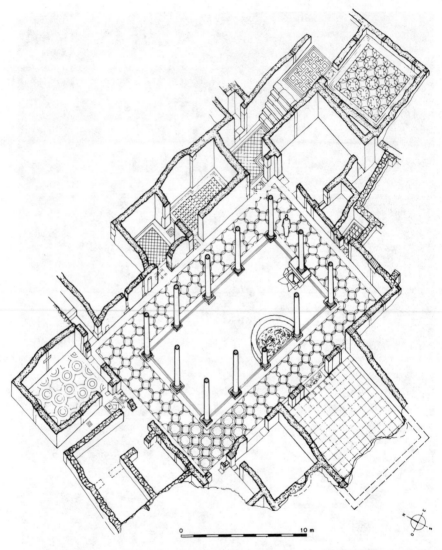

FIG. 3.   House of Neptune, axonometric plan (Artist: S. Gibson).

with Dr. Aïcha Ben Abed, INAA, and with the help of American and Tunisian students. Professor Brown served as advisor and consultant. The archeological data are particularly important, since few of the objects from the French excavations are published, and we have been unable to consult existing archives.

While ours is not a full-fledged excavation, our methods and procedures conform to standard archeological practice. The work is confined primarily to soundings related directly to existing mosaics, in order to study the foundations, establish stratigraphical sequences, and secure datable finds. Additional soundings were sometimes made if they might clarify the structural development of a building and thus establish more precisely the context and relative chronology of its pavements. One of the most revealing soundings was that in the annex of the Market basilica (fig. 4) where four floor levels were uncovered (the fragments of cocciopesto are not visible in the photograph), dating from at least the 2nd-5th centuries. Careful probing of the foundations frequently revealed a quantity of tesserae, even fragments of mosaics, often the only evidence of earlier pavements.

Soundings were made in some 30 structures, producing a wide variety of objects—fragments of pottery, lamps and frescos, bits of glass, metal and bone, an occasional piece of a figurine, and coins. They were cleaned, catalogued, and drawn by Ms. Noelle Soren. Fragments of vessels and lamps were the most common finds. The earliest, including also two nearly intact pots, are of Punic date. A few lamp fragments and sherds of African A ware of the early 1st century A.D. were found in Area I. A quantity of African Red Slip ware and common ware sherds, datable to the late 1st-early 2nd centuries, turned up all through the site. Most date from late 2nd to early 3rd centuries. Some sherds, particularly from certain houses in Area IIIb, near the Winter Baths, and from the fill for the top level mosaic in the Market basilica, date to the 4th and to the end of the 5th-early 6th centuries. In Areas I and IIIb sherds of the early 7th century were found in the surface fill. Dr. Soren has made a general study of the pottery which we hope will be published. The sherds from four houses in Area IIIb were analyzed by Dr. Ben Abed; the results are included in her dissertation for the University of Aix-en-Provence.

Several legible coins of the 2nd-5th centuries, but also including a Punic one, were recovered in or beneath floor foundations or imbedded in walls. Like the sherds, they provide a *terminus post quem* for the mosaics and for certain structural changes.

Architectural studies, under the supervision of Dr. Brown, have permitted us to identify some buildings. The so-called portico (Ma3) of the Market was recognized as a two-story basilica. The building beside it (Th2), described by the excavators as a house with rooms for bathing, was identified as a small bath. Combined archeological, architectural, and mosaic studies have established a general structural history for many edifices. The buildings were surveyed and plans drawn by one or more of the architects Charles Peirce, Sheila Gibson, Judith Saltzman, and Richard Trimble. One set of plans shows the buildings in their present state, with areas of existing mosaics indicated in a uniform grey; the other presents simplified plans in which the basic decorative scheme of each mosaic is reconstituted. The site was surveyed and a detailed plan (fig. 1) drawn by Mr. Peirce.

During the course of our work, a couple of devices were invented to solve particular practical problems. Mr. Peirce constructed a plane table, a simple mechanical alidade using a tape for direct measuring of distance. It permits surveying at distances up to 20 meters at a speed of 25 points per hour with an accuracy of plus or minus 2 centimeters. Photographer William A. Graham devised a monopod for photographing mosaics in situ, including those of considerable extent, without distortions or shadows (see fig. 4). It can also be adapted for photographing mosaics high on the walls of museums (see fig. 5).

The results of our researches can be summarized in an accounting of some of the contributions they have made to the history of Thuburbo and its mosaics (Merlin, 1933; Maurin, 1967). That there was a Punic settlement was already known, but the finding of a Punic kiln, along with common ware sherds of the 3rd-2nd centuries B.C., near the W gate considerably extends its limits. Evidence for 1st century A.D. habitation, rarely noted, was discovered in Area I in the form of shaved-down walls and floors of cocciopesto, lime and sand, and terrazzo. Most existing monuments and mosaics date from the period of great urban expansion under the Antonines and Severans. Among the earliest are the baths (Th2) behind the Capitolium. The few sherds unearthed beneath the mosaic in the apodyterium are dated 150-250, but the black and white geometric mosaics, of a type common in the 1st-early 2nd centuries, help to fix the date in the second half of the 2nd century. Of about the same period is the simple geometric mosaic in the lowest visible level of the sounding in the Market basilica (fig. 4). The mosaic immediately above it has a rich polychrome geometric and floral design typical of those of the Severan epoch at Thuburbo Majus. It paved the original annex of the basilica which was part of a grand building scheme for the Forum starting with the dedication of the Capitolium in 168 and ending with that of the Temple of Mercury in 211.

The buildings and mosaics which can be assigned to the first half of the 3rd century are too numerous to mention. They include the Summer and Winter Baths, most of the temples, and a majority of the houses. For most of these structures, and for several previously excavated but not published, we have been able to provide considerable information on building and mosaic phases and to provide quite secure dates for many of the mosaics. The elaborateness of the mosaic decoration can be surmised from the multiplicity of designs shown in the axonometric plan of the House of Neptune in Area I (fig. 3).

FIG. 4.   Market basilica annex, sounding (Photographer: W. A. Graham).

FIG. 5.   Baths of the Labyrinth, Theseus and the Minotaur (Photographer: W. A. Graham).

During the troubled second half of the 3rd-early 4th centuries, few monuments were erected. The *area sacra* of a small temple (T3) was paved; sherds found in a sounding date from the 2nd to the end of the 3rd century. On the basis of style we can propose a similar date for two figural mosaics coming from the Baths of the Labyrinth, including that (fig. 5) which gave its name to the structure.

Fig. 6. House of Nicentius, dining-room mosaic (Photographer: W. A. Graham).

In the 4th century, the city witnessed a certain revival and a changing economy evidenced in the establishment of small industries such as oil mills and dyeing establishments. Some houses were partially repaved, as for example a house on the E corner of the Forum. It was built and paved in the late 2nd century; a lamp fragment dating to the end of the 2nd-early 3rd centuries was found under one of the delicate floral mosaics. Later the peristyle and dining-room (fig. 6) were repaved in the heavy style characteristic of the first half of the 4th century, a date confirmed by sherds. The mosaics came from the workshop of Nicentius, as an inscription in the doorway proudly asserts. New houses were constructed, particularly in Area IIIb, with trifolia and paved with figural mosaics (fig. 7) which, judging from objects found in the soundings, must date to the mid-4th century.

FIG. 7. House of the Protomes, mosaic of the protomes (Photographer: W. A. Graham).

Renovations to the Summer and Winter Baths are documented by two precisely dated inscriptions of the end 4th-beginning 5th centuries. We have recognized some, including several new pavements. Partial reconstruction of a house near the Capitolium, using large ashlar blocks probably taken from that temple, can now be dated to the 5th century on the basis of a sherd found in

FIG. 8.   House of the Crater, apse mosaic (Photographer: W. A. Graham).

the nucleus of the mosaic (fig. 8), perhaps Christian, which paved the apse built into one of the rooms. A bit later, judging from sherds and Vandal coins dating from 428 to 484, the annex of the Market basilica was rebuilt in apsidal form and paved with a black and white mosaic (fig. 4, top level).

The only structure datable to the 6th century is the church built into the Temple of the Cereres (Duval, 1971); fragments of the pavement and parts of two tomb mosaics survive. But the quantity of 6th-century sherds found on the surface, particularly in the NE and SW sectors, attest to the continued life of the city. That it survived into the 7th century is evidenced in a horde of gold coins of the time of Heraclius found several years ago near the Forum. Thuburbo was abandoned soon after; none of the sherds pulled from the accumulated debris in the ruins dates later than the mid-7th century.

The full documentation of the researches summarized above will be published in Volume II of the *Corpus*. Fascicle 1, by A. Ben Abed and M. Alexander with S. Ben Mansour and D. Soren, is in press. Fascicle 2, by M. Spiro, A. Ben Abed, M. Ennaïfer, and D. Soren, and Fascicle 3, by A. Ben Abed, will be published in 1982-83. Fascicle 4, by M. Alexander, A. Ben Abed, and M. Spiro, will be published in 1984. It also includes a catalogue of the mosaics from Thuburbo, now in the Musée du Bardo, whose original context cannot be determined, as well as the few mosaics coming from the region. It contains an essay on the typological and stylistic development of the mosaics and their place in the broader context of Tunisian mosaics. It concludes with various tables, concordances, and analytical indices.

REFERENCES

ASSOCIATION INTERNATIONAL POUR L'ETUDE DES MOSAÏQUES ANTIQUES (AIEMA)
  1973.   Répertoire graphique du décor géométrique dans la mosaïque antique. Bulletin, fasc. 4, Paris.
CHARLES-PICARD, GILBERT
  1977.   Recherches archéologiques franco-tunisiennes à Mactar, I, La maison de Vénus.   Paris and Rome, Ecole Française de Rome.
DRAPPIER, LOUIS
  1920.   Les thermes de Thuburbo Majus.   Bulletin archéologique du Comité des Travaux historique et scientifique, pp. 55-75.
DUVAL, NOEL
  1971.   Le temple à cour de Thuburbo Majus, dit "Temple des Cereres," et son église.   Bulletin archéologique du Comité des Travaux historique et scientifique, n.s., vol. 7, pp. 277-290.
ENNAIFER, MONGI
  1976.   La cité d'Althiburos et l'édifice des Asclepieia.   Tunis, Institut National d'Archéologie et d'Art.
GAUCKLER, PAUL, and MERLIN, ALFRED
  1910.   Inventaire des mosaïques de la Gaule et de l'Afrique, II, Afrique Proconsulaire.   Paris, Académie des Inscriptions et Belles Lettres.   Supplement published in 1915.
LEZINE, ALEXANDRE
  1968.   Thuburbo Majus.   Tunis, Société Tunisienne de Diffusion.
MAHJOUBI, AMOR
  1978.   Recherches d'histoire et d'archéologie à Henchir el-Faouar (Tunisie).   Tunis, Université de Tunis.
MAURIN, LOUIS
  1967.   Thuburbo Majus et la paix vandale.   Cahiers de Tunisie, pp. 225-254.
MERLIN, ALFRED
  1922.   Le Forum de Thuburbo Majus, Tunis.   Tunis, Direction des Antiquités et Arts.
  1933.   L'histoire municipale de Thuburbo Majus.   Ve Congrès international d'Archéologie, Alger, pp. 205-225.

MARGARET A. ALEXANDER

The Amino Acid Dating of African Fossil Bones

Principal Investigator: Jeffrey L. Bada, Scripps Institution of Oceanography, University of California, San Diego, La Jolla, California

Grant Nos. 1175 and 1929.   In support of a study of amino acids and their use in dating African fossils.

During the past several years, a new method of dating fossil materials, called amino acid racemization dating, has been developed (see Masters and Bada, 1978, for review). This geochronological technique is the first to use an organic reaction. The amino acid dating method is based on the fact that all of the amino acids commonly found in protein, with the exception of glycine, can exist in two different isomeric forms, which are called the D and L isomers. The chemical and physical properties of these isomers are identical, with the exception that they rotate plane polarized light in equal but opposite directions.

Over 120 years ago Pasteur demonstrated that the amino acids present in the proteins of living organisms consist of only the L isomers. This is especially true in higher organisms. However, under chemical equilibrium conditions, both D- and L-amino acids are present in exactly equal abundance. A living organism thus maintains a state of disequilibrium; this is accomplished by using enzymes that can utilize only L-amino acids. After an organism dies, the biochemical reactions that maintain the disequilibrium state cease and a process called racemization begins. In the racemization process, the L-amino acids are reversibly converted into the corresponding D-amino acids and this reaction continues to take place until there are equal amounts of the D and L isomers present in the system. Racemization was first found to occur in strong acidic and basic solutions nearly a hundred years ago. During the past ten years, however, it was found that this reaction also occurs in fossils, and it is possible to use this reaction as a dating tool.

In order to understand the principles used in the amino acid dating of fossil bone, it is necessary first to discuss kinetics of the racemization reaction. The kinetic equation (referred to as equation (1) in this paper) for the racemization reaction can be written as

$$\mathrm{Ln} \left\{ \frac{1+\mathrm{D/L}}{1-\mathrm{D/L}} \right\} - \mathrm{constant} = 2 \cdot k \cdot t \qquad (1)$$

23

where k is the interconversion rate of the D- and L-isomers of a particular amino acid; t is the age of the sample; and D/L is the amino acid isomeric ratio in the sample. The constant in the above equation is necessary to account for some slight racemization that occurs in sample processing.

The above equation illustrates that there are two variables that determine the extent of racemization in a fossil bone, time (t) and k, which in turn is a function primarily of temperature. In order to determine one of these variables, the other must be known. To date a fossil bone, for example, a value of k must be available for the site under investigation. The value of k at a particular location is determined by a "calibration" method, wherein a sample of known age from the area of interest is analyzed for its D/L isomeric ratio. The age and the D/L ratio of the "calibration" sample are substituted into the above equation and an in situ k value is thus determined. This k value represents an average integrated value over the age of the "calibration" sample. Any change in the temperature or other environmental parameters of the locality is thus evaluated when the calibration constant, k, is determined. Once k has been determined at a particular site, this value can then be used to date other bones from the general area (this procedure is subject to certain limitations which are discussed elsewhere, i.e., Master and Bada, 1978).

The aspartic acid racemization reaction has been the most widely used in fossil-bone dating because it has the fastest racemization rate of any common stable amino acid. Easily detectable aspartic acid racemization occurs in a time period datable by radiocarbon; thus the racemization analysis of carbon-14 dated bones can be used to provide the necessary calibration constants which are required in order to date other fossil bones whose ages are unknown.

Because of the large number of well-characterized sites and the findings of numerous potentially datable hominid remains, Africa appeared to be one of the best areas to test the application of the amino acid-racemization dating in paleoanthropology. Thus, during the summer of 1973, I spent several months in Africa visiting various individuals and sites and collecting samples. The results of the analyses of some of these samples are described in this report.

Collection of Samples and Methods

The itinerary of the 1973 collecting trip is listed below:

June 29-July 2: *Capetown, South Africa*. Visited Q. B. Hendy, South Africa Museum. Discussed the Saldanha site; obtained 4 samples from the site.

July 2-4: *Bloemfontein, South Africa*. Visited H. Oberholzer, National Museum, and discussed dating of Florisbad. Obtained several samples from this site, including a piece of the Florisbad human skull. An afternoon was spent at the Florisbad site.

July 4-6: *Johannesburg, South Africa.* Visited with numerous scientists, including P. Beaumont, Prof. R. Dart, Prof. R. Mason, Dr. Cruickshank, and Prof. P. Tobias at the University of Witwatersrand and the Bernard Price Institute of Palaeontology. Discussed possible dating of several important South African human skeletons. Samples were obtained from several sites, including Kalkbank, Cave of Hearths, and pieces of the human skeletons found at Border Cave.

July 7-12: *Border Cave, Swaziland, South Africa.*

July 13-16: *Pretoria, South Africa.* Visited with Drs. Brain and Vogel and discussed dating of various South African sites. One day was spent at Swartkrans.

July 17-Aug. 20: *Kenya and Tanzania, East Africa.* Several days were spent in Nairobi visiting people at the National Museum. The remaining time was spent at Olduvai Gorge with Dr. Mary Leakey. The dating of samples from the Olduvai area was extensively discussed. More than 16 samples were collected from Olduvai Gorge under the supervision of Dr. Leakey; samples were also collected from the newly discovered hominid site at Lake Ndutu.

The samples I obtained or collected were returned to Scripps for analysis. Processing was carried out according to the procedures described elsewhere (Masters and Bada, 1978). In general, approximately 5 to 10 grams of bone were used for analysis. The samples were first cleaned, using an ultrasonication procedure. After this cleaning, the sample was hydrolyzed in 2x-distilled 6 m HCl, usually for 24 hours. After hydrolysis the sample was desalted on cation exchange resin. The aspartic acid was then isolated from the other amino acids by using anion exchange chromatography. The D/L aspartic acid ratios were determined, using the method described by Bada and Protsch (1973). The extent of racemization of isoleucine to alloisoleucine was determined from analyses of the total isolated amino acids on the automatic amino acid analyzer.

Results

SOUTH AFRICAN SAMPLES

Saldanha faunal material. Faunal material from the Saldanha has been dated at 40,570 ± 1,080 years by the UCLA Radiocarbon Laboratory (UCLA 1742). However, radiocarbon ages this close to the upper dating level of radiocarbon should be viewed with caution. Thus racemization analysis of the Saldanha material was carried out in an attempt to test the validity of the UCLA radiocarbon age. A piece of the Saldanha faunal material dated by the UCLA Radiocarbon Laboratory was analyzed and found to have a D/L aspartic acid ratio of 0.44. Using the racemization results from bones from another

South African coastal locality, i.e., Nelson Bay Cave (Bada and Deems, 1975; Masters and Bada, 1978), it was possible to make a rough calculation of the racemization age for Saldanha. Using equation (1) and the k_{asp} value determined for Nelson Bay Cave gave an age of about 80,000 years for the material dated by the UCLA C-14 Laboratory; this age is considerably older than the radiocarbon age. In an attempt to verify the racemization age, a piece of *Megantereon* bone (identification no. 3059) from Saldanha, obtained from Q. B. Hendy, was analyzed. This saber-toothed cat became extinct in South Africa at the beginning of the Upper Pleistocene, i.e., about 120,000 years ago (Hendy, 1974). The D/L aspartic acid ratio for this sample was found to be 0.51. Thus, if the *Megantereon* bone is greater than 120,000 years old, then the Saldanha faunal material with a D/L aspartic acid ratio of 0.44 must be greater than 100,000 years old. The racemization analyses of the Saldanha material thus indicate an age closer to 100,000 years, which is consistent with the age estimated from faunal evidence by Klein (1974).

Florisbad hominid. A piece of the Florisbad skull was generously provided by Dr. H. Oberholzer. However, the racemization analysis of this material was complicated by the fact that there appeared to be a large amount of glue or some similar substance on the bone. Attempts to remove this were unsuccessful. The subsequent racemization analyses yielded very low D/L ratios for several amino acids. This suggests that the Florisbad bone had been badly contaminated with secondary amino acids (probably from the glue), and thus this material was not datable by the racemization method.

Racemization results for Border Cave. Border Cave has yielded several hominid skeletons that could be of considerable importance to our understanding of the evolution of modern man. Anatomical investigations of these skeletons suggest that they are representatives of *Homo sapiens sapiens* (de Villiers, 1973). However, the context in which the skeletons were discovered casts doubt on their antiquity. Although the layers in the cave from which the skeletons were alleged to have been found have been dated at greater than 40,000 years (Beaumont and Vogel, 1972), there is concern that the skeletons might be intrusive into the deposits and thus could be considerably younger than the ages of the stratigraphic units in which they were found.

I was provided with samples of all three of the Border Cave hominid materials (infant A-1106; adult cranium A-1102a; and adult mandible A-1102b). These were generously provided by Professor P. Tobias and Dr. P. Beaumont. Analyses of all three samples indicated that they had essentially identical D/L aspartic acid ratios. The average ratio of the infant bones, cranium, and mandible was found to be 0.72 ± 0.03. However, because of the complexity of the site and some inconsistencies in the racemization ratios determined on the faunal material from various stratigraphic horizons in the cave, no direct calibration sample is available to date the human remains. An approximate age for the Border Cave hominids, however, can be estimated by using the Nelson Bay Cave k_{asp} value and the temperatures of the Nelson Bay Cave and the Border Cave regions. The present temperature along the South African coast in the vicinity of Nelson Bay Cave is on the order of 17°C. On the other hand, the present-day temperature of Nsoko, a town a kilometer or so from Border Cave, is about 22°C. If we assume that this temperature difference has existed throughout the past, then we can adjust the Nelson Bay Cave k_{asp} value to the Border Cave temperature. Based on this temperature information, and using the procedures we have outlined elsewhere (Bada, Schroeder, and Carter, 1974; Bada and Helfman, 1975), the k_{asp} value estimated for Border Cave is about $1.4 \times 10^{-5} \mathrm{yr}^{-1}$. If we substitute this value and the measured D/L aspartic acid ratio of the various hominid remains into equation (1), the estimated age is about 60,000 years. This result does indeed suggest that the human remains are not intrusive and are contemporaneous with stratigraphic units in which they were found. Moreover, the fact that they are greater than 40,000 years old makes them some of the oldest representatives of *Homo sapiens sapiens* in the world. They therefore are extremely important to our understanding of the origin of modern human beings.

SAMPLES FROM OLDUVAI GORGE AND VICINITY

Samples were collected under the direction of Dr. Mary Leakey from various stratigraphic units in Olduvai Gorge. The analysis of these samples indicated that, in general, samples from only the Upper Pleistocene deposits contained indigenous aspartic acid; bones from the older layers in Olduvai Gorge were found to contain mainly secondary aspartic acid contamination. This result therefore indicates that the aspartic acid racemization dating of bones from the Olduvai Gorge region would be limited to samples less than 100,000 years old.

One interesting result that was obtained concerned a sample from the Upper Ndutu Beds. A large sample was collected, most of which was sent to the UCLA Radiocarbon Laboratory for carbon-14 dating. A small amount was retained at the Scripps Amino Acid Dating Laboratory; analysis of the sample yielded the D/L aspartic acid ratio of 0.5 which, using the k_{asp} value established earlier for Olduvai Gorge (Bada and Protsch, 1973), indicated an age of about 33,000 years. The C-14 dating of the sample, on the other hand, yielded an age of only 3,340 ± 800 years (UCLA 1903) — obviously considerably younger than the racemization age. The racemization age is more consistent with the estimated age of the Upper Ndutu Beds deposits from other independent evidence (Hay, 1976). The radiocarbon dating of calcareous materials, and the geological interpretation of the deposits, indicate that the Upper Ndutu Beds are greater than 30,000 years old, which is consistent with the racemization age. The radiocarbon age of the Ndutu bone is thus much too young and therefore must be considered erroneous, whereas the racemization age of the bone seems reasonable. This result suggests that bones that are so badly contaminated with secondary carbon that they yield erroneous carbon-14 ages can still be dated by racemization.

Some measurements of the extent of racemization of isoleucine suggested that this amino acid may be useful in dating bones that are not datable by aspartic acid because they are either too old or because they are contaminated with secondary aspartic acid. The results of Hare, Turnbull, and Taylor (1978) for older stratigraphic sections in Olduvai Gorge show that the extent of isoleucine racemization in tooth enamel is stratigraphically consistent (i.e., the ratio of alloisoleucine to isoleucine increases in going from Bed IV/III to Bed I). Comparing their results with the alloisoleucine/isoleucine (allo/iso) ratios determined for bones collected from some of the younger units at Olduvai suggests that these bones may also be datable using isoleucine racemization. For example, a bone from the base of the Masek Beds was found to have an allo/iso ratio of about 0.6. Based on the results of Hare, Turnbull, and Taylor (1978), this would suggest that the base of the Masek Beds at Olduvai Gorge is about 460,000 years old. This age appears somewhat too young in comparison to the age estimated from geological evidence (Hay, 1976), so some slight isoleucine contamination may be present in this sample.

It is also important to mention that the analysis of bones from the first occupational floor at the Lake Ndutu site yielded an allo/iso ratio of about 0.6, the same as the Masek Bed bones from Olduvai Gorge. This suggests that the Lake Ndutu site is comparable in age to the Masek Beds at Olduvai, although this conclusion should be viewed with caution because of the possibility of contamination, which might make this comparison invalid.

These results indicate that further studies of the isoleucine racemization dating should be conducted, since this method offers the opportunity to determine ages of bones which are difficult or impossible to determine by other methods.

Conclusions

The racemization analyses of the samples collected during the trip to Africa in 1973 have proven to be extremely valuable, not only in testing the application of amino acid racemization dating to African fossil bones, but also in our understanding of various aspects of human evolution. For example, the age determined for the Saldanha deposits suggests that *Homo sapiens rhodesiensis* in South Africa has an age in excess of 100,000 years. This is consistent also with the racemization age of the hominid skeletons found at Broken Hill (Bada et al., 1974). An age in excess of 100,000 years for *Homo sapiens rhodesiensis* has been suggested from faunal evidence by Klein (1973, 1974). This is considerably older than had originally been estimated by anthropologists (Protsch, 1975).

The racemization age of the Border Cave hominids also suggests that the origin of modern human beings occurred much earlier than had originally been estimated. Heretofore it was thought that modern human beings first appeared in southern Europe or the Middle East approximately 35,000 years ago. The racemization ages for the Border Cave hominids suggest that, in fact, *Homo sapiens sapiens* may have appeared much earlier in Africa.

The results discussed here provide convincing evidence that the racemization method is a powerful technique that can be used to deduce important information about the chronological age of fossil bones. Fossil bones that are undatable by other methods can be dated by racemization, and therefore their chronological location in the scheme of human evolution can be ascertained. One other important advantage of the racemization method is that only very small amounts of bone are required for the analyses. Thus, valuable human skeletons do not have to be destroyed for racemization analysis.

Further trips to Africa are anticipated in order to collect additional samples which will also be analyzed by racemization. It is hoped that these racemization results will provide still further chronological information useful to our understanding of human evolution.

REFERENCES

BADA, JEFFREY L., and DEEMS, LYDIA
    1975.   Accuracy of dates beyond the C^{14} dating limit using the aspartic acid racemization reaction.   Nature, vol. 255, pp. 218-219.
BADA, JEFFREY L., and HELFMAN, PATRICIA M.
    1975.   Amino acid racemization dating of fossil bones.   World Archaeology, vol. 7, pp. 160-173.
BADA, JEFFREY L., and PROTSCH, REINER
    1973.   Racemization reaction of aspartic acid and its use in dating fossil bones.   Proc. Nat. Acad. Sci., vol. 70, pp. 1331-1334.
BADA, JEFFREY L.; SCHROEDER, ROY A.; and CARTER, GEORGE F.
    1974.   New evidence for the antiquity of man in North America deduced from aspartic acid racemization.   Science, vol. 184, pp. 791-793.
BEAUMONT, PETER M., and VOGEL, JOHN C.
    1972.   On a new radiocarbon chronology for Africa south of the equator.   Afr. Stud., vol. 31, pp. 66-90.

De Villiers, Hertha
  1973.   Human skeletal remains from Border Cave, Mgwarruma District, Kwa-
            zulu, South Africa.   Ann. Transvaal Mus., vol. 28, pp. 229-265.
Hare, P. Edgar; Turnbull, H. F.; and Taylor, R. E.
  1978.   Pp. 7-12 *in* "Views of the Past, Essays in Old World Prehistory and
            Paleoanthropology," Leslie G. Freeman, ed.   Mouton Publishers, The
            Hague.
Hay, Richard L.
  1976.   Pp. 136-137, 152-154 *in* "Geology of the Olduvai Gorge."   Univer-
            sity of California Press, Berkeley, California.
Hendy, Q. B.
  1974.   Faunal dating of the late Cenozoic of Southern Africa, with special refer-
            ence to the Carnivora.   Quaternary Res., vol. 4, pp. 149-161.
Klein, Richard
  1973.   Geological antiquity of Rhodesian man.   Nature, vol. 244, pp. 311-
            312.
  1974.   Environment and subsistence of prehistoric man in the Southern Cape
            Province, South Africa.   World Archaeology, vol. 5, pp. 249-284.
Masters, Patricia M., and Bada, Jeffrey L.
  1978.   Advances in amino acid racemization dating of bone and shell.   Pp.
            117-138 *in* "Archaeological Chemistry," vol. II.   Advances in Chemis-
            try Series, no. 171, American Chemical Society, Washington, D. C.
Protsch, Reiner
  1975.   The absolute dating of upper Pleistocene sub-Saharan fossil hominids
            and their place in human evolution.   Journ. Human Evolution, vol. 4,
            pp. 297-322.

Jeffrey L. Bada

Pig Rearing and the Domestication Process in New Guinea and the Torres Strait Region

Principal Investigator: James A. Baldwin, Indiana University, Indianapolis, Indiana (formerly at University of Akron, Akron, Ohio).

Grant Nos. 1249 and 1624.   In support of an investigation of the cultural and ecological aspects of the domestic and wild pig complex in New Guinea.[1]

The domestication of plants and animals was one of the more important steps taken by man in his long rise to a position of ecological dominance on this planet. One of the most stimulating efforts to explain how plant and animal domestication came about, how man surrendered his ancestral hunting and gathering way of life in favor of the direct manipulation of lesser organisms, is Carl Sauer's *Agricultural Origins and Dispersals* (1952). In this work Sauer constructs a series of arguments, among them that man's agricultural systems are of two basic types, a largely tropical system based on root crops and "household" animals (dogs, chickens, pigs) and a largely extra-tropical system based on grasses, other seed crops, and herd animals (sheep, goats, cattle); that Southeast Asia, where certain isolated upland peoples continue to practice forms of agriculture utilizing tubers and household animals, was quite likely the scene of man's earliest experiments in domestication; that noneconomic, and especially religious, factors played critical roles in early man's movement toward domestication; and that domestication must be considered not as a single revolutionary historical event, but rather as a long evolutionary process involving a series of gradual shifts in the increasingly symbiotic relationship of man to the plant and animal world.

The distinction between tropical tuber-based agriculture and extra-tropical grass-based agriculture is now widely accepted by researchers. Archeological evidence unearthed in Southeast Asia has strengthened Sauer's claim for the antiquity of agriculture in that region (Solheim, 1971). Southeast Asian archeological evidence also provides evidence that noneconomic factors were

[1] Anthony L. Crawford of the National Cultural Council of Papua New Guinea must be thanked for providing much valuable advice and assistance. I am of course indebted to the Gogodala people for their hospitality and patience.

linked with early man's interest in and familiarity with other animal species: e.g., a pig's tooth found in Borneo and dating to perhaps 20,000 B.C. seems to have been employed as a burial charm (Medway, 1960). Finally, the work of a number of recent investigators (e.g., Johannessen, 1966; Lynch, 1973) has stressed the necessity for considering domestication as a process of evolving man-plant-animal relationships, and the Simoons's (1968) monograph on the "free ranging" mithan, a cow-like creature of eastern India, demonstrates how human groups can develop quite close relationships with "semi-wild" animal species. My own earlier work on the cat argues that man's developing relationship with semi-wild village cats was a vital first step in the cat domestication process (Baldwin, 1975).

The tuber-based agriculture that initially developed in Southeast Asia spread eastward from that region to reach most of the islands of the Pacific, although the practice failed to reach Australia (Baldwin, 1976). Archeological evidence of plant cultivation may date to 7000 B.C. in the Papua New Guinea Highlands; from the same region pig remains have been tentatively identified in sites dating to about 8000 B.C. (Bulmer, 1976, p. iv).

New Guinea is thus assuming increased importance in the study of early agriculture, and not only because of the island's apparently quite early dates for plant and animal husbandry. Living in New Guinea today are approximately three million people who have been isolated for millennia from most of the currents of cultural evolution which have transformed the peoples of the Asian continent and the nearby Indonesian and Philippine archipelagoes. Writing, the development of cities, the adoption of universal religions, and—most relevant for this discussion—the cultivation of rice and the breeding of bovines (particularly the water buffalo) have long set most of the peoples of Indonesia apart from those of New Guinea.

One way, then, of furthering our understanding of early Asian agriculture and animal husbandry is to investigate the agriculture and animal husbandry of contemporary New Guinea peoples. In particular, the pig—which Sauer has argued is one of the most ancient Asian domesticates but whose importance in that region has declined greatly with the spread of Hinduism, Buddhism, and Islam—survives today as the most important domestic animal in the culture, economy, and ecology of the native peoples of New Guinea.

Many researchers have not realized that it is possible to identify in New Guinea two very different systems of pig husbandry, systems which I term "pig breeding" and "pig rearing." The distinguishing feature of New Guinea's pig breeding societies is the intentional manipulation of the genetic heritage of the village pig population, usually by means of the maintenance of stud boars kept especially for breeding purposes. Only about 30 percent of

New Guinea's ethno-linguistic groups, however, practice such intentional pig breeding (Baldwin, 1978b, p. 24). The remainder of New Guinea's ethno-linguistic groups do keep pigs, but according to the regimens of a much less intensive pig husbandry system. These groups castrate all their village boars and consequently, in order to maintain a "domestic" pig population, depend on the continual capture of wild piglets to be adopted, tamed, and raised as village animals. This relatively loose system I term pig rearing.

Most of New Guinea's pig breeding societies are located in the densely populated mountain valleys of the central backbone of the island. Most of the pig rearing societies, however, are located along the coast or along the banks of the many rivers which descend out of the mountainous interior, particularly the Sepik and the Fly. Ethnographers have investigated the societies of the New Guinea Highlands in great detail, and much has become known in recent years about the mechanisms of pig husbandry in the New Guinea Highlands and of the key role of the so-called "pig complex" there (e.g., Rappaport, 1968; Vayda, 1972). In contrast, comparatively little is known about the mechanisms of pig rearing in the lowland societies of New Guinea. This study, based on a field investigation of a sample lowland New Guinea "pig rearing" group, was initiated with the goal of partially balancing this situation.

1. The Gogodala of Papua New Guinea

The first task of the study was to locate a lowland New Guinea society among whom it would be possible to investigate ecological adaptation in general and pig rearing in particular. The group selected were the Gogodala, six thousand people occupying about twenty villages, most of which lie along the swampy middle reaches of the Aramia River, just north of the mouth of the great Fly River, in Papua New Guinea's Western Province. The Gogodala were the subject of a brief ethnography published in the 1930's (Wirz, 1934), but relatively little ethnographic material has appeared in print since then. Fieldwork quickly revealed, though, that the Gogodala remain quite well adapted to their Everglades-like homeland. Because of a total lack of stone in their swamps, the Gogodala have even developed the interesting and apparently unique custom of manufacturing club-heads from the sclerotia of a local fungus (Price, Baldwin, and Simpson, 1978).

I first arrived in the Gogodala country in June 1975 and completed the field portions of the study in June 1976. For approximately ten months (September 1975 to June 1976) I lived in the Gogodala village of Isago (8°S, 142°40′E), one of the more conservative villages and at that time the only vil-

FIG. 1.   Longhouse at Isago village (117.4 meters in length).

lage occupying a traditional longhouse dwelling. At 117.4 meters in length, the Isago longhouse must be one of the largest examples of primitive architecture existing in the world today (fig. 1). It was in Isago that data were gathered on all aspects of Gogodala ecological adaptation; this material, focusing particularly on agriculture, hunting, diet, and nutrition, is reported in detail elsewhere (Baldwin, 1979a). Presented here is a summary of the place in Gogodala life of the pig, an important animal for understanding Gogodala life and also, I maintain, for furthering our understanding of early animal domestication.

SUBSISTENCE

Gogodala subsistence is highly dependent on the freshwater swamp habitat in which the people have lived for generations, even though that habitat also supports certain dangerous diseases, most particularly malaria (Baldwin, 1978a.). Food surveys carried out from February 9 to 24 and from April 27 to June 10, 1976, at the height of the wet season and at the beginning of the dry, reveal that Gogodala diet consists in large part of sago, a starchy high-calorie foodstuff processed from the pith of the swamp-growing sago palm, and freshwater fish. Little if any serious malnutrition is obvious, with the exception of

FIG. 2. Recently captured wild piglet, tethered in the women's section of the longhouse.

some children who have difficulty in weaning. Gogodala diet seems nutritionally adequate, both from the perspective of total calories consumed and from the perspective of the variety of nutrients ingested.

Pigs, perhaps surprisingly, contribute little to Gogodala subsistence. Pig flesh, whether taken from slaughtered village pigs or from hunted wild animals, supplies much less than 1 percent of a Gogodala's average daily calorie consumption and less than 1 percent of his daily protein intake. Thus, even though the Gogodala spend much time and attention in the rearing and the hunting of pigs, and even though pigs do play an important role in local mythology and ritual, the Gogodala could subsist quite well should pigs vanish completely from their villages and from their hunting territories.

PIG REARING METHODS

Among the Gogodala the hunting of wild animals, even though contributing only negligibly to subsistence, is a favorite masculine activity. When Gogodala men return from their hunting expeditions they not infrequently carry back with them live animals of various sorts. Baby wallabies, small birds, and even certain nonvenomous snakes are presented to children as pets, or rather as playthings, and as a rule remain alive only for a brief period of time.

In contrast, small piglets captured in the wild, almost always after the mother pig has been killed in the hunt, are given to the women to raise. Recently captured piglets are kept tethered in the women's section of the communal longhouse (fig. 2) and are offered sago, premasticated by the women, as food. When a piglet will not accept such sustenance, perhaps because of fright or because it has not yet been weaned off its mother, a woman will offer it her breast. Such breast-feeding of infant animals, a practice quite widespread in New Guinea and indeed in many parts of the world (Simoons and Baldwin, 1980), serves two important functions. Not only does it insure the survival of the young animals, it also functions as a very effective taming mechanism. Young piglets, by being suckled by humans and also by being continually petted and carried about as if they were human infants (they may even be addressed as "my child"), become "imprinted" on their human foster mothers. In this way born-wild pigs are made relatively easy to manage in captivity.

Shortly after being introduced to Gogodala village life from the bush, all male piglets are castrated (fig. 3). The Gogodala maintain that castration serves to keep the animals gentle and encourages them to grow bigger and fatter. Following a young pig's operation, the testicles are placed in a small bag and suspended beneath the ridgepole of the village longhouse, the most sacred space in the building, in fact the place where the clans' totemic objects and initiation regalia are traditionally stored. The Gogodala believe that the suspension of a pig's severed testicles in the longhouse serves to prevent the animal from wandering too far away from the village and "going bush."

The Gogodala practice no intentional breeding of pigs. Occasionally, though, a litter of piglets may be born to a village sow. In such cases the progenitor of the litter can usually be identified as an adult wild boar, who was able somehow to mate with the sow as she roamed about beyond the confines of the village. Piglets born in the village, however, endure a high mortality rate, suffering from neglect, poor diet, and especially attacks from village dogs.

Gogodala village pigs, once mature enough to forage by themselves and to protect themselves from village dogs, are left pretty much to themselves. They are provided with only a minimum amount of food. I estimate that an adult village pig obtains only about 5 percent of its diet directly from human beings; this 5 percent is largely in the form of coconuts which Gogodala men cut open and give to their pigs. Gogodala village pigs must therefore scavenge for the great bulk of their food supply. They accomplish this by "free ranging" around the village, consuming discarded foodstuffs, garbage, and feces, both

FIG. 3. Adult (castrated) village boar.

animal and human. They also venture into the nearby bush, where, being omnivorous, they seek out and consume such diverse wild foods as fruits, roots, worms, grubs, as well as reptiles and small mammals.

To prevent scavenging pigs from rooting in gardens, the septums of the animals' snouts may be fitted with sago thorns. These simple devices make it too painful for the pigs to dig for taro, yams, sweet potatoes, or other tubers in the always unfenced garden plots. Village pigs are also sometimes fitted with ear tassels. The ears of the animals are pierced and pieces of woven string attached. These "brands" enable a Gogodala hunter in the bush immediately to distinguish a truly wild animal from a wandering village pig.

No Gogodala village pig, born in the wild but lovingly raised in the village by a human "mother," ever dies a natural death. The men, who retain ownership of the animals they have captured, eventually reclaim them for slaughter, always as part of some ceremonial or ritual event. The slaughter of village pigs among the Gogodala involves an interesting cultural echo of the hunting tradition. An animal selected to be killed is chased about the village, sometimes for hours, pursued by men and boys armed with clubs and spears. Eventually the confused and terrified animal is cornered and dispatched, its flesh to serve as the principal course at an important feast or ritual. Meanwhile the woman who raised the victim, and who perhaps suckled the animal when it was newly arrived in the village, understandably wails and mourns as if for a murdered human offspring.

THE PIG IN CULTURE, ECONOMY, AND ECOLOGY

Even though not a fully domesticated animal, the pig is one of the more significant components of Gogodala culture. No ceremonial or ritual occasion is complete without the consumption of pork; the pig functions as one of the primary clan totems of the society; the animal is always the focus of much attention, symbolism, and metaphor. As an example of the latter, the Gogodala draw an analogy between the village longhouse, the central spatial focus of their culture, and a pig. The word for "pig's head" is used to refer also to the front end of a longhouse, while the word for "pig's tail" is used to refer to the back side of the building. In addition, the word for "backbone" is used for the ridgepole of the longhouse, and is also the word meaning "village" in general.

In the economic sphere the village pig functions as a convenient medium of exchange and as an important measure of a man's wealth or importance. Being quite rare (the pig-to-man ratio among the Gogodala is about 0.1:1, compared to ratios of up to 2.5:1 in some New Guinea Highland societies), village pigs are traditionally among the most valuable commodities a Gogodala might aspire to own.

Village pigs also play an important role in Gogodala ecology. Their dung is occasionally added as fertilizer to gardens, particularly to gardens devoted to the cultivation of tobacco, a notably soil-exhausting crop. As has been noted elsewhere in New Guinea (Aitchison, 1960, pp. 164-165), the excessive rooting of pigs around a village may contribute to soil erosion and, since pigs consume large quantities of fruits, nuts, and seeds, to the gradual replacement of tree vegetation by grasses. In fact, each Gogodala village is surrounded by large tracts of grassy savanna country, created not only by generations of foraging village pigs but also by man's frequent use of fire in hunting and gardening.

Any discussion of the ecologic role of pigs among the Gogodala must include a mention of their function as handy village "garbage disposals." By consuming waste foods, garbage, and feces, village pigs make a great contribution to village sanitation and thus serve as an efficient check on the spread of many diseases. One might speculate that sedentary village life in this humid tropical environment would be impossible without the scavenging village pig. Finally, one might also note that village pigs, by occasionally attacking and consuming venomous snakes, serve to check a serious threat to human life in this part of the world.

RECENT CHANGES IN THE SYSTEM

Missionaries have been active among the Gogodala since the late 1930's. These individuals, most of whom were sent to New Guinea by evangelical churches in Australia, have discouraged any expression of traditional Gogodala ceremonial life. Thus for a period of about two decades the distinctive Gogodala art tradition was in real danger of extinction; fortunately this art tradition has recently been revived (Baldwin, 1979c; Crawford, 1975).

Unlike art, traditional subsistence has been little influenced by missionaries or other outside influences. Certain changes have begun to occur in the traditional pig husbandry system, however. Three interrelated innovations have recently been adopted by the Gogodala, largely because of contact with missionaries and other outsiders. These include: one, the keeping of imported European pigs; two, the building of "pig-houses" for the confining of pigs; and three, the conscious and purposeful breeding of pigs within the villages. The long-range impact of these innovations for the local ecosystem is difficult to predict, although there are some indications that the total number of pigs kept by the Gogodala may be increasing. And since some Gogodala are now confining their animals, it is necessary that such confined animals be provided with all their food, an ominous situation which for the first time puts the village pig population in direct competition with the human population for subsistence.

CONCLUSION

As Sauer noted, domestication must be considered as a gradual process and not as a single historical event. There thus exists—not only in the archeologic past but in the ethnographic present as well—a "continuum of domestication," involving many degrees of intimacy between human groups and different species of animals. In other words, man chooses to exert varying degrees of control over the various animals with which he has entered into relationship. The Gogodala and groups like them elsewhere in New Guinea represent a stage intermediate, and I maintain transitional, between the two extremes of the pig domestication continuum. Gogodala village pigs, born in the wild but reared and protected by man, are "neither fish nor flesh," neither truly wild nor truly domestic animals.

2. Man and Pig in the Torres Strait Region

In July 1976, following a year of research among the Gogodala of the Western Province of Papua New Guinea, the support of an additional grant from the National Geographic Society enabled me to visit the nearby Torres

Strait, the 150-kilometer-wide body of water that separates New Guinea and Australia. Not only does this relatively shallow and narrow strait separate two major landmasses, it also forms the border between two generally accepted major culture areas, Melanesia and Australia.

The purpose of this visit to the islands of the Torres Strait was to gather data relating to the traditional human ecology of this interesting and little-known region. Specifically I was most eager to learn what I could about the traditional pig-keeping practices of the islanders. Operating out of Thursday Island, I was able during my stay in the area to visit Horn, Prince of Wales, and Hammond islands. Although the islanders are by now well acculturated into the general pattern of Australian life (all of the islands in the Strait are politically a part of Queensland), I was able to accumulate useful data by talking to older islanders and by visiting homesteads and gardens. The gardens are generally well-tended and produce harvests of bananas, sweet potatoes, and other crops. The most favored cultivated crops are various yams (*Dioscorea* spp.), which are also important crops on the New Guinea mainland to the north, for example among the Gogodala. Yams (wild yams, that is) are also important economic plants among Australian Aborigines living on the Cape York Peninsula, just to the south of Torres Strait (Harris, 1976, p. 659).

Pigs occur now as feral populations on most of the larger islands of Torres Strait, and do considerable damage to native gardens. Pigs are currently kept as domestic livestock by only a few individuals. In pre-contact times pigs were not bred in the islands, but rather were traded into the islands from peoples living on the New Guinea mainland, who commonly captured live piglets in the bush. This trade continues today, in spite of the fact that an international boundary must now be crossed, often illegally. A notice posted in Daru, the capital of Papua, New Guinea's Western Province, warns that "No person may take animals (dogs, pigs, wallabies) from Papua to the Torres Strait Islands"; punishment for this infringement of "international law" is fine or imprisonment.

Two principal hypotheses, both dealing with the role of Torres Strait as a transition zone between New Guinea and Australia, have developed out of my interest in that area. First, I have argued that the Torres Strait trade system acted as a "cultural filter" which allowed certain culture traits to pass through and diffuse into Australia, but which—because of a dependence of many islanders on traded foodstuffs—blocked the passage of the cultural complex of agriculture (Baldwin, 1976).

I have also advanced the hypothesis that pigs had been introduced to the Cape York Peninsula at some time prior to European contact and that pigs existed there as a feral population before the time of Captain Cook (Baldwin,

1979b). The argument to support this hypothesis begins with the fact that pigs were carried as trade items in the traditional Torres Strait trade system, a system in which the Cape York Aborigines were active participants. I assume that live pigs, traded across the Strait from New Guinea and landed on the Australian mainland, would have found it easy to escape from human groups not accustomed to the rigors of animal husbandry. Other more direct evidence in support of this hypothesis includes several unmistakable depictions of cloven-footed pigs in the Aboriginal rock art of the Cape York Peninsula, the presence of a typically New Guinea intestinal parasite in the Cape York wild pig population, and the observation that the Cape York wild pigs are much closer in physical appearance to the rather small and bristly pigs of New Guinea *(Sus scrofa papuensis)* than to European/Australian pigs *(Sus scrofa scrofa).*

One important general conclusion of this research is that Torres Strait cannot be considered to be a firm and fixed boundary between "agricultural" and "hunting and gathering" ways of life. With respect to pigs, the peoples of the central New Guinea highlands (to the north of the region under consideration here) habitually breed their pigs, thus practicing full pig domestication. The lowland peoples of southern New Guinea (e.g., the Gogodala) do not breed their pigs, but are continually dependent on the capture of wild piglets to be reared as tame village animals. The Torres Strait islanders import their pigs from the nearby New Guinea mainland. Finally (if indeed wild pigs did exist in pre-European times on the Cape York Peninsula), the Cape York Aborigines were limited to the hunting of wild pigs. Thus, in one 800-kilometer transect from central New Guinea to northeastern Australia, one runs what is I think an historically significant gamut from full domestication, to institutionalized pig "rearing," to the trading of captive wild pigs, and finally to the hunting and killing of truly wild animals.

REFERENCES

AITCHISON, T. G.
1960.   The pig and its place in the impact of the New Guinean on vegetation. Pp. 158-167 *in* "Symposium on the Impact of Man on Humid Tropics Vegetation." A. J. Arthur, Government Printer, Canberra.
BALDWIN, JAMES A.
1975.   Notes and speculations on the domestication of the cat in Egypt. Anthropos, vol. 70, pp. 428-448.
1976.   Torres Strait: Barrier to agricultural diffusion. Anthrop. Journ. Canada, vol. 14, no. 2, pp. 10-17.
1978a.   Interrelationships of disease, nutrition, and population among the Gogodala of Papua New Guinea. Paper read at the annual meeting of the East Lakes Division, Association of American Geographers, East Lansing, Michigan.

1978b. Pig rearing vs. pig breeding in New Guinea. Anthrop. Journ. Canada, vol. 16, no. 3, pp. 23-27.

1979a. The ecology of domestication in a lowland Papua New Guinea community. Ph.D. thesis, University of California, Davis, 247 pp., illus.

1979b. Pre-Cookian pigs in Australia? Paper read at the 76th annual meeting of the Association of American Geographers, Philadelphia.

1979c. Renaissance artistique chez les Gogodala (Papouasie). Journ. Soc. Océanist., vol. 63, pp. 115-118.

BULMER, SUSAN

1976. The prehistory of the New Guinea Highlands. Oceanic Prehistory Records, no. 1, 231 pp., illus. Department of Anthropology, University of Auckland, Auckland, N.Z.

CRAWFORD, ANTHONY L.

1975. Gogodala culture: A revival. Journ. Anthrop. Soc. South Australia, vol. 13, no. 2, pp. 4-11.

HARRIS, DAVID R.

1976. Land of plenty on Cape York Peninsula. Geogr. Mag., vol. 48, no. 11, pp. 657-661.

JOHANNESSEN, CARL L.

1966. The domestication process in trees reproduced by seed: The pejibaye palm in Costa Rica. Geogr. Rev., vol. 56, pp. 363-376.

LYNCH, THOMAS F.

1973. Harvest timing, transhumance, and the process of domestication. Amer. Anthrop., vol. 75, pp. 1254-1259.

MEDWAY, LORD

1960. Rhinoceros' and pigs' teeth as Niah charms? Sarawak Mus. Journ., no. 12, pp. 637-638.

PRICE, TERENCE V.; BALDWIN, JAMES A.; and SIMPSON, JACK A.

1978. Fungal club-heads in Papua New Guinea. Nature, vol. 273, pp. 374-375, illus.

RAPPAPORT, ROY A.

1968. Pigs for the ancestors: Ritual in the ecology of a New Guinea people. 311 pp., illus. Yale University Press, New Haven.

SAUER, CARL O.

1952. Agricultural origins and dispersals, 110 pp., illus. Amer. Geogr. Soc., New York.

SIMOONS, FREDERICK J., and BALDWIN, JAMES A.

———. Breast-feeding of animals by women: Its sociocultural context and geographic occurrence. Department of Geography, University of California, Davis. Anthropos. (In press.)

SIMOONS, FREDERICK J., and SIMOONS, ELIZABETH S.

1968. A ceremonial ox of India: The Mithan in nature, culture, and history, 323 pp., illus. University of Wisconsin Press, Madison.

SOLHEIM, WILHELM G., II

1971. New light on a forgotten past. Nat. Geogr. Mag., vol. 139, no. 3, pp. 330-339, illus.

VAYDA, ANDREW P.
    1972.   Pigs.   Pp. 905-908 *in* "Encyclopaedia of Papua and New Guinea," vol.
        2, Peter Ryan, ed.   Melbourne University Press, Melbourne.
WIRZ, PAUL
    1934.   Die Gemeinde der Gogodára.   Nova Guinea: Uitkomsten der Nieuw-
        Guinea-Expedities, vol. 16, no. 4, 120 pp., illus. Leiden.

JAMES A. BALDWIN

Survey of Ancient Shipwrecks in the Mediterranean

Principal Investigator: George F. Bass, American Institute of Nautical Archaeology, Philadelphia, Pennsylvania.

Grant Nos. 1203,   For a survey for ancient shipwrecks off the Turkish coast,
1252, 1317.   1973 and 1974.

Between early August and the end of October 1973, the American Institute of Nautical Archaeology, with grants from the National Geographic Society, conducted a survey for ancient shipwrecks off the Turkish coast between Antalya and the vicinity of Bodrum. The aim of the expedition was to locate one or more wrecks suitable for future excavation.

Staff included G. F. Bass, director; John Broadwater, Donald A. Frey, and Donald M. Rosencrantz, electronics technicians and divers; John Gifford, in charge of diving equipment and chamber; and Joseph K. Alexander, Merih Karabag, and Cumhur Ilik, divers. The 35-foot fishing boat *Günyel* was captained by Ibrahim Günyel, and the 65-foot trawler *Kardeshler* by Mehmet Turgut Tekkin, who also was in charge of all local arrangements for the expedition. Yüksel Egdemir was commissioner from the Turkish Department of Antiquities; he acted also as unofficial codirector of the survey, and through his efforts some of the most interesting wrecks were located.

Diving and electronic equipment were provided largely by the University Museum of the University of Pennsylvania; the latter had been purchased with a grant from the National Science Foundation in 1971.

During the first half of the survey a random search was made with side-scanning sonar and underwater television from the *Günyel*. Although the equipment performed well, only one wreck (no. 7, below) was found in this way. A few leads from local sponge divers were also followed by diving, but because the Institute's new recompression chamber (purchased with a grant from F. Alex Nason) had not yet arrived, little deep diving was done at this time.

In midseason the expedition moved from the *Günyel* to the *Kardeshler* because the trawler was large enough to carry the new chamber, which had by then arrived from the United States. From that time most searching was done by divers, always following directions from various sponge divers we met in coastal villages or at sea.

The sites located are catalogued below as follows: Date of discovery, general location, depth, description, date, and present evaluation. By agreement with the Turkish Department of Antiquities we will not publish precise locations of wrecks; the seriousness of looting was brought home by the discovery that almost all sites had suffered some damage at the hands of modern divers.

1. August 21. Knidian Peninsula. 90 to 110 feet. Cargo of bowls, cups, plates, and lamps, partly on rock and partly in sand. 1st century B.C. Worth excavation, although probably few hull remains are to be expected.

2. August 22. Knidian Peninsula. 25 to 30 feet. Broken amphora fragments on rock. Probably 3rd century A.D. Not worth excavation.

3. August 22. Knidian Peninsula. 15 to 20 feet. Broken amphoras and cooking ware on rock, in two groups about 50 feet apart. Not yet dated. Too badly broken for excavation.

4. August 28. Kerme Bay. 20 to 30 feet. Two large piles of badly broken, concreted pottery, mostly on rock. Two amphora handles of Cypriot or Phoenician type point to a date of the 7th or 6th century B.C. Sandy area at bottom of slope should be investigated further; otherwise site warrants little additional effort.

5. August 30. Kerme Bay. 30 feet. Pottery fragments, including amphoras and *pithos* (open-mouthed storage jar). No sign of further wreckage in deeper water. Not yet dated. Not worth excavation.

6. August 31. Kerme Bay. 85 to 95 feet. Cargo of roof tiles on rocky slope with some sand covering; galley wares mark one end. Probably 7th century A.D. Probably worth excavating, although hull remains may be scanty.
This wreck, although visited and catalogued, is not included among the 17 sites listed as found during the survey. It was discovered in 1958 by Peter Throckmorton, and described by him and by Honor Frost (see References).

7. September 8. Near Iassos. 70 feet. Scattered pottery lying on surface of deep mud bottom; visibility limited to a few inches (the site was located by sonar). Probably Late Roman or Byzantine. The thick mud may conceal and protect a well-preserved hull. The site is worth further investigation, although its excavation will require new techniques.

8. September and October (several visits). Southwest coast. 10 to 110 feet. Assorted pottery fragments and tiles, found over a wide area in a harbor mouth, date from 7th or 6th century B.C. through Hellenistic, Roman, and Byzantine times. All may be simply jetsam, but a thorough survey of the area might be productive.

9. September 23. Near Bozburun. 110 feet. A large mound of amphoras in deep sand. Byzantine (exact date unknown). A perfect site for excavation.

10. September 24. Near Marmaris. 90 feet. Scattered amphoras, including one

1st-century A.D. pseudo-Koan type. Very little now visible, although ex-sponge-diver claimed it was a good wreck; possibly thoroughly looted.

11. September 26. Near Cape Gelidonya. 120 to 135 feet. Large cargo of bowls and plates, partly on sand and partly on rock. Second century B.C. to 1st century A.D. Cargo worth excavating, but probably little or no hull will be found. This site and the following had been seen originally by Dr. Frey and Mr. Egdemir in 1971, but had not been photographed.

12. September 26. Near Cape Gelidonya. 140 feet. Cargo of square terracotta tiles, heavily concreted and mostly on rock. Undated. Worth investigation if wreck no. 11 is excavated, but is probably not worth a separate campaign; the two wrecks lie about 100 yards apart.

13. October 1. Near Kalkan. 120 feet. Scattered amphora fragments. The site has been thoroughly looted. Byzantine. There may be substantial material left under the sand, but virtually all surface pottery, reported as having been considerable, has been stolen in recent years.

14. October 3. Southwest coast. 110 feet. Cargo of glass ingots and broken glass vessels, with mound of amphoras at one end of site. Late Byzantine or Medieval. The wreck is in deep sand and is most suitable for excavation.

15. October 5. Southwest coast. 110 feet. Knidian amphoras of ca. 300 B.C. The site has been badly looted of cargo but is still most worthy of excavation. Hull remains, personal possessions, and additional cargo almost surely exist under the deep sand; a small part of the wreck may lie on rock.

16. October 7. Knidian Peninsula. 100 to 110 feet. Large cargo of tiles and pottery is scattered over a rocky slope. Probably 1st century B.C. No hull will be preserved on the rock, but the cargo is worth further study, especially if neighboring wreck no. 1 is the subject of a full-scale excavation; the wrecks lie about 100 yards apart.

17. October 12. Kerme Bay. 110 feet. Pottery spread over rocky slope, with large jars well preserved in thick sand just below. Probably 7th century B.C. The early date makes this the most important site for excavation, although probably much or most of hull has disappeared.

18. October 14. Kerme Bay. 110 feet. Cargo of Rhodian amphoras. Site has been partially looted, revealing small fragments of wooden hull under the sand. From 1st century B.C. or A.D. A good wreck for excavation.

From this catalogue it is evident that the survey was successful. Wrecks 1, 9, 11, 14, 15, 16, 17, and 18 are all sites worthy of excavation, representing a variety of periods: Iron Age, late Classical or early Hellenistic, Hellenistic, Roman, Byzantine, and Late Byzantine or Medieval. The excavation of these sites will contribute greatly to our knowledge of the history of ships and seafaring. Wreck no. 7 may prove to be the most interesting of all, but it requires further investigation before this can be determined.[1]

After this report was written, however, two of the sites (nos. 17 and 14) were excavated in their entirety, and in 1979 we began the excavation of a third (no. 15). Wreck no. 17, at Sheytan Deresi, proved to be from about 1600 B.C., much older than estimated when found. Wreck no. 14, at Serçe Liman, was dated to about A.D. 1025.

In 1974 we planned to begin the excavation of the most interesting of the shipwrecks discovered during the 1973 survey, that of the Iron Age (Archaic Period). After staff and equipment had been assembled in Turkey, however, the Cyprus War brought all coastal excavations in the Aegean to a halt. Thus not a single dive was made on the new site.

---

[1] Illustrations of samples raised from the various wrecks, for dating purposes, appeared in *Türk Arkeoloji Dergisi* and the *International Journal of Nautical Archaeology*. A popular account of the survey appeared in *AINA Newsletter*, vol. 1, no. 1 (Spring 1974).

REFERENCES

BASS, GEORGE F.
   1970.   Archaeology under water, 175 pp., illus.   Penguin Books, Ltd., Hammondsworth, England.
   1972.   A history of seafaring based on underwater archaeology, 320 pp., illus., George F. Bass, ed.   Walker & Co., New York.
   1974.   Survey for shipwrecks, 1973.   Int. Journ. of Nautical Archaeology, vol. 3, no. 2, pp. 335-338, illus.
   1975.   Underwater survey—1973.   Türk Arkeoloji Dergisi, vol. 22, no. 2, pp. 33-38, illus.
   1976.   Sheytan Deresi: preliminary report.   Int. Journ. of Nautical Archaeology, vol. 5, no. 4, pp. 293-303.
   1977.   The wreck at Sheytan Deresi.   Oceans, vol. 10, no. 1, p. 34-39, illus.
   1978.   Glass treasure from the Aegean.   National Geographic, vol. 153, no. 6, pp. 768-793, illus.
   1979.   The shipwreck at Serce Liman, Turkey.   Archaeology, vol. 32, no. 1, pp. 36-43, illus.
   1979.   A medieval Islamic merchant venture.   Archaeological News, vol. 8, nos. 2/3, pp. 84-94, illus.
BASS, GEORGE F., and VAN DOORNINCK, JR., FREDERICK H.
   1978.   An eleventh-century shipwreck at Serce Liman, Turkey.   Int. Journ. of Nautical Archaeology, vol. 7, no. 2, pp. 119-132, illus.
FROST, HONOR
   1963.   Under the Mediterranean, 278 pp., illus.   Prentice-Hall, Inc., Englewood Cliffs, New Jersey. (See pp. 215-217, figs. 42, 43.)
THROCKMORTON, PETER
   1964.   The lost ships, 260 pp., illus.   Atlantic Monthly Press, Little, Brown & Co., Boston. (Includes 2 photographs of the wreck.)

GEORGE F. BASS

Spectroscopic Provenience Analyses of Archeological Amber Artifacts

Principal Investigators: Curt W. Beck, Vassar College, Poughkeepsie, New York. A. Colin Renfrew, University of Southampton, Southampton, England.

Grant No. 1225:   In support of a spectroscopic provenience analysis of archeological amber artifacts.

Grant No. 1491:   For an analysis of patterns of trade of prehistoric amber.

The wide occurrence of amber objects in archeological excavations throughout Europe and the Near East and during all prehistoric and early historic periods since the Late Stone Age shows that the "amber trade" has been an important part of the commercial and cultural relations between ancient peoples and that from its systematic study much can be learned about travel and traffic in these early times.

Until quite recently the mapping of "amber routes" was severely hampered by the impossibility of ascertaining the geographical origin of an archeological amber find. Thus the many amber ornaments found by Heinrich Schliemann in the shaft graves of Mycenae are certainly imports, but whether they are imports of Baltic, Rumanian, or Sicilian amber will make a very large difference in our views of the external contacts of the Mycenaean civilization. In 1964, infrared spectroscopy was found to identify Baltic amber, or succinite, unambiguously (Beck, Wilbur, and Meret, 1964). That variety of amber is found over a very considerable portion of northern Europe, viz, from the east coast of England and the eastern part of the Netherlands, through northern Germany and southern Scandinavia, and well into Poland and western Russia. Still, the southern boundaries of the natural occurrence of Baltic amber are well defined and coincide with the limits of glaciation, which, geologists believe, carried the amber from its primary source in Scandinavia to its present deposits.

Since 1964 the infrared provenience analysis of archeological amber artifacts has been carried out at Vassar College and, more recently, in several laboratories in Italy (Catacchio and Guerreschi, 1970) and Poland (Jaworski et al., 1972), with a view of assembling a comprehensive inventory and analysis of all the prehistoric amber finds of Europe (a *Corpus Sucinorum Veterum*), which can serve as a data base for any future study of the amber trade.

Beyond the distribution of Baltic amber in Europe, evidence of export of this material to the Near and Far East will add to our knowledge of intercontinental trade in early times.

Within this larger context the present grant from the National Geographic Society served to collect and analyze archeological amber artifacts from France, Czechoslovakia, Lebanon, and Japan.

France

In collaboration with Dr. Jean-Louis Roudil, Directeur de la Circonscription des Antiquités Préhistoriques du Langue doc-Roussillon, amber excavated by Dr. Roudil in the Grotte du Hasard (Gard) has been analyzed and found to be of Baltic amber. These finds are typologically particularly significant since among them are two so-called "spacer beads," a form of amber ornament that provides a "missing link" between similar beads in Denmark and England on the one hand and Greece of the 16th-15th centuries B.C. on the other. These spacer beads lend strong support to the views held by the late Professor Spiros Marinatos of Athens, that northern amber reached the Aegean by a route crossing Europe along the Rhine and Rhone Rivers to the Marseille area and thence by sea to the eastern Mediterranean. A report on the analyses of these finds has been published (Beck and Liu, 1976).

Additional amber finds of the southern French Bronze Age were collected in the fall of 1973 and have been analyzed. The fact that all of about 40 identifiable samples were of Baltic amber further supports the role of the Midi in the transit of Baltic amber to the Aegean. A report on these analyses awaits publication in France.

A complete series of Bronze Age amber finds from the tumuli of the Forest of Haguenau, Alsace, has been analyzed and found to be of Baltic amber. These finds, which include spacer beads, had been believed to be of southern origin (Schaeffer, 1926). Their northern provenience, now firmly established by infrared spectroscopy, further strengthens the evidence for the Rhine-Rhone amber route and suggests that the similar and roughly contemporary amber finds in southern Germany (Hachmann, 1957) indicate a branch from the central north-south amber route. A report of the amber finds from Haguenau has been published (Beck, Liu, and Nunan, 1975).

Czechoslovakia

More than one hundred Bronze Age amber artifacts, collected in Czechoslovakia in 1971 and 1972, have now been analyzed. The results will be published in one or more papers jointly with Dr. Antonin Beneš, of the Czech Academy of Science, who has been our principal collaborator in this area.

Near East

Forty-five amber artifacts of various periods of Near Eastern pre- and protohistory were supplied by Lady Gloria Dale of Beirut, Lebanon. Their analysis is complete, but publication of the results has been delayed by political events in that country. The finds, unfortunately without firm excavation data, are of Baltic amber.

Japan

About twenty samples of archeological and naturally occurring amber were sent to us by Professor Teruko Muroga of the University of Kyoto, Japan. These samples are the beginning of a joint project at Kyoto and Vassar to date the first appearance of Baltic amber in Far Eastern archeology and art history. A report on the results has been published (Fujinaga et al., 1974).

CURT W. BECK

Great Britain[1]

The analyses have shown that all the identifiable samples except one are of Baltic amber; the exception is a bead from Dun Ardtreck on the Isle of Skye, northwest Scotland, most probably dating to the Roman Iron Age. These results refute recent suggestions that fossil resins available from local sources in Britain were being used; however, it does not exclude the possibility that the Baltic amber used was collected on the east coast of Britain, which it had reached by natural means. Any decision on this matter must be made on other grounds.

The chronological distribution of British amber finds which has emerged from compilation of the corpus is unsurprising: one or two Paleolithic/Mesolithic finds, one or two Neolithic occurrences, and a few in Bell Beaker contexts; the majority are in the "Wessex Culture" graves, together with a

[1] A National Geographic Society grant (No. 1491 in 1975) awarded jointly to Professor C. W. Beck, Vassar College, and to Professor A. C. Renfrew, University of Southampton, England, led to the appointment of Dr. S. J. Shennan to complete a corpus of prehistoric amber in Britain and to collect samples for analysis by Professor Beck. During 1975-76 virtually all museums in Britain with amber finds were visited; drawings were made, the finds were weighed, and all available details of context were noted; samples of over eighty beads were also taken.

number in Late Bronze Age contexts, especially hoards; finally, there is a rather limited Iron Age use.

In order to understand the British pattern of use it is helpful to make comparisons with the continent. In the Middle Neolithic Trichterbecher-kultur period amber is found extensively in Denmark and also occurs in the Dutch megaliths and the Seine-Oise-Marne culture graves of the Paris basin. Further east, at a similar date, amber is found as far south as Bohemia in Globular Amphora contexts, and in Bernburg and Globular Amphora contexts in central Germany. There is a very similar general pattern in the succeeding Corded Ware phase.

It is noteworthy that Britain does not seem to share in this distribution of Baltic amber. There is very little use of amber in the British Neolithic: a couple of beads from the east Yorkshire area, most probably made from amber picked up on the nearby east coast, and a find of axe-shaped amber and jet beads from Lanarkshire, Scotland, which may indicate Scandinavian contact, since the shape is a Danish Middle Neolithic type.

The initial large-scale (although the quantities should not be over-emphasized) use of amber in Britain, in the Wessex Early Bronze Age, provides a marked contrast with Denmark, first in the date at which it begins, and secondly, because it does not seem to be concentrated close to the potential local source, the east coast. Examination of the reasons for the relative lack of amber finds in eastern areas suggests that it is genuine and not simply a result of the nature of the evidence. Thus, even if it is assumed that the Wessex amber came from the east coast of England, the simplest type of exchange, with the commodity decreasing in quantity with distance from the source, does not seem to be operating.

The question of whether human agency was responsible for bringing the amber from Jutland or simply from the British east coast is obviously important. A case can be made out for preferring the traditional view that it was intentionally brought from Jutland. In particular, the appearance of amber in Wessex coincides with a marked increase in the amount found elsewhere in Western and Central Europe in the Early and Middle Bronze Age. This almost certainly came from Denmark and traveled considerable distances overland into Central Europe. In these circumstances it seems unnecessary to invoke a separate origin for the amber found in Wessex. A second point to be taken into account is the lack of a tradition of Neolithic amber use in eastern Britain, apart from the rare exceptions noted above, a situation which contrasts markedly with that in Denmark. This lack of amber continues into the Bronze Age and the few fine amber objects which have been found in East Anglia, such as the well-known necklace from Little Cressingham, Norfolk, suggest that here too amber was a prized material.

Attention has already been drawn to certain distinctions between Britain and Denmark in terms of their use of amber, but two more should also be mentioned. The first is the quantity of known amber finds, which is several orders of magnitude greater in Denmark than in Britain. The second is the different social and economic context of early extensive use in the two areas, in Denmark among Mesolithic and Early Neolithic communities and in Britain in the Wessex Early Bronze Age. An initial impression, which is being further investigated, would also suggest that the amber is found in the richer Early Bronze Age graves. On this basis it may be reasonable to distinguish between the use of amber simply as an attractive material for ornaments, and its use with a socially ascribed value concomitant with high status, its attractiveness and unusual qualities providing one reason for this value, but its rarity, or at least inaccessibility, providing another. This presupposes that the development of ranking led to the creation of a demand for symbolic distinction.

The Wessex pattern, for it remains in Wessex that the amber finds are largely concentrated, seems to be an indication of directional trade, not the "down-the-line" exchange apparently operating in the distribution of amber on the continent in the later Neolithic, when the quantity of amber gradually thins out southward. This in itself may be seen as suggesting some degree of more complex social organization, which fits in with the usual interpretation of the Wessex graves. Work still going on indicates that the amber probably went initially to the highest ranking groups within the Wessex area and was then redistributed by them to their supporters; such systems of exchange are well documented ethnographically and may have operated in other parts of Britain as well as in the Wessex area.

The other main series of British amber objects belongs to the later Bronze Age and is completely different in distribution. Here there is less evidence than in other periods to enable a decision on whether the finds accurately reflect the patterns of use of amber in the period, or simply the distribution of certain types of hoard deposition. The majority of the finds, which usually consist of fairly large necklaces of graduated beads, come from Ireland. There are also some from Western Britain and here too the beads are often of Irish type; these could well have been secondarily derived from Ireland, especially in view of their distribution. In both Britain and Ireland the amber, when it occurs, is generally in hoards or isolated finds. Many of the Irish finds come from peat bogs, where they may well have been deposited as offerings, but the many hoards from English rivers, which may well be roughly comparable, do not contain amber. The reasons for this major shift in the distribution of amber compared with the Early Bronze Age, for which there is only a single amber bead known from Ireland, remain unknown at present and it is doubtful whether consideration of the amber alone is likely to reveal them.

Finally, a comment may be made on the Iron Age evidence for use of the material. This is fairly rare, but there are reasons for believing that the evidence is not representative. Burials are rare in the British Iron Age until the later part, and even then most of them are cremations. Where inhumations do occur, for example in east Yorkshire, occasional amber artifacts are found, and an amber necklace was associated in a burial with a mirror from Birdlip, Gloucestershire. But most Iron Age sites are settlements and such contexts present problems, first because it is unlikely that much amber would find its way into archeological deposits, and secondly because on most sites the amber would be likely to occur in the process. At the Glastonbury and Meare Lake villages, where conditions were favorable for amber preservation, a number of beads and pendants were found, and it seems unreasonable to take the view that amber was actually restricted to these settlements in the Iron Age.

Investigation of the problems raised by the work is continuing; it is concentrated primarily on the Early Bronze Age amber, which has most significance from the point of view of British prehistory, and secondarily on the Late Bronze Age distribution, which is also of considerable interest (Shennan, 1980).

REFERENCES

BECK, CURT W., and LIU, T.
  1976.   Origine de l'ambre des Grottes du Hasard et du Prevel.   Gallia Préhistoire, vol. 19, pp. 201-207.
BECK, CURT W.; LIU, T.; and NUNAN, R.
  1975.   Die Herkunft der Bernsteinfunde vom Hagenauer Forst.   Beitr. Archäol. und Kunstgesch. (Bericht der Staatlichen Denkmalspflege im Saarland), vol. 22, pp. 5-17.
BECK, CURT W.; WILBUR, ELIZABETH; and MERET, SILJA
  1964.   Infra-red spectra and the origin of amber.   Nature, vol. 201, pp. 256-257.
CATACCHIO, N. NEGRONI, and GUERRESCHI, G.
  1970.   La promblematica dell' ambra nella protostoria italiana.   Studi Etruschi, vol. 38, pp. 165-168.
FUJINAGA, T.; TAKENAGA, T.; and MUROGA, TERUKO
  1974.   The origin of the archaeological amber in Japan—studies by infrared spectra.   Journ. Chem. Soc. Japan, 1974, pp. 1653-1657.
HACHMANN, R.
  1957.   Bronzezeitliche Bernsteinschieber.   Bayer. Vorgeschichtsblätter, vol. 22, pp. 1-36 and the literature cited therein.

JAWORSKI, M.; KRAUSE, J.; LEMPKA, A.; and RICHTER, S.
1972.   Badania metodami chromatograficzną i spektrofotometryczną prczdmio-
tów bursztynowych pochodzących z wykopalisk archeologicznych.
Fontes Archaeol. Posnan., vol. 21, pp. 230-238.
SCHAEFFER, C. F. A.
1926.   Les tertres funéraires préhistoriques dans la Forêt de Haguenau, I: Les tu-
mulus de l'âge du bronze, 279 pp.   Haguenau.
SHENNAN, STEPHEN J.
1980.   Exchange and ranking: The case of amber.   Paper read at the 45th annual meeting of the Society for American Archeology, May 1, 1980,
Philadelphia, Pa.

STEPHEN J. SHENNAN

Archeological, Paleontological, and Geological Research at the Lubbock Lake Site, Texas, 1973-1974

Principal Investigators: Craig C. Black, Eileen Johnson, and Charles A. Johnson II, Museum of Texas Tech University, Lubbock, Texas.

Grant Nos. 1152 and 1318.   In support of archeological, paleontological, and geological investigations at the Lubbock Lake site.

The Lubbock Lake site is an archeological locality situated in an old meander bend in Yellowhouse Draw, just north of the city of Lubbock, Texas. The site is approximately 110 acres in extent (fig. 1) and has an occupational record from Clovis to Historic times. A unique aspect of this locality is the occurrence of a detailed geological and faunal stratigraphy in conjunction with this cultural sequence. The site was discovered in the late 1930's, with intermittent testing conducted by various people (Black, 1974). The Lubbock Lake Project, under the auspices of the Museum of Texas Tech University, began excavations at the site in 1973.

The 1973 Season

We conducted excavations at the site from May 15 to July 31, 1973. Three previous test excavations by various groups had yielded material from the Folsom, early and late Archaic, Ceramic, and Historic levels. A well-made scraper came from the probable Clovis level, although it was unassociated with any faunal remains. Clovis points were found in dump material dredged from the site. Although the cultural history of the site is limited to the last 12,000-15,000 years, faunal and geological history go back to the early Pleistocene. Such animals as *Borophagus* sp., *Stegomastodon* sp., *Nannipus* sp., and *Geochelone* sp. have been recovered from a green-sand stratum below the Clovis sands. The summer's efforts were concentrated in a number of areas and were exploratory in nature. With a crew of 30 students from various colleges and universities across the country, six major areas at the site were explored. A late Archaic living surface was uncovered at the northeast end of the site, with associated cultural and faunal material (including remains of the modern *Bison bison*).

57

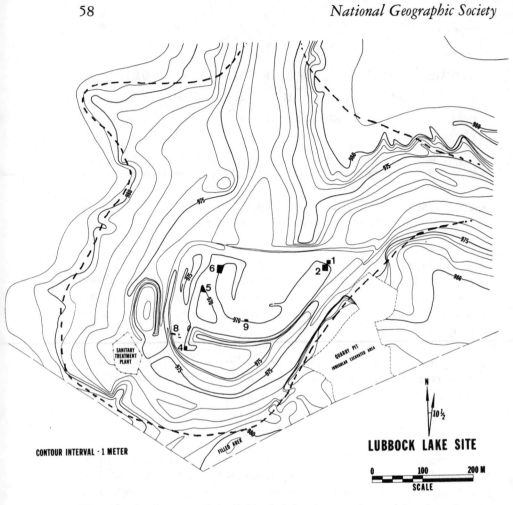

FIG. 1.   Areal extent of the Lubbock Lake site complex and location of excavation areas of the Lubbock Lake Project.

Two Folsom bison kill/butchering locales were partially excavated, yielding butchered skeletal elements of *Bison antiquus* and associated butchering
tools. The partial remains of a juvenile *Bison antiquus* were uncovered in a
post-Folsom level. This probably represents a natural death occurrence since
no associated cultural material was found, nor was any butchering evidence
seen on the bones.

A partial skeleton of a quite large, probably male, *Bison antiquus* was uncovered lying in the bank of an outlet channel of one of the Folsom period

ponds. The outlet channel was literally choked with bone and will be further explored next season. This area undoubtedly will yield a wealth of faunal data as well as geological information about the drainage patterns during Folsom time.

Lithic materials were recovered from all levels except the Clovis sands.

One of the more interesting finds, in terms of the faunal material, was the excavation of a front leg of a late Pleistocene horse. Although no associated cultural material was found, the remains come from what is most probably the Clovis level. On the basis of material recovered from previous excavations and the 1973 efforts, at least two types of late Pleistocene horses appear to have been present in the site area: a large horse, *Equus scotti,* and a medium- to small-sized horse, which is as yet unidentified. Besides such late Pleistocene animals as horse and extinct bison, mammoth and camel were recovered. Although bison remains were the most numerous, a variety of other animals was found, including a number of carnivores, rabbits, rodents, turtles, birds, and fishes.

A detailed picture of the site's geology is a major aspect of the project. A large number of geological features and materials are available for determining the site's environmental history. Geological work at the site has shown that from Clovis times onward there is a good sequence of buried soils and other time-stratigraphic marker units present. Besides discovering the Folsom pond outlet channel and Clovis period stream gravel channels, such features as mud-cracked surfaces that formed during both the Clovis and Folsom periods have been uncovered at various areas of the site. Lacustrine, fluvial, eolian, and colluvial sediments make the site's geologic history complex but provide a welcome diversity of depositional environments. Also, the essentially complete stratigraphic record, which spans the last 12,000-15,000 years, makes the Lubbock Lake site of great importance in unraveling the cultural and environmental history of man on the South Plains. Approximately 2,000 pounds of sediment from various features within the site were washed to recover the smaller vertebrates, invertebrates, and plant material. These concentrates are still being sorted but have yielded to date a variety of gastropods (both freshwater and terrestrial), bird bones, and several types of rodents.

A number of researchers have studied various aspects of the site's deposits: Vaughn Bryant, Texas A & M, looked at the pollen record, while Hal Pierce and Joseph Compton, Texas Tech University, studied the invertebrates and the diatoms respectively. During the fall of 1973 and the winter of 1974 preparation of the faunal material recovered during the summer was completed.

In late November, Eileen Johnson presented a paper on the preliminary analysis of the faunal material at the annual meeting of the American Anthropological Association. A symposium on all aspects of work, both past and present, at the Lubbock Lake site was held March 22-23, 1974, at the Museum of Texas Tech University. Participants included Joe Ben Wheat (University of Colorado), Glen Evans, James Judge (University of New Mexico), C. Vance Haynes (Southern Methodist University), W. C. Holden (Lubbock), Ernest Lundelius (University of Texas), and the principal investigators.

The 1974 Season

The second field season of the project extended from May 19 to August 18, 1974. A crew of 40 students continued excavations in some areas and tested new excavation locales. In total, seven areas (1, 2, 4, 5, 6, 8, and 9) were opened, with material recovered from the major cultural periods (fig. 1). Geologic testing was initiated with the aid of a backhoe. A limited number of profile trenches were cut to view the stratigraphy and correlate various facies changes. This type of testing will be expanded in future field seasons in an attempt to create paleotopographic maps for the major cultural and geological periods. In order to maximize data return, all excavated soil was waterprocessed through nested screens of decreasing mesh size. This matrixwashing operation was a modification of the one developed by Guilday and McCrady (Guilday et al., 1964). Recovery rate of microvertebrates, invertebrates, and small cultural items was high for most features, providing data that would have been overlooked otherwise.

The Historic period, or post-Hispanic contact, was defined at the site on the presence of modern horse *(Equus caballus)* in the deposits. Sections of two Historic processing stations were uncovered in Areas 1 and 5 (fig. 1), within substratum 5C. This substratum was a soil that developed on the valley slopes and basin margins around the marsh deposits of substratum 5B. Processing stations were areas where secondary butchering and distribution took place. Only parts of carcasses (butchering units) were taken there, the kill and initial butchering being done elsewhere. As such, a variety of game animals was recovered from these stations. The most common remains were of modern bison *(Bison bison)*, but other animals butchered included modern horse, pronghorn antelope *(Antilocapra americana)*, coyote *(Canis latrans)*, and wolf *(Canis lupus)*. Most remains of all these animals showed butchering evidence in the form of cut lines, blow marks, or bone breakage. Many of the bison bones and a few remains of horse were broken for marrow extraction. Remains of a variety of microvertebrates were recovered from the matrix concentrates associated with these features, the most common being prairie-dog *(Cynomys ludovicianus)*. Numerous flakes, scrapers, and broken bifaces, mainly of Edwards

Plateau chert, were recovered among the faunal material from both stations. A glass scraper and a bone awl came from the feature in Area 1. Two projectile points and a midsection of a third were recovered from the processing station in Area 5. One was a Washita point, made of chalcedony. No radiocarbon dates were associated with this point type in this area, although Hughes (1972) estimated a terminal date of A.D. 1600. The second point, of Edwards Plateau chert, was known locally as a Lott point. It has not yet been formally defined, and no radiocarbon dates were associated with this type.

Parts of two more processing stations were uncovered in the Ceramic period levels of substratum 5B in Areas 1 and 5. Possessing the same characteristics as the Historic stations, similar materials were recovered. The main difference was the absence of horse. Butchered remains of modern bison, pronghorn antelope, coyote, and wolf were strewn across the stations. Prairiedog was the dominant microvertebrate in the concentrates. Flakes and scrapers, mainly of Edwards Plateau chert, were common in both stations. A core from Potter's chert and a midsection of a point from Edwards Plateau chert were recovered from the station in Area 1. A Garza point (Tecovas chert), a Harrell point (chalcedony), and Apache pottery (black micaceous ware) were located in the Ceramic station in Area 5. Although no radiocarbon dates were associated with Garza points, a post-A.D. 1500 date was suggested for the type locality. Harrell points were generally found in association with Garza points in this region (Runkles, 1964).

Several weeks of testing in Area 8 (fig. 1) revealed various occupation levels within the Historic and Ceramic periods. All six activity areas located represented camping locales, and several hearths were excavated. Testing operations were limited in areal extent, and only the edges of these features were uncovered. A scattering of burned caliche, flakes, and a broken drill (Edwards Plateau chert) represented a Historic period occupation surface. A second Historic level was located below this activity area, consisting of a double hearth in a large rock-lined pit. Flakes and a few bison bones were recovered in and around the pit. The edge of a Ceramic period chipping station was located, yielding over 200 small flakes within a 2-meter area. The majority of flakes were of Edwards Plateau chert, with a few of chalcedony. Although no projectile points were recovered, through stratigraphic correlation these features were probably associated with the ones uncovered in Areas 1 and 5. Economic pursuits, i.e., hunting and butchering, were taking place around the marsh-stream area, while camping activities were located on higher ground.

The edge of a bone bed of extinct bison *(Bison antiquus)* was located in substratum 4A, the Early Archaic level, during limited testing operations along the east side of Area 5. No lithic material was located in the bed, either in situ or from matrix concentrates. The bones were in poor preservation and no butchering evidence was noted. However, less than 4 meters were exposed. More work is needed in this feature before determining whether it is a cultural or natural phenomenon.

A late Paleoindian camping area was located in Area 6 (fig. 1) within the cienaga deposits of substratum 2C. The feature consisted of an extensive scatter of lithic material with some food debris. Flakes were numerous, and a few cores were located. Most of the tools recovered (scrapers, choppers, utilized flakes) were broken. Edwards Plateau chert and Morrison quartzite were the most common lithic sources. A midsection of a projectile point, possibly an Eden, was found among the debris. Butchered remains of extinct bison formed the bulk of the food debris. Remains of prairie-dog and muskrat *(Ondatra zibethicus)* were common in the matrix concentrates. The deposits were extensive and the material relatively abundant. Although a large area was uncovered, only a section of the camping locale was exposed. The center of the camp remains to be found in future excavations.

A limited amount of time (less than two weeks) was spent in testing operations in Areas 4 and 9 (fig. 1). However, the returns were fruitful. These areas produced new bison kill/butchering locales within the late Paleoindian deposits. Two skulls *(Bison antiquus)*, assorted postcranial elements, and a flake (Edwards Plateau chert) were recovered in a sandy deposit (substratum 2F) in Area 4. Area 9 revealed a near-shore facies (substratum 2E) of the pond deposits. Several resharpening flakes of chalcedony and Edwards Plateau chert were recovered among a small stack of bison bones. Only a 2-by-3-meter unit was opened in each area.

A major excavation area for the season was in Area 2 (fig. 1), within the sands and gravel deposit (substratum 1B) of the Clovis period. Expanding the work begun during the 1973 season, butchered remains of two mammoths *(Elephas* cf. *columbi)* were recovered. These remains, of a baby mammoth and an adult, were concentrated around large caliche boulders. Bones from extinct horse *(Equus* sp.) and camel *(Camelops* cf. *hesternus)* were also recovered in this activity area. Although no direct butchering evidence was noted on these remains, their presence in the feature indicates their probable utilization by Clovis hunters. No lithic material was recovered, but a bone tool was located among the bone debris. Remains from a variety of small animals were common, particularly in the matrix concentrates. These animals included prairie-dogs, muskrats, voles *(Microtus pennsylvanicus* and *M. ochrogaster)*, turtles *(Trionyx* sp. and *Chrysemys scripta)*, and frogs *(Rana* sp.). The actual kill area for this feature was not located, the pattern recovered probably representing a processing station. Given the bulk and weight of mammoths, however, the kill area probably was not too distant from the station.

The 13 weeks of fieldwork of the 1974 season at the Lubbock Lake site were productive, particularly within the Paleoindian levels. Investigations into both camping activities and economic pursuits demonstrated both the multipurpose and repeated use of the site through time. The washing technique proved successful. The microvertebrates recovered from the concentrates will be instrumental in the paleoenvironmental reconstructions for the various periods.

REFERENCES

BLACK, CRAIG C., ed.
1974. History and prehistory of the Lubbock site. Mus. Journ., vol. 15, pp. 1-160. West Texas Museum Association.
GUILDAY, JOHN E.; MARTIN, PAUL S.; and McCRADY, ALLEN D.
1964. New Paris no. 4: A Pleistocene cave deposit in Bedford County, Pennsylvania. Bull. Nat. Speleol. Soc., vol. 24, no. 4, pp. 121-194.
HUGHES, JACK T., ed.
1972. Projectile point types of Texas and bordering states, 1 p. Anthropological Society, West Texas State University, Canyon, Texas.
RUNKLES, FRANK A.
1964. The Garza site: A Neo-American campsite near Post, Texas. Bull. Texas Archaeol. Soc., vol. 35, pp. 101-126.

CRAIG C. BLACK
EILEEN JOHNSON
CHARLES A. JOHNSON II

Studies on the Genetics of Darwin's Finches

Principal Investigator: Robert I. Bowman, San Francisco State University, San Francisco, California.

Grant No. 1274:   To support a genetic analysis of evolutionary patterns in Galápagos finches.

Evolutionary studies on Darwin's finches of the Galápagos and Cocos islands of the eastern tropical Pacific Ocean have been concerned initially with anatomical variations (Darwin, 1845; Swarth, 1931; Lack, 1945, 1947; Bowman, 1961, 1963; Cutler, 1970), secondarily with behavioral variations (Eibl-Eibesfeldt, 1961; Eibl-Eibesfeldt and Sielmann, 1962; Curio, 1964; Curio and Kramer, 1964; Bowman and Billeb, 1965; De Benedictis, 1966; Millikan and Bowman, 1967; Bowman, 1979, and most recently with variations in population ecology (Abbott et al., 1975, 1977; Grant et al., 1975a, 1975b). The studies summarized below are among the first to consider comprehensively genetic variations at the chromosomal and genotypic levels (cf., Sibley, 1970; Ford et al., 1974). More detailed presentations appear elsewhere (Jo, 1981; Polans, 1981).

The present study was supported by grants from the National Geographic Society and from the Chapman Fund of the American Museum of Natural History. The portion on the karyotype of Darwin's finch was primarily the work of Nancy Jo; that on enzyme polymorphism was primarily the work of Neil O. Polans.

Karyotype of Darwin's Finches

This part of the genetic study was intended (1) to analyze quantitatively the chromosomal morphology of the finches, (2) to correlate the findings with the known structural and behavioral patterns of the birds, and (3) to assess this information in the light of the various proposed relationships within the avian family Fringillidae, which includes the finches, sparrows, and buntings (Wetmore, 1940).

METHODS

A total of 257 finches was obtained in the Galápagos Islands during January and February, 1974, and included 12 species from 12 islands (table 1).

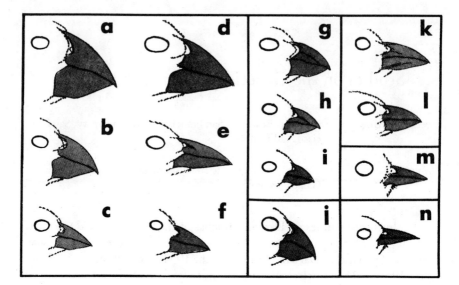

FIG. 1.   Profiles of the bills of 14 species of Darwin's finches. a, *Geospiza magnirostris;* b, *Geospiza fortis;* c, *Geospiza fuliginosa;* d, *Geospiza conirostris;* e, *Geospiza scandens;* f, *Geospiza difficilis;* g, *Camarhynchus psittacula,* h, *Camarhynchus pauper;* i, *Camarhynchus parvulus;* j, *Platyspiza crassirostris;* k, *Cactospiza pallida;* l, *Cactospiza heliobates;* m, *Certhidea olivacea;* n, *Pinaroloxias inornata.* (After Swarth, 1931.)

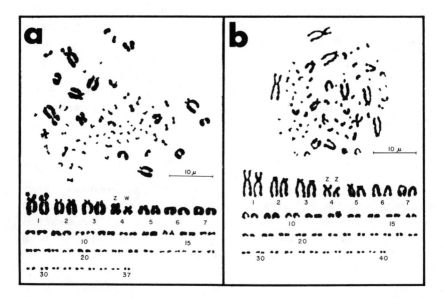

FIG. 2.   Karyotypes of two species of Darwin's finches. a, *Geospiza magnirostris,* Isla Marchena (female; NJ 179); b, *Camarhynchus parvulus,* Isla Santiago (male; NJ 201).

TABLE 1.   Island Sources of Population Samples of Darwin's Finches

SPECIES	Santa Cruz	Santa Fe	San Cristóbal	Española	Floreana	Isabela	Fernandina	Pinta	Marchena	Genovesa	Santiago	Pinzón
Geospiza												
magnirostris								3	3	1	2	
fortis	7	2			3	6		1	2	4	9	
fuliginosa	4	2	4	4	4	7	1	4			4	2
conirostris				5								
scandens	4	4						4				
difficilis								1		1		
Camarhynchus												
psittacula										1		
pauper					2							
parvulus	7			2							4	
Cactospiza												
pallida			1									
Platyspiza												
crassirostris					1					3	2	
Certhidea												
olivacea	4				4				1	1		

Chromosomal analyses were performed on 138 specimens using the in vivo technique described by Patton (1967). Details of techniques of preparation and analyses are presented in Jo (1981).

Among the 12 species and 5 genera examined (fig. 1), the karyotype shows a striking uniformity in the mean number of chromosomes ($N=76$) and gross anatomy (fig. 2). Like most birds, Darwin's finches have a typical avian karyotype with two well-marked groups of chromosomes, the so-called macrochromosomes and the microchromosomes. Members of the former group, which number seven pairs, are usually recognized by their size and distinct structure. The remaining members, belonging to the latter group, are small and show acrocentric configurations.

The sex chromosomes of Darwin's finches occupy fourth place in the series of macrochromosomes arranged in order of decreasing size. The female is heteromorphic with a "ZW" constitution, and the male is homomorphic with a "ZZ" constitution.

Karyotypic Uniformity. The uniformity in karyotype of Darwin's finches may be explained in two ways. First, if chromosomal rearrangements have occurred, they are of the paracentric inversion type or they are symmetrical translocations, which are not detectable with standard karyotypic techniques. Application of differential staining techniques, such as G-banding, will be necessary to detect the presence or absence of possible differences. Second, the apparent pan-specific uniformity of the chromosomes suggests that the 14 species of Darwin's finches have been derived from a common ancestor (i.e., have a monophyletic origin). In other words, evolutionary changes could have occurred at the structural gene level (revealable by means of protein electrophoresis) rather than at the level of the gene rearrangements (revealable by karyotypic studies such as this or as supplemented by banding techniques). Using the same specimens that were employed in the karyotypic study, Polans (see below and 1981) found "fast" esterase bands and band patterns that display various degrees of specificity.

Comparison of Karyotypes. Gross karyotypic characteristics of the 12 species of Darwin's finches, when compared with those of 4 continental species of finch of the same family (Fringillidae), suggest three possible interpretations of the karyotypic condition in the Galápagos species. One possible interpretation points to chromosomal similarity (homology?) between Darwin's finches (subfamily Geospizinae) and the canary, *Serinus canarius,* and the chaffinch, *Fringilla coelebs* (subfamily Fringillinae), as a consequence of close phyletic lineage. A structural analysis of the unfused palato-maxillary bones of the skull (Tordoff, 1954) suggests an affinity between Darwin's finches and the genus *Fringilla.*

Another possible interpretation would attribute the karyotypic similarity to chromosomal convergence, assuming that geospizines and fringillines do not have a very close genetic affinity. This idea is supported by electrophoretic data on egg-white proteins. Sibley (1970) found that 2 species of Darwin's finches, *Geospiza magnirostris* and *G. fortis,* show protein bandings similar to those of New World members of the subfamily Emberizinae. If, on the other hand, we assume that the Geospizinae (species of Darwin's finches) and the Emberizinae (represented by the American species *Zonotrichia albicollis* and *Junco hyemalis,* the white-crowned sparrow and slate-colored junco, respectively) are closely allied genetically, then the karyotypic data for these groups suggest chromosomal divergence. This could mean that geospizine finches have evolved into an insular group significantly distinct from their ancestral emerizine finches on the continent, as suggested by Beecher (1953) and Bowman (1961). Features of the geospizine syringeal musculature, described by Cutler (1970), would justify placing emberizine and geospizine finches in separate systematic groupings.

Lastly, there is the "relictual hypothesis" of Tordoff (1954), which suggests that several genera of the family Fringillidae, possessing primitive unfused or partially fused palato-maxillary bones, have persisted in remote or isolated regions located at the periphery of the central landmass of North

America. For example, in Central America the "peripheral" southeastern area includes the islands of the Caribbean; the "peripheral" southwestern area includes Cocos Island, Costa Rica, and the Galápagos Archipelago. And, if we carry the "peripheral" (= relictual) hypothesis further, we may think of the volcanoes of the Central American highlands as refugia for "primitive" genera of Fringillidae, i.e., those with unfused palato-maxillary bones. Present karyotypic data might be interpreted as favoring Tordoff's hypothesis since the geospizine finches survive today in one of the isolated peripheral locations, and they show unfused palato-maxillary bones and only slight chromosomal divergence from the presumed ancestral stock (subfamily Fringillinae) of the family Fringillidae. Moreover, Cutler (1970) has suggested that the geospizines possess an "unspecialized" type of syringeal structure, which possibly was characteristic of the ancestral oscine group now surviving mainly in isolated locations.

Future investigations of the various members of the family Fringillidae, using advanced cytological techniques, will be necessary to permit a singular interpretation of the chromosomal data for Darwin's finches. The present situation in Darwin's finches is similar to that which prevailed in our understanding of the phylogenetic relationships of phyllostomatid bats of the genera *Choeroniscus* and *Carollia,* before Stock (1975) investigated the banding patterns of their chromosomes. He clearly demonstrated that the presumed close phylogenetic affinities of these genera, reported by earlier authors on the basis of gross karyotypic characteristics, were invalid, an opinion shared by Patton and Gardner (1971).

Enzyme Polymorphisms in Darwin's Finches

Using patterns of banding derived from the electrophoresis of finch proteins, attempts were made (1) to characterize the genotypes of enzyme band patterns, (2) to estimate the degree of polymorphism and heterozygosity existing in natural populations of the finches, and (3) to measure the degree of genetic affinity between the 12 species of Darwin's finches and thereby independently evaluate traditional taxonomic categorizations.

Tissues from 257 finches (table 1) were used to determine enzyme polymorphisms with gel electrophoresis techniques pioneered by Hubby and Lewontin (1966), Lewontin and Hubby (1966) and Harris (1966). Assays include the esterases alpha-glycerophosphate dehydrogenase (a-GPD) and supernatant malate dehydrogenase.

Data from these assays, consisting of various protein bands and their groupings into specific band patterns or band phenotypes, vary in accordance with the enzyme being surveyed. In the case of malate dehydrogenase, every finch develops the same single band, while the same four-banded a-GPD pattern is present in 241 birds. Twelve remaining finches, for which patterns can be scored, possess one of three other a-GPD band "phenotypes." Two bands of "slow" esterases (that group located distinctively near the cathode after electrophoresis) also appear in each bird examined, accompanied by a third band in only a small number of finches. The bands of "fast" esterases (that group located distinctively near the anode after electrophoresis), however, display the greatest degree of band and band-pattern variation. Eleven bands, distributed throughout the 12 species, yield 32 different band patterns.

On the basis of these band data, the following relationships are considered: the number of shared bands according to species, the number of shared bands according to island location, frequency distribution of bands among species and among island locations, interspecific band correlations, frequency distribution of putative alleles among species and among island locations, genetic identity, and genetic distance.

Comparisons involving band data and locality data reveal that the presence of a particular band at a given location generally results from the presence of a particular species or group of species. Band frequency and distribution, consequently, appear to be much more a function of species presence than species location. An apparent exception to this rule is the presence of the only variable a-GPD locus in the heterozygous state exclusively on Isla Pinta, and of the homozygous state only on islas Santa Fe and Española. The suggestion of a possible ecological/environmental basis for this structure derives from a categorization of the Galápagos Islands by Bowman (1961) into groups according to area, elevation above sea level, floristic diversity, and the multiplicity of vegetation zones. Pinta, a moderately large island with a comparatively diverse flora, areas of high elevation and multiple vegetation zones, would seemingly offer a varied environment in which enzymatic variation might be advantageous. Both Santa Fe and Española, on the other hand, are smaller, have less diverse floras, are of low elevation and exhibit only a coastal vegetation zone. Perhaps within the constraints of less diverse environments there is less need for variability of an a-GPD. It is important to note, however, that this same relationship does not generally hold true for most of the islands of the archipelago. In fact, heterozygosity levels are remarkably similar across the three major island groups of Bowman (1961).

The only other readily observable correlation between electrophoretic data and ecology is the differentiation of the 4 samples of *Certhidea olivacea,* collected in the upper transition and *Scalesia* forest zones of Isla Santa Cruz, from the 12 samples collected on islas Marchena, Genovesa, and Española.

The Santa Cruz sample shows unusually high frequencies of 2 esterase bands. Three enzyme assays undertaken in this study are presumed to involve 10 genetic loci, including 1 malate dehydrogenase locus, 4 a-GPD loci, and 5 esterase loci. Across all 12 species, 50 percent of these loci are polymorphic (an allele being designated as such if it occurs with a frequency ≥ 0.01); although, within the 7 species represented by 10 or more individuals, the percentage of polymorphic loci ranges between 20 percent and 40 percent, with a median and mean of 30 percent.

The weighted average proportion of heterozygous loci per individual, (H̄), is 0.054 ± 0.023 across all 12 species of Galápagos finch. This estimate of H̄ is similar to those reported in the literature for other avian species (see Selander, 1976, p. 35).

Among the species examined in this study there was no significant degree of difference detected. Whether comparisons are made on the basis of individual band frequency, number of bands in common, specific band patterns, or genetic similarity, such data differences as do exist are small and subtle in character. Differences do exist, however, and all the comparison tests of the data support most of the previous taxonomic groupings within the subfamily Geospizinae.

The most obvious relationships established by these phylogenetic comparison schemes are intergeneric. The species of *Geospiza* are most closely related to each other. The other 3 genera examined are less closely related to *Geospiza* or to each other. This fact would seem to reinforce the validity of existing generic classification. *Camarhynchus* seems to be the closest of the 3 genera to *Geospiza*, followed by *Platyspiza*. *Certhidea* is the most distantly related. *Camarhynchus parvulus* is particularly close to the 6 species of *Geospiza* (see fig. 1) on the basis of electrophoretic information and, allowing for the exclusion of a vast array of anatomical, behavioral, and ecological data, might easily be placed among them.

Within the genus *Geospiza* several interesting relationships are revealed. In keeping with prior classification schemes, *Geospiza magnirostris, G. fortis,* and *G. fuliginosa* appear to be very closely related, although *fuliginosa* and *fortis* seem to be closer to each other than to *magnirostris*. An unexpected finding is the close relationship between *G. fuliginosa* and *G. scandens,* a propinquity more than rivaling that of *G. fuliginosa* to *G. fortis* and *G. magnirostris*. Ford, Ewing, and Parkin (1974), having observed this same unexpected relationship, referred to Lack's (1947) belief that the seed-eating, small-billed groundfinch, *G. fuliginosa,* and the more specialized cactus finch, *G. scandens,* are a subgenus apart. The electrophoretic evidence does not support this notion.

TABLE 2.   Genetic Identity Distance Between 12 Species of Darwin's Finches

SPECIES	olivacea	pallida	parvulus	pauper	psittacula	crassirostris	conirostris	scandens	difficilis	fuliginosa	fortis	magnirostris
Geospiza												
magnirostris	.866	.968	.972	.968	.951	.919	.972	.980	.982	.981	.992	.008
fortis	.856	.982	.985	.982	.963	.924	.986	.993	.993	.993		.019
fuliginosa	.862	.975	.992	.975	.958	.929	.991	.999	.982		.007	.018
difficilis	.853	.989	.977	.989	.962	.883	.987	.979		.018	.007	.020
scandens	.863	.975	.992	.975	.961	.940	.988		.021	.001	.007	.028
conirostris	.852	.986	.990	.986	.959	.881		.012	.013	.009	.014	.084
Platyspiza												
crassirostris	.820	.879	.920	.879	.906		.127	.061	.125	.073	.079	.050
Camarhynchus												
psittacula	.833	.975	.980	.975		.099	.042	.040	.039	.043	.038	.033
pauper	.835	1.000	.978		.026	.129	.014	.026	.011	.025	.018	.028
parvulus	.864	.978		.022	.020	.083	.010	.008	.023	.008	.015	.033
Cactospiza												
pallida	.835		.022	0.000	.026	.129	.014	.026	.011	.025	.018	.144
Certhidea												
olivacea		.181	.146	.181	.182	.199	.160	.148	.160	.148	.155	

Because of the paucity of electrophoretic information on *Cactospiza* (only one specimen of *C. pallida* was analyzed), little can be said about the distinctiveness of the genus (compare the opinions of Swarth, 1931, and Bowman, 1961, with Lack, 1945 and 1947). No specimens of *Pinaroloxias inornata* from Cocos Island were available.

Based upon measures of genetic distance, using the method of Nei (1975), approximate divergence times are established for species of Galápagos finches, ranging from 5,000 years to nearly 1,000,000 years (table 2). Recent evidence summarized by Cox (1981) on the geological age of the islands, gives support to these crude estimates extracted solely from electrophoretic data. According to Cox, the oldest islands of the Galápagos Archipelago, namely the central and southeastern islands, are about 4,000,000 years or less in age, with some, perhaps 2,000,000 years or less. The more recently formed islands may be less than 700,000 years old. If these datings (by paleomagnetic techniques) are reasonably accurate, the notion is upheld that most of the speciation among the finches has occurred within about 1,000,000 years or so, as predicted by the electrophoretic analyses.

REFERENCES

ABBOTT, I.; ABBOTT, L. K.; and GRANT, P. R.
  1975. Seed selection and handling ability of four species of Darwin's finches. Condor, vol. 77, pp. 332-335.
  1977. Comparative ecology of Galapagos ground finches (*Geospiza* Gould): Evaluation of the importance of floristic diversity and interspecific competition. Ecol. Monogr., vol. 47, pp. 151-184.
BEECHER, W. J.
  1953. A phylogeny of the oscines. Auk, vol. 70, pp. 270-333.
BOWMAN, R. I.
  1961. Morphological differentiation and adaptation in the Galápagos finches. Univ. Calif. Publ. Zoöl., vol. 58, pp. 1-302.
  1963. Evolutionary patterns in Darwin's finches. Occas. Papers Calif. Acad. Sci., vol. 44, pp. 107-140.
  1979. Adaptive morphology of song dialects in Darwin's finches. Journ. für Ornith., vol. 120, no. 4, pp. 353-389.
BOWMAN, R. I., and BILLEB, S. L.
  1965. Blood-eating in a Galápagos finch. The Living Bird, vol. 4, pp. 29-44.
COX, A.
  ———. The age of the Galápagos Islands. *In* "Recent Advances in Galápagos Science," Bowman, R. I. and A. Leviton, eds. Amer. Assoc. Adv. Sci., Pac. Div. (In press.)
CURIO, E.
  1964. Zur geographischen Variation des Feinderkennens einiger Darwinfinken (Geospizidae). Verh. Deutsche Zoöl. Ges. Kiel, vol. 12, pp. 466-492.

CURIO, E., and KRAMER, P.
1964. Vom Mangrovefinken (*Cactospiza heliobates* Snodgrass und Heller). Zeitschr. für Tierpsychologie, vol. 21, pp. 223-234.

CUTLER, B. D.
1970. Anatomical studies on the syrinx of Darwin's finches. M. A. thesis, San Francisco State University.

DARWIN, C.
1845. Journal of researches into the natural history and geology of the countries visited during the voyage of H.M.S. "Beagle" round the world, under the command of Capt. Fitz Roy, R. N. John Murray, London, 2 ed., rev.

DE BENEDICTIS, P.
1966. The bill-brace feeding behavior of the Galápagos finch *Geospiza coniros-tris*. Condor, vol. 68, pp. 206-208.

EIBL-EIBESFELDT, I.
1961. Über den Werkzeuggebrauch des Spechtfinken *Camarhynchus pallidus*. Zeitschr. für Tierpsychologie, vol. 18, pp. 343-346.

EIBL-EIBESFELDT, and SIELMANN, H.
1962. Beobachtungen am Spechtinken *Cactospiza pallida* (Sclater und Salvin). Journ. für Ornith., vol. 103, pp. 92-101.

FORD, H. A.; EWING, A. W.; and PARKIN, D. T.
1974. Blood proteins in Darwin's finches. Comp. Biochem. Physiol., vol. 47B, pp. 369-375.

GRANT, P. R.; GRANT, B. R.; SMITH, J.N.M.; ABBOTT, I.; and ABBOTT, L. K.
1975a. Darwin's finches: population variation and natural selection. Proc. Nat. Acad. Sci., U.S.A., vol. 73, pp. 257-261.
1975b. Finch numbers, owl predation and plant dispersal on Isla Daphne Major, Galápagos. Oecologia (Berlin), vol. 19, pp. 239-257.

HARRIS, H.
1966. Enzyme polymorphisms in man. Proc. Roy. Soc. London, vol. B164, pp. 298-310.

HUBBY, J. L., and LEWONTIN, R. C.
1966. A molecular approach to the study of genic heterozygosity in natural populations. 1. The number of alleles at different loci in *Drosophila pseu-doobscura*. Genetics, vol. 54, pp. 577-594.

JO, NANCY
———. Karyotypic analysis of Darwin's finches. *In* "Recent Advances in Gala-pagos Science," R. I. Bowman and A. E. Leviton, eds. Amer. Assoc. Adv. Sci., Pac. Div. (In press.)

LACK, D.
1945. The Galápagos finches (Geospizinae): A study in variation. Occas. Pa-pers Calif. Acad. Sci., vol. 21, pp. 1-159.
1947. Darwin's finches, x + 208 pp., illus. Cambridge University Press.

LEWONTIN, R. C., and HUBBY, J. L.
1966. A molecular approach to the study of genic heterozygosity in natural populations. 2. Amount of variation and degree of heterozygosity in nat-ural populations of *Drosophila pseudoobscura*. Genetics, vol. 54, pp. 595-609.

MILLIKAN, G. C., and BOWMAN, R. I.
1967.   Observations on Galapagos tool-using finches in captivity.   The Living Bird, vol. 6, pp. 23-41.
NEI, M.
1975.   Molecular population genetics and evolution.   North-Holland/American Elsevier, Amsterdam.
PATTON, J. L.
1967.   Chromosome studies of certain pocket mice, genus *Perognathus* (Rodentia: Heteromyidae).   Journ. Mammalogy, vol. 48, pp. 27-37.
PATTON, J. L., and GARDNER, A. L.
1971.   Parallel evolution of multiple sex-chromosome systems in the Phyllostomid bats, *Carollia* and *Choeroniscus*.   Experientia, vol. 27, pp. 105-106.
POLANS, NEIL O.
_____.   Enzyme polymorphisms in Galapagos finches.   In "Recent Advances in Galápagos Science," R. I. Bowman and A. E. Leviton, eds.   Amer. Assoc. Adv. Sci., Pac. Div.   (In press.)
SELANDER, R. K.
1976.   Genic variation in natural populations.   Pp. 21-45 *in* "Molecular Evolution,"F. J. Ayala, ed.,   Sinauer, Sunderland, Mass.
SIBLEY, C. G.
1970.   A comparative study of the egg-white proteins of passerine birds.   Peabody Mus. Nat. Hist., Bull. 32.
STOCK, A. D.
1975.   Chromosome banding pattern homology and its phylogenetic implications in the bat genera *Carollia* and *Choeroniscus*.   Cytogenetics and Cell Genetics, vol. 14, pp. 34-41.
SWARTH, H. S.
1931.   The avifauna of the Galapagos Islands.   Occas. Papers Calif. Acad. Sci., vol. 18, pp. 1-299.
TORDOFF, H. B.
1954.   A systematic study of the avian family Fringillidae based on the structure of the skull.   Misc. Publ. Mus. Zool. Univ. Mich., vol. 81.
WETMORE, ALEXANDER
1940.   A systematic classification for the birds of the world.   Smithsonian Misc. Coll., vol. 99, pp. 1-11.

NANCY JO
NEIL O. POLANS

Antipredator Adaptations of Neotropical Salamanders (Supergenus *Bolitoglossa,* Family Plethodontidae)

Principal Investigator: Edmund D. Brodie, Jr., Adelphi University, Garden City, New York.

Grant Nos. 1173 and 1436.   In support of two expeditions into Central America for the study of antipredator mechanisms of Neotropical salamanders.

There has been considerable recent interest in the presence and selective advantages of salamander antipredator mechanisms. The adaptations have been studied and are especially well developed in terrestrial species because of the different and perhaps greater predation pressures facing the terrestrial salamander. Morphological and behavioral antipredator mechanisms of terrestrial salamanders are:

Morphological Adaptations	*Behavioral Adaptations*
Tail autotomy	Escape
Toxic skin secretions	Biting
Noxious skin secretions	Vocalization
Ribs projecting through body wall	Immobility
Coloration and pattern	Posturing
Cryptic	
Aposematic	
Pseudoaposematic	

They interact in a synergistic manner that increases the protection afforded the salamander (Brodie, 1977). Prior to the present research the largest and most terrestrial group of salamanders had not been studied. These (Bolitoglossini, Plethodontidae) are confined largely to the Neotropical realm and occupy a wide range of ecological niches (Wake, 1966). The goal of this research was to study the antipredator adaptations of this most advanced group of salamanders and to compare these with previous observations on temperate plethodontid species (Brodie, 1973; Brodie et al., 1974b).

During the two expeditions, in 1973 and 1975, into Costa Rica, Guatemala, and Mexico, the 21 species listed below, belonging to 5 genera, were

77

Locality	*Species*
Volcán Poas Prov., Alajuela, Costa Rica	*Bolitoglossa subpalmata*
Cerro de la Muerte, border Prov. San José-Cartago, Costa Rica	*Bolitoglossa cerroensis* *Bolitoglossa subpalmata*
El Angel Waterfall, border Prov. Heredia-Alajuela, Costa Rica	*Chiropterotriton picadoi* *Oedipina poelzi* *Oedipina uniformis* *Bolitoglossa robusta*
Near San Marcos, Dept. San Marcos, Guatemala	*Bolitoglossa englehardti* *Bolitoglossa flavimembris* *Bolitoglossa franklini* *Bolitoglossa morio* *Bolitoglossa resplendens* *Chiropterotriton bromeliacia* *Pseudoeurycea brunnata* *Pseudoeurycea goebeli*
Volcán Tajumluco, Dept., San Marcos, Guatemala	*Bolitoglossa rostrata* *Pseudoeurycea rex*
2 kilometers east of San Rafael Pie de la Cuesta, Dept. San Marcos, Guatemala	*Bolitoglossa occidentalis*
Llanos de las Flores, Oaxaca, Mexico	*Pseudoeurycea smithi* *Thorius macdougalli*
El Chico National Park, Hidalgo, Mexico	*Chiropterotriton dimidiatus* *Chiropterotriton multidentatus*

collected and their antipredator adaptations were studied and photographed. More than 1,000 live specimens were returned to the laboratory for tests on the effects of temperature on immobility and the palatability of these salamanders to avian and mammalian predators. Observational and experimental methods were as previously published (Brodie and Howard, 1973; Howard and Brodie, 1971, 1973; Dodd et al., 1974; Hensel and Brodie, 1976; Johnson and Brodie, 1975). Some results of these studies have been presented at meetings (Dodd and Brodie, 1974, 1976a; Brodie, 1976) and published

(Dodd and Brodie, 1976b; Brodie and Tumbarello, 1978). Preserved specimens have been deposited at the Museum of Zoology, University of Michigan.

Presumably, tail loss when grasped by a predator would allow the escape of the salamander, and, since the autotomized segment of the tail twitches actively, one might assume that the predator would devote its attention to the tail rather than the body of the animal itself. The autotomized tails of two *Bolitoglossa subpalmata* (31 and 51 mm in standard length, measured from the snout to the posterior angle of the vent) continued to writhe for more than 10 minutes at 12°C. in the field. A *Chiropterotriton multidentatus* survived under experimental conditions, while a short-tailed shrew (*Blarina brevicauda*) attacked the actively writhing tail. The tail is an important fat storage organ in at least some salamanders (Wake and Dresner, 1967), and its loss, while enhancing immediate survival, could decrease the likelihood of long-term survival. Tail loss might also decrease the likelihood of successful mating of males since the tail is often used in courtship (Arnold, 1972). It was assumed by Wake and Dresner (1967), and I agree, that the loss of the entire tail, "discarded and twitching violently, is probably more efficient in distracting a predator, or acting as a decoy, than part of a tail."

The basal tail constriction in bolitoglossines apparently gives the salamander more behavioral control over tail loss, since the percentage of broken tails is significantly lower (p = < 0.001) for this group than for those salamanders with slender tails and the wound-healing specialization (Wake and Dresner, 1967). Apparently, even those salamanders with basal tail constrictions must have the tail restrained in order for breakage to take place, but observations by Esterly (1904) and Stebbins (1951) suggest that the tail of *Ensatina* might be shed under stress conditions without restraining the tail, and unpublished observations on *Bolitoglossa subpalmata* support this idea.

Skin secretions as salamander antipredator adaptations have been extensively studied (Brodie, 1968a, 1968b, 1971; Brodie and Gibson, 1969; Brodie et al., 1974a). The presence of skin secretions which irritate or repel predators is probably the most important antipredator adaptation of terrestrial salamanders. Members of the tribe Bolitoglossini were found to be the most variable group of salamanders in regard to noxiousness of skin secretions. *Batrachoseps* (at least *attenuatus*) are not distasteful but their secretions cause a drying sensation to the tongue and mouth. The secretions of *Chiropterotriton* (*bromeliacia, dimidiatus, multidentatus*) and *Pseudoeurycea brunnata* are astringent but are not bitter or burning. The secretions of *P. gadovii, P. smithi,* and *Oedipina poelzi* are astringent and bitter, burn the membranes of the mouth slightly, and cause nausea, which lasts several minutes.

The skin secretions of 7 species of *Bolitoglossa* were tested. My responses to these secretions were similar. The clear mucous secretion from mildly irritated *Bolitoglossa* produced a mild astringent feeling to the tongue not unlike that of *Chiropterotriton*. After further irritation the milky granular secretion was exuded onto the tail dorsum. A small droplet of this secretion produced a painful, bitter and burning sensation to the tongue, which spread and numbed the mouth, lips, and gums. In the most distasteful species there was increased salivation, yet the throat became dry, and I became nauseated, light-headed, and dizzy. *B. flavimembris* and *B. cerroensis* were the least distasteful and the burning was slight, lasting for only a minute or two. *B. rostrata, B. morio,* and *B. subpalmata* were more distasteful than the aforementioned species but less distasteful than *B. franklini* and *B. resplendens*. The nausea caused by a droplet of secretion from these last species placed on the tongue may last for more than 15 minutes. There are at least three types of skin secretion found on some of these *Bolitoglossa,* a clear mucous secretion as is found in all salamanders and two types of thicker secretion (presumably from the granular glands). One of these secretions is white and the other is yellow. Some species have only one of these secretions and others have both. The significance of these two types of granular secretion is currently unknown.

Immobility and antipredator postures are common and well developed in Neotropical salamanders. These adaptations and bright warning coloration, which has not yet been systematically studied, are thought to be dependent on the presence of noxious skin secretions and act synergistically with the tail autotomy specialization. The immobile response in salamanders has only recently been considered in more than a superficial manner (Brodie et al., 1974b; Dodd and Brodie, 1976b).

While immobility per se might convey a selective advantage upon an immobile prey individual it is always associated with some other line of defense in salamanders. Presumably immobility in salamanders is a form of crypsis, and as such any alteration in shape of the salamander such as coiling or contorting the body will project stimuli that may not fit the search image of the predator (illustrated by Brodie et al., 1974b; Dodd and Brodie, 1976b). Particularly important may be the positioning of the limbs during immobility. If the limbs are clasped along the body, the salamander resembles a twig or straw rather than a salamander with limbs. Immobility is further advantageous in those salamanders that have noxious skin secretions since the predator contact with the salamander, if it does take place, will be of less intensity and after experiencing the noxiousness of the salamander avoidance will follow. Immobility thus reduces the potential of injury to an inedible salamander.

Many salamanders flipped the body wildly prior to becoming immobile (e.g., *Batrachoseps attennatus, Oedipina poelzi, Pseudoeurycea brunnata, P. goebeli, P. rex, Bolitoglossa englehardti, B. franklini, B. resplendens, B. subpalmata*). The body may be coiled and uncoiled rapidly or the limbs may be used in jumping, but, in any case, the sudden change of shape, position, and location of the salamanders could startle and confuse the predator. Since this movement is protean (Chance and Russell, 1959) or erratic, the predator would be unable to predict the movement and the salamander would be difficult to seize (Klopfer, 1962; Alcock, 1975). This behavior also has a component of the flash display seen in many insects in that it starts and stops suddenly thereby disorienting pursuing predators (Robinson, 1969).

It was established that at least some species of salamanders (*Chiropterotriton multidentatus*) remain immobile for a shorter time after stimulation when acclimated at normally experienced temperatures than at higher and lower temperatures (Dodd and Brodie, 1976b). The logical interpretation is that under stressful conditions the salamanders utilize different adaptive strategies (immobility) from those at normal temperatures where they attempt to avoid predators by running. It was also observed that juveniles of *Bolitoglossa subpalmata* remained immobile for a shorter period of time than adults.

Immobility is also important in antipredator displays and could, in fact, be an evolutionary precursor to these in salamanders. Most individuals of each species studied exhibited immobility under field and laboratory conditions. This immobility was often associated with specific postures, which were categorized as follows (Dodd and Brodie, 1976b):

1. Body arched—The midpoint of the dorsal surface was elevated above both pectoral and pelvic girdles. Such arching may be accompanied by body elevation, tail arching, tail undulations, or combinations of these.
2. Body elevated—The body was raised off the ground by stiffening the front, rear, or all four limbs.
3. Body coiled—Coiling is usually tight with the head near the base of the tail. The limbs and the tail may or may not be coiled around the body.
4. Limbs extended—The limbs are held straight out from the body in a rigid manner.
5. Limbs clasped—The limbs are held posteriorly along the sides or venter of the body or tail in a rigid manner.
6. Coil-uncoil flip—The body is flipped by alternate rapid coiling and uncoiling. The limbs are clasped and are never used in flipping. The body is rigid.
7. Running flip—The body is flipped, the tail used as the main propulsive element. The body is flexible and not held rigid as in coil-uncoil flipping. This type of flipping occurs as the animal is running.
8. Serpentine flip—This type of flipping is characterized by a rigid snakelike writhing of the body producing a flipping movement; the limbs are clasped and the forepart of the body may be elevated.

9. Tail arched—The midpart of the tail is higher than either the proximal or distal ends.
10. Tail elevated—The distal portion of the tail is raised higher than any other part.
11. Tail undulated—The tail is moved slowly back and forth in a serpentine manner; it is usually associated with an arched or elevated tail.

FIG. 1.   Top, *Pseudoeurycea leprosa* in tail-arched posture, from which tail is lashed center, immobility of *Chiropterotriton picadoi* with limbs extended (note the disruptive nature of the ventral pattern); bottom, *Oedipina poelzi* (note the silver sides and black venter).

Summarized in table 1 are the antipredator behaviors observed in Neotropical salamanders. The minus sign, which means a behavior was not observed, does not rule out the existence of a certain behavior. Six species of *Pseudoeurycea* were studied. Guatemalan species (*P. brunnata, P. goebeli, P. rex*)

FIG. 2.   Top, *Bolitoglossa occidentalis* in antipredator posture, with body coiled, limbs
clasped, tail elevated and undulated; center, *Bolitoglossa resplendens* in body-arched
posture, from which the tail may be arched and undulated; bottom, *Bolitoglossa franklini* with body coiled and tail arched and undulated.

exhibited weak defensive postures, slightly elevating and undulating the tail while they held the body immobile. Mexican species (*P. gadovii, P. leprosa, P. smithi*) were more active in their tail postures (fig. 1, top). The tail was arched high, undulated, and lashed toward stimuli when touched.

All the *Chiropterotriton* examined exhibited immobility (fig. 1, center) and a few individuals of each species elevated and undulated the tip of the tail. There seemed to be a distinct difference in the flipping behavior preceding immobility between Mexican species (*C. dimidiatus, C. multidentatus*) and Central American species (*C. bromeliacia, C. picadoi*), but further studies are needed (Dodd and Brodie, 1974, 1976b).

Only one species of *Thorius, T. macdougalli*, has been examined and only 2 of 21 individuals arched slightly and undulated the tail. The other individuals exhibited immobility, often in a coil following flipping.

TABLE 1.   Antipredator Behavior of Bolitoglossine Salamanders
(A minus sign indicates that this behavior was not observed.)

Species	Immobility	Flip	Limbs clasped	Body coiled	Body arched or elevated	Tail arched or elevated or undulated
Bolitoglossa cerroensis	+	–	+	–	+	+
B. englehardti	+	–	+	+	+	+
B. flavimembris	+	–	+	+	+	+
B. franklini	+	+	+	+	+	+
B. morio	+	–	+	+	+	+
B. occidentalis	+	–	+	+	+	+
B. resplendens	+	+	+	+	+	+
B. robusta	+	–	+	–	+	+
B. rostrata	+	–	+	+	+	+
B. rufescens	+	–	+	+	+	+
B. subpalmata	+	+	+	+	+	+
Chiropterotriton bromeliacia	+	+	+	–	–	+
C. dimidiatus	+	+	+	+	–	+
C. multidentatus	+	+	+	+	–	–
C. picadoi	+	+	+	+	–	+
Oedipina poelzi	+	+	+	–	–	+
O. uniformis	+	+	+	–	–	+
Pseudoeurycea brunnata	+	+	+	+	+	+
P. goebeli	+	+	+	+	+	+
P. rex	+	+	+	+	–	+
P. smithi	+	+	+	+	+	+
Thorius macdougalli	+	+	+	+	–	+

Members of the genus *Oedipina* are the most elongate of the bolitoglossines and their defensive behavior is correlated with their morphology. *O. poelzi* randomly flip their body and become immobile when uncovered. They flip a greater distance (3-4 meters in one series of flips) than observed for any other salamander, and while immobile they repeat the flipping and immobility if touched. This rapid change of position and activity could startle and confuse the would-be predator. In *O. poelzi* there is also an apparent change in coloration as the animal flips by coiling and uncoiling. The dorsum is brown, the sides are silver and the venter is black with white flecks (fig. 1, bottom). The sides and venter flash during flipping but as the animal stops flipping it usually rights itself exposing the cryptic dorsum and becomes immobile.

The other *Oedipina* observed, *O. uniformis*, is not similarly pigmented and has a different posture. They sometimes writhed their bodies and tails stiffly with their limbs clasped along their bodies; the forebody was elevated. This behavior is reminiscent of the protean writhing of a small black snake *Geophis zelodoni* in the same habitat and the potential of mimicry exists.

The genus *Bolitoglossa* is by far the largest and most diverse genus of salamanders; it is also quite variable and advanced in defensive postures although only 11 species have been studied (table 1). The least-developed displays are those of *B. occidentalis* and *B. rufescens*, which consist of elevating and undulating the tail while the limbs are clasped along the body which is usually coiled and immobile (fig. 2, top). The tail is not swung toward a touch and the rear of the body is not elevated as is normally the case when a salamander arches and undulates the tail.

The most advanced display was observed in *Bolitoglossa resplendens*, *B. franklini*, and *B. subpalmata*, three brightly pigmented species. These normally assume a defensive posture immediately when uncovered; 49 of 55 *B. subpalmata* (16-59 mm standard length) behaved in this manner and the other 6 postured when touched. These three species elevate the posterior portion of the body or arch the body while they arch and undulate the tail (fig. 2, center). The body was often coiled with the head under the tail (fig. 2, bottom), and the body and tail were leaned toward any tactile stimulation. Animals without tails or with regenerated tails assumed the same posture as those with tails and all sizes behaved the same. These behavior patterns serve to increase the apparent size of the salamander and to place concentrations of granular glands with their antipredator secretions in closest proximity to the predator. The tail displays additionally increase the survival value of tail autotomy. When compared with other terrestrial genera of salamanders the bolitoglossines are among the most diverse in the world (table 2).

TABLE 2. Antipredator Adaptations of Terrestrial Salamanders
(A minus sign indicates that this adaptation was not observed.)

Adaptations (see listing below)

Genus	a	b	c	d	e	f	g	h	i	j	k	l	m	n	o	p	q	r	s	t	u
Salamandra	+	+	–	–	–	–	–	–	–	+	+	–	+	–	–	–	+	–	+	+	–
Salamandrina	–	–	–	–	–	–	–	–	–	+	+	–	–	–	+	+	–	–	–	–	–
Chioglossa	–	–	–	–	–	–	–	–	–	–	–	–	–	–	–	+	–	–	–	–	+
Neurergus	–	–	–	–	–	–	–	–	–	–	–	–	–	–	–	+	–	–	–	–	–
Triturus	–	–	–	+	+	+	–	–	–	–	–	+	+	+	–	–	+	–	+	+	–
Cynops	–	–	–	+	–	–	–	–	+	–	–	+	+	–	–	–	+	–	+	+	–
Taricha	–	–	–	+	–	–	–	–	–	–	–	+	+	+	–	–	+	–	+	+	–
Notophthalmus	–	–	–	+	–	–	–	–	+	–	–	+	+	+	–	–	+	–	+	+	–
Paramesotriton	–	–	–	+	–	–	–	–	+	–	–	+	+	–	–	–	+	–	+	+	–
Pleurodeles	–	+	–	–	–	–	–	–	–	+	+	–	–	+	+	–	–	+	+	+	–
Tylototriton	–	+	–	–	–	–	–	–	–	–	–	–	–	–	–	–	–	+	–	–	–
Euproctus	–	–	–	–	–	–	–	–	–	–	–	–	–	–	–	+	–	+	+	+	–
Dicamptodon	–	–	+	–	+	–	–	–	–	+	+	–	–	+	+	–	+	–	–	+	–
Rhyacotriton	–	–	+	–	–	–	+	–	+	–	–	–	+	–	–	–	–	–	–	+	–
Rhyacosiredon	–	–	+	–	+	–	–	–	–	–	–	–	–	–	–	–	–	–	–	+	–
Ambystoma	+	–	+	–	+	+	+	–	+	+	+	–	+	+	–	–	+	–	–	+	–
Hynobius	–	–	+	–	–	+	–	–	–	–	–	–	–	–	–	–	+	–	–	+	–
Onychodactylus	–	–	–	–	–	–	–	–	–	–	–	–	–	–	–	–	–	–	–	–	–
Ranodon	–	–	–	–	–	–	–	–	–	–	–	–	–	–	–	–	–	–	–	–	–
Desmognathus	–	–	–	–	–	–	–	–	–	–	–	–	–	–	+	+	–	–	–	–	–
Phaeognathus	–	–	–	–	–	–	–	–	–	–	–	–	–	–	–	–	–	–	–	–	–
Eurycea	–	–	+	–	–	–	+	–	+	+	–	–	+	–	–	–	+	–	–	+	+
Gyrinophilus	–	–	–	–	–	–	+	+	+	–	–	–	–	–	+	+	–	–	–	–	–
Hemidactylium	–	–	+	–	–	–	+	+	+	–	–	+	+	–	–	–	+	–	–	+	+
Pseudotriton	–	–	–	–	–	–	+	–	+	+	–	–	–	–	–	+	–	–	–	–	–
Typhlotriton	–	–	+	–	–	–	+	–	+	+	–	–	+	–	–	–	–	–	–	+	+
Aneides	–	–	+	–	–	–	+	+	+	+	–	–	+	+	+	–	+	–	–	+	+
Plethodon	+	–	+	–	+	+	+	+	+	–	–	–	+	+	+	–	+	–	–	+	+
Ensatina	+	–	+	–	+	+	–	–	–	+	–	–	+	–	–	–	+	–	–	+	+
Batrachoseps	–	–	–	–	–	–	–	+	+	–	–	+	–	–	–	–	–	–	–	–	+
Hydromantes	–	–	–	–	–	–	+	–	–	+	–	–	–	–	–	–	+	–	–	+	–
Bolitoglossa	–	–	+	–	+	+	+	+	+	–	–	+	–	–	–	–	+	–	–	+	+
Chiropterotriton	–	–	–	–	–	–	+	+	+	–	–	–	+	–	–	+	–	–	–	+	+
Lineotriton	–	–	–	–	–	–	–	–	–	–	–	–	–	–	–	–	–	–	–	–	+
Oedipina	–	–	–	–	–	–	+	+	–	–	–	–	+	–	–	–	–	–	–	+	+
Parvimolge	–	–	–	–	–	–	–	–	–	–	–	–	–	–	–	–	–	–	–	–	+
Pseudoeurycea	–	–	+	–	+	–	+	+	+	+	–	–	+	–	–	–	+	–	–	+	+
Thorius	–	–	–	–	–	–	+	+	+	–	–	–	+	–	–	–	–	–	–	–	+

(a) Parotoid glands
(b) Lateral warts
(c) Glandular concentrations on tail dorsum
(d) Uniform distribution of skin glands

(e) Tail lashed
(f) Tail wagged
(g) Tail undulated
(h) Body flipped

(i) Body coiled
(j) Body elevated
(k) Head butted

Table 2.—continued

(l) Venter exposed in posture	(q) Aposematic coloration
(m) Immobility	(r) Ribs extend through body wall
(n) Vocalize	(s) Toxic skin secretions
(o) Bite	(t) Noxious skin secretions
(p) Pseudoaposematic coloration	(u) Specialization for tail autotomy

REFERENCES

ALCOCK, JOHN
1975. Animal behavior: An evolutionary approach, 547 pp., illus. Sinauer Associates, Inc., Sunderland, Massachusetts.
ARNOLD, S. J.
1972. The evolution of courtship behavior in salamanders. Unpublished dissertation, University of Michigan, Ann Arbor.
BRODIE, EDMUND D., JR.
1968a. Investigations on the skin toxin of the adult rough-skinned newt, *Taricha granulosa*. Copeia, 1968, pp. 307-313.
1968b. Investigations on the skin toxin of the red-spotted newt, *Notophthalmus viridescens viridescens*. Amer. Midl. Nat., vol. 80, pp. 276-280.
1973. Defensive mechanisms of plethodontid salamanders. Hiss: News Journ., vol. 1, p. 55.
1976. Altitudinal differences in antipredator behavior of the Neotropical salamander, *Bolitoglossa subpalmata*. Proc. Ann. Meet. Animal Behav. Soc., 1976, p. 227.
1977. Salamander antipredator postures. Copeia, 1977, pp. 523-535.
BRODIE, EDMUND D., JR., and GIBSON, S.
1969. Defensive behavior and skin glands of the northwestern salamander, *Ambystoma gracile*. Herpetologica, vol. 25, pp. 187-194.
BRODIE, EDMUND D., JR.; HENSEL, JOHN L.; and JOHNSON, JUDITH A.
1974a. Toxicity of the urodele amphibians *Taricha, Notophthalmus, Cynops,* and *Paramesotriton* (family Salamandridae). Copeia, 1974, pp. 506-511.
BRODIE, EDMUND D., JR., and HOWARD, RONNIE R.
1972. Behavioral mimicry in the defensive displays of the urodele amphibians *Notophthalmus viridescens* and *Pseudotriton ruber*. BioScience, vol. 22, pp. 666-667.
1973. Experimental study of Batesian mimicry in the salamanders *Plethodon jordani* and *Desmognathus ochrophaeus*. Amer. Midl. Nat., vol. 90, pp. 38-46.
BRODIE, EDMUND D., JR.; JOHNSON, JUDITH A.; and DODD, C. K., JR.
1974b. Immobility as a defensive behavior in salamanders. Herpetologica, vol. 30, pp. 79-85.
BRODIE, EDMUND D., JR., and TUMBARELLO, M.
1978. The antipredator functions of *Dendrobates auratus* skin secretions in regard to a snake predator. Journ. Herp., vol. 12, pp. 264-265.

CHANCE, M.R.A., and RUSSELL, W.M.S.
1959.   Protean displays: A form of allesthetic behaviour.   Proc. Zool. Soc. London, vol. 132, pp. 65-70.
DODD, C. K., JR., and BRODIE, EDMUND D., JR.
1974.   Antipredator mechanisms in selected members of the Neotropical salamander genus *Chiropterotriton* with comments on the effects of temperature on the immobile response.   Herp. Rev., vol. 5, p. 74.
1976a. Defensive mechanisms of Neotropical salamanders with an experimental analysis of immobility and the effects of temperature on immobility. Herpetologica, vol. 32, pp. 269-290.
1976b. Antipredator mechanisms of Neotropical salamanders.   Herp. Rev., vol. 7, p. 79.
DODD, C. K., JR.; JOHNSON, JUDITH A.; and BRODIE, EDMUND D., JR.
1974.   Noxious skin secretions of an eastern small *Plethodon, P. nettingi hubrichti.*   Journ. Herp., vol. 8, pp. 89-92.
ESTERLY, C. O.
1904.   The structure and regeneration of the poison glands of *Plethodon.*   Univ. California Publ. Zool., vol. 1, pp. 227-268.
HENSEL, JOHN L., JR., and BRODIE, EDMUND D., JR.
1976.   An experimental study of aposematic coloration in the salamander *Plethodon jordani.*   Copeia, 1976, pp. 59-65.
HOWARD, RONNIE R., and BRODIE, EDMUND D., JR.
1971.   Experimental study of mimicry in salamanders involving *Notophthalmus viridescens viridescens* and *Pseudotriton ruber schencki.*   Nature, vol. 233, p. 277.
1973.   A Batesian mimetic complex in salamanders: Responses of avian predators.   Herpetologica, vol. 29, pp. 33-41.
JOHNSON, JUDITH A., and BRODIE, EDMUND D., JR.
1975.   The selective advantage of the defensive posture of the newt *Taricha granulosa.*   Amer. Midl. Nat., vol. 93, pp. 139-148.
KLOPFER, PETER H.
1962.   Behavioral aspects of ecology, 200 pp.   Prentice-Hall, Inc., Englewood Cliffs, New Jersey.
ROBINSON, M. H.
1969.   Defenses against visually hunting predators.   Pp. 225-259 *in* "Evolutionary Biology III," T. Dobzhansky, ed.   Appleton-Century-Crofts, New York.
STEBBINS, ROBERT C.
1951.   Amphibians of Western North America, 539 pp.   University of California Press, Berkeley.
WAKE, DAVID B.
1966.   Comparative osteology and evolution of the lungless salamanders, family Plethodontidae.   Mem. Southern California Acad. Sci., vol. 4, 111 pp.
WAKE, DAVID B., and DRESNER, I. G.
1967.   Functional morphology and evolution of tail autotomy in salamanders. Journ. Morph., vol. 122, pp. 265-305.

EDMUND D. BRODIE, JR.

Some Energetic Aspects of Behavior in a Montane Hummingbird Nesting Habitat

Principal Investigators: William A. Calder III, Department of Ecology and Evolutionary Biology, The University of Arizona, Tucson, Arizona.

Grant Nos. 1281 and 1454. In support of an investigation of the utilization of time and microhabitat by the rufous hummingbird.

The specialization of biology has led to a situation in which the biology of a species is rigidly compartmentalized. The physiologist, the morphologist, the ecologist, and the behaviorist each analyze one aspect while tending to ignore the whole. The animal, however, functions as a whole, compromising between optimization of individual variables in order to survive and reproduce as effectively as possible, with natural selection deciding what is effective.

That being the case, how much observable behavior can be explained by the physiology or ecology of the animal's situation? For the past nine years, the nesting of hummingbirds has been studied in this regard. As a consequence of small body size and intense metabolic requirements, small hummingbirds would seem to have major difficulty in maintaining nest temperatures and adult energy balance in the nocturnally cold climates of high mountain valleys.

Nest-site microclimate studies conducted during the summers of 1971-1976 were funded by the National Science Foundation and the National Geographic Society (1973, 1974, 1975, 1978). Measurements of air velocities, radiation exchanges, and temperature of nests, outside air, and surfaces of the hens have shown the importance of overhead branches in shielding the bird from the cold night sky; the insulation of the nest has also been measured (Calder, 1973b, 1974, 1975).

The objectives of the 1978 field season were:

1. Acquisition of additional nests (following abandonment) for insulation measurement.

2. Measurement of the female's metabolism while incubating at night.

3. Follow-up studies of nesting population and nest-site utilization.

The timing of the nesting season is set by the immediate weather conditions and by the consequences of the spring and winter just passed. If snow accumulation was heavy and melt-out of the valley slow, the flowers will be delayed in blooming and thus the energy supply of nectar will not be available as early as in other years. Conversely, if spring or early summer storms intervene, an early season may turn into a late season.

The 1978 season followed unusually heavy winter and spring snows which totaled 13.7 meters. However, warm temperatures in late May and early June resulted in extremely rapid melting and high runoff from the remaining accumulation, with the net result that incubation began in the middle of the range of early and late dates of previous years.

The total number of nests located was 15, of which two were not completed or incubated. Numbers of incubated nests may be compared to abundances in previous years in figure 1. The number of nests discovered is a function of at least two variables: the actual size of the breeding population and the effort and experience in locating nests. The first year of study was one of forming a search image. With the experience of knowing where to look, how the hens behave while building and incubating, etc., and the addition of a paid assistant, the number of nests located was highest (30) in 1972. An equivalent effort (principal investigator plus employment of competent and highly motivated undergraduate assistants) yielded 30 percent fewer nests in 1973. Field studies in Alaska in 1974 limited observations at Gothic, Colorado, to a part-time basis until we arrived in late July to check the old nest sites. Increased experience and accumulated knowledge of sites used in past years should have offset the reduced effort partially, but the number of nests declined 47 percent from 1973 to 1974, and has fluctuated around that level in 1975 and 1976, years in which the study was continued but with emphasis on priorities other than finding a maximum number of nests. Research and meetings overseas on other projects limited the 1977 season at Gothic to a brief visit at the end of the season. This year (1978), with renewed effort and assistance, the effort was qualitatively similar to that of 1972 and 1973, but yielded about the same results as 1974-1976.

Thus we conclude that the number of nesting females declined from 1972 to 1974 and has leveled off. The decrease seems to have been independent of the lateness of the previous year and the climate during the summer as reported by colleagues there all season.

A successful nest is defined as one at which the fledging of one or both chicks is observed, fledging size and behavior are attained (at which time any approach of a potential predator would stimulate fledging), or typical deformation of nest by large chicks has occurred (see fig. 5, Calder, 1973a). The average yearly success has been 46 percent, ranging from 18 percent in 1976 to 62 percent in 1973, and the success rate was higher than average for both years (1972, 1973) that were followed by fewer nestings in the succeeding

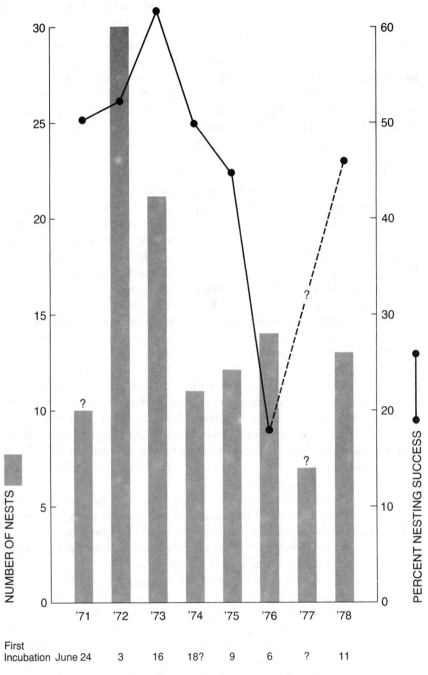

FIG. 1. Number of nests related to percent of nesting success.

year. Thus the decline from 30 nests in 1972 to an average of 12½ from 1974-1978 (except 1977, inadequate observation) does not correlate with nesting success of previous years. Nesting success has not been affected by our studies at the nest—the procedures and equipment have not had any measurable effect on the outcome. There were 3 nests out of the 109 studied wherein our manipulations resulted in egg breakage, or sudden frightening resulted directly in abandonment, but this small fraction could not have had the observed impact.

The only other factor which we could offer to perhaps account for the decline is the fact that either our studies or those of other biologists studying pollination and feeding behavior have required the cooperation of Gothic residents in refraining from putting out hummingbird feeders in the years 1972-1978. The previous availability of an artificial source of food may have increased the "carrying capacity" of the local area significantly, holding in more birds than could breed successfully on the nectar supply available naturally. If this were the case, the nest numbers should increase with completion of studies and resumption of hummingbird-feeding as a human pastime.

We have heard frequent reports from people who have female hummingbirds that return to the same nest "year after year." Frequently nests are found which have been built upon the matted remains of old nests from past years. In no case has banding established that a female returned to the same site, although that could prove to be the case with sufficiently extensive bird studies.

The apparently crucial importance of locating the nest site for proper sheltering would favor reuse of the best sites. Also, the apparent energy cost of hovering to gather spider-webbing and fine bark flakes for the well-insulated hummingbird nests would seem to make the use of old material for the nest base desirable. It is thus interesting to examine the records for reuse of nest sites.

Of 109 nestings, 29 (27%) have been in the same position as nests observed in previous seasons. Of these reuses of the same branches, 60 percent have been in successive years, the other 40 percent having been vacant for one year or more between reuses. At those sites used two or more years in succession, 53 percent had successful nests in the previous season.

If the use of a nest site were unsuccessful, we might expect the female to go elsewhere, learning to avoid the scene of predation, intrusion or inadequate shelter. That sites, when reused, are almost equally likely to follow tragedy as success, suggests that other females are involved, in other words, that the hens' search image for a favorable site is behaviorally standardized. Lacking a record of the previous outcome, a new hen would then be likely to accept an apparently good site even though her predecessor met with grief.

That over one-fourth of the observed nestings were at previously used sites seems to confirm the favorable-site-image hypothesis. The slight edge of 60 percent to 40 percent for successive reuses compared to alternately vacant sitings may well reflect the addition of a component of experience.

Because the study could not be pursued throughout the summer of 1977, it is difficult to utilize 1978 observations fully, except in the case of one nest obviously built upon a last-year nest and one that was observed in use during the brief inspection of 1977 as well as in 1975, 1976, and 1978.

Limiting the data to the 1971-1976 period, the success rates can be compared between sites used only one time (43% successful, n = 65), reused but not successively (67% successful, n = 6), and used again in successive seasons (92% successful, n = 12). These figures seem indicative of a synergistic effect between favorable site and experience.

With the comparatively small number of nests in 1978, and the fact that most of these happened to be located too high in thin trees or too far out over the river during a record high runoff, the incubating female was inaccessible for field measurements of oxygen consumption in all but one nest. The design, fabrication and placement of a closing chamber around that one nest all proceeded smoothly. The female accepted the addition to her surroundings and even permitted partial remote closure of the doorway that would be necessary to ensure a controlled airflow for measurement of oxygen consumption, without taking flight. After a period of stormy nights the weather broke and a night of recording was planned. The door was not closed until 2:00 a.m. when the bird was sleeping on the nest. Unfortunately, the female panicked, left the nest, and when released from being "trapped" inside, flew off into the night, never to return. The abandoned nest was later collected for thermal conductance measurements, as were two naturally abandoned nests. The nesting population and success are being followed further as a sidelight to a new project on fluid balance, because the background of information now available on the Gothic nesting population of the broad-tailed hummingbird makes it the most extensively documented hummingbird population anywhere, thanks to National Geographic Society research grants, National Science Foundation grants, and the research of our colleagues, Drs. Nickolas Waser, David Inouye, Graham Pyke, and Mary Price.

REFERENCES

CALDER, WILLIAM A.
1973a. Microhabitat selection during nesting of hummingbirds in the Rocky Mountains. Ecology, vol. 54, pp. 127-134.
1973b. An estimate of the heat balance of a nesting hummingbird in a chilling climate. Comp. Biochem. Physiol., vol. 46A, pp. 291-300.

CALDER, WILLIAM A.—*continued*

1974.   Consequences of body size for avian energetics.   *Avian Energetics*, R. A. Paynter, Jr., ed.   Publ. of the Nuttal Ornithological Club, No. 15, Cambridge, Mass., pp. 86-151.

1975.   Factors in the energy budget of mountain hummingbirds.   Pp. 431-442 *in* "Perspectives of Biophysical Ecology; Ecological Studies: Analysis and Synthesis," D. M. Gates, ed.   Springer-Verlag, New York, Heidelberg, Berlin.

1976.   Energetics of small body size and high latitude: The rufous hummingbird in coastal Alaska.   Int. Journ. Biometeor., vol. 20, pp. 23-35.

1981.   Heat exchange of nesting hummingbirds in the Rocky Mountains and utilization of time and microhabitat by the rufous hummingbird, Nat. Geogr. Soc. Research Reports, vol. 13, pp. 179-203.

WILLIAM A. CALDER III

SARA HIEBERT

Status of the Rare and Endangered Black-footed Ferret in Wyoming

Principal Investigator: Tim W. Clark, Idaho State University, Pocatello, Idaho.

Grant No. 1254:   To study the interrelationships of prairie-dogs and black-footed ferrets in Wyoming.

"Black-faced prairie-dog" was the name given the currently rare and endangered black-footed ferret (*Mustela nigripes*) by Sioux Indians. The Sioux name is indicative of the close association ferrets have with prairie-dogs. As a result of their rarity and nocturnal habits, large gaps still exist in our knowledge of them. The purposes of this paper are: (1) to report results of an extensive and intensive search for ferrets in Wyoming, and (2) to compare the results of this investigation with data from South Dakota (the only place where they can be consistently found) and elsewhere and with the ferret's nearest living relative—the Amur Siberian polecat (*Mustela evensmani amurensis*).

Background and Search Procedures

The ferret search covered 25 months (October 1973-October 1975). The procedures were similar to those used successfully in South Dakota to locate ferrets there. First, a review of the locations of ferret sightings in Wyoming was completed (Clark, 1973). Also, biologists in adjacent states (Nebraska, South Dakota, Montana, Utah, and Colorado) were contacted about ferret sightings along Wyoming's borders.

Second, self-addressed postcards, picturing ferrets and briefly explaining survey objectives and ferret habits, were sent to all Bureau of Land Management, Soil Conservation Service, Fish and Wildlife Service, and Wyoming Game and Fish offices and to county agents, county assessors, and all high schools and colleges in the state. Cards were passed out to ranchers in areas likely to contain ferrets and were posted in conspicuous places in towns nearest the sightings. About 9,000 cards were distributed in all.

Third, numerous newspaper releases and longer articles (e.g., in *Wyoming Wildlife*) were written; the combined circulation exposure was about 100,000. These articles briefly described the ferret-search project and told of ferret biology. They requested people to be on the lookout for ferrets and to

95

pass along any sightings or other evidence they might have on ferrets, regardless of how old the information might be.

Fourth, a few radio stations carried short ferret-search announcements as a public service. They requested that individuals report any pertinent information.

Fifth, a few public talks were given to Lions Clubs, conservation groups, and others. A slide series and a ferret movie (courtesy of C. Hillman and G. Titus, respectively) were used in these presentations.

Sixth, in 1975, 500 ferret "wanted" posters were distributed picturing a ferret with its description and announcing a $50 reward for a photograph or information leading to my taking a photograph.

When a ferret sighting was reported, contact was made with the individual by letter for more details. On the basis of this standardized report form, the reports were evaluated and, if considered reliable or possibly so, respondents were contacted personally. They were first asked to describe in as much detail as possible what they saw. Next, plate 6 (p.53) in Burt and Grossenheider's *A Field Guide to Mammals* (1964) showing color pictures of weasels, mink, and ferrets (with species names masked out) was shown to respondents, and they were asked to choose the animal most like what they saw. If the observation still seemed credible, a site visit was frequently made with the respondent and details of the sighting again requested.

On the basis of all this information, either the report was discarded as a misidentification or because too little information was available for a valid evaluation or else it was classified into one of the three following categories:

1. Positive—the observer produced some physical evidence such as a hide or photograph accompanied by trenches, plugged burrows, and ferret scat. Or a credible description was given by observers who were biologists or professional field-oriented persons (e.g., geologist, range manager). This person articulated a credible account and may have recently seen live ferrets in South Dakota or ferret skins in museums. The region has a documented history of ferret reports. Also the habitat was characterized by abundant ground-dwelling sciurids, especially prairie-dogs. If seen in white-tailed prairie dog habitat an alternate prey source is readily available during winter months.

2. Probable—The observer gave an accurate description of a ferret; selected a ferret out of a series of mustelid pictures; and characterized the behavior of the animal in detail. The report was supported by other sightings in the immediate area by individuals judged to be "positive" or "probable."

3. Possible—The observer described some characteristics of a ferret (e.g., black feet), but because of poor memory for details or an obscured view was unable to give a fully detailed account of the animal. However, the descrip-

tion did contain strongly suggestive information. The report was also supported by other evidence as described in "positive" above.

If the respondent's observations constituted at least a "possible" ferret sighting, a detailed search in the area of the sighting was conducted. It consisted of locating prairie-dog colonies in the area (within 3.0 kilometers) and searching here for ferret signs by day and for ferrets by night. Prairie-dog colonies encountered were systematically mapped and enumerated for future census.

Results

Nearly 300 alleged ferret sightings were reported; approximately half of these were discarded because of lack of sufficient information or because of an obvious misidentification. From 1851, when the first ferret was described by Audubon and Bachman, to 1975, 145 sightings of at least 167 animals were evaluated as valid or likely sightings. A list of these is available from me (Clark, 1980).

Of the 145 reports, 93 were classed as positive, 37 probable, and 15 as possible. Many earlier reports were accompanied by supporting evidence (i.e., skin and skull) or were made or recorded by very reputable observers (e.g., from the Biological Survey, universities, or state and Federal game and fish departments).

Evaluation of recent reports is by no means an unequivocal process. However, the diversity and competence of the respondents lend credence to their reported sightings; two of the respondents had previously observed ferrets in South Dakota with competent biologists. Respondents have included Wyoming game and fish biologists, experienced U. S. Fish and Wildlife Service personnel, members of U. S. Forest Service, Bureau of Land Management people, academic wildlife scientists, wildlife photographers, and others. Such evidence overwhelmingly indicates that black-footed ferrets still exist in Wyoming.

Remains of 23 ferrets from Wyoming were located, including the type skin (no. 1; numbers correspond to entries in a list available from me) and eight other preserved skins (nos. 4, 5, 7, 8, 9, 10, 11, 16) on deposit in the U. S. National Museum (Smithsonian); four (no. 3) associated with the Plains Indian Museum, Cody; four (no. 3) in the Chief Plenty Coups Museum (maybe from southern Montana), Pryor, Montana; two (nos. 40, 46) in the University of Wyoming Zoology Museum; two in collection at Old Trail West, Cody; and two in private collections (D. Prager, Garrett, and J. Fillmore, Sheridan). One skeleton (no. 8) and at least eight skulls are represented.

Little Box Elder Cave in Converse County, an archeological site of the late Pleistocene, yielded skeletal remains of 15 ferrets and at least 73 prairie-dogs (Anderson, 1968).

The 145 reports from 1851 to 1975 were plotted on a Wyoming map (fig. 1). The numbers correspond to entries in a list (available from me) where information on dates, location, animal(s), sources, notes, and evaluation is given for each report. Reported sighting locations fall in areas of highest human population densities and along major roads. Since the sample shown in figure 1 is not random, it may not indicate the complete range (either historic or current) and population concentrations of ferrets.

Ferrets were reported from all counties except Yellowstone National Park. Yellowstone is bordered by mountains to the east and south and vegetated with dense stands of timber; coniferous forests are not considered "typical" ferret habitat.

The distribution of recent sightings (1970 to 1975) follows the pattern of earlier records (1851-1969) with one major exception—the southeastern portion of Wyoming (fig. 2). No recent ferret reports come from a five-county area, including Laramie, Goshen, Platte, Niobrara, and Converse. Johnson, Teton, and Uinta counties showed no recent reports.

Of the 167 different animals reported, 34 or 35 (21%) were of dead animals. Ten or 11 (6%) (nos. 13, 15, 24, 29) were caught in coyote traps, two (1%) (nos. 20, 21) in badger traps, one (no. 46) was shot, one (no. 40) was road killed, and one (no. 94) was drowned in a stock tank. The remaining ferrets were preserved in some manner and are discussed above.

Additional ferret mortality is attributed to poisoning for coyotes by several respondents. For example, David Prager, who saw two ferrets (nos. 30, 61) in the same area and heard of several others, said these observations preceded a "heavy poisoning program put on this area for coyotes and I never heard of any ferrets after this time." Report no. 24, originally noted by Don Fortenbery, U. S. Fish and Wildlife Service, cites that seven or eight ferrets were caught in coyote traps in southern Converse County between 1932 and 1936. It is likely that other such incidents have gone unreported. Attempts to obtain detailed data on the distribution and volume of a variety of poisons used for prairie-dog and predator eradication were generally thwarted or data were unavailable. No published data exist on the effects of ferrets eating strychnine-poisoned prairie-dogs, or their susceptibility to cyanide gas bombs. Another ferret was found "with its whole front end full of porcupine quills. It was in bad shape and nearly helpless." The quills were extracted from the captured ferret and it was released. It ran off into the vegetation and disappeared.

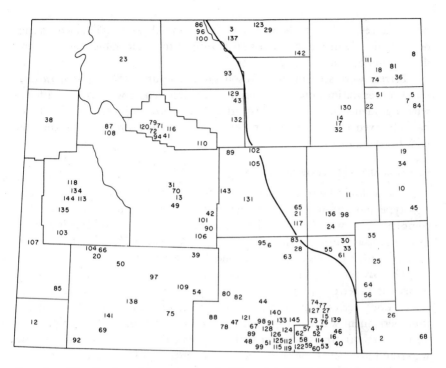

FIG. 1.   Distribution of ferret reports in Wyoming (1851-1975); numbers correspond to entries, listed chronologically, available from the author. Left of the dark
line is the range of the white-tailed prairie-dog and to the right, that of the black-
tailed prairie-dog.

In all, 121 ferret reports clearly fell within the range of one of the two
largely allopatric prairie-dog species in the state (fig. 1): 88 (73%) reports fell
in the range of white-tailed prairie-dogs *(Cynomys leucurus)* and 33 (27%) in
the range of the black-tailed *(C. ludovicianus).*
   The distance that ferret reports were from the nearest prairie-dog concentration was determined in 31 cases. In 26 instances, ferrets were a mean of 0.4
kilometer (range 0.0-0.8 kilometer) from whitetails and in five instances were
a mean of 0.8 kilometer (range 0.3-3.2 kilometers) from blacktails.
   The only published information on prairie-dog distribution indicated
that prairie-dogs occupied approximately 52,800 hectares in Wyoming in the
early 1970's (Clark, 1973). Prairie-dog distribution is patchy and many colonies are only a few hectares in size. Stromberg (1975) presents evidence that
ferrets may need prairie-dog colonies that contain burrow systems with multi-

ple entrances; such systems seem to be found on old, well-established prairie-dog colonies. Prairie-dogs are currently subject to considerable poisoning and destruction by shooting and gassing.

Ferrets were seen on Richardson ground-squirrel *(Spermophilus richard-sonii)* concentrations on two occasions. A single report was given of a ferret with a golden-mantled ground squirrel *(S. lateralis)* in its mouth. Dr. Hub-bard observed a ferret catching millers (moths) under a street light at the edge of Wheatland in 1933.

ECOLOGICAL CONTEXT OF SIGHTINGS

The ecological setting of each sighting was categorized in terms of vegeta-tion type and distance to a perennial watercourse and an extensive meadow complex. This was determined for 105 observations. Most sightings were made in a sagebrush-grassland habitat type (N= 102, 97%), two ferrets were seen in coniferous forests (2%), and one was seen in a meadow (1%).

The distance to perennial water and an associated meadow was deter-mined for 44 ferret reports. Of the 34 reports in association with white-tailed prairie dogs, ferrets were a mean of 0.7 kilometer (range 0.0-0.8 kilometer) from permanent water and associated meadows. This contrasts sharply for the 10 ferret reports in association with black-tailed prairie-dogs. No standing water and associated meadows were closer than 1.6 kilometers in these 10 cases; the exact distance in all cases was not determined.

Discussion

Evidence gathered from this study verifies that ferrets still exist in several locations in Wyoming (fig. 2). Data on ferret distribution and ecology were derived from numerous reports by a wide variety of observers. No estimates of present ferret numbers are possible. There is mounting evidence, however, that the black-footed ferret mentioned in the lore of Blackfeet, Cheyenne, Crow, Sioux, and Pawnees was more abundant in American prehistory than in recent times (Henderson et al., 1969; Hillman, 1974; Clark, 1976). As dis-cussed by Hillman and Linder (1973), locating ferrets is a very difficult task—characteristic ferret signs are nearly nonexistent; positive identification of fer-ret activity is difficult during all seasons. Solicitation of ferret observations is one of the most efficient means of obtaining potential information on ferrets (Henderson et al., 1969).

A noteworthy pattern of geographic distribution of ferret reports emerged. Most observations were from western Wyoming in association with white-tailed prairie-dogs. The only previously published information shows

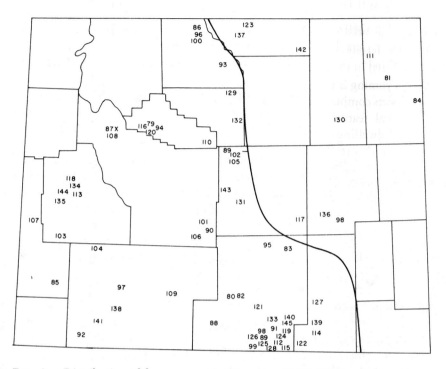

Fig. 2. Distribution of ferret reports in Wyoming (1970-1975); numbers correspond to entries, listed chronologically in a list available from the author. Left of
the dark line is the range of the white-tailed prairie-dog and to the right, that of the
black-tailed prairie-dog.

ferrets occurring only in eastern Wyoming in association with black-tailed
prairie-dogs. Information in Hall and Kelson (1959) and Long (1965) was
based on the eight ferret skins known from museum collections or information
from early sources (mostly before ca. 1950). Both accounts of the historic distribution in the state suggested that ferrets existed only in the eastern part.

Reasons for the differences in early reports on ferret distribution in Wyoming and results of this study are not clear. The extent of early biological surveys in western versus eastern Wyoming is unknown, and if most collecting in
earlier periods was concentrated in eastern Wyoming, then it is not surprising
to learn that no ferrets were reported from the western area. Two of the most
recent ferret reports from Colorado are in the northernmost tier of counties
just south of Uinta and Sweetwater counties in southwestern Wyoming and in
the range of white-tailed prairie-dogs (Torres, 1973). Valid reports from

Utah, in association with white-tailed prairie-dogs, show ferrets to have occupied range even farther west than western Wyoming (Sparks, 1973). It is likely that ferrets have always occupied western Wyoming but have gone
unreported in the scientific literature.

Wyoming is very diverse in vegetation and physiography, but despite ferret reports coming from across this broad region the reports tend to have some
ecological features in common, i.e., habitat type and association with
ground-dwelling sciurids, especially prairie-dogs. Nearly all ferret reports received in this study (where sufficient background data existed) showed that
ferrets were most often seen in a sagebrush-grass habitat type. In other areas of
North America ferrets are frequently found in short- and mid-grass prairies
(Henderson et al., 1969). The Amur Siberian polecat, the black-footed ferret's closest living relative, also lives in open landscapes and rarely in forests
(Zverev, 1931; Brom, 1954; Kolosov, 1939). The two ferret reports in this
study from timbered areas are not unique for Wyoming. Warren (1942) lists
two similar records from Colorado: the first record in the early 1900's is of a
specimen taken from an area west of Pikes Peak Range, Teller County (3,070
meters). The second record is of a dead ferret found in Lake Moraine, El Paso
County (3,400 meters); the lake is surrounded by mountains with dense
stands of timber. Other Colorado reports come from South Park, a large
mountain valley 160 kilometers southwest of Denver and from the mountain
town of Meeker (Torres, 1973).

Survival of ferrets seems closely linked to, if not dependent on, prairie-
dogs (Linder et al., 1972). Prairie-dogs serve as their principal prey; burrows
are used for shelter and to raise young (Sheets and Linder, 1969). Nearly all
ferret sightings are on prairie-dog towns (Hillman and Linder, 1973). As
prairie dogs are eradicated, essential ferret habitat is apparently lost. Ferrets
seem unable to compete effectively with weasels, minks, and badgers, etc., on
a year-round basis outside prairie-dog colonies.

The interior of North America underwent radical changes with the coming of Europeans. As part of the transformations, the grasslands were either
plowed under or turned into pastures for livestock production. Prairie-dogs
were considered economic pests and massive long-lasting eradication programs have been carried out against them (Clark, in preparation). Now, over
all parts of their former range, prairie-dogs have been totally extirpated or
greatly reduced in numbers. There are, however, exceptions to this, and a few
areas still contain sizable prairie-dog populations. Hillman and Linder (1973)
state that information is lacking on the status and distribution of prairie-dogs
over much of the ferret's original range and the success of intensive ferret
searches depends on our knowledge of prairie-dog numbers and distribution.

They go on to say that prairie-dog surveys are an important part of any effort to determine the ferret's current status. The current information from this study on the ferret's ecology and ethology shows its biology in western Wyoming to be similar to that of the Amur Siberian polecat and somewhat different during the winter months from what we know of ferret biology in South Dakota. Stroganov (1969) reports that the Siberian polecat needs an abundance of rodents (marmots, susliks=ground squirrels, etc.) and that polecats occur in highest concentrations where these rodents are abundant. In western Siberia, polecats live in different biotopes (habitats) at various seasons; this is a function of changes in seasonal availability of prey. The major seasonal change in feeding conditions results from the hibernation of susliks from late fall to late spring. Black-footed ferrets in South Dakota are thought to remain on or near blacktailed prairie-dog colonies throughout the year; since blacktails do not hibernate, they provide a potential perennial food source. Ferrets in western Wyoming and elsewhere, living in association with white-tailed prairie-dogs, which do hibernate, are forced to alternate prey during the winter months. Siberian ferrets move onto meadows in early winter and prey on several genera of small mammals *(Clethrionomys, Microtus, Peromyscus, Mus,* etc.). These same genera are found in meadows of western Wyoming. One characteristic of ferret sightings in western Wyoming revealed in this study was that ferrets were most often found less than 0.5 kilometer from permanent water and associated meadows. This suggests that ferrets in western Wyoming may adopt a strategy of alternating prey as Siberian polecats do.

REFERENCES

ANDERSON, E.
1968.   Fauna of the Little Box Elder Cave, Converse County, Wyoming: The Carnivora.   Univ. Colorado Stud., earth sci. ser., no 6, 60 pp.
BROWN, I. P.
1954.   [Data on the biology of the Transbaikalian polecat.]   Inst Siberi i Dal' nego Vostoka, 12. Irkytsk. (In Russian.)
BUREAU OF LAND MANAGEMENT, U. S.
1974.   Draft environmental impact statement: Eastern Powder River Coal Basin II, p. 1529.
BURT, WILLIAM H., and GROSSENHEIDER, R. P.
1964.   A field guide to the mammals, 284 pp., illus.   Houghton Mifflin Co., Boston.
CAHALANE, VICTOR H.
1954.   Status of the black-footed ferret.   Journ. Mamm., vol. 35, pp. 418-424.

CLARK, TIM W.
   1973.   Prairie dogs and black-footed ferrets in Wyoming. Pp. 88-101 *in*
           "Black-footed Ferrets and Prairie Dogs in North America," R. L. Linder
           and C. N. Hillman, eds.   South Dakota State University, Brookings.
   1976.   Some relationships of prairie dogs, black-footed ferrets and Paleo- and
           modern Indians.   Plains Anthrop., vol. 13, pp. 275-280.
   1978.   Current status of the black-footed ferret in Wyoming.   Journ. Wildl.
           Management, vol. 42, no. 1, pp. 128-134.
   1980.   A listing of blackfoot ferret reports in Wyoming (1851-
           1977).   Northw. Sci., vol. 54, pp. 47-54.
   _____.   Prairie dogs—Range and relationships: A review.   (In preparation.)
HALL, E. RAYMOND, and KELSON, KEITH R.
   1959.   The mammals of North America, 1,083 pp., illus.   Ronald Press, New
           York.
HENDERSON, F. R.; SPRINGER, P. F.; and ADRIAN, R.
   1969.   The black-footed ferret in South Dakota.   South Dakota Dept. Game,
           Fish, and Parks Tech. Bull. no. 4, 37 pp.
HILLMAN, C. N.
   1968.   Field observations of black-footed ferrets in South Dakota.   Trans.
           North Amer. Wildl. and Nat. Res. Conf., vol. 33, pp. 133-143.
   1974.   Status of the black-footed ferret.   Paper presented before Conference on
           Rare and Endangered Wildlife, Washington, D. C., summer 1974.
HILLMAN, C. N., and LINDER, RALPH L.
   1973.   The black-footed ferret.   Pp. 10-23 *in* "Blackfooted Ferret and Prairie
           Dog Workshop."   South Dakota State University, Brookings.
KOLOSOV, A. M.
   1939.   [Mammal fauna of the Altai and adjacent Mongolia in relation to prob-
           lems of zoogeography.]   Zool. Zhurnal, vol. 18, p. 2. (In Russian.)
LINDER, RALPH L.; DAHLGREN, R. B.; and HILLMAN, C. N.
   1972.   Black-footed ferret–prairie dog relationships.   Pp. 22-37 *in* "Sympo-
           sium on Rare and Endangered Wildlife of the Southwestern United
           States, Sept. 22-23, 1972, Albuquerque, New Mexico."
LONG, CHARLES A.
   1965.   The mammals of Wyoming.   Univ. Kansas Publ., Mus. Nat. Hist.,
           vol. 14, pp. 483-735.
SHEETS, R. G., and LINDER, RALPH L.
   1969.   Food habits of the blackfooted ferret *(Mustela nigripes)* in South Dakota.
           Proc. South Dakota Acad. Sci., vol. 48, pp. 58-61.
SPARKS, E. A.
   1973.   Prairie dogs and black-footed ferrets in Utah.   Pp. 102-104 *in* "Black-
           footed Ferrets and Prairie Dogs in North America," R. L. Linder and
           C. N. Hillman, eds.   South Dakota State University, Brookings.
STROGANOV, S. U.
   1969.   Carnivorous mammals of Siberia.   Izdatel'stvo Akad. Nauk SSSR,
           Moskva, 1972. (Translated from the Russian by Israel Program for Sci-
           entific Translations, Jerusalem, 1969.)

STROMBERG, M.
 1975. Aspects of habitat of black-tailed prairie dogs: Vegetation, soils, comparative burrow structure and spatial patterns, 120 pp. M. S. dissertation, University of Wisconsin.
TORRES, J. R.
 1973. The future of the black-footed ferret in Colorado. Pp. 27-33 *in* "Black-footed Ferrets and Prairie Dogs in North America," R. L. Linder and C. N. Hillman, eds. South Dakota State University, Brookings.
WARREN, EDWARD R.
 1942. The mammals of Colorado, ed. 2, 330 pp., illus. University of Oklahoma Press, Norman. (1st ed., 1910, 300 pp., G. P. Putnam's Sons, New York.)
ZVEREV, M. D.
 1931. [Data on the biology and agricultural significance of polecats and other Carnivora of the family Mustelidae in Siberia.] Trudy Zashchite Rastenii Sibiri, vol. 1, no. 8. (In Russian.)

TIM W. CLARK

Research Toward Satellite Tracking of Migrating Birds

Principal Investigator: Frank C. Craighead, Jr., Environmental Research Institute, Moose, Wyoming, and Atmospheric Sciences Research Center, State University of New York at Albany.

Grant Nos. 1189, In support of the development of an ultra-high-frequency
1636. radiolocation system for studying birds and continued research toward satellite tracking of raptors.

The objective of this research has been to advance toward the ultimate goal of tracking and monitoring migrating birds by satellite. This has required a number of different yet related steps. It has involved the development and employment of both a high frequency (VHF) and an ultra high frequency (UHF) radiolocation system for conventional ground and airplane tracking; the development and testing of a Nimbus 6/RAMS (Random Access Measurement System) DCP miniaturized transmitter (56 g.) on a satellite compatible frequency (401 MHz); and work with transmitter attachment methods and techniques on a variety of birds, both trained and wild. This has been done in conformance with National Aeronautics and Space Administration guidelines (Anonymous, 1973, and Wolff et al., 1975).

Development and Application of a VHF-UHF Telemetry System

In order to test and evaluate various transmitter-attachment methods, a combination 148-MHz and 462-MHz bird-telemetry system was acquired and put into operation. Basically, it consisted of a 148-MHz system (Beaty, 1972) with a UHF to VHF converter on the UHF receiver antenna. The miniaturized transmitters weighed 2.8 grams.

Transmitters on 32, 148, 220, 401 and 462 MHz were also tested and performance compared.

Twenty birds were instrumented with various transmitters. These included 6 golden eagles *(Aquila chrysaetos)*, 4 bald eagles *(Haliaeetus leucocephalus)*, 6 ravens *(Corvus corax)*, 3 red-tailed hawks *(Buteo borealis)*, and 1 prairie falcon *(Falco mexicanus)*. These were divided equally among trained and wild birds (Craighead and Dunstan, 1976).

107

Tests using 32-MHz transmitters were not conducted in this series of tests but transmitters on this frequency were used operationally in tracking elk and grizzlies for hundreds of tracking days. The performance of this frequency using comparable tracking systems was compared with the other field-tested systems, and a judgment decision formulated.

In field use it takes a great deal of time and tracking experience to learn all the idiosyncrasies of a radio tracking system. The directivity varies with terrain, attachment methods, subject activity, equipment configuration, and other variables. Nevertheless, the impressions obtained in using and comparing the different systems are that the range at which signals could be received was more consistent with the 32-MHz frequency than with the others. At this frequency signals could be picked up with hills and low mountains intervening, and transmission and reception were better than line-of-sight. When transmitters were low (1-2 m. above the ground) signal range and directivity were more consistent on 32 MHz. Although signal directivity as well as range was excellent in line-of-sight and ground-to-air with the higher frequencies, terrain absorption seemed to be proportionately greater, as was directive "bouncing," or signal reflection.

In very rugged country shielding effect or signal reflection could at times make position location and tracking quite difficult when a 400-MHz frequency was used, but change of receiving position tended to eliminate errors. A decided advantage of the 400-MHz frequency is the very small transmitting and receiving antennas that are used. A UHF frequency permitting small receiver and transmitter antennas appears to be suitable not only for satellite tracking but also for many applications of ground-to-ground location while tracking migrating birds.

The 400-MHz frequency also has been used to study movements of herring gulls. The performance of this UHF system versus VHF systems is summarized by Lawson et al. (1976, p. 362). They found the range of the telemetry system to be limited primarily by the radio horizon; strong signals were received at a distance of 84 kilometers, and the system was effective through 1 kilometer of forest and over low hills. In their experience, the "range of comparable 150-MHz and 432-MHz systems is similar in light forest and low hills, and the latter is superior for open water or flat country."

Animal-Instrument Interphase-Attachment Methods and Techniques

The attachment of an electronic package to an animal is basic to acquiring position/location and other pertinent information. The method of attachment selected depends on the animal's characteristics, but it must be done with care so as not to harm the animal or introduce an unacceptable physiological or behavioral variant. Such aberrations will degrade the value of any data acquired (Anonymous, 1973). The smaller the gear for attachment to an animal, the greater the number of species on which it can be effectively used. The package size varies with transmitter power, life, size, encapsulation, and harnessing requirements. A program was conducted to test and evaluate various transmitter-attachment methods with the realization that the final satellite package itself might weigh between 100 and 200 grams.

Four approaches to instrumenting or harnessing were tried: transmitter attachment to the tarsus (tarsometatarsus), attachment to the retrices or tail feathers, the backpack harness (Dunstan, 1972), and the backsack attachment (figs. 1 and 2). Each of the four methods has advantages for some species of birds, and one may be favored over the other, depending on objectives.

BACKPACK HARNESS

The backpack harness (fig. 1) as designed by Dunstan (1972), a modification of earlier such body attachments, was used in this study on ravens and golden eagles. The transmitter, power source and transmitting antenna were either embedded in perm dental acrylic or sealed in layers of epoxy to waterproof them and to prevent breakage. Neck and body straps of both nylon and tubular Teflon were used to form the harness. The attainable weight of a satellite transmitter package appears to be in the neighborhood of 180 grams. Total weight will, of course, vary with battery requirements. It seemed logical that weights ranging between 100-200 grams could best be carried by a bird when attached to the back. The maximum package weight used on ravens was 45 grams. A wild golden eagle successfully carried a 180-gram package while nesting (Craighead and Dunstan, 1976).

BACKSACK HARNESS

Radio packages prepared as backpacks (fig. 1) were sewn within a "backsack" made of tough, durable fabrics (Craighead and Dunstan, 1976). The backsack protects the transmitter antenna and also serves as a color marker before and after battery failure. Straps made of 1- or 1.4-centimeter-wide tubular Teflon were centered and embedded with acrylic into the ventral surface of the package. The straps formed a harness for use on bald eagles, golden eagles, and other birds.

When placed on an eagle, the two straps are passed around the body so that they cross and are joined at the middle of the breast (fig. 1). Straps and harness fit are adjusted to allow for growth of nestlings and molt and body size

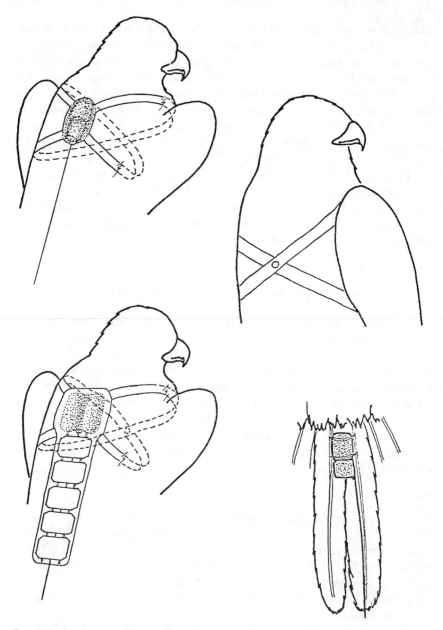

FIG. 1.   Transmitter attachments: Backpack (top), backsack (lower left), and tailfeather (right), showing ventral view of rectrices.

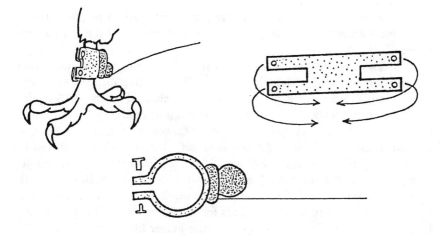

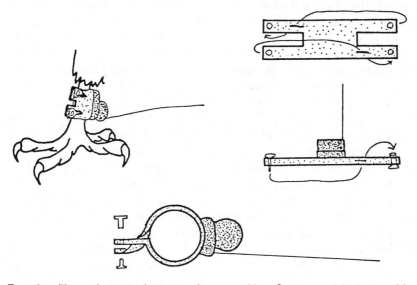

FIG. 2.   Transmitter attachment to the tarsus: Top, flat-type, with rivet, and bottom, jess-type joint.

changes in full-grown eagles. Straps are joined with various suture materials which biodegrade over time and will release the harness after the desired term of use.

The use of solar cells to recharge transmitter batteries has been increasing and is being perfected, although there are still packaging difficulties (Beaty, pers. comm.). Solar panels kept the batteries recharged on the IRLS equipment used to track elk *(Cervus canadensis)* (Craighead et al., 1972, and Craighead et al., 1978). They have been used successfully on turkeys *(Meleagris gallopavo)* and mule deer *(Odocoileus hemionus)* (Patton, Beaty, and Smith, 1971). Solar cells have been tested with 30-gram, 400-MHz transmitters designed for use on herring gulls *(Larus argentatus)* (Williams and Burke, 1973). The antenna sheath used to prevent antenna breakage by golden eagles could readily be modified to house solar cells for recharging of satellite transmitter batteries as depicted in fig. 1, thus assuring longer life at reduced weights. This is an area for further development and experimentation and may be essential to obtaining long life with light-weight packages.

Evidence indicates that the radio transmitter backsack works well on nestling, fledgling, and adult eagles. Antenna breakage is minimized, and, after the transmitter power source fails, the backsack acts as a color marker for continued use. More than one transmitter with separate antennas can be placed in a backsack. With use of two transmitters it is possible to combine a slow-pulsed transmitter (1 per minute) for satellite tracking with a more rapidly pulsed transmitter (1 per second) for location from the ground. This combination, or a single transmitter timed to switch to a more rapid pulse rate for ground tracking, would facilitate global location via satellite during migration, yet permit ground observations for behavioral and recapture studies. It should also be possible to locate a satellite-directed transmitter from the ground, using more sophisticated antenna arrangements. Both types of data, long-range movement and precise location, are important in movement/behavior studies. The post-nesting-season range of an immature red-tailed hawk instrumented and tracked in this study embraced 320 square kilometers (125 square miles) and measured 30.4 kilometers (19 miles) at its longest dimension. This fall hunting range contrasted in size to nesting territories of mature birds in the same area measuring from 4.6 square kilometers (1.8 square miles) to less than 2.5 kilometers, or about one square mile. (fig. 3). The relation of this immature bird to adults was observed, and hunting behavior was recorded (Craighead, 1975). This bird may migrate over 1,000 miles to wintering areas of unknown dimensions. To determine the habitat requirements of a species, the full spectrum of its ecology must be known.

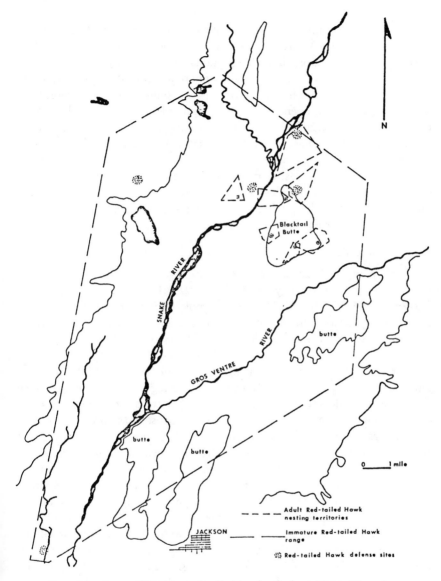

FIG. 3.   Areas utilized by red-tailed hawks. Jackson Hole, Wyoming.

The theoretical minimum weight of the current one-watt demonstration RAMS transmitter is 56 grams. The smallest available battery pack capable of operating it weighs approximately 33 grams, and antenna and harness weigh about 10 grams. Operating life of the 33-gram lithium battery pack would be 3.2 months. A 99-gram lithium battery pack would increase the weight but provide an estimated operating time of eight months as opposed to about three. Because of weight considerations the backpack and backsack harnesses appear to be the first choices for satellite feasibility experiments. The backsack has the drawback that it is not readily dropped or released when the package is no longer functioning. Using materials that disintegrate when exposed to sunshine should permit ultimate release at a roughly precalculated time. This can be accomplished by sewing with biodegradable thread the four attachment straps where they join.

TAILFEATHER ATTACHMENT

Various types of tailfeather attachments (figs. 1 and 4) have been tried with a variety of birds (Bray and Corner, 1972; Dunstan, 1973). The tailfeather attachment falls off when the bird molts—both an advantage and a liability. Its operational life is limited to periods between molts, and its use is not feasible just before molting. Sooner or later the transmitter is dropped and the bird is free of any encumbrance, a decided asset.

For the tail attachment, a 4.3-gram lithium battery (2.80 volts) was glued to the 2.8-gram miniature transmitter using fast-drying epoxy. Two strands of heavy dental floss were tied around the transmitter and knotted so as to leave eight loose ends or four ties. These were used to secure the transmitter to the two inner tail feathers (figs. 4 and 5). Two square knots were tied around the shaft of each feather, one above the other. The transmitter rested against the ventral surfaces of the feather shafts, and the knots were tied on the dorsal side. Prior to being placed on a bird, the transmitter, dental floss wrapping and battery were covered with several coats of epoxy. While the tail attachment was being secured, either the bird was hooded by means of a standard falconry hood, or its head and eyes were covered with a stocking. This had a calming effect and minimized struggling. In some cases the task was made easier by lightly binding the bird's wings to its sides, using several wrappings of cheesecloth or towel. With the bird immobilized, the transmitter was quickly tied to the two central tailfeathers about 4 centimeters below the point of feather insertion. Each tie on both the ventral and dorsal side of the feather was then epoxied—a precaution found necessary to prevent slippage. The antenna was tied to the shaft of one tail feather about 5 centimeters from the tip of the feather. This knot also was coated with epoxy to prevent

FIG. 4.   Instrumenting a red-tailed hawk with a tail-attachment radio.

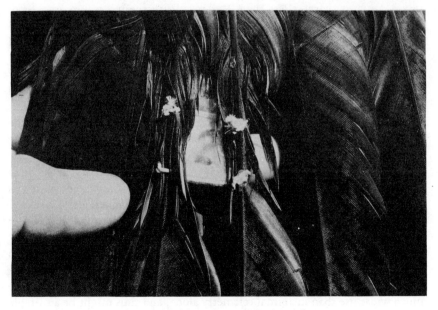

FIG. 5.   Radio fastened to tail feathers of a raven.

breaking or untying when picked at by the bird. The antenna length was as near one quarter wavelength as feasible but varied with the subject. Shortening the antenna length reduced operating range in proportion to the reduction. The antenna extended between 2.5 and 12.5 centimeters beyond the end of the tail. The whip antenna varied from 24 to 30 centimeters in length.

TARSAL ATTACHMENT

The tarsal attachment (fig. 2) was prepared by cutting an unoiled pattern of leather to fit around the leg of the species of bird to be instrumented. The transmitter with attached battery was epoxied to the leather. Two snaps permitted rapid attachment or removal. When the transmitter was to be kept on the bird for an extended period of time, a drop of epoxy was placed on each snap. Most tests were made with trained birds that could be released for varying periods of time and then retrieved. The tarsal transmitter assembly was readily snapped on the subject's leg while the bird was sitting on the gloved hand. Hooding the hawks simplified the task. The tarsal attachment was used or tested with a variety of birds—ravens, red-tailed hawks, prairie falcons, and in previous years horned owls *(Bubo virginiana)*.

The tail attachment proved to be quite suitable for raptors and ravens. However, this package weighed under 10 grams: transmitter 2.8 grams, battery 4.3 grams, harness less than 2 grams. With the maximum amount of miniaturization available from present advanced technology, the RAMS transmitter for satellite use conceivably could be reduced to 20 grams and could be used to track golden and bald eagles using the tailfeather attachment. Such miniaturizing developments, however, are far in the future.

The tail assembly was received well by all subjects. After a little initial preening, the birds ignored the transmitter, and it had no noticeable effects on flight performance. However, comparison of flight performance when the transmitter is attached to one rather than to two tailfeathers should be explored.

The tarsal attachment proved largely unsuccessful for raptors, as the birds often bent, twisted, and even completely broke off the whip antennas. It was quite useful and convenient for instrumenting birds for periods of tracking lasting only a few days. It should prove more useful for waterfowl, but winter use with freezing conditions would definitely present problems. Completely waterproofing any of the transmitter packages may prove to be a problem with waterfowl and ocean birds. This is an area that would benefit by further research and development. Better or improved waterproof encapsulents have much wider use than in animal telemetry alone, and thus might be a suitable subject for NASA funding.

The backpack and backsack harnesses are the logical choices for most situations where RAMS satellite transmitters will be employed. The models used were within the weight allowances determined for birds of between 3 and 5 percent of body weight (Anonymous, 1973). Adult bald and golden eagles weigh in the neighborhood of 5,000 to 7,000 grams. The largest backsack used—180 grams—is between 2.6 and 3.6 percent of the eagle weights. The current demonstration RAMS transmitter package using a 99-gram lithium battery is also within this weight range.

Development of a Satellite-Compatible Transmitter

A Nimbus 6/RAMS DCP one-watt 401-MHz transmitter was developed by the investigators Joel R. Varney and Roger L. Pope (1974). The development work was sponsored jointly by the National Geographic Society and NASA's Ames Research Center through contracts with the Environmental Research Institute. The aim of the transmitter development was to work toward an electronic package that would be as small as possible and one needing little or no modification when fastened to the smallest as well as the largest animal that could be feasibly studied. This approach tends to standardize equipment and eliminate duplication. Since this project was completed, however, the Nimbus Satellite Program has been effectively terminated.

This random access measurement system (RAMS) used the Doppler location technique (Balmino et al., 1968). The RAMS system transmits at predetermined intervals as compared with an ordered system such as IRLS (Interrogation, recording, and location system), which responds to an interrogation from the satellite (J. J. Craighead et al., 1971). It permits large-scale experiments at low cost using simple data-collection equipment. The RAMS system aboard the Nimbus 6 satellite could accommodate up to 1,000 platforms per orbit, thus permitting studies of birds on a worldwide scale. The platforms transmit a one-second message to the satellite at the rate of once per minute. The satellite recorded a Doppler frequency measurement and a time lag and formats the received data. This information was stored aboard the satellite for readout every 108 minutes over the Fairbanks, Alaska, ground station, followed by transmission to Goddard Space Flight Center for processing. At Goddard the position location coordinates of each platform were computed and the data were transmitted to the investigators. Eight data-acquisition channels allowed for simultaneous reception of up to eight transmissions (Cote et al., 1973).

Briefly the system operates in the following fashion: Each instrumented bird carries a transmitter that transmits a constant frequency. The signals received by the Doppler equipment aboard the satellite contain the Doppler frequency shift caused by the motion of the satellite. The frequency received at the satellite varies as the satellite passes near the instrumented animal. The characteristics of the signal received at the satellite, combined with the known orbit of the satellite, define two lines on the surface of the earth that run parallel to the track or orbit of the satellite. The instrumented animal is located on one of these two lines. The time at which the signal received at the satellite changes most rapidly occurs when the satellite is closest to the transmitter. At this time, a plane normal to the orbit of the satellite is defined. The intersection of this plane and the surface of the earth produces a line that bisects the orbit lines on one of which the transmitter or electronic animal package is located. The instrumented animal (bird) must be at one of these two intersections. These intersections are normally several hundred miles apart on the surface of the earth. Knowledge of the previous position of the animal can be used to eliminate one of the intersections (Balmino et al., 1968).

Test Results of Nimbus 6/RAMS DCP Transmitter

Before feasibility experiments could be conducted on free-flying raptors, it has been mandatory to test the RAMS breadboard transmitter designed by Varney and Pope (1974) with the Nimbus 6 satellite. The opportunity to do this occurred in 1977, and stationary tests were run by Joel Varney from January 28 through November 21, 1977. The transmitter was placed on the roof of the Ford Aerospace Facility in Palo Alto, California (Varney, 1977).

The location results from a transmitter having less than optimum frequency stability are encouraging. (NASA frequency specifications for the Nimbus 6 require no more than a 4-Hz drift in 15 minutes.) The average error for location was 19 kilometers (12 miles). Typical one-pass location errors were 6.4 kilometers (4 miles) for night passes and 32 kilometers (20 miles) for day passes. The frequency of contact with the satellite using a whip antenna was quite good. Sufficient messages for a location calculation were generally received for at least four passes per day (two noon, two midnight passes). Research and development on antennas done by Georgia Tech under a NASA contract may be applicable in improving antenna performance (Schuchardt et al., 1976). Our test results indicate that, with minor modification, transmitters for field use can be constructed and a feasibility experiment carried out on free-flying migrating birds. Location accuracy can be improved, but it is more than adequate for many migration and movement studies under consideration. Computer programming would be essential for data reduction and analysis.

Feasibility Experiment Possibilities

Although further equipment development and testing will be required, we have now reached a point where we can consider various feasibility experiments with the Nimbus, or equivalent, satellite, using a large instrumented raptor as the subject. The approximate 100- to 200-gram weight of the RAMS transmitter package is well within the weight-carrying capacity demonstrated for golden or bald eagles. The current weight precludes all but the backpack attachments, but this does not appear to offer any real deterrents. Whether a bald or golden eagle is selected may well depend upon the time of year when experiments can be undertaken. Timing will depend upon a number of factors, one of which will be the construction and testing of two to six transmitters for field use in a feasibility experiment. The major objective will be to track accurately an instrumented bird or birds over a considerable distance for an extended period of time, perhaps a minimum of three months. Ideally the experiment not only should demonstrate the feasibility of satellite tracking, but also should provide information not hitherto available. It appears as though a nongame bird such as a golden or bald eagle would be the candidate for a first experiment, but large waterfowl or oceanic birds could be considered. User agency demand for future satellite tracking programs may well develop in the area of migratory tracking of waterfowl.

Numerous feasibility experiments are possible, but only a selected few of the more promising are treated here on a tentative priority basis. Through the Environmental Research Institute we are continuing our efforts to conduct a first feasibility experiment.

GOLDEN EAGLE

The tracking of a mature or an immature golden eagle (fledgling) from a far northern nesting site, perhaps within the Arctic Circle, would provide a long flight over a relatively short period of time. A three-month battery life would suffice, though longer would be desirable. In 1976 a limited survey was made of nesting golden and bald eagles in Alaska with the specific objective of locating active nests that could be readily reached on short notice. Both the golden and bald eagles tend to return to and use the same nest year after year or they switch to a nearby alternate nest site. The time for instrumenting an adult eagle would be mid-July to early September. Fledglings could be fitted with a transmitter in late August. Trapping methods for capturing adults have been worked out for practically any time of year.

Golden eagles as well as bald eagles regularly concentrate in very localized areas during winter months and in some cases in spring. Such concentrations are primarily related to sources of available food. Adult eagles of either species trapped and instrumented at concentration sites should provide migratory or dispersal data and shed information on where golden eagles come from or disperse to from such concentration sites as those in Colorado or Texas. These movements could be extensive or rather limited in length as compared to northern nesting migrants instrumented in the fall of the year.

There is an expressed interest and suggested support for satellite tracking of eagles to obtain information for management decisions. The golden eagle is protected by federal law, yet its predatory habits continually bring it in conflict with ranchers. There is growing pressure to develop management plans for this bird that take into consideration their actual or assumed predation on domestic lambs. This is an economic problem that, in view of the eagles' protection, can be solved only by obtaining factual biological data. One such situation that presents such a biologic-economic problem and lends itself to at least partial solution by satellite tracking is presented by golden eagle concentrations at spring lambing areas.

Near Dillon, Montana, on the Helle and Christensen ranches, immature golden eagles concentrate during the spring lambing season. At this time (May) eagles take some lambs and they also feed on carrion, that is, lambs that have died at birth or from other causes. Recently, some eagles have been trapped and marked with colored wing discs (patagial markers) as well as with leg bands. If one or more of these immature golden eagles were instrumented with a transmitter and tracked by satellite in a feasibility experiment, some data on the concentration and dispersal of these eagles might be quickly obtained, with good probability of more data from an expanded program. The information would be most useful in fashioning a management program for these eagles, the cost might be less than that of using conventional methods, and solutions to a predation problem of economic concern might be expedited. Funding for such a project should be available. The captured eagles should be instrumented in April or May.

Intensive studies of nesting golden eagles and associated raptors have been carried out on the Snake River Birds of Prey Natural Area near Boise, Idaho. This area is under the jurisdiction of the Bureau of Land Management, and the research is supported by this federal agency. Information is scarce, yet desirable, on the migratory movements of the adult nesting eagles as well as on the movement of fledglings. Satellite tracking of these birds could provide needed information for management of the eagle population on this federal preserve. Bureau of Land Management officials have expressed interest in helping to fund equipment development leading to satellite tracking.

BALD EAGLE

The bald eagle, our national bird, was given protection under the Bald Eagle Act of June 1940. Numerous federal, state, and private programs are under way to protect this bird and its habitat and to gather a wide range of information that will ensure that it receives adequate protection. Data for management are needed on bald eagle movements and migration. Information has been and is being obtained through banding operations. Banding of eagles and other migratory birds falls under the jurisdiction of the United States Fish and Wildlife Service and the Canadian Wildlife Service. Since 1955 about 2,000 bald eagles have been banded, but as of August 1975, only 232 returns had been filed (Spencer, 1976). Information on migration is thus slow in accumulating. It could be greatly speeded up and enhanced through a program of satellite tracking. Because of the bald eagle's national importance, large size, and migratory movements, it is a suitable bird for one or more feasibility experiments in satellite tracking.

The majority of breeding bald eagles are found along the coasts of Alaska and western Canada. Estimates range between 30,000 and 50,000 birds (Spencer, 1976). Southeast Alaska alone has an estimated breeding population of 8,000 eagles (King et al., 1972). Some 2,760 eagle nests have been located along 5,600 kilometers (3,500 miles) of surveyed coastline in southeast Alaska (Robards and Hodges, 1976). Both fledgling and mature bald eagles could readily be instrumented in southeast or northern Alaska but there would be less assurance of a long flight than would be the case with the golden eagle.

Bald eagles, like the golden eagles, also form winter concentrations where food such as fish, wounded waterfowl, and carrion is available. Capturing and instrumenting for satellite tracking can most easily be performed at or near nest sites or in the vicinity of winter concentrations.

Very little is known about the movements of West Coast bald eagles. One or more bald eagles concentrating along the Skagit River in Washington could be readily trapped, instrumented, and its dispersal flight pattern monitored by satellite. A mature bird would probably move to a spring nest site. Such a project could be conducted cooperatively with the Washington Department of Game, the United States Fish and Wildlife Service, the Nature Conservancy, and interested researchers. The optimum time for instrumenting would be December. Similar but much larger concentrations occur along the Chilkat River, Alaska, in the fall of the year. Here a cooperative project of trapping and marking could be worked out with the State of Alaska, the National Audubon Society, and the United States Fish and Wildlife Service. Bald eagles could also be trapped and instrumented at a number of winter concentration areas throughout the United States such as McDonald Creek, Montana, along the Mississippi in Illinois, or in the San Luis Valley of Colorado.

Discussion

In all of the suggested satellite tracking feasibility projects, movement studies of birds are emphasized. However, a vast and varied amount of data on the ecology of numerous species can be secured. The complexity of the studies will vary with objectives and funding. Migration flights can be correlated with simultaneous weather data from Tyros satellites. Migration routes and stop-over or staging areas can be related to habitat and physiographic features using Landsat multi-spectral imagery. Critical habitat for some species can be delineated more specifically than presently possible. Information can be accumulated to shed light on bird orientation and navigation. The potential for research on and management of migratory birds using satellite technology is tremendous, almost unlimited, once a tested miniaturized system is available at reasonable cost and the research can be carried out on a global basis in cooperation with scientists from other countries.

Suggestions for Expediting a Future Program

There should be a sustained effort to organize a future program of satellite tracking of birds while work progresses on carrying out feasibility experiments. A key to this is creating interest and obtaining support of user agencies and other organizations. User agencies that could benefit from a program of satellite tracking of birds and that have expressed an interest are:

> The U. S. Fish and Wildlife Service, Dept. of the Interior
> The Bureau of Land Management, Dept. of the Interior
> National Oceanic and Atmospheric Agency, Dept. of Commerce
> National Marine Fisheries Service, Dept. of Commerce
> The Bureau of Reclamation, Dept. of the Interior
> The U. S. Corps of Army Engineers, Dept. of Defense
> U. S. Forest Service, Dept. of Agriculture
> Various state agencies—e.g., Washington State Game and Fish Dept.
> Private organizations such as: The National Geographic Society, Nature Conservancy, Eagle Valley Environmentalists, Inc., and the Environmental Research Institute
> Researchers from various universities

Field researchers who could expedite a future program were contacted, and their names, addresses, subjects of interest, and abstracts of proposals listed (Craighead, 1978).

New and improved data-gathering techniques that will enable state and federal agencies to better carry out their responsibilities are desired by the above-listed agencies. Tracking and remote sensing by satellite could expedite numerous research projects, provide information needed for management plans of migratory species, provide data for Environmental Impact Statements and obtain critical information not now available on some endangered species. Of all the organizations listed, the U. S. Fish and Wildlife Service would probably have the most to gain from a bird satellite tracking program.

After feasibility experiments have been successfully carried out, it is up to the user agencies to expedite and finance their programs. Initially most of the support for such a program must of necessity come from federal and state agencies using appropriated funds. However, if NASA could support and help finance a number of "feasibility experiments" once the first one proves successful, it should provide tremendous impetus for getting a program going, and it would tend to eliminate a gap of inactivity between a first experiment and later operational programs—a gap that otherwise seems inevitable.

The potential of satellite tracking and monitoring for learning more about our wildlife environments, for gathering significant ecological data for studying specific species of birds or mammals is truly staggering (Buechner et al., 1971). It could have immediate application in determining migratory routes and wintering areas of endangered species such as the peregrine falcon *(Falco peregrinus)* (Hickey, 1969, and White and Cade, 1971). Studies could then be conducted on pesticide levels in their winter habitat (Craighead and Dunstan, 1976). Other raptors that through migration and concentration help regulate high densities of prey populations could be studied. Such birds include the American rough-legged hawk *(Buteo lagopus s.-johannes)* and the short-eared owl *(Asio flammeus)*. A better understanding of the movement of sea birds could be obtained and their migration linked to their influence on ocean food chains and this in turn to the effect of possible or actual oil spills. Another quite apparent application would be the instrumenting of birds that are being reestablished in a former habitat. This would apply to the Aleutian Canada goose *(Branta canadensis leucopareia)* now being reintroduced on Agattu Island. When these birds are released it is important to know where they go, what happens to them, and whether some return in spring to establish a breeding population.

The Next Priority and Estimated Costs

The next step in the continuation of this research is the miniaturization of the existing hardware (RAMS transmitter) into a configuration that is compatible for later volume production and that would perform with the required precision. The result would be six prototype pre-tested transmitters ready to put on free-flying birds in the field. In other words, this would set the stage for feasibility experiments with bald or golden eagles. A 1978 cost estimate by Telonics, Inc., for the development of six such transmitters was about $50,000. With the demise of Nimbus, the only viable alternative is the Argos/Tiros System. Recent development work on transmitters conforming to this system, with its more stringent frequency requirements, have met difficult technological setbacks. At present, the ball-park estimate for development of an Argos-compatible miniaturized transmitter is $500,000. Volume production and cost-efficient production would greatly decrease the cost of future transmitters for satellite tracking programs.

Acknowledgments

This research project was conducted under National Geographic Society Grant 1636 and a NASA-Ames Grant NSG-2157. The earlier research resulting in the development of a prototype Nimbus 6 RAMS transmitter was supported in part by NASA Order-A-91082 and National Geographic Grant 1189. The author wishes to acknowledge the help and collaboration of Joel R. Varney, Roger L. Pope, and Charles E. Cote. Special thanks are due Joel Varney for his time and effort in testing the RAMS transmitter. The advice and administrative support and encouragement of Paul Sebesta is gratefully acknowledged. Thomas C. Dunstan contributed significantly to the field research. David P. Mindell, James Berthrong, Jana Craighead, F. Lance Craighead, and Charles S. Craighead assisted. David Winter, Chief of NASA's Biological Science Division encouraged the work through his expressed interest in the future potential of the project. Volker A. Mohnen, Director of Atmospheric Sciences Research Center, State University of New York at Albany, likewise gave encouragement and support, as did directors of the Environmental Research Institute.

REFERENCES

ANONYMOUS
   1973.   Report on 1973 Santa Cruz summer study on wildlife resources monitoring. 2 vols.   National Aeronautics and Space Administration.
BALMINO, G.; CRISWELL, J.; FERNALL, D. L.; JENTSCH, E. H.; LATIMAR, J.; and MAXWELL, J. C.
   1968.   Animal tracking from satellites.   Smithsonian Astrophys. Obser. Spec. Report 289. 40 pp.

BEATY, D. W.
  1972.   Instruction/operation and usage manual for the magnum MK-1 telemetry transmitter series, models M-1 and MM-1.   Telonics, Inc., Mesa, Arizona.
BRAY, O. E., and CORNER, G. W.
  1972.   A tail clip for attaching transmitters to birds.   Journ. Wildl. Management, vol. 36, pp. 640-642.
BUECHNER, H. K.; CRAIGHEAD, F. C., JR.; and CRAIGHEAD, J. J.
  1971.   Satellites for research on free-roaming animals.   BioScience, vol. 21, no. 24, pp. 1201-1205.
COTE, C. E.; DuBOSE, J. F.; and COATES, J. L.
  1973.   The Nimbus 6 Random Access Measurement System.   Paper presented to the Fifth Annual Southeastern Symposium of System Theory. 5 pp.
CRAIGHEAD, F. C., JR.
  1975.   Progress Report: Development of an ultra high frequency radiolocation system for studying birds.   Nat. Geogr. Soc. Progress Report. Unpublished. 17 pp.
  1978.   Assessment of needs for satellite tracking of birds and suggestions for expediting a program.   Mimeo report, 73 pp.   Environmental Research Institute. Moose, Wyoming.
CRAIGHEAD, F. C., JR.; CRAIGHEAD, J. J.; COTE, C. E.; and BUECHNER, H. K.
  1972.   Satellite and ground radiotracking of elk. Pp. 99-111 *in:* "Animal Orientation and Navigation: A Symposium."   NASA Spec. Publ. 262. Supt. of Documents, Washington, D. C.
CRAIGHEAD, F. C., JR.; CRAIGHEAD, J. J.; COTE, C. E.; and BUECHNER, H. K.
  1978.   Satellite tracking of elk, Jackson Hole, Wyoming.   Nat. Geogr. Soc. Research Reports, 1969 Projects, pp. 73-88.
CRAIGHEAD, F. C., JR., and DUNSTAN, T. C.
  1976.   Progress toward tracking migrating raptors by satellite.   Raptor Research, vol. 10, no. 4, pp. 112-119.
CRAIGHEAD, J. J.; CRAIGHEAD, F. C., JR.; VARNEY, J.R.; and COTE, C. E.
  1971.   Satellite monitoring of black bear.   BioScience, vol. 21, no. 24, pp. 1206-1212.
DUNSTAN, T. C.
  1972.   A harness for radio-tagging raptorial birds.   Inland Bird Banding News, vol. 44, no. 1, pp. 4-8.
  1973.   A tail feather package for radio-tagging raptorial birds.   Inland Bird Banding News, vol. 45, pp. 3-6.
HICKEY, J. J.
  1969.   The peregrine falcon: life history and population literature. Pp. 3-42. *in* "Peregrine Falcon Populations, their Biology and Decline," J. J. Hickey, ed.   Univ. Wisconsin Press, Madison, xxii + 596 pp.
KING, JAMES G.; ROBARDS, F. C.; and LENSINK, C. J.
  1972.   Census of the bald eagle breeding population in southeast Alaska.   Journ. Wildl. Management, vol. 36, no. 4, pp. 1292-1295.
LAWSON, K.; KANWISHER, J.; and WILLIAMS, T. C.
  1976.   A UHF radiotelemetry system for wild animals.   Journ. Wildl. Management, vol. 40, no. 2, pp. 360-362.

PATTON, D. R.; BEATY, D. W.; and SMITH, R. G.
　1971.　Solar panels as an energy source for radio transmitters.　Rocky Mountain Forest and Range Exp. Sta., Fort Collins, Colo.
ROBARDS, F. C., and HODGES, J. I.
　1976.　Observations from 2,760 bald eagle nests in southeast Alaska.　Dept. of Int., U. S. Fish & Wildlife Service Eagle Management Studies. Juneau, Alaska.
SCHUCHARDT, J. M.; SMITH, G. S.; RICE, R. W.; BASSETT, H. L.; COVINGTON, D. W.; KEAHEY, J. A.; and BIRD, R. W.
　1976.　Wildlife Resources Antenna Concept Study.　Final Technical Report (A-1749).　Georgia Institute of Technology, Atlanta, Georgia.
SPENCER, D. A.
　1976.　Wintering of the migrant bald eagles in the lower 48 states.　Nat. Agric. Chem. Assoc., Washington, D. C.
VARNEY, J. R.
　1977.　Status Report: RAMS transmitter location accuracy test.　Ford Aerospace Facility, Western Development Laboratories Division, 3939 Fabian Way, Palo Alto, Calif.
VARNEY, J. R., and POPE, R. L.
　1974.　Final report Nimbus 6/RAMS DCP transmitter miniaturization feasibility study for the Environmental Research Institute, Moose, Wyoming. Technical memo 74-6, 20 Dec. 1974. Philco-Ford Corp. Western Development Laboratories Division, 3939 Fabian Way, Palo Alto, Calif.
WHITE, C. M., and CADE, T. J.
　1971.　Cliff-nesting raptors and ravens along the Colville river in arctic Alaska.　The Living Bird, Tenth Annual, Cornell Lab. of Ornithology.
WILLIAMS, T. C., and BURKE, E. J.
　1973.　Solar power for wildlife telemetry transmitters.　American Birds, vol. 27, no. 4, pp. 719-720.
WOLFF, E. A.; COTE, C. E.; and PAINTER, J. E.
　1975.　Satellite data collection user requirements workshop report.　Communications and Navigation Division, Applications Directorate, Goddard Space Flight Center, Greenbelt, Maryland.

FRANK C. CRAIGHEAD, JR.
FRANK LANCE CRAIGHEAD

Development of Behavior in the Golden Eagle

Principal Investigators: John J. Craighead, University of Montana, Missoula, Montana, and David H. Ellis, Institute for Raptor Studies, Oracle, Arizona.

Grant No. 1169:   For a study of the nesting behavior of the golden eagle.

The behavior of an adult vertebrate can be compared to a complex web; the individual strands are the distinct behavior patterns. The construction of the web is the behavioral ontogenic process.

From the laying of the first strand (when the eaglet emerges from the egg) until the web is geometrically complete (when the eaglet fledges), the bird undergoes a rapid transformation. A quantitative and descriptive documentation of this metamorphosis is contained in my report (Ellis, 1973, 1979), of which these paragraphs are a summary.

Data for the report were gathered in all-day watches from blinds near the eyries. Of over 150 eaglet observation days, 106 were mechanically recorded via a keyboard-chart recorder system. All but a few of the 82 behavior patterns were quantitatively followed from hatching to fledging. Supplemental observations were made on captive birds for 7 years.

From the quantitative performance data, developmental trends are identified and generalized patterns in behavioral performance are described. These patterns are compared with previously published schemes which attempt to describe the development of behavior as a series of stages. The performance data for the eagle suggest that there are no discrete stages in nestling development. Behavioral ontogeny emerges from the study as a vast array of overlapping processes.

The report also presents a scheme for separating groups of organisms according to the precocity of the young. The treatment is based on the timing of the first appearance of the behavior patterns. The most precocial birds had a post-hatching peak in the number of behavior patterns appearing. A scheme for more precisely defining the degree of precociousness is described. Ideally, this scheme (defining precocial-altricial ranks) will be a collation of the parameters of parental care, physical development, and behavioral maturation.

127

REFERENCES

ELLIS, DAVID H.
1973.   Behavior of the golden eagle: An ontogenic study.   Unpublished Ph.D. dissertation, University of Montana, Missoula, Montana.
1979.   Development of behavior in the golden eagle, 94 pp., illus.   Wildlife Monogr. 70 (Suppl. to Journ. Wildl. Management, vol. 43, no. 4 [October]).

DAVID H. ELLIS

In Search of Garífuna, Beachfolk of the Bay of Honduras

Principal Investigator: William V. Davidson, Arkansas State University,[1] State University, Arkansas.

Grants No. 1168,   For field research on the cultural geography of the Black
1300.   Caribs (Garífuna) of Central America.[2]

Presently living along the shores of Caribbean Central America is a group of people known in the anthropological literature as "Black Caribs." Locally, they are called *morenos, Caribs,* or *Garífuna,* the latter term being preferred by members of the group to denote their own language and culture. Garífuna are unified and characterized primarily by the language they alone speak and by rituals based on the remembrances of their ancestors. Their songs, dances, and folk-stories are also important to maintain continuity with the past. Females have an unusual devotion to home, and to female companions; they practice an agriculture and food preparation that centers on bitter manioc *(Manihot esculenta,* see fig. 1). Male attention is traditionally to the sea, and to fishing-related activities (see fig. 2). They are a coastal folk, living virtually always within a few hundred yards of the Caribbean Sea.

Before 1970, information on this Negroid population could be found in a few scholarly monographs, most prominently those by anthropologists Taylor (1951), Coelho (1955), Gonzalez (1969), and Beaucage (1970), and in some of the travel literature of the 19th century, beginning with Galindo (1832). These studies, however, were confined to relatively small areas and to specialized topics, and did not attempt to portray the broader picture of Garífuna cultural geography. It therefore became the purposes of this project to examine in some detail the most fundamental aspects of their existence: (1) the size of their population and the range of settlement in the western Caribbean, (2) the origin and historic dispersal of the group, and (3) the hierarchy of habitats in which modern Garífuna live.

---

[1] Present affiliation: Department of Geography and Anthropology, Louisiana State University, Baton Rouge, Louisiana 70803.
[2] Additional funding for this project was provided by the Faculty Research Committee, Arkansas State University; the University Council on Research, Louisiana State University; and the American Council of Learned Societies.

FIG. 1. Garífuna woman holds a *ruguma*, or woven, snake-like squeezer, which is used to process the staple food —bitter manioc. (From Río Esteban, Honduras.)

To these ends, field investigations were carried out in Central America during the summers of 1973 and 1974. The resulting publications are here summarized.

Population and Extent of Settlement

The search for Garífuna-speaking people began at Dangriga (formerly Stann Creek) in Belize and continued south and east around the Bay of Honduras to Plaplaya, Honduras (see fig. 3). Along this 400-mile littoral virtually every coastal village is inhabited predominately by the Garífuna. Of their 54 settlements, 6 are in Belize, 2 are in Guatemala, and 44 are under the jurisdiction of the Republic of Honduras (Davidson, 1974). Outside the Bay of Hon-

FIG. 2.   Garífuna fisherman hurls his *siríwia* (thrownet) in the freshwater lagoon near Tornabé, Honduras.

duras, a two-village enclave was located in 1974 at Pearl Lagoon, Nicaragua (see below). Only one village, Punta Gorda, on Roatán Island, is not on the mainland of the isthmus.

The Garífuna are obviously beachfolk. With only four exceptions, their settlements are located on beaches. The "interior" settlements range as far inland as 10 miles. In Belize, the single interior Carib village, Georgetown, is the result of a government resettlement project after hurricanes damaged coastal villages. A second resettlement community, at Silk Grass, Belize, no longer houses the several Garífuna families that lived there originally; they moved back to the seacoast and rebuilt their village. The other, more "artificial" interior settlements in Honduras, at Cayo Venado, Rosita, and Monte Pobre have grown near fruit company railroads to take advantage of a market for their fruits and oil palm produce.

Generally, Black Carib settlements are distributed in a highly clustered pattern. However, Belizean villages may be separated by as much as 50 miles. Those of Honduras are much closer, being on the average about 5 miles apart. This is the case particularly in far eastern Honduras, where 13 villages are concentrated along a 40-mile stretch of coast. Villages normally have a linear pattern parallel to the sea that makes for small distances between them. In fact, a number of settlements are so near to each other and interact so frequently that they could be considered "twin-villages" (Travesía-Baja Mar, Tornabé-San Juan, Cayo Venado-Rosita, Guadalupe-San Antonio, Cristales-Río Negro, Santa Rosa de Aguán-Barra de Aguán, Punta Piedra-Cusuna, Sangrelaya-Cocalito, Tocomacho-San Pedro, and Batalla-Pueblo Nuevo).

Using house counts from my air photographs taken in 1973, in situ villages censuses, and interpolations from the most recent national censuses, I have been able to calculate that between sixty and seventy thousand Garífuna currently live in Central America, distributed in 1978 approximately as follows:

Country	Garífuna population	% total population of country
Belize	11,000	7.85
in 6 settlements	8,700	
elsewhere	2,300	
Guatemala	5,000	0.083
in 2 settlements	3,100	
elsewhere	1,900	
Honduras	48,000	1.71
in 44 settlements	42,750	
elsewhere	5,250	
Nicaragua	1,000	0.05
in 2 settlements	750	
elsewhere	250	
Total population	65,000	

Only in Belize, where approximately 8 percent of the population is Garífuna, do they comprise a significant proportion of a country's total population. Settlements vary in size from those extended family compounds of about 50, to Dangriga, which has more than 8,000 residents. In 1978, in terms of approximate size, 6 Garífuna settlements had a population of less than 100; 17, of from 100-500; 12, from 500-1,000; 13, from 1,000-2,500; 5, from 2,500-5,000; and 1, over 5,000.

Less than 3 percent of the total number of Garífuna live outside the villages. Isolated single-family habitations are rare. There are, however, increasing seasonal migrations from the villages to the larger cities. Garífuna from northeast Honduras, for example, now work for up to four months at a time in

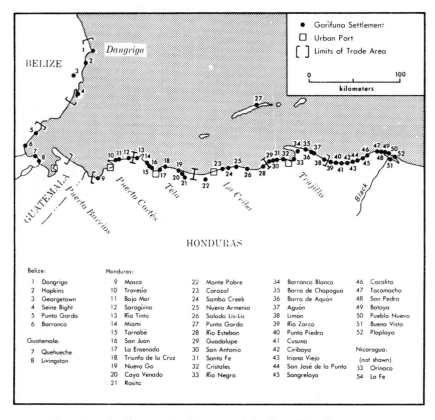

FIG. 3. Garífuna settlements around the Bay of Honduras, 1975.

interior towns such as Tegucigalpa, San Pedro Sula, and Santa Rosa de Copán, and there are increasing indications that Carib enclaves will develop in the larger cities (Davidson, 1979c). Also, a few thousand Garífuna live in New York, Boston, Los Angeles, and New Orleans.

Origin and Dispersal

Garífuna are not native to Central America. Their genesis can be traced to the Lesser Antillean island of St. Vincent, where during the 17th century black Africans, from slave ships and as runaway slaves, gradually mixed with the native Carib Indian islanders. Although details of the fusion are slight, the growing hybrid population, physically Negroid but with Amerindian culture traits (hence, "Black Caribs"), dominated the northern sector of the island un-

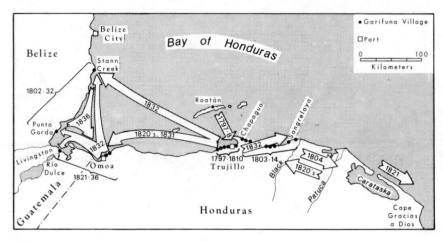

FIG. 4.   Dispersal of Garífuna around the Bay of Honduras, 1797-1836.

til the late 18th century. Then, the British, after a 2-year war, subdued the islanders and exiled virtually the entire population (perhaps 5,000) to the western Caribbean in the spring of 1797.

The site of the disembarcation was the uninhabited island of Roatán, just off the north coast of Honduras. From there, urged and aided by Spanish officials from the mainland, most went to Trujillo on the adjacent coast. Until the present, Trujillo has remained their ethnic "capital." From this new Central American hearth, over the next four decades, Garífuna spread around the Bay of Honduras, reaching the maximum extent of their settlement and establishing one-third of the modern villages (see fig. 4). Afterwards, with the exception of the villages in Nicaragua, founded in the late 19th century, new sites and relocations have taken place within the 1836 limits (Davidson, 1979b).

At Trujillo the Garífuna migrants dominated and transformed the hinterland immediately. The four or five thousand Garífuna listed in the 1801 census of Honduran Governor Anguiano must have absolutely overwhelmed the previous one thousand residents. The most restless Garífuna began an outward movement as soon as they reached the mainland, wandering to the east into Mosquitia and sailing to Belize in dugout watercraft, but most remained near Trujillo and established settlements at Río Negro, Cristales, Santa Fe, San Antonio, and Guadalupe (see fig. 4). It was not until 1832, after losing battles to the Central Americans during the war of independence, that Garífuna finally scattered from Trujillo—mostly to the safety of British territory in Belize.

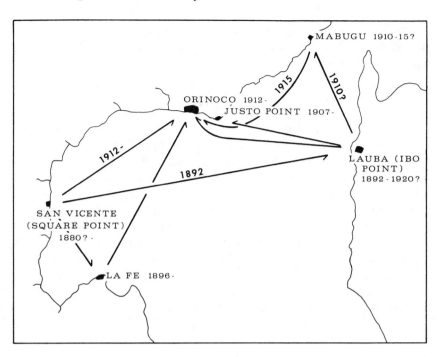

Fig. 5.   Garífuna settlements on Pearl Lagoon, Nicaragua.

After four decades of dispersal around the Bay of Honduras, pressures to relocate abated. Settling new lands had opened new plots for agriculture and enlarged the fishing grounds; life must have eased in the new sites. Then, more than a generation from their homeland in the far southeastern Caribbean, Garífuna began to organize for permanence in Central America.

The Nicaraguan Enclave

During the second field session (summer 1974), rumors of a Garífuna enclave in Nicaragua were investigated. Two villages were located on the north and west shores of Pearl Lagoon, about 30 miles north of Bluefields. A reconstruction of the history of settlement was pieced together from travel literature on eastern Nicaragua, the historic cartography of Pearl Lagoon, and detailed oral histories collected from the present families of the two settlements, Orinoco and La Fe (Davidson, 1978b).

Following the arrival of Garífuna from northeastern Honduras near the end of the nineteenth century, as shown in figure 5, they have occupied six sites on Pearl Lagoon. Isolated for almost a century from their relatives on the Bay of Honduras, the Nicaraguan Garífuna are on the verge of losing their language and their culture.

Hierarchy of Habitats

Within the long, narrow, discontinuous Garífuna culture realm that fringes the southwestern Bay of Honduras (see fig. 3), at least four spatial units can be identified by which Garífuna organize their culture in the physical world. Because of the consistent selection of coastal sites for settlement, the dominant aspects of physical geography for each village are relatively similar (Davidson, 1976). Trade winds blow onshore from the east and northeast over warm currents of the Bay and moderate temperatures of the littoral. Because of the slight variation in temperature throughout the year, seasonality is expressed most clearly in the distribution of rainfall: June to December is the rainy period, December to June is dry. Of course, local habitats vary in topography, soils, sources of fresh water, etc., but nowhere in the realm are differences so great that subsistence production is significantly affected. Throughout the tropical, wet-dry, windy shoreland, Garífuna know that they can travel and visit, without invitation, and be assured that the warmth of family awaits their arrival.

TRADE AREAS

Although most economic activities of the Garífuna are carried out within the immediate vicinity of their settlements, in recent times trade contacts with distant towns have occurred on a regular basis. In fact, most Garífuna villages are now attached to a larger, usually non-Carib population center in a trade network. Six such trade centers (shown in italics on figure 3) and their hinterlands can be identified. Within the trade areas there is at least weekly contact between each village and the trade center. Only in eastern Honduras between Punta Piedra and Plaplaya are the settlements so isolated that frequent trade contacts do not occur with the larger coastal towns.

Beachwalks are the normal mode of transportation between village and port, but frequently, particularly when heavy produce is involved, the trips are in small watercraft or truck-buses. The exchange of produce normally consists of coconuts, palm oil, fish, coconut bread, and cassava from the villages, and fuel, ice, citrus, dry goods, and hardware from the ports. Also, a fleet of Garífuna-produced trading vessels ply the coast to carry Ladino foodstuffs to the port markets.

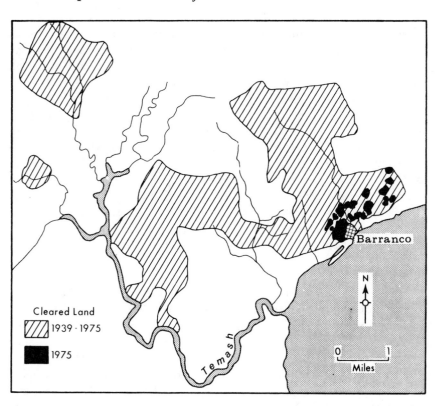

FIG. 6.   Land clearing for agriculture near Barranco, Belize, 1939-1975. (After Lundberg, 1978.)

The relationship of trade center and Carib village is of importance beyond the economic exchange that takes place. Trade areas are economic "meso-habitats," but they also provide the framework for the incorporation of Garí-funa into Central American life. It is from the urban ports that non-Garífuna ways are introduced into the villages. It is from the ports that Garífuna men are drawn onto the merchant ships that carry them to the United States and elsewhere over the globe.

VILLAGE SUBSISTENCE REGION

A second spatial system envelops the village and provides a resource base from which the local inhabitants receive their daily sustenance. The cultivated lands that lie behind the settlement are included, as are the offshore waters and nearby coastal lagoons that serve as fishing grounds. The Garífuna have so consistently chosen similar physical environments for their villages that an idealized habitat can be reconstructed. The ideal site is one located less than one hundred yards from the sea on beachland very near the mouth of a small stream or river. Preferably, the settlement is backed by a narrow, fresh water lagoon, across which cultivable hill lands are easily reached by dugout.

Cultivated lands are often several miles from the village, usually on public, or national, territory. In their use of shifting field, slash-and-burn farming techniques, some Garífuna travel several miles to plots while others farm relatively near home. The amount and location of cleared land (but not necessarily farmed) has varied greatly historically. For example, small "plantations" of the residents of Barranco, Belize, during the period of commercial banana operations before the Second World War were extensive, covering a few thousand acres and ranging 12 miles from the village. Today, that area has shrunk to about 140 acres within one-and-a-half miles of town (see fig. 6).

SETTLEMENTS

Because they are delimited by the distribution of dwellings, settlements are the most easily recognized and bounded space in the hierarchy of Garífuna settlement patterns. Here are concentrated the material expressions of Garífuna culture. Generally, houses and outbuildings are closely clustered. Such agglomeration probably reflects the highly social nature of the residents. Smaller villages are linear, normally with the ridge poles of the houses parallel to the sea. As settlements enlarge, a few rows of houses develop inland, and further growth usually brings nucleation near the middle of the line village (see fig. 7). Settlements large enough to support public buildings exhibit centrality in the location of schools, churches, and stores (see fig. 8).

Settlement landscapes are dominated by Garífuna dwellings, which traditionally are constructed in two distinctive forms. Both have cahoon palm thatching for the roof, but one has walls of wattle-and-daub, the other has horizontal strips of royal palm bark *(yagua)*. Partitioned into two rooms (for eating and for sleeping), these houses are unusual in folk design for Central America because their roofs have a high pitch and are rectangular in form.

FAMILY COMPOUNDS

Internal subdivisions, here called family compounds, exist within each settlement. Very little can be seen in the landscape to distinguish one sector from another. Yet, inhabitants categorize sections of their villages, primarily on the basis of family residence. In size, compounds range from a small cluster of dwellings and outbuildings belonging to the local members of an extended family to *barrios,* or neighborhoods, of over one hundred homesteads.

FIG. 7.   An elongated Garífuna village on the north coast of Honduras.

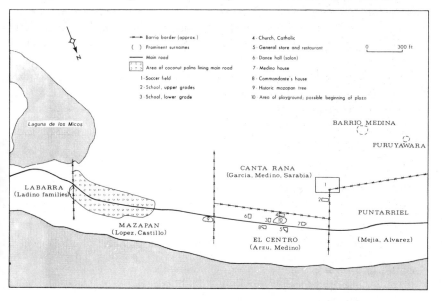

FIG. 8.   Tornabé, Honduras: Barrio subdivisions, approximate for 1976. (Source: King, 1976.)

Because settlement usually occurs first along the waterfront, and is family-related, as compounds grow they seem to enlarge perpendicular to the sea. Access to the water is therefore assured via family land. Also, later entrances by nonfamily (or non-Garífuna) relegates new settlers to the periphery. Tornabé, Honduras, for example, a village of about 1,800 inhabitants, has five locally-recognized internal sections, including one recently occupied by Ladino in-migrants (see fig. 8).

Clearly, it is through the agency of family-related activities of the compound that Garífuna maintain their cultural continuity. Within the borders of the compounds children receive their socialization and attachment to family, adult females gather for processing cassava and food preparation, and *barrio* residents sponsor dance groups and host ritual observances. The compound-based reverence for ancestors is the primary matrix that allows Garífuna ways to persist in a modernizing world.

Other Research Activities

Other activities associated with this research project have included the preparation of a 135-item bibliography of research (Davidson and Pierce, 1977) and the organization of a symposium for the 42nd International Congress of Americanists in Paris (Davidson, 1979a). Further, a paper on the general nature of research in coastal ethnogeography in Central America was presented at a symposium on research techniques in coastal environments (Davidson, 1978a).

At this date, field studies continue along the littoral of the Bay of Honduras, and a forthcoming monograph will culminate research on the historical and cultural geography of these most hospitable and imaginative beachfolk of the Central American shorelands.

REFERENCES

ANGUIANO, GOV. R.
    1801.   Población de las provincia de Honduras—matricula del año 1801. Manuscript, Guatemala Indiferente 1525, no. 11, Archivo General de Indias, Sevilla.
BEAUCAGE, P.
    1970.   Economic anthropology of the Black Carib of Honduras. Ph.D. dissertation, University of London, 1970.
COELHO, R.
    1955.   The Black Carib of Honduras. Ph.D. dissertation, Northwestern University, 1955.

DAVIDSON, W. V.
1974. The Caribs (Garífuna) of Central America: A map of their realm and a bibliography of research. National Studies (Belize), vol. 2, no. 6, pp. 15-25.
1976. Black Carib (Garífuna) habitats in Central America. Pp. 85-94 *in* "Frontier Adaptations in Lower Central America," 178 pp., M. Helms and F. Loveland, eds. Institute for the Study of Human Issues, Philadelphia.
1978a. Research in coastal ethnogeography: the east coast of Central America. Pp. 277-284 *in* "Research Techniques in Coastal Environments," 320 pp., J. Walker, ed., vol. 18, Geoscience and Man, Louisiana State Univ. School of Geoscience, Baton Rouge.
1978b. The Garífuna of Pearl Lagoon: ethnohistory of an Afro-American enclave in Nicaragua. *In* "New Approaches in Afro-American Ethnohistory," R. Stoffle and D. Shimkin, eds., special issue of Ethnohistory, in press. (Presented orally, American Society for Ethnohistory, Austin, Texas, 1978.)
1979a. The Garífuna symposium: an introduction. Actes du XLIIe Congrès International des Américanistes (Paris 1976), vol. 6, pp. 447-449.
1979b. Dispersal of the Garífuna in the western Caribbean. Actes du XLIIe Congrès International des Américanistes (Paris, 1976), vol. 6, pp. 467-474.
1979c. Coastal imperative lost?: village abandonment among the Honduran Garífuna. Actes du XLIIe Congrès International des Américanistes (Paris, 1976), vol. 6, pp. 571-576.
DAVIDSON, W. V., and PIERCE, J. K.
1977. The Garífuna of Central America: a bibliography of research. Louisiana State Univ. Dept. of Geography and Anthropology, Baton Rouge, 12 pp.
GALINDO, J.
1832. Notice of the Caribs in Central America. Journ. Royal Geogr. Soc. (London), vol. 3, pp. 290-291.
GONZALEZ, N. S.
1969. Black Carib household structure. University of Washington Press, Seattle.
KING, P.
1976. A descriptive and comparative study of the barrios of Tornabé, Honduras. Pp. 71-79, *in* "Field Studies in Central America I: Tela and Vicinity, Honduras," 140 pp., W. V. Davidson, ed. Louisiana State Univ. Department of Geography and Anthropology, Baton Rouge.
LUNDBERG, P. A.
1978. Barranco: A sketch of a Belizean Garífuna (Black Carib) habitat. M. A. thesis, University of California, Riverside.
TAYLOR, D.
1951. The Black Carib of British Honduras. Viking Fund Publ. in Anthrop. no. 17. Wenner-Gren Foundation, New York.

WILLIAM V. DAVIDSON

Cenozoic Vertebrates and Floras in the Arctic

Principal Investigators: Mary R. Dawson, Carnegie Museum of Natural History, Pittsburgh, Pennsylvania; Robert M. West, Milwaukee Public Museum, Milwaukee, Wisconsin; and Leo J. Hickey, National Museum of Natural History, Smithsonian Institution, Washington, D. C.

Grant Nos. 1178, 1600, 1749, and 2044.   In support of prospecting for and study of Cenozoic biota in the eastern Arctic.

Two major lines of evidence led to our project of searching for Cenozoic biota in the eastern Arctic. First, it has long been recognized that early Eocene (Sparnacian–Wasatchian) mammal faunas of western North America and western Europe show a remarkably high degree of similarity at the generic level—at least 50 percent—which is higher than at any other time during the Cenozoic. In the succeeding interval (Lutetian–Bridgerian) the generic similarity drops to about 10 percent and endemism increases.

The second line of evidence comes from data supporting the plate tectonics theory, according to which there was a North Atlantic land connection between the northeastern Canadian Arctic, Greenland, and continental Europe, which appears to have been broken by further plate motion around 45 to 48 million years ago, just after the time, around 49 million years ago, of the Sparnacian–Wasatchian mammalian similarity. Thus, fossils found along the postulated North Atlantic route might show whether this was indeed an area of biotic continuity between North America and Europe.

The presence of Late Cretaceous to Paleogene plant-bearing deposits, the Eureka Sound Formation, on various islands of the Canadian Arctic Archipelago makes the eastern Canadian Arctic a logical place to search for fossils that might provide evidence for North American–European land connections. These rocks are especially well exposed on Ellesmere and Axel Heiberg islands, and occur in more scattered exposures on Devon, Cornwallis, Somerset, Banks, Ellef Ringnes, Melville, and Lougheed islands. The Eureka Sound Formation is a thick sequence of sandstones, mudstones, shales, and limestones with some interbedded conglomeratic channel deposits. Fossil plant remains are one of the outstanding features of the unit, but until our work no invertebrate or vertebrate fossils had been reported definitely from the formation.

Fragmentary vertebrate fossils found by members of the Canadian Geological Survey on Devon Island led us to widen our project into the Neogene deposits bearing these remains. Thus, we have lengthened the temporal span of our project, going from one dealing exclusively with late Cretaceous and Paleogene fossils to one extending also through the later Tertiary. These younger deposits open up the possibility of tracing Arctic biotic developments through the Tertiary.

Procedure

Paleontological work in 1973, 1976, and 1977 was done in the Eureka Sound Formation on Ellesmere, Axel Heiberg, and Devon islands. By far the most work was done in the excellent exposures on Ellesmere Island. In the 1979 field season we worked again in the Eureka Sound Formation but added a project in later Tertiary lake sediments within the Haughton Astrobleme, Devon Island. Working out of over twelve base camps during the course of our field seasons, we have covered many regions that appeared to be paleontologically interesting. During our first years our work was entirely by foot, but in the later years surveying for sites was done from a helicopter. The helicopter support and much of our fixed wing flying was provided by Polar Continental Shelf Project, Canadian Department of Energy, Mines and Resources.

Paleontological Results

Our first results were somewhat disappointing, since in 1973 only incomplete remains of marine fishes were found. However, a return trip to Ellesmere Island by Dawson and West in 1975 produced the first record of Tertiary terrestrial vertebrates from the Eureka Sound Formation and even from within the Arctic Circle anywhere. The 1976, 1977, and 1979 expeditions were still more successful. A vertebrate fauna of over twenty taxa indicating an early Eocene age was discovered in the upper part of the Eureka Sound Formation in the Strathcona Fiord–Bay Fiord area, Ellesmere Island, and a younger, probably Bridgerian level with about eleven taxa was also found. Amphibians, reptiles, birds, and mammals are represented. All of the terrestrial vertebrates so far known are from high in the formation in this one area of Ellesmere Island. Continued prospecting in the lower parts of the formation and in other areas has yielded some fish remains but no other terrestrial vertebrates.

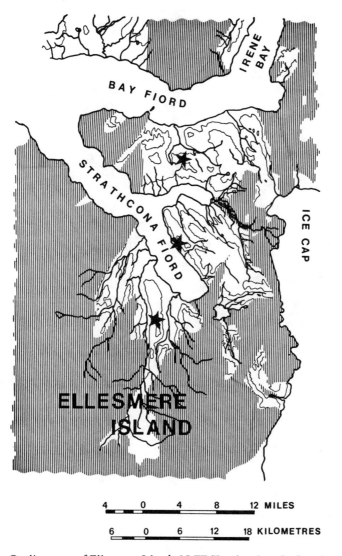

FIG. 1.   Outline map of Ellesmere Island, N.W.T., showing the locations of the
seven field camps used during the 1973 fieldwork and collecting areas of the same
names. The primary areas of Eureka Sound Formation are indicated.

1, Irene Bay	5, Strathcona Fiord
2, Vesle Fiord	6, Canon Fiord
3, Sawtooth	7, Lake Hazen
4, Clinker	

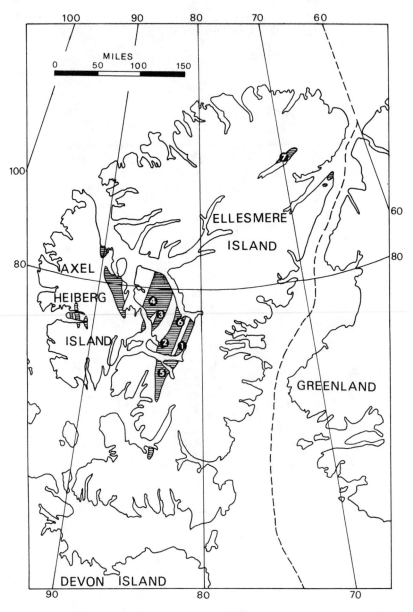

Fig. 2.   Sites of 1976 fieldwork.

The lake sediments in Haughton Astrobleme, Devon Island, produced a peculiar assemblage of vertebrates dominated by fish and a very large pika (family Ochotonidae). The only other well-represented mammal is a peculiar artiodactyl. The age of this fauna is probably late Miocene.

Fossil leaves and wood are abundant in the Eureka Sound Formation. In the first year of the project, some specimens were collected but this was not done systematically until 1977, when palynological samples were made from two localities in the Eureka Sound Formation. A more extensive paleobotanical project was undertaken in 1979, when fossil leaves, wood, and pollen were collected from one area on Axel Heiberg Island and four areas on Ellesmere Island.

Collecting invertebrate fossils has not been a primary object of our work, but samples of marine and nonmarine invertebrates have been collected.

Interpretations

Although detailed taxonomic studies of the vertebrates and plants are still in progress, preliminary identifications have enabled us to suggest some distributional and climatic hypotheses for the Paleogene. Geographic affinities of the faunas are strongest with North America, and less so with Europe and Asia but strong enough to suggest that there may have been faunal connections both eastward across the North Atlantic and westward across the Bering region. The Eocene climate was warm temperate, and a distinct summer-winter regime of light and dark intervals probably prevailed. We do not yet know enough of the Miocene fauna to interpret later Tertiary conditions.

Stratigraphic studies have been part of our project. Sections through the Eureka Sound Formation on Axel Heiberg and Ellesmere islands have been made, attempting to relate areas to one another. Our lowest sections are on Fosheim Peninsula, Ellesmere Island, where the formation includes Cretaceous marine invertebrates. The uppermost sections are in the Strathcona Fiord–Bay Fiord area. The formation includes, broadly speaking, a lower part with abundant plants, a middle part with marine incursions, and an upper part with well-represented plants and vertebrates that extends into the middle Eocene.

REFERENCES

DAWSON, MARY R.; WEST, ROBERT M.; LANGSTON, WANN; and HUTCHISON, J. HOWARD
    1976.   Paleogene terrestrial vertebrates: northernmost occurrence, Ellesmere Island, Canada.   Science, vol. 192, pp. 781-782.

DAWSON, MARY R.; WEST, ROBERT M.; RAMAEKERS, PAUL; and HUTCHISON, J.
HOWARD
1975.   New evidence on the paleobiology of the Eureka Sound Formation, Arc-
         tic Canada.   Arctic, vol. 28, no. 2, pp. 110-116.
WEST, ROBERT, M., and DAWSON, MARY R.
1977.   Mammals from the Paleogene of the Eureka Sound Formation: Ellesmere
         Island, Arctic Canada.   Geobios, Mem. Spécial, vol. 1, pp. 107-124.
1979.   Vertebrate paleontology and the Cenozoic history of the North Atlantic
         region.   Polarforschung, vol. 48, no. 1/2, pp. 103-119.
WEST, ROBERT M.; DAWSON, MARY R.; HICKEY, LEO J.; and MIALL, A. D.
1981.   Upper Cretaceous and Paleogene sedimentary rocks, eastern Canadian
         Arctic and related North Atlantic areas.   Pp. 279-298 *in* "Geology of
         the North Atlantic Borderlands," J. W. Kerr and A. J. Fergusson, eds.,
         Canadian Soc. Pet. Geol., Mem. 7.
WEST, ROBERT M.; DAWSON, MARY R.; and HUTCHISON, J. HOWARD
1977.   Fossils from the Paleogene Eureka Sound Formation, N.W.T., Canada:
         occurrence, climatic and paleogeographic implications.   Milwaukee
         Public Mus., Spec. Publ. Biol. Geol., vol. 2, pp. 77-93.
WEST, ROBERT M.; DAWSON, MARY R.; HUTCHISON, J. HOWARD; and RAMAEK-
ERS, PAUL
1975.   Paleontologic evidence of marine sediments in the Eureka Sound Forma-
         tion of Ellesmere Island, Arctic Archipelago, N.W.T., Canada.   Cana-
         dian Journ. Earth Sci., vol. 12, no. 4, pp. 574-579.

MARY R. DAWSON
ROBERT M. WEST

Gravitational Deflection of Light: Solar Eclipse of June 30, 1973[1]

Principal Investigator: Texas Mauritanian Eclipse Team. Co-leaders: Bryce S. DeWitt and Harlan J. Smith, University of Texas, Austin, Texas.[2]

Grant No. 1186:   For improved measurement of the gravitational light-deflection effect.

The deflection of light by large masses is one of the simplest effects predicted by currently viable theories of gravity, and an accurate observation of the effect is of fundamental importance in the determination of which theory is correct. By far the most accurate observations to date have been obtained by radio interferometry,[3,4] and this technique may remain the most accurate for years to come. Nevertheless it will always remain desirable to have observations at optical frequencies as well, to provide a measure in a radically different wavelength range, differing in possible systematic errors. Moreover, the day will ultimately come when the observations can be performed from a space

---

[1] A more complete account of the expedition and of the data reduction procedures will be found in: Texas Mauritanian Eclipse Team, Astron. Journ., vol. 81, p. 452 (1976); B. F. Jones, idem, p. 455. In addition to support from the National Geographic Society the expedition received funds from the Research Corporation (New York), NATO (Brussels), the University of Texas, and the National Science Foundation, which supplied the bulk of the financial assistance.

[2] The project team consisted of R. Allen Brune, Jr., Charles L. Cobb, Bryce S. DeWitt (co-leader), Cecile DeWitt-Morette, David S. Evans, Johnnie E. Floyd, Burton F. Jones, Raymond V. Lazenby, Maurice Marin, Richard A. Matzner, Alfred H. Mikesell, Marjorie R. Mikesell, Richard I. Mitchell, Michael P. Ryan, Harlan J. Smith (co-leader), Sy Alassane, and Charles D. Thompson, plus the secretarial, fiscal, engineering, and maintenance staffs of the Department of Astronomy and Center for Relativity of the University of Texas.

[3] K. A. Weiler, R. D. Ekers, E. Raimond, and K. J. Wellington, Astron. Astrophys., vol. 30, p. 241, 1974.

[4] C. C. Counselman III., S. M. Kent, C. A. Knight, I. I. Shapiro, T. A. Clark, H. F. Hinteregger, A.E.E. Rogers, and A. R. Whitney, Phys. Rev. Letters, vol. 33, p. 1621, 1974.

platform. The optical measurements should then surpass the radio measurements in accuracy.

No method has as simple a concept or as little dependence on secondary parameters as the classical method, which makes use of photography during a solar eclipse.[5] The older eclipse observations can be criticized on several grounds, including failure to use identical optics for eclipse and reference exposures, failure to obtain night plates with exactly the same instrumental setup as used for day plates, absence of temperature control, and the unavailability of modern microdensitrometric reduction techniques. However, by far the most serious drawback of eclipse observations is the necessity of photographing under field conditions, at the mercy of uncontrollable meteorological elements. The Texas expedition suffered seriously from the latter and consequently may, in the light of future history, prove to have been the last expedition for its purpose to receive major funding. Nevertheless, the results obtained compare favorably in accuracy with earlier observations obtained under fine weather conditions, and may be regarded as a good test of current technology.

The solar eclipse of June 30, 1973, was a member of the "grand cycle" of the 20th century, which included also the "Eddington eclipse" of 1919 (three saroses earlier and with a rather similar track) during which the first successful photographs of the light deflection were made. The period of totality lasted over 7 minutes at maximum, the sun was in a rich Milky Way star field, and sunspot (and hence coronal) activity was fairly low. These facts influenced the decision to undertake the expedition.

Advance members of the field team arrived at the oasis of Chinguetti, Mauritania, 25 kilometers north of the eclipse center line,[6] on the 18th of May. A semipermanent well-insulated building was first assembled to house the telescope and to provide a dust-free and thermally controlled environment in the desert. The building, 16 feet square and 12 feet high, was of plywood and styrofoam construction braced with bolted 2-by-4-inch studs. A gasketed movable roof section provided access to about 1 hour of sky and 30° of declination. Otherwise the building was completely caulked and sealed. It was provided with a two-door entrance "air lock" (to permit entry and egress during sand and dust storms), a workbench and tool rack, a darkroom with refrigerator, an evaporative cooler (to maintain the telescope at typical night tempera-

---

[5] H. von Klüber, Determination of Einstein's light deflection in the gravitational field of the sun.   *In* "Vistas in Astronomy," A. Beer, ed.   Pergamon Press, London, 1960.

[6] Lat. 20°27′N., long. 12°22′W., elevation about 350 meters.

tures and to provide filtered air and positive inside pressure), and a compressor type air-conditioner (to control darkroom temperature near 20°C.). Electricity in May and June was provided by a logistic support team and in November by a gasoline-powered generator.

The telescope itself was assembled as soon as the building was completed. Initial instrument design had called for a red-corrected 3-meter-focal-length camera. Because of funding limitations, the purchase of new optics was not possible. Through the courtesy of Prof. R. Michard and Jean Texereau the expedition was able to borrow a 4-element astrometric-quality blue-corrected flat-field telescope (lens and tube) from the Paris Observatory. This 2.1-meter-focal-length telescope had been designed by Prof. André Danjon, delivered to him shortly before his death in 1967, and never used. The original desire for a red-corrected lens arose partly from a wish to discriminate predominantly yellow stars against the (blue) sky. In fact, at Chinguetti the sky was gray-white, not blue, during the eclipse, and so the blue correction was not a liability. After 3 months of tuning in Austin, knife edge and other tests showed the lens to be of excellent quality. In order to enhance this quality the lens elements were antireflection-coated, the 20-centimeter aperture was stopped down to 16.5 centimeters, and a blue filter was added. The lens was hand carried from Austin to Chinguetti, and image quality on field plates indicated that the excellent optics were maintained intact.

The telescope tube carried a cylindrical hood, or dew cap, with sky diaphragm at its upper end. The telescope mount, of equatorial type, had been constructed by Calvert in England about 1880. The right ascension drive worm and gear were replaced by a rigidly framed tangent-screw assembly driven for tracking by a 115-volt synchronous motor run by a 60 Hz. crystal-controlled power supply, which drew its energy from a 12-volt battery. The whole assembly could be shifted in right ascension and declination by unclamping. Fine control in declination was obtained through hand-operated screws and in right ascension through a push-button-controlled variable-speed motor.

No manual guiding was attempted at any time, and examination of the eclipse plates reveals no trace of tracking error. During the actual eclipse run the telescope was driven unbalanced, heavy to the east, to eliminate the effects of any possible play in the precision screw. An auxiliary "guide" telescope was used in the alignment process. This instrument was intended to be used also for the final aiming of the camera on eclipse day. But the sky proved to be so bright that the guide star (ε Geminorum) could not be seen, even a few seconds before second contact, and an emergency backup telescope, a Questar aimed directly at the sun, had to be used instead.

The expected outdoor temperature at mid-eclipse was 29°C. (it turned out, because of a dust storm, to be 36°C.). Photographic plate focus runs and adjustments were made with the lens at precisely this temperature. Thermal invariance was achieved by holding the building at 29° for several hours until equilibrium was reached and by exposing the hooded lens to the night sky only for brief periods. At all other times the open end of the lens hood was covered by several layers of aluminum foil. A similar aluminum blanket covered the plate end of the telescope except during exposure runs. The entire telescope tube, including the hood, was wrapped in fiberglass blanketing 10 centimeters thick, and the uniformity of its temperature was monitored by means of thermistors mounted along its length, and on the lens elements.

Outside temperature and humidity were measured by a mercury thermometer and wet-bulb hygrometer located outside the building on the shady side (south in June). June humidity measurements frequently reached as low as 10 percent. During night-time test exposures prior to the eclipse, great difficulty was encountered with plate spotting due to static electricity arising from the extreme aridity. (The evaporative cooler was generally not running at night, and hence not supplying humidified air.) This problem was at length solved by placing wet sponges inside the tube near the plate.

At eclipse time rigid temperature control was maintained for 24 hours prior to second contact. During the night, after reaching thermal equilibrium, the eclipse plates were prepared for use and mounted in plateholders. Each was provided with a rectangular grid of artificial star images, or fiducial marks, contact printed from a master plate. The lattice spacing of the grid was 1 centimeter, and the artificial images were uniform and circular, each with a diameter of 50 μ. A chief purpose of the grid was to monitor emulsion creep, but it is not difficult to imagine other uses for the grid in the plate reduction process.

In addition to the grid, each plate was provided with step-tablet wedge patterns on two opposite corners and in the center, and with graded star-image sensitometric scales on the other two corners. It had been planned to use the patterns as sensitometric standards in the plate reduction process, in order to control image displacements arising from nonlinear emulsion response and nonuniform background. The noise level on the actual eclipse plates, however, made it impossible to achieve an accuracy for which such effects could become significant.

To prepare for a range of possible sky brightness levels, a slow, fine-grained plate (Kodak III-0) was chosen as the primary plate, and a faster, grainier plate (Kodak IIa-0) was chosen as a backup in case of an exceptionally dark sky. A photometer aimed well away from the sun was used to determine the background level during the eclipse. The III-0 plates were those in fact used. All plates were 1/4 inch, microflat, and 12 inches square, yielding a 7.5° by 7.5° field with the Danjon optics. Bottled Evian water, trucked to the site, was used for developing.

The weather on the morning of the eclipse was execrable. A strong wind blew from the north, as on the several preceding days. Although the airborne dust made them difficult to see, there were also some thin clouds in front of the solar disk. At approximately 10 minutes before totality, however (shortly after the opening of the building roof), the wind began to drop until by totality the air was almost completely still. Moreover, the clouds dissipated so that only the very fine suspended dust remained to interfere with the view of the sun. Measurements by Peterson, Kieffaber, and Buehler[7] indicated 82 percent extinction of the solar light coming through this dust. The sky, moreover, remained unusually bright. Only Venus was easily visible.

At 1 minute before totality the thermal blanket on the front end of the telescope was removed, but the lens was still covered by a hand-held shutter so that no sunlight ever touched it. Exposures began approximately 5 seconds after totality began. Each plate was exposed to the eclipse field for 60 seconds and to a comparison field 10° away in declination (nearly identical in altitude and likewise in the Milky Way) for 30 seconds. Five seconds were allowed after each major telescope handling for vibrations to damp down before the shutter was opened again. Three plates in all were exposed, the exposure sequence being (comparison, eclipse), (eclipse, comparison), (eclipse, comparison). A rotating sector, a few millimeters above the plate surface, was used to reduce saturation near the sun, so that images of a few of the brighter stars might be secured in the outer coronal region. The corona was not large, but there are several prominent streamer images on the plates, one of which wiped out a hoped-for star.

The plates were developed on-site during the afternoon of the same day, dried, inspected, and packed for transit the same night. Had the sky been clear, over a thousand eclipse-field star images would have appeared on each plate. In fact only 150 measurable images were found in addition to 60 comparison-field images. Yet this was surprisingly good, poor conditions considered, and it was decided to adhere to the original plan to send a second team 5 months later. On July 1 the building was sealed and placed under guard, with the telescope left in exactly the final eclipse position but with the tangent drive returned to the position it had at the beginning of the eclipse run.

---

[7] A. W. Peterson, NSF Solar Eclipse 1973 Bull. no. 5, p. 40

The second team arrived on November 6 and found the guard on duty. When the building was opened everything was in perfect order. Generators, refrigerator, air conditioners, and telescope-tracking system all worked, and first observations were attempted through clouds on November 7. Last observations were taken the night of November 16. Several nights in this interval, including that when the moon was centered in the eclipse field, were lost because of overcast sky and even rain. The first observations of importance were made after the housing interior was maintained for 48 hours at its 29°C. mideclipse temperature. For the last two nights the temperature was that of the current outside ambient, 24°C. The key series of exposures at each temperature precisely duplicated the hour angle and time sequence of the eclipse exposures. Contrary to preliminary fears, seeing turned out to be excellent, even on the plates exposed when the air inside the building was considerably warmer than outside. As in June, processing of the plates was carried out effectively, and the disassembly of equipment was not undertaken until the last plate was seen to be good.

Both the June and November plates were first measured at the Royal Greenwich Observatory, Herstmonceux, on the Galaxy II comparator. They were then brought to Texas for further analysis and measurement on a PDS microphotometer.

Two unfortunate facts emerged from the plate analysis: (1) The grid-point positions differ from one plate to another by small amounts that can be most readily explained by supposing that the master grid was not firmly in contact with each plate when the points were put on. (2) Variable scale changes occurred between the eclipse and comparison-field exposures. Although some scale change was inevitable (owing to flexure of the instrument as it was moved from one position to the other) it had been hoped that the change would be the same from plate to plate. It was not.

It is quite possible that fact number (1) resulted from a decision that was made in the field not to brush the plates before preparing them for exposure. This decision was made because of fear of static electricity, but it meant that grains of dust or very fine sand may have found their way to and remained on the emulsion surfaces, preventing perfect contact with the master grid. It is also possible that simply not enough pressure was applied to the master grid.

The most likely explanation for fact number (2) is imperfect instrument design. The telescope was constructed to register all plates identically with the lens. During exposure each plate rested against steel buttons at the back of the telescope, *independently of the plateholder.* However, pressure was applied to the plate through springs mounted on the plateholder. It was discovered in the field that these springs, as they came from the machineshop, were exerting insufficient force. Pads were therefore mounted on the springs to increase the force by what was thought to be an adequate amount. Evidently it was not. The plate measurements show clear scale-change correlations between plates that had been exposed in a given plateholder, but the "signature" of each plateholder was not reproducible with sufficient accuracy for the comparison field to be used for scale control.

Both of the above problems could have been discovered, and corrected, had there been time to make a dry run of the exposure procedures and plate analysis before the instrument was shipped to Mauritania. In the end, however, neither difficulty significantly affected the accuracy that could be obtained, which was almost entirely determined by the adverse sky conditions and consequent "noise" on the eclipse plates. An outer ring of eclipse-field stars on each plate was reserved exclusively for scale determination. It is not difficult to show[1] that unless the scale change between eclipse and comparison fields can be held constant from one plate to another to a very high degree of accuracy (beyond that obtainable in the present case, given the atmospheric conditions) only an inner ring of eclipse-field stars should be used in the determination of the light deflection, even under much more favorable "noise" conditions. Hence no stars were wasted in the actual reductions. The final value obtained for the light deflection extrapolated to the solar limb was

$$L = \{.95 \pm .11\} \times L_E$$

where $L_E \{= 1''.75\}$ is Einstein's value. The error indicated is one standard deviation and compares favorably with the errors reported from earlier eclipse expeditions.[5]

BRYCE S. DEWITT

Search for the *Monitor* and Development of a Camera for Horizontal Underwater Photography

Principal Investigators: Harold E. Edgerton, Massachusetts Institute of Technology, Cambridge, Massachusetts; John G. Newton, Duke University Marine Laboratory, Beaufort, North Carolina; Robert E. Sheridan, University of Delaware, Newark, Delaware; and Gordon P. Watts, North Carolina Department of Cultural Resources.

Grant Nos. 1219, 1297, 1336, 1382, 1421.   For search for the wreck of the *Monitor* and geologic investigation of the ridge off Cape Hatteras, and for development of a camera system for horizontal underwater photography.

An oceanographic expedition off North Carolina in August 1973 had dual objectives: geological study of a ridge and swale on the Continental Shelf off Cape Hatteras, and a search for the Civil War ironclad USS *Monitor*. Two weeks of ideal weather and a group of diverse but compatible specialists aboard three vessels brought both goals to successful conclusions.

The geological study offered evidence of ancient estuarine environments, buried channels, and upwarping of the strata beneath the ridge.

The archeological search yielded, in the area of interest, more than 22 contacts. These were detected by side-searching sonar, vertical sonar, or magnetometer. Two of these targets were selected for thorough investigation by photographic and television cameras. One target was revealed to be a fishing trawler; the second was identified as the wreck of the ironclad USS *Monitor,* lost in 1862.

Subsequent expeditions to the wreck site in March–April 1974 and August 1974 offered reinforcing evidence through detailed vertical photography, oblique television recordings, and sampling of artifacts from the sea floor around the wreck.

Details of the search for the *Monitor* and underwater photographs of the vessel are contained in the articles listed in the references.

After several trial and error designs, plus numerous tests in Boston Harbor, final design of an underwater camera capable of horizontal photography was completed. It provides a high-resolution, 35-mm underwater camera, with synchronized strobe lights and a surface TV viewing system that enables the surface operator to take photographs, the direction of the camera being controlled by torque from water jets.

Positioning of the ship above the target is accomplished by use of two or three nylon anchor lines and the ocean currents. A winch is used to raise and lower the assembly to the desired height with respect to the target. Considerable seamanship is required when currents and winds are present.

An expedition was mounted by the Monitor Research and Recovery Foundation, through John Newton, Robert Sheridan, and Harold Edgerton in early April 1977. Dr. Sheridan, of the University of Delaware, served as the

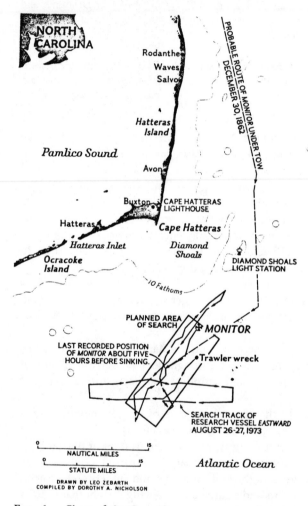

FIG. 1.   Chart of the Cape Hatteras area, showing the area searched with side-scan sonar to locate the *Monitor* wreck.

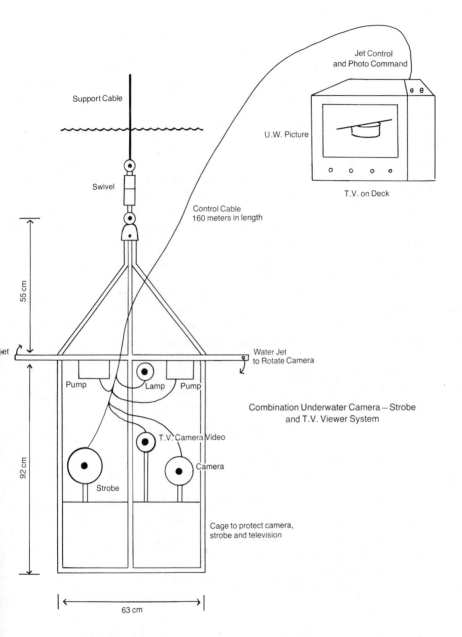

FIG. 2.   An underwater camera with synchronized strobe light. Television viewing enables a surface operator to trigger the camera at the proper moment. Water jets are used to rotate the assembly.

principal scientist on the research vessel *Cape Henlopen* out of Lewes, Delaware. We were unable to obtain site-view photographs of the turret.

Further investigation of the *Monitor* was accomplished during July and August 1977 by an expedition headed by NOAA, with the cooperation of Ed Link and his Harbor Branch Foundation, including their two research vessels and submarines. It was determined, for example, that the *Monitor*'s turret portholes were closed. The divers could not see into the turret. (At the moment, we do not know if the two 11-inch cannons are still in the turret, but I believe that they are.) Confirmation was made of the unusual position of the wreck. It is resting on one edge of the turret, so that the divers could swim under it. There is no distortion to the heavy side armor which bears the weight of the wreck. Link stated that it should be possible to put cables under the wreck, using the side armor and the heavy deck as a pan to lift the entire ship and its contents, except for the turret, which has broken away from the *Monitor,* and gradually to float it into shallow water where archeologists can work under more favorable conditions. The numerous photographs made by the expedition would be useful in making a plan for this recovery operation and other studies.

The horizontal underwater camera/strobe/TV system is now in the Strobe Laboratory of the Massachusetts Institute of Technology, ready for any assignment that might come along. A number of minor improvements are scheduled to be incorporated into it in the near future.

The encouragement and backing of the National Geographic's Research Committee for this project assisted us greatly in our objectives.

REFERENCES

EDGERTON, HAROLD E.
    1975.   The *Monitor* is found.   Mass. Inst. of Techn., Technology Review, February 1975, p. 8.
    1975.   Lost camera on the *Monitor.*   Skin Diver Magazine, June 1975, pp. 40-41.
NEWTON, JOHN G.
    1975.   How we found the *Monitor.*   National Geographic, vol. 147, no. 1 (January), pp. 48-61.
SHERIDAN, ROBERT E.
    1976.   An epic quest, recovery of the USS *Monitor.*   Univ. of Delaware News, winter 1976-77, pp. 3-10.

HAROLD E. EDGERTON
JOHN G. NEWTON

Water Balance in Insects of the Namib Desert, South West Africa

Principal Investigator: Eric B. Edney, University of California, Los Angeles, California.

Grant No. 1146: In support of studies of the water balance of insects of the Namib Desert.

One of the reasons why insects as a group are so biologically successful is that they possess highly efficient mechanisms for maintaining water balance, often in very dry surroundings. Deserts provide very good material for the study of these mechanisms, because the extremely hot, dry conditions that occur there have led to a maximum expression of the adaptations concerned. In South West Africa (Namibia) the geologically old Namib Desert contains a rich fauna of tenebrionid beetles, the various species of which are specialized in different ways to live in the different biological niches that the desert affords. During the past decade or so, interest in these problems has been developing, and the facilities for field study afforded by the Namib Desert Research Station at Gobabeb[1] have attracted several insect biologists to work in the area. I have visited Gobabeb several times, and with the valuable cooperation of Erik Holm, Prof. Gideon Louw, and Dr. Mary Seely (the present director of the Station) I have worked on some of the numerous problems that call for investigation. The National Geographic Society kindly supported my visit in November and December 1973—the subject of this report.

The Namib beetle fauna can be divided into three ecologically more or less distinct groups: those in the "stony" desert to the northeast of the (usually dry) Kuiseb River bed, those in the river bed and the bordering vegetation, and those in the vast, virtually vegetationless sand-dune country between the river and the coast, some 65 kilometers distant. The fauna in the dunes is nourished largely by plant detritus blown into the area, sometimes from great distances. Food is important to these beetles not only for energy and nourishment but also for the free water that it contains (albeit in small quantities) and

---

[1] Founded by the late Dr. C. Koch, whose studies on the taxonomy of African tenebrionids is basic to all the subsequent ecological and physiological work on the group.

as a source of metabolic water that results when even completely dry food is oxidized in the body.

Holm and Edney (1973) observed that the behavior of the sand-dune species is such that each takes advantage of the food resource in its own way. Activity patterns (through annual as well as daily cycles) are distinct—different species using different times of the day and of the year to forage, the patterns varying seasonally. Thus a diurnal species such as *Onymacris plana* shows a bimodal daily activity pattern in the summer, but this becomes unimodal in the winter as midday temperatures become less extreme. Furthermore, the activity patterns correspond well with physiological attributes of the species concerned; thus species with higher cuticular water loss rates are active only by night (e.g., the species of *Lepidochora*). In this connection, Seely and Hamilton (1976) have recently shown that *Lepidochora* spp. drink the water that condenses from advective fog on small sand ridges built up by beetles themselves. *Onymacris unguicularis*, on the other hand, although normally diurnal, may emerge at night when fog is present and drink the water formed by condensation on their bodies (Hamilton and Seely, 1976). In 1973, Mary Seely and I extended my earlier work to a study of the biology of *Onymacris plana* and a common riverine species, *Onymacris rugatipennis*. *O. plana* lives in the dunes but is usually associated with clumps of the cucurbitaceous plant *Acanthosicyos horrida* (whose vernacular name is *nara*), and we were interested in finding its food preferences. By labeling various possible food materials with radioactive ^{32}P, we found that *plana* always prefers fresh flower buds to other parts of the plant or to *nara* detritus (although it will eat the latter). In our experiments the beetles did not feed on wind-blown fibrous grass detritus when this was offered although it was common in the area. Fresh flower buds contain about 83 percent water, while dry buds as detritus contain only 5 percent. Adult *O. plana* beetles lose about 10 milligrams per gram per day by transpiration (measured in dry air at 27°C. Unfortunately we do not have data for such loss in natural conditions), and calculations based on reasonable assumptions for fecal water loss and metabolic water show that a 1-gram beetle would have to eat only about 12 milligrams of *nara* buds per day to remain in water balance. Beetles were allowed to feed on radioactive buds for 48 hours and then counted for radioactivity (in whole body Anton counters). These counts indicated a mean ingestion of 96.85 milligrams per gram of beetle, but the actual amounts were certainly larger than this because of the quenching effect of the beetles' bodies and of loss by defecation. Thus for these desert sand-dune beetles, water balance is readily maintained provided *Acanthosicyos* is available.

Earlier work (Holm and Edney, 1973) had determined the temperatures and humidities to which certain sand-dune species are exposed both at and below the surface during a 24-hour cycle in the summer. In 1973 I extended these observations by measuring conditions in the habitat of *O. plana* (a large, *nara*-topped sand hillock). As might be expected, both temperature and humidity 30 centimeters below the surface were relatively equable, even though surface temperatures rose to 41°C. and humidities fell to below 10 percent. These beetles therefore have a comfortable retreat in which they may avoid the harsh ambient conditions.

During my 1973 visit, Mary Seely and I also obtained information about the feeding habits of the common riverine species, *Onymacris rugatipennis*. First we measured the water content of various available food materials. This was about 61.7 percent (standard deviation 3.26 percent) for detritus (mostly flowers) of *Acacia albida* collected at 11:15 a.m., and about 3.5 percent higher for the same material collected early in the morning at 6:30 a.m. Detritus collected at 5 p.m. and left overnight in 100 percent relative humidity gained 16.9 percent by absorbing water. Fresh *Nicotiana* leaves had a water content of about 88 percent, and radioactive labeling showed that beetles preferred this food over other offerings, although they fed quite readily on *Acacia giraffae* and *Euclea* flower and fruit detritus.

I had already observed the activity patterns, water-loss rates, and body temperature relationships of this species, and in 1973 we recorded the distribution of detritus-feeding activity during a 24-hour cycle. Such information may be important because, as we had found, in nature the moisture content of the detritus changes with immediate climatic conditions. The feeding distribution was measured by labeling artificial food (we used cornflakes) with ^{32}P and offering it to successive groups of 4, 5, or 6 beetles, at each hour from 6 a.m. to 6 p.m. (We knew that the beetles are inactive at night.) Each group was allowed to feed for 2 hours, after which individuals were counted for radioactivity. Numbers were small and variances large, but there was a significant trend: feeding increased from a low in the 6 a.m. group to a maximum during the 2 hours after noon, and fell again to a low in the 6 p.m. group. Observed changes in water content considered, this feeding pattern would not seem to be optimal for water uptake, but our work was done in the laboratory, and further observations in nature, and at other times of the year, are necessary.

Finally we wanted to know whether beetles take more food either when it is moist rather than dry or when the beetles themselves are dehydrated rather than in good water balance. For these experiments we used *rugatipennis* and the artificial food (cornflakes) labeled with ^{32}P. The answers were quite clear: the beetles always took more moist than dry food, irrespective of whether they themselves were fasted or were short of water. Such behavior could be advantageous if the amount of water present in dry food is less than the water content of the feces produced. This has been shown by Loveridge (1974) to be true for desert locusts, but we do not yet have sufficient information for a conclusion in the case of *O. rugatipennis*.

Conclusion

This research answered a few questions and uncovered several others, and the results will be incorporated in a book to be published shortly (Edney, 1977). We now know a little more about the water problems of desert insects and the adaptations by which they are solved. From this and other work the over-all impression that emerges is one of a multiplicity of solutions to the same general problem (how to remain in water balance in a hot dry desert). Differences in size, color, microhabitat, behavior, and physiological attributes combine to determine the particular strategy adopted by each species. In all probability adaptations in reproductive mechanisms also play an important part, but of these little or nothing is yet known.

Since the above was written Henwood (1976) has described the parts played by behavior and surface color on body temperature in two very long legged beetles, the black *Stenocara phalangia* and the white *S. eburnea;* and Holm and Scholtz (1980) have published a very full description of diurnal and annual activity periods in all Namibian sand-dune arthropods.

REFERENCES

EDNEY, ERIC B.
1977.   Water balance in land arthropods.   Zoophysiology and Ecology series,
        no. 8, 282 pp.   Springer-Verlag, New York.
HAMILTON, WILLIAM J., III, and SEELY, MARY K.
1976.   Fog basking by the Namib Desert beetle, *Onymacris unguicularis*.   Na-
        ture, vol. 262, pp. 284-285, illus.
HENWOOD, K.
1976.   A field tested thermoregulation model for two diurnal Namib tenebrio-
        nid beetles.   Ecology, vol. 56, pp. 329-342.
HOLM, ERIK, and EDNEY, ERIC B.
1973.   Daily activity of Namib Desert arthropods in relation to climate.   Ecol-
        ogy, vol. 54, pp. 43-56.
HOLM, E., and SCHOLTZ, C. H.
1980.   Structure and pattern of the Namib desert dune ecosystem at Gobabeb.
        Madoqua, vol. 12, pp. 5-39.
LOVERIDGE, J. P.
1974.   Studies on the water relations of adult locusts, II: Water gain in the food
        and loss in the faeces.   Trans. Rhodesia Sci. Assoc., vol. 56, pp. 1-30.
SEELY, MARY K., and HAMILTON, WILLIAM J., III
1976.   Fog catchment sand trenches constructed by tenebrionid beetles, *Lepido-
        chora,* from the Namib Desert.   Science, vol. 193, pp. 484-486, illus.

                                                        ERIC B. EDNEY

The Cooperative Breeding System of African Bee-eaters

Principal Investigator: Stephen T. Emlen, Cornell University, Ithaca, New York.

Grant Nos. 1216,   For a study of cooperative breeding among African bee-
1419.   eaters.[1]

Sociobiology is a new field of biology that combines ecology, animal behavior, and evolutionary theory. One of the most important and exciting challenges in this new field is to explain the evolution of cooperative or altruistic behavior in genetic and ecological terms. Under what conditions should an animal help another if it involves a risk to itself? When should one animal devote time and energy to help rear young that are not genetically its own? How much "cooperation" do helpers really provide and do they provide it to all other individuals equally, or selectively to their own relatives? Answers to these questions are essential if we are going to be able to explain or to understand better why some animals cooperate with one another and others do not.

True cooperation is extremely rare in animal societies. We generally think that "helping one another" is a behavior found only among mammalian social carnivores, primates, and man. But "helping" or mutual cooperation is known to occur also in a small number of species of tropical birds. Birds are excellent animals in which to study such problems. This is because they combine elements of simplicity (sufficient stereotypy of displays to allow behavioral interpretations; short generation times to allow collection of population success data) with sufficient complexity of social organization to make the results applicable as models of similar behavior in higher animals.

In 1973 Natalie J. Demong and I took sabbatical leave from Cornell University to initiate studies of the cooperative breeding of bee-eaters in East Africa. Bee-eaters are colorful birds belonging to the family Meropidae, order Coraciiformes. Several species are found commonly in East Africa, and the

---

[1] This research was initiated in 1973 and followed up in the spring of 1975 under grants from the National Geographic Society and the John Simon Guggenheim Foundation. Co-leader: Natalie J. Demong (Emlen).

white-fronted bee-eater, *Merops bullockoides,* was selected as a subject for intensive study on this project. The first six weeks were spent mapping out the distribution of white-fronted bee-eater colonies in the Rift Valley and selecting two sites as locations for intensive observation. We then studied the breeding chronology, trapped and color-marked 96 individuals for individual identification, made demographic studies of reproductive success, and recorded detailed behavioral observations at these sites.

In the spring of 1975 we again returned to Kenya and spent four months continuing our bee-eater studies. The results from these initial studies reveal a bee-eater social organization more complex than those previously described for most Temperate Zone avian species and even for most species of group-territorial cooperative breeders. Some of the most interesting features of bee-eater cooperative social organization are described below.

White-fronted bee-eaters show a degree of social complexity rarely found among birds, involving as it does at least three levels of social bonding between individuals. The basic social unit is a communally breeding group of two to seven individuals. But many such groups nest together, forming large colonies of up to several hundred individuals. A network of additional friendships and social alliances crisscrosses throughout the colony as a whole.

The bee-eaters have a sophisticated and graded system of vocal communication signals, allowing a wide range of signals and moods to be conveyed between colony members. Such graded systems of vocalization were previously thought to occur primarily among higher primates.

The bee-eaters show a high development of cooperative behavior. The groups of up to seven individuals include only one male and one female parent; the remaining individuals help in all aspects of the work of nesting, from building the nest (which is dug deep into vertical cliffs along river banks) to incubating the eggs, feeding the young, and defending the nestlings against predators. Only about half of the sexually mature adults in a colony are actually breeders. The remaining birds are devoting their full time and energy to sharing the work load in order to rear young that are not genetically their own. Surprisingly, the cooperating "helpers" are not merely young birds that were reared the year before and hence are helping their parents to raise more young. Rather, membership in the communal groups is open, with different individuals joining and leaving the groups as the year progresses. This argues against a kin-selection model for the evolution of altruism and raises a series of fascinating questions about cooperative societies in general.

The nonbreeding, helping adults in the bee-eater colony are primarily males. Sex ratios obtained both in the field and from museum skins indicate a heavy skew of between 1.6 and 2.0 males per female. The sex ratio of young birds at the age of fledging, however, is 1:1. It appears that dispersal from the home colony is carried out primarily by females, which incur a much higher mortality than do males. Our preliminary observations and demographic data reveal that helpers frequently do not help. This became evident by following individually marked birds throughout the long breeding season. Certain individuals diligently brought food to their foster young, while others contributed only minimally or actually brought food but then ate it rather than presenting it to the young. The actual reproductive success of the bee-eaters was drastically different in the two years of study. In 1975, when drought conditions were severe, reproductive success was extremely low (11 percent) and there was some indication that having extra birds share in the work load did result in a benefit for the parents (but not for the "helpers"). In 1973, reproductive success was slightly higher (average = 24 percent), and helpers appeared to be unimportant, contributing insignificantly to increased reproductive success. Thus it may turn out that the occurrence of helpers at the nest, and their importance to increased reproductive success, may vary directly with environmental conditions such as insect abundance or rainfall. Perhaps the basic question should not be whether parent birds benefit by having other bee-eaters help with their work load but rather whether the individual helper gains by contributing its help. Our preliminary hypothesis is that all birds benefit by living in groups and the survival of adults from one year to the next is greater among individuals that belong to large social units. If this is correct, then the evolution of cooperative behavior might not be best explained in terms of the paradox of decreased evolutionary fitness of the individual "helper" during times of breeding, but rather in terms of increased survival of the same individual by virtue of its membership in a tight social unit outside of the breeding season.

To answer the evolutionary question of why cooperation develops in certain animal societies and not in others, it is important that we follow individual bee-eaters from the time they hatch until they become sexually mature, reproducing adults. It will be necessary to know the parentage of these individuals in order to relate their activity to those of their genetic kin. After several years of such observation, it should be possible to calculate the lifetime reproductive fitness of different individuals. Such research is currently under way. We plan to continue to monitor the individual birds that were first marked in 1973 and 1975.

Through a combination of field approaches—by building up longitudinal dossiers on known individual birds, by collecting information on population success, and by making detailed behavioral observations—we hope to come to a fuller understanding of "altruism" among bee-eaters. The information that we hope to obtain should lead to a better understanding of both the evolution and the functioning of cooperation in animal societies in general.

REFERENCES

EMLEN, STEPHEN T.

1977.   Cooperative breeding in the white-fronted bee-eater.   Kenya Wildlife Club Bull., 1977, pp. 8-11.

1978.   The evolution of cooperative breeding in birds.   Pp. 245-281 *in* "Behavioural Ecology: An Evolutionary Approach," J. Krebs and N. Davies, eds.   Blackwell Scientific Publications Ltd.

————.   Altruism, kinship, and reciprocity in the white-fronted bee-eater.   *In* "Natural Selection and Social Behavior," R. D. Alexander and D. Tinkle, eds.   Chiron Press. (In press.)

————.   Breeding options, behavioral conflicts, and the evolution of helping behavior.   American Naturalist. (In press.)

EMLEN, STEPHEN T.; DEMONG, NATALIE J.; and HEGNER, ROBERT E.

————.   Bee-eaters: An alternative route to cooperative breeding?   *In* "Proceedings of XVII International Ornithological Congress," Berlin.   (In press.)

HEGNER, ROBERT E.,; EMLEN, STEPHEN T.; DEMONG, NATALIE J.; and MILLER, CAROLYN E.

1979.   Helping at the nest in the white-fronted bee-eater.   Scopus, vol. 3, pp. 9-13.

STEPHEN T. EMLEN

Fiestas in Manco Capac Province, Department of La Paz, Bolivia: An Ethnographic and Ethnomusicological Survey

Principal Investigator: Edwin E. Erickson, Department of Anthropology, University of Virginia.

Grant No. 1214:   For an ethnographic and ethnomusicological survey of the Copacabana Festival (Bolivia).

This project, funded in its entirety by the National Geographic Society, was planned as an analysis of the social and cultural meanings of the Fiesta of the Virgin of Copacabana, celebrated each year in early August. Discoveries in the field made it necessary to broaden the scope of the study considerably, because it became quickly apparent that the Festival of the Virgin is merely the centerpiece of a large and very complex system of pilgrimages, fairs, and festivals that take place annually in and around the town of Copacabana. The totality of ritual events, and especially those concentrated in the months of July and August convert Copacabana and its surrounding area (Manco Capac Province of La Paz Department) into a religious capital, not only for Bolivians, but also for residents of the southern third of highland Peru.

During these two months, the town and the province are involved in an almost continuous round of ritual activity. For example, on August 6 and 7 (and, informally for some days before and after), there are masses, processions, dances, and feasts in honor of the Virgin of Copacabana, celebrated in and around the basilica built in her honor. In mid-July, there is a large fiesta in honor of the Virgin of Carmen, who is widely venerated throughout the Andes (and more widely in the Hispanic world), and who is the national Patroness of Bolivia. Also concentrated in these two months are numerous local (village level) patronal fiestas (e.g., that of Santiago Apostol, in late July, celebrated at the village of Collasuyu). And throughout the period, throngs of people make the climb to the Calvario de la Virgen, a precipitous hill some 200 meters high, for the purpose of seeking the protection and bounty of a thinly disguised pre-Christian Earth Mother (Pachamama), who is sometimes identified with one or another manifestation of the Virgin Mary. The leaders in these rituals are lay readers (*maestros cantores*), who combine Roman Catholic prayers and hymns with such indigenous ritual practices as pouring libations of beer on the ground as a gift to Pachamama.

171

Throughout the year, moreover, Copacabana draws pilgrims from all over Bolivia and from much of Peru, most of them supplicants for restoration of health or for success in a new marriage or a recently established business. Out of the fiesta season, such supplicants normally visit and pray to the image of the Virgin and attend (and sometimes commission) masses in the basilica. In addition, they almost always make the climb of the Calvario, where numerous *maestros cantores* wait daily to provide their ritual services.

This project was designed as both an ethnographic and an ethnomusicological survey. In addition to the principal investigator, project staff consisted of Karen Poe Bromley, then a graduate student at the University of Virginia, and Stella Erickson. The principal investigator took primary responsibility for the recording of musical performances, observation of main festival events, and of interviewing key informants in Copacabana. Ms. Bromley was based principally in an agrarian community (Yumani) on the Island of the Sun, in the middle of Lake Titicaca, her purpose there being to provide a rural and local perspective on the ritual events. Ms. Erickson took primary responsibility for photography and, in addition, spent many days in observation at the top of Calvario.

Background

Copacabana, a town whose permanent population in 1973 was about 6,000 people, is the seat of Manco Capac Province, a subdivision of La Paz Department. With a 1973 population of about 39,000 and an area of 367 square kilometers, Manco Capac is far and away the most densely populated rural province of the department (about 107 persons per square kilometer; Poe, 1979, p. 45). Prior to the 1953 land reform (Blanchard et al., 1963), most of the land in Manco Capac was occupied by *haciendas*—large landed estates worked by entailed peasants and mostly absentee-owned. Much of the farmland lies in sheltered valleys and coves near the lake shore and, in consequence, enjoys a climate much milder than one would expect at the mean altitude of 12,600 feet above sea level. In prereform times and at present, the province has been one of the most productive agricultural zones in the Bolivian Altiplano, or plateau.

The town of Copacabana lies on a large bay of Lake Titicaca that harbors a considerable fleet of fishing vessels. It is also on a main road connecting La Paz and other parts of Bolivia to Puno Department, Peru. From Inca times (and perhaps before), Copacabana has been an important way station for traders and other travelers in the Central and Southern Andes. Geographically, Manco

Capac Province is a peninsula jutting eastward into the lake, attached territorially to Peru, rather than to Bolivia. From Copacabana to Yunguyo and other towns in southern Peru, the trip is made by an uninterrupted all-weather road; the trip to La Paz and elsewhere in Bolivia entails a ferry passage at the Strait of Tiquina.

A MAGNET OF PILGRIMAGE

Lake Titicaca (and particularly the bay and the islands near Copacabana) figures importantly in the origin myths of the Inca Empire. Accordingly, with the establishment of Inca control over the Collasuyu (southern province), several shrines were constructed by various Inca rulers. Some of the more important shrines were established on the Island of the Sun and at various other sites near Copacabana. The town is believed to have been founded for the purpose of housing Inca colonists (*mitimacuna*) to service the ritual establishment (Garcilaso de la Vega, 1966, pp. 189-190), but apparently it came early to be a major pilgrimage center in its own right (Helfritz, 1946).

In Inca times, pilgrimages were a major part of the annual cycle (Bennett, 1949). Not only were awesome supernatural personages confronted and supplicated, but a lively interregional trade was organized. In the tightly and minutely controlled society of the Inca, pilgrimages and regional fairs provided the major relief from drudgery and monotony. Normal barriers to travel were temporarily lowered and individuals were permitted to trade off their small surpluses for foodstuffs and other goods not available in their home territories.

The first task in the charter of the Spanish conquerors who arrived in the 16th century was to Christianize the Quechua- and Aymara-speaking masses of the Inca Empire and to extirpate all traces of idolatry. The process was reported as complete within a century of the arrival of the Pizarro expedition. How this task was accomplished is a long and complex story (see Kubler, 1946). Through the exercise of the doctrine of "missionary tolerance" (which separates "superstition," a venial sin, from "idolatry" and "heresy," mortal ones), it was possible to make the new faith more attractive to the converts by permitting the persistence of local ritual custom (which was theoretically divorced from the old matrix of pre-Christian beliefs). In addition, the early missioners managed to emphasize feast days that corresponded in time to the major festivals of the old religion. Thus, old feast days and old pilgrimage sites maintained their importance, though they were associated with new supernaturals.

It is not surprising, therefore, that before the end of the 16th century the Copacabana site had acquired a miraculous image of the Virgin, whose devotions formed then—and form today—the core of a pilgrimage festival. Early writers (e.g., Salas, 1618; Calancha, 1939) tell us that the image of the Virgin of Copacabana was carved some time late in the 16th century by an Indian of noble lineage, Don Francisco Titu Yupanqui, as an act of personal devotion. Almost immediately, miracles came to be associated with the image, and it was borne reverently about the territory surrounding the city of La Paz. In 1583, it was carried across the Strait of Tiquina, into what is today Manco Capac. As the bearers approached Copacabana, they discovered that they were making extraordinary speed and that their burden had become almost weightless. By these and other signs, it was decided that the Virgin had chosen the old shrine center as her permanent abode, and the image was sheltered there on the second of February. Nearly a century later, in 1670, construction was begun on a basilica that still houses the image and the official acts of her devotion (presently in the charge of Franciscans).

George Kubler (1946) has shown that Copacabana was but one of several pilgrimage sites in early colonial times. In the first prosperous days of the Spanish Viceroyalty, when gold and silver from the Andes made Spain the preeminent economic power in Europe, there was a proliferation of fairs and festivals, which provided variety and excitement in the life of the Indian peasants. Each of these festivals, now associated with one or another Christian personage, followed most of the patterns of the older celebrations—the combination of public ritual, private supplication, dance, and retail marketing.

At the same time, figures and images of Christian (and especially Spanish) festivals were introduced to the syncretic mix. Clowns, caricatures, and heroic representations from far and wide across medieval Europe came to lend a strain of uniformity to fiestas and pilgrimages from Mexico to Chile. Thus, for instance, the imagery of Christians vs. Moors, associated with an apparition of Santiago Apostol (St. James the Apostle) as the knight-hero of Spain are to be seen in festivals throughout Spanish America (Turner and Turner, 1978, pp. 169-170). As syncretized as the Andean pilgrimages were, they were part and parcel of a Marian tradition represented at Monserrat, Loreto, Guadalupe, and Czestochowa (Turner and Turner, 1978).

Toward the end of the colonial period, with a decline in overall prosperity, most of the Andean pilgrimages had ceased to be celebrated. Copacabana was one of the few that survived, at least on its traditional scale. In recent years, it has continued to draw, for the August festival alone, about 50,000 pilgrims from a large catchment area. The vigor and longevity of the Copacabana fiesta invite speculation on its social functions. It was toward these speculations that the research project was aimed.

RESEARCH HYPOTHESES

Three areas of anthropological theory were addressed in the research design. First, and most generally, is the question of the functions of the fiesta and the pilgrimage in the social, political, and economic life of the nation. Anthropologists have long seen ritual as symbolizing and reinforcing strategic relationships and salient concerns in human societies. This point, for example, was emphasized in the case of the nations of Subsaharan Africa in a review article by Victor W. Turner (1973). Quite aside from the literal supernatural (theological and hagiographic) content of the rituals, cultural identity, social usage and economic interchange are all brought into relief. Thus, for example, E. Z. Vogt (1965), analyzing a set of rituals in a Highland Maya community, finds the structural replication of centuries of social tradition. History is preserved in ritual dances of Christians and Moors and of Incas and Spaniards. The theme of trade, salient not only in the Andean tradition, but also in the Marian pilgrimages of Europe (Turner and Turner, 1978, pp. 36-37), presents the richness and variety of resources available within the vast area from which the pilgrims come.

To put it most briefly, the first research hypothesis was that the fiesta of Copacabana serves as a paradigm of the important social, economic, and political concerns of its participants. In some senses, it was anticipated, the festival could be seen as a dramatization of what is important and permanent in the lives of the participants. Functional reasoning is, as many of its critics have pointed out, logically dangerous, because it asserts that an effect, an outcome, is a cause. On the other side of the dispute, the empiricist would emphasize the consistency of the outcome and argue that a series of behaviors that recur almost predictably must, indeed, have an important function. This function, to restate the first hypothesis, is one of reaffirming and outlining the social, economic, and political relationships and concerns of the society.

The second theoretical area addressed by the study concerned what Julian H. Steward (1955) called levels of sociocultural integration. In his 1955 article, Steward argued that it is useful to analyze sociocultural behavior at several different levels, i.e., at the family, folk, and national levels. The basis for Steward's model is the proposition that roles, institutions, values, and symbols in complex societies are at least partly segregated at specific levels of integration. Thus, for example, there is a level of sociocultural functioning specific to life in family units. The elements of functioning at this level have to do mainly with the establishment of primary identities and loyalties. Another set of elements is identified at the "folk" or "community" level, functionally linked to everyday subsistence activity, social control and the ordering of relationships among kinship units. The third and highest level is that of the state, whose institutions and values integrate its many regional, ethnic, socioeconomic, and community components. In Steward's formulation, phenomena at each of these levels must be studied in at least partial independence of those at other levels. What exists at the community level, for instance, is only partially understandable in terms of what happens at the family level; and the institutions of the state can be explained only incompletely by reference to the functioning of its lower components.

Steward's essay contains three general points of relevance to this research. (1) He emphasized that, for each of the levels, there is a corresponding segregation of ritual and symbolic systems; in other words, there are specific rituals and symbols appropriate to each of the levels. (2) The levels form a "nested hierarchy," in the sense that each level contains elements of sociocultural feature specific to lower levels; thus, the ritual system of the state would be expected to contain elements and referents specific to the community and family levels. (3) The model provides a valuable heuristic for the explication of sociocultural change.

With respect to the third point, Steward provides a brief, but provocative account of the effects of Spanish conquest upon the Inca national society. The effects of conquest, he said, varied regularly at each level: At the state level, the native system was virtually obliterated: native priesthoods were supplanted by Catholic orders, and the native systems of political and economic control were taken over by those of the Spanish Crown. At the community level, the impact was less complete, because the institutions and structures of indirect rule provided a considerable buffer. The family level—embracing such aspects as language, primary loyalty, face-to-face sociality, and folk religious belief—proved most refractory to the effects of conquest, because life at this level was contained within the partly protected community structure. Steward's analysis laid particular stress on ritual and belief. He pointed out that at the highest (and most bureaucratized) levels, the churches and priests of Roman Catholicism completely supplanted the temples and priests of the previous religious system. At the level of the community, the official religion prevailed to the extent that a parochial organization and a system of religious education were implanted. But, at the same time, religious belief and practice, as they were expressed in community life, came quickly to form a synthesis of the new and the native systems, with a considerable influence of curers, magicians, and other native magicoreligious practitioners. Here, of course, lies the main locus of the rich local color of folk Catholicism in the Andes (and elsewhere in Indo-America). Finally, at the family level, baptism, church marriage, and Christian burial joined, but did not supplant, a rich tradition of life crisis, fertility, and curing rituals.

A review of the literature on Andean Indian ritual shows that Steward's model works very well. Most scholars have concentrated on the community-level rituals, showing how they syncretize European and indigenous themes and how they integrate local social life. A smaller body of research has been focused on rituals specific to the family level. For example, Sergio Quijada Jara (1957) provides an extensive description of the Santiago festival in central Peru. In this context, St. James, thoroughly syncretized with a native mountain deity, is a patron of animal increase. His festival is celebrated by family groups, rather than by any group organized at the community level. As would be expected from Steward's model, song, dance, and symbology are almost entirely native. Virtually the only Spanish element is the association of the honored supernatural with a Christian Saint. In the Aymara-speaking areas of Bolivia and southern Peru, Tschopik (1951), Carter (1968), and Patch (1971) are among the few anthropologists who have studied family-level ritual.

This project was designed with the expectation that the three levels of functioning would be apparent in the Copacabana festival. It was hypothesized that an analysis of the whole festival would result in the segregation of three levels of functioning—the highest and most bureaucratized involving political and church officialdom, the next lower involving groups organized in their communities of origin, and the lowest involving family groups. It was further hypothesized that these three levels would show (from highest to lowest) an increasing content of indigenous cultural symbolism.

The third area of theory concerned music as a cultural indicator. Nearly twenty years ago, Alan Lomax (1962; Lomax et al., 1968) developed a system for the standardized description and comparison of song styles. This system, cantometrics, has been shown (Lomax, 1962; Lomax and Erickson in Lomax et al., 1968; Erickson, 1974) to be a very effective taxonomic device for identifying stylistic traditions and relating them to culture-historic traditions. It is possible, for example, to show that mestizo song styles bear varying resemblances to European and native American styles, and also to specify the aspects and degrees of resemblance. It was hypothesized that musical performances recorded at various levels of ritual (national, community, and family) would be increasingly indigenous in style and instruments the lower the level.

Research and Results

In briefest summary, the expectations expressed in the foregoing hypotheses were oversimplified. To be sure, elements of national, community, and family level functioning were found in the ritual acts of the Copacabana fiesta and several other festivals observed in the area. The musical styles observed in the various ritual acts did show considerable variation between the poles of European and indigenous (Aymara). On the other hand, the expectation that the August fiesta of Copacabana would show clear traces of functioning at Steward's three levels was not supported by the data. Except for the Calvario rituals, little at the family level was observed in that fiesta, and the organization of main festival events (processional, masses, dances, and feasts) largely transcended community groupings, being coordinated centrally among many different participants from many different localities. In the Copacabana fiesta, most of the song and dance material was in a style (mestizo, to be sure) that is broadly common throughout Bolivia and southern Peru. There was little in the recorded performances that resembled the main native Aymara style represented in Alan Lomax's cantometric sample (Naroll, 1970, Appendix E). Two major conclusions, discussed below, can be stated. First, the Copacabana August pilgrimage/festival is organized overwhelmingly at the national (perhaps better, considering the participation of Peruvians, international) level. It is, in sum, the enactment of social and cultural themes that far transcend the boundaries of communities, though it is accompanied by family-level rituals. Second, even the numerous community-level observances (village patronal fiestas and the like) contain much more cosmopolitan symbology—identified in Catholic festivals elsewhere—than had been expected.

DATA COLLECTION

We entered the field at Copacabana on June 25, 1973. After six days of orientation, Ms. Bromley took up residence in Yumani, on the Island of the Sun, where she remained for most of the next two months. The Ericksons settled in at Copacabana, although the principal investigator made frequent trips to various parts of the province in a survey of the busy schedule of ritual.

In all, slightly more than 20 hours of music (most of it dance accompaniment) were recorded at fiestas in and around Copacabana and at rehearsal sessions. At the request of personnel of the National Directorate of Culture, Ministry of Education, about half of this material was transcribed for deposit in the National Folklore Archive. At the time of writing, a preliminary analysis had been performed to place the music (in terms of instruments and cantometric characteristics) in one of three categories: mostly indigenous; mestizo; and mostly European. The criteria employed in the stylistic characterizations included melodic form (litany for indigenous; strophe for European and mestizo) and melodic interval (wide for indigenous; diatonic for European, varied for mestizo), among others. The instrumental characterization was based upon historic origins: brasses and chordophones (e.g., the charango) from European sources, and panpipes (*sicuris* and *zampoñas*) and flutes (e.g., *luribay, pinkillu* and *kena-kena*) from the indigenous tradition.

The principal source of interview data was provided by key informants, i.e., people actively involved in the events being studied. These included: (1) Civil authorities in Copacabana and in surrounding communities—officials of the provincial (subprefectural) government, village mayors (*jilacatas*), and officials of the Agrarian Reform organizations (*sindicatos campesinos*); (2) priests of the resident Franciscans in charge of the basilica; (3) many of the *maestros cantores* who perform on Calvario; (4) a lifelong resident and amateur folklorist in the town; and (5) participants in the main events of the August fiesta and other ritual occasions. In addition, a large number of pilgrims—from most departments of Bolivia and from various nearby points in Peru—were interviewed for periods varying between half an hour and about two hours.

During the August 6-7 fiesta and for some days before and after, the entire team endeavored to observe as many events at various locations as possible. Ms. Bromley joined the Ericksons and observation sites were coordinated in order to maintain maximal coverage of the town plaza (the main site) and other places of ritual and celebration. The principal investigator also witnessed substantial portions of festivals in outlying communities, most notably (1) the *octava* (eighth day) celebration of the Virgin of Carmen, in the village of Viluyo; (2) a secular (school-organized) folkloric festival, at the regional school in Huacuyo; and (3) the patronal fiesta of Santiago Apostol, in Collasuyo community. Finally (July 16), the Ericksons observed the fiesta of the Virgin of Carmen, the Patroness of the Bolivian Republic and its armed forces.

Observation of festival events was accompanied by extensive photography, both still and motion picture. It was possible, therefore, to capture numerous details of the costuming, spatial organization, and choreography of dance groups. In addition, Ms. Bromley undertook a detailed survey of the layout of the Copacabana fair during the August fiesta.

THE COPACABANA FIESTA: A COSMOPOLITAN CELEBRATION

Even cursory observation reveals that the fiesta of the Virgin of Copacabana is a cosmopolitan event—supranational in its scope. On August 4, 1973, trucks and buses began pouring into the town bearing license plates of every accessible Bolivian department and of the Peruvian departments of Puna, Arequipa, and Cuzco. Represented in the multitudes were numerous persons of Hispanic culture; rural mestizos; Aymara-speaking Indians from La Paz and Oruro Departments and from Puno in Peru; and Quechua-speaking Indians, wearing costumes from such farflung points as Chuquisaca Department, Bolivia, and Cuzco Department, Peru.

A closer scrutiny of fiesta organization gives further evidence of the overarching scope of the event. Although they provide logistical support, trade in the fair, and form an audience to the festival, the residents of Copacabana and its environs are not the main participants. Indeed, numerous informants were agreed that the August festival is overshadowed in importance by several other celebrations during the ritual year—among them the Feast of La Calendaria (February 2), which also commemorates the arrival of the Virgin; the Day of the Crosses (May 3); and the Virgin of Carmen. In these and other fiestas the sponsorship and performance is dominated by local people.

As for the August fiesta, its organization and performances are in the hands of outsiders. The principal sponsorship, exercised by persons called *prestes* (*priostes* in many other parts of Hispanic America), is entrusted to a group of merchants resident in the capital city of La Paz. Many of these individuals have relatives somewhere in Manco Capac, but not all do. The dance groups that provide the centerpiece of color and action for two days are drawn overwhelmingly from other places—La Paz, Oruro and, on occasion, Puno. Very few of them are from Manco Capac. Indeed, in 1973, only one group (*kena-kena* dancers) was from the province. Most of the groups (e.g., the famed *diabladas* or devil dancers of Oruro) are made up of semiprofessionals who spend much time traveling from fiesta to fiesta throughout the country. Similarly, groups of bull-dancers (whose costume is the model of a bull fitted at the waist) dance in numerous fiestas in the city of La Paz and throughout the department.

By written accounts (e.g., Helfritz, 1946) and according to older residents of the town, this cosmopolitan aspect has long been the case. Before the construction of the motor road, pilgrims used to arrive from various lake ports on chartered vessels. Even in long-term cultural change, the cosmopolitan theme persists. One older resident of the town expressed regret that many of the former trappings of costume had disappeared. Such trappings included skins of jungle animals and feathers of the Lake Poopo flamingo (*pariguana*). Indeed, they had disappeared by 1973. At the same time, virtually every item of dance and processional costume had been manufactured and purchased in La Paz (where a whole crowded neighborhood is given over to costume shops) or Oruro. Always, the emphasis in costumes and trappings has been on the novel and cosmopolitan.

The music accompanying the dance groups that dominate the August processions turned out to fall overwhelmingly in the "predominantly European" category. The *diabladas, morenos,* and most of the other groups in the two processions were accompanied by orchestras of instruments exclusively out of the European tradition. Stylistically, the medodies fell into the European category. One of the priests of the basilica, himself a musician, commented that, over more than a decade of observation, he had seen the annual adoption of new popular (radio-broadcast) music to the dance tunes of the procession. Of the mestizo melodic style—*mesomusic* in Carlos Vega's terms (1966), only the *waca-wacas* (bull dancers) provided a clear example in the main processions. In the "clearly indigenous" category, the dance music in the August fiesta contained only the performance of a lone group of *kena-kena* dancers who were not in the main procession, but danced unofficially in one corner of the church square.

Beyond the official events of the Copacabana fiesta—the masses on two successive days, the processions following the masses, and a series of feasts following the processions—many other important things take place. Most visible, for the centrality of its location and the amount of space it occupies, is the fair. The square in front of the basilica is occupied by the stands of more than a hundred merchants, selling merchandise of many different varieties. Several other open places in the town are given over to marketing activities, as well, mostly by people from nearby places in Peru.

In the church square, the central portion is occupied, during the festival and for some days before and after, by stands set up by retailers from the city of La Paz. About three-quarters of the stands in the central portion (61 out of 83) were given over to the sale of clothing. In the latter category, urban-European clothing stands were more numerous than those selling items of folk costume (37 to 21; 3 stands offered combinations). Other categories of merchandise sold in the central portion of the plaza included household goods (mostly kitchen utensils) and electrical appliances (mostly radios and record players). The peripheries of the central market space were given over to food vendors, the sellers of musical instruments (mostly indigenous), jewelers and service people (e.g., bootblacks and photographers). Nearest the basilica were vendors of religious objects—images of the Virgin and of Jesus, amulets and medals. In the same area were many stands offering the uniquely Bolivian goods of *Alasitas*—miniatures of such consumer items as sacks of flour, bales of coca, household utensils and the like, paper money, houses, trucks and other items that stand as tokens of wish fulfillment in the January festival of Ek'eko, the Aymara god of plenty, celebrated throughout Bolivia. In other market spaces throughout the town, Peruvian vendors offered pottery and handicrafts from their home villages.

The activities and the organization of the August fiesta are very broad in scope. Merchandise and handicrafts are brought from all over Bolivia and from parts of nearby Peru. The dance groups that dominate the major processionals are those that perform at many other festival centers. The major sponsorship and organization, exercised by the two *prestes* are in the hands of people from the national capital of La Paz. Overall, then, the Copacabana festival, if it is a

symbolic focus of any recognizable level of social activity, symbolizes and focuses activity at the national and international levels. The expectation that all
the levels of Steward's model would be found somewhere in the festival was
not met entirely.

THE CALVARIO SCENE

As spectacular as the processionals, fairs, feasts and other activities in the
town may be, it is impossible for the observer to ignore the events taking place
on Calvario. Calvario, a precipitous hill about 200 meters high, rises out of
the town about three blocks from the church plaza. Its peak is reached by a
zigzag path, a large portion of which is occupied by Stations of the Cross.
About halfway up the path, the way opens onto a relatively broad and flat saddle connecting Calvario with a neighboring hill called *Boca del Sapo* (frog's
mouth). After the saddle, the path becomes even more precipitous until the
summit is reached. At the summit, a long and narrow flat area, there is a series
of stations representing the incidents of the Passion.

On the days of the August fiesta, the Calvario path is alive with streams of
pilgrims making the climb to the summit. On the saddle, numerous groups
(mostly families) of pilgrims will be found resting, picnicking, celebrating,
and performing rituals. One of the most unavoidable aspects of the scene is
provided by a more or less continuous sound of explosions of quarter-sticks of
dynamite, touched off by visitors from the Bolivian tin mines. Over the explosions and murmur of numerous voices, the occasional sound of a chant can be
heard. The chant comes from a *maestro cantor* who has been contracted to bless
the dream of one or another pilgrim. The dream, itself, is a topographical representation of an ideal farmstead, laid out on the ground and bounded by a perimeter marked in pebbles, that surrounds a house built of flat stones and a
series of corrals also marked off in pebbles.

Pilgrims proceed from the saddle to the peak. There they are greeted by a
multitude of *maestros cantores* and vendors. The latter offer beer, soft drinks and
foodstuffs, and miniatures, mostly of trucks and houses. It is interesting to
note that the house miniatures represent, for the most part, multiple dwellings of an urban style reflecting the origins of most of the pilgrims.

The *maestros cantores* can be found at the peak of Calvario on most days of
the year, because pilgrims come to Copacabana in a continuous stream—
sometimes a flood and sometimes a trickle. They pray, sing hymns, and perform rituals in honor of the Virgin Mary; they also offer libations to Pachamama. Their blessings are conferred on marriages, the future state of one's
health, and one's best hopes for prosperity in the coming year. The main ritual

opens with the performance by the *maestro cantor*, in Spanish, of a hymn to the Virgin of Copacabana:

A vuestros pies, Madre,	To your feet, Mother
Llega un infeliz,	Comes an unhappy one,
Cercado de angustia	Hemmed in by anguish
Y de penas mil.	And by pains a thousand.

Intermittently, the *maestro* censes the supplicant and, if appropriate, the miniature (e.g., of a house) and prays and sings in Aymara. At the end of the ritual, he sprays the ground, the supplicant and the miniature with beer that has been provided by the supplicant, usually calling on the kindness of Pachamama.

In addition to the miniatures that have been blessed by the *maestros*, the pilgrims in many cases come away from the summit with such miniature items as perfect replicas of cigarette packages and household utensils which they will affix to the effigy of the Aymara god of plenty, Ek'eko, who is kept in a place of honor in their houses. The aura of the Calvario blessing lends them a great importance.

The rituals of Calvario are important not only to the multitudes who come to the August festival, but also to the train of those who come to Copacabana during the year. In no sense does it have the sanction of official religion, but it is an important part of the total pilgrimage. It is performed in the midst of Christian symbology, but its focus, as it turns out, is on a Virgin whose identity is thoroughly syncretized with that of the pre-Christian Pachamama. Perhaps most fundamentally, it reflects the fact that Copacabana is a site of awesome holiness—the home of the revered Virgin and the continuing abode of Pachamama.

THE COPACABANA FIESTA CYCLE

One of the main discoveries in the fieldwork was the fact that the residents of Manco Capac Province, though thoroughly caught up in the annual round of ritual, looked upon the August festival as something belonging to outsiders (and mostly city folk). They celebrate numerous local fiestas—many of them in the same season as that of the Virgin—and they maintain a tightly structured version of what anthropologists have called the civil-religious hierarchy. Numerous anthropologists, both in Andean South America and in Meso America (Mexico and upper Central America) have described village level leadership in terms of the model of tandem political and ritual leadership. In both areas, civil office of progressively higher rank is invested in individuals who have served as fiesta sponsors on a progressively larger scale.

Since colonial times, the assignment of religious and civil offices has been in the hands (officially, at least) of the Roman Catholic clergy. Thus, for example, in many parts of Peru, village mayors were named and took office for one year during the course of Christmas mass, the nomination having been made by the priest after consultation with the villagers. The criterion of nomination was distinction in service as sponsor of fiesta events. In many parts of Bolivia and Peru, social change has brought about a diminution in the importance of fiesta sponsorship as a prerequisite to civil office (see Buechler and Buechler, 1971, pp. 71, 86). Moreover, minor civil authorities have become much less responsive in general to the leadership and requests of parish priests. This is most manifestly not the case in Manco Capac Province. As traditionally in most Aymara localities, the territory is organized into complementary segments, *Urinsaya* and *Aransaya* (translatable as "lower side" and "upper side"), which bear alternating responsibility for various tasks of church maintenance and the leaders of which form distinctive ritual groups at masses and other ceremonials. The entire corps of traditional Indian officials—*jilacatas* (mayors) and *campos* (subordinates)—continues to function with its symbols of office, and it forms an important part of the operation of the parish.

It is interesting to note that this traditional politico-religious organization has survived a revolution that redistributed farmlands, enfranchised the Indian masses and, in later years, resulted in a vast increase in cosmopolitan influences in peasant communities. Not only has it survived in the Copacabana area, it has also absorbed a newer level of officialdom, the leadership of the peasant unions *(sindicatos campesinos)*, who provide a link with the national government in La Paz. On major ritual occasions, the *sindicato* leaders are seen with the *jilacatas,* and in the councils of political and civil matters, the *jilacatas* appear to have an important voice.

Along with the traditional organization of local authority, Manco Capac has maintained a very active ritual year. Because this project extended only for two months, many of the major festivals were missed in actual observation. Nonetheless, project personnel were in the province during a very busy part of the ritual calendar and it was possible, both through observation and interviewing to formulate some ideas on the functions and meanings of the fiesta round.

First of all, the outpouring of community-level culture, in the sense of more indigenous and conservative performance styles, expected but not found in the main fiesta, did turn up in the local fiestas. The cosmopolitan dance groups (*diabladas,* for instance) were absent in the village festivals observed. Furthermore, dances absent from the August fiesta (some of them reported to have been performed in earlier years) did show up in the villages. Among these were the dance of the *auqui-auquis* (the grandfathers) and a dance called the *lichiwayo,* both accompanied by music on indigenous instruments in a style that is mainly indigenous. It should be emphasized, though, that even in the village fiestas, there were elements of a changing, cosmopolitan culture. At the Santiago fiesta in the village of Collasuyo, there were two dance orchestras of young musicians who were hoping to make the big city circuit and looked upon their local performance as a kind of rehearsal.

The presence of the outside world was apparent in many other aspects of the local fiestas. For example, during the fiesta of the Virgin of Carmen in Copacabana, much of a ceremonial gathering of *jilacatas,* provincial officials, and *sindicato* leaders was taken up by a presentation by the Ministry of Labor on an agricultural migration project in the lowlands, *Promigra 73,* in which young men were recruited for work in the cotton harvests. The entire presentation was in the Aymara language and aimed at the assembled *jilacatas.* A rapid survey of participants in the local festivals, moreover, discloses that many are permanent residents of other localities (most notably La Paz and migrant centers in the eastern lowlands) who had been born in the host community. Homeland pilgrimages for participation in patronal fiestas is an old pattern in Andean migration (see Valcárcel, 1946). Kinship loyalties and trading partnerships are thus maintained between the peasant villages of the Altiplano and the cities and workplaces of all parts of the Republic. Maintenance of rights under the laws of agrarian reform underscore for many the importance of keeping close ties with the natal community.

In summary, the patronal fiesta provides in one a celebration of local identity (being, after all, in honor of the local patron) and a point of contact with many parts of the outside world. The government clerk who came to Collasuyu to dance in the *waca-wacas* rejoined resident kinsmen and childhood friends in an important (and expensive) act of traditional ritual. He also brought with him novelties of costume from La Paz.

IMAGES OF DANCE

Informants long familiar with the main Copacabana festival report a pattern of continuous change in the costuming and performance of the main dance groups. Most particularly, they report the virtual disappearance of the older and more indigenous forms like the *lichiwayos* and the *auqui-auquis,* which do tend to show up in the local fiestas. In 1973, the main dance groups in the processions included *diabladas, morenadas* (blackface), *waca-wacas,* and *Incas.* In addition to the plaza performances, the groups danced at the numerous private feasts provided by fiesta sponsors at various locations in the town.

Overall, the impression was one of long practice and professionalism; processional dancers perform at major festivals in many different places.

In the local fiestas observed, the overwhelming majority of dance groups were either from the host community or from nearby places. Many of the more indigenous dances accompanied by native aerophones (flute and panpipe) were observed, though the more European forms appeared as well. The variety of dance figures was, in aggregate, greater than that seen in the August fiesta.

One striking aspect of the whole pattern of fiesta dance in Manco Capac (as, indeed, elsewhere in Indo-America) is the amount of comic content and satire. The *waca-wacas,* garbed as bulls, are accompanied in their dance by clown figures (*kusillos*) who, with a combination of trickiness and studious clumsiness, burlesque the bullfighter. Both in dance groups and as accompanying clowns, some men dress in tails and top hats of exaggerated height (the costuming effect reminding one of Der Inspektor in the old comic strip "The Katzenjammer Kids"). These are the *doctorcitos* (little doctors), who lampoon the learned gentlemen of the city. At two local festivals, there were dance troupes of *soldados y prisioneros* (soldiers and prisoners). The soldiers were garbed in khaki and pith helmets, carried toy rifles with which they menaced the onlookers and were constantly losing their lightly bound prisoners through inattention and clumsiness. Another figure of burlesque was the *cholita* (the peasant woman), played by men dressed in native women's clothes. The main theme of humor in this case was provided by *kusillos* chasing the "women" and endeavoring to lift their skirts. Many aspects of common experience are exposed to satire. Probably the principal victims are the powerful, heroic and bombastic figures of the dominant Spanish culture. Interestingly, the variety (and sharpness) of satirical figures is greater in the local festivals than in the vast cosmopolitan August fiesta.

Also interesting, and requiring much more research and analysis, is the widespread distribution of many of the dance characters. Much of what is seen in Manco Capac appears to be part of a universal idiom of fiesta performance in Spanish America. Bull dancers, with and without clowns, are found, indeed, throughout Catholic Europe, as well as broadly in Meso America (Kurath, 1967, p. 184). Learned doctors, women, and old men are burlesqued in much the same way throughout Meso America (Bricker, 1973). How much of the broad resemblance in fiesta themes is explained by diffusion (e.g., in the context of Santiago celebrations) is open to question. For such figures as Christians and Moors and the bulls, there can be little doubt. On the other hand, the dance ridiculing old people is reported as aboriginal for many parts of America, for example among the Aztec (Bricker, 1973, p. 201), and may, indeed, be a widespread native theme. In any case, a salient aspect of the fiestas of Manco Capac Province is that, no matter how the local patrons celebrated, the celebration is expressed in themes that are widely shared in time and space.

Conclusion

One expectation carried to the field turned out to be mostly incorrect. Very little by way of aboriginal ritual and music was found in the fiestas; this was especially the case with the focal fiesta of August. To be sure, much pre-Christian ritual is reported from the Aymara areas (see Buechler and Buechler, 1971, ch. 7). Alan Lomax's Aymara and Quechua song samples are dominated by styles that are nearly unmodified by European influences (see Lomax et al., 1968, p. xvi, for acknowledgment of sources).

In terms of Steward's model, it was possible to isolate elements of ritual at each of the three levels of integration. But the main Copacabana fiesta was absolutely dominated by rituals and referents at the national level. Its principal events are organized and supported by people living in the city of La Paz. The fair associated with the festival involves the participation of merchants who normally operate in the large-scale urban retail trades. Music and dance performances are dominated by styles and performers associated with the national scene.

To be sure, family-level ritual, with large components of pre-Christian practice is to be seen on the Calvario, and this activity builds to a crescendo during the August fiesta. On the other hand, the same activity goes on continuously outside the fiesta period. A large majority of pilgrims who come to Copacabana, at any time during the year, go to Calvario as a part of the visit. This hill is the home of Pachamama, a supernatural whose beneficence is aimed at the domestic level of life.

More of a local focus is to be seen in the other fiestas of the ceremonial year. The *prestes* and other sponsoring officials, the dancers and other personnel, are drawn either from among residents or from among those who have ties to the host community. Musical and dance styles, on the average, tend to be more local. Even in this case, though, it must be noted that (1) the family-level rituals hardly occur and (2) there is a focus on the national level. What is being satirized is at the national level of experience: soldiers, scholars, historic figures, and the like. In such dances as the *morenadas,* what is exotic to the local scene (in this case, people of African origins) is emphasized in caricature. The fiesta, in other words, seems to bring into focus what lies outside the local horizons. Where, then, are the family level rituals? In Copacabana, the question is simply answered. Following the saddle of Calvario, then the rise of the adjacent hill, Boca del Sapo (itself draped with abandoned terraces probably dating from Inca times), one reaches a high, flat, open area, overlooking the Lake and providing a magnificent view of the Island of the Sun in the distance. This hilltop is littered with the remains of *mesas* (burnt offerings of llama fetuses, candies, herbs, and amulets) dedicated to Aymara supernaturals who have, as it turns out, no place in the fiestas. On Calvario we found no remains of *mesas*. On Boca del Sapo we found them in abundance. They are also to be seen on another hill near the town: Colla Juana, which is the abode of an *achachila,* a powerful Aymara place spirit.

In summary, a revised view of the Manco Capac fiestas—the local ones and the Copacabana pilgrimage—must emphasize the link to national society and national culture. In the act of celebrating their supernaturals, the participants focus their attention on national traditions, national images, national trading networks and, in general, things that transcend the local scene. The anthropologists Karl and Judith-Marie Buechler (1971, p. 89) express the point very well, in writing about the fiestas of Compi, a village closer to La Paz:

> . . . we would see in it an important means of communicating both continuity and change in social relationships. It furnishes a symbolic system which in the Bolivian highlands is common to peasant communities, towns and cities in which both internal social differentiation and/or integration and . . . farflung networks of interpersonal ties can be expressed.

That such an important symbolic exercise happens so frequently and intensively in the area of Copacabana is probably best explained by the age-old sacredness of the place.

REFERENCES

BENNETT, WENDELL
  1949.   Religious structures. Vol. 5, pp. 29-52, *in* "Handbook of South American Indians," J. H. Steward, ed. Smithsonian Institution, Washington, D. C.
BRICKER, VICTORIA REIFLER
  1973.   Ritual humor in highland Chiapas. University of Texas Press, Austin, Texas, and London.
BUECHLER, HANS C., and BUECHLER, JUDITH-MARIE
  1971.   The Bolivian Aymara. Holt, Rinehart and Winston, New York.
CALANCHA, ANTONIO DE
  1939 (orig. 1638). Cronica moralizada. Biblioteca Boliviana, La Paz, Bolivia.
CARTER, WILLIAM E.
  1968.   Secular reinforcement in Aymara death ritual. American Anthropologist, vol. 70, pp. 238-263.

ERICKSON, EDWIN E.
1974. La canción como huella histórica: Estilos de cantar y la historia cultural Americana. America Indígena, vol. 34, pp. 973-992.
GARCILASO DE LA VEGA, EL INCA
1966 (orig. 1616-17). Royal commentaries of the Incas, I. University of Texas Press, Austin, Texas, and London.
HELFRITZ, HANS
1946. La fiesta de la Vírgen de Copacabana. Revista Geografica Americana, vol. 25, pp. 69-74.
KUBLER, GEORGE
1946. The Quechua in the colonial world. Vol. 2, pp. 331-410, *in* "Handbook of South American Indians," J. H. Steward, ed. Smithsonian Institution, Washington, D. C.
KURATH, GERTRUDE PROKOSCH
1967. Drama, dance and music. Vol. 6, pp. 158-190, *in* "Handbook of Middle American Indians," Robert Wauchope, ed. University of Texas Press, Austin, Texas, and London.
LEGTERS, LYMAN H.; BLANCHARD, WENDELL; ERICKSON, EDWIN E.; FORTENBAUGH, SUSAN G.; MADAY, BELA C.; POPKIN, NATHAN S.; TELEKI, SUZANNE; and WEAVER, JOHN O.
1963. Area handbook for Bolivia. Government Printing Office, Washington, D. C.
LOMAX, ALAN
1962. Song structure and social structure. Ethnology, vol. 1, pp. 425-451.
LOMAX, ALAN; ARENSBERG, CONRAD; ERICKSON, EDWIN E.; GRAUER, VICTOR; BERKOWITZ, NORMAN; BARTENIEFF, IRMGARD; PAULAY, FORRESTINE; HALIFAX, JOAN; AYRES, BARBARA; MARKEL, NORMAN N.; RUDD, ROSWELL; VIZEDOM, MONIKA; PENG, FRED; WESCOTT, ROGER; and BROWN, DAVID.
1958. Folksong style and culture. American Association for the Advancement of Science, Washington, D. C.
NAROLL, RAOUL
1970. What have we learned from cross-cultural surveys? Amer. Anthropologist, vol. 72, pp. 1227-1288.
PATCH, RICHARD W.
1971. Agriculture and the supernatural. American Universities Field Staff Reports. West Coast of South America Series, vol. 18, no. 4.
POE, KAREN M.
1979. Land and labor in the Titicaca basin: An ethnohistory of an Aymara Community. Ph.D. dissertation, University of Virginia.
QUIJADA JARA, SERGIO
1957. Canciones del ganado y de pastores. Amigos del Libro, Huancayo, Peru.
SALAS, BALTASAR
1901 (orig. 1618). Documents included in J. Vizcarra, Copacabana de los Incas. Palza Hermanos, Bolivia.
STEWARD, JULIAN H.
1955. Theory of culture change. University of Illinois Press, Urbana, Illinois.

TSCHOPIK, HARRY S.
1951.   The Aymara of Chucuito, Peru.   American Museum of Natural History, New York.
TURNER, VICTOR W.
1973.   Symbols in African ritual.   Science, vol. 179, pp. 1100-1105.
TURNER, VICTOR W., and TURNER, EDITH
1978.   Image and pilgrimage in Christian culture: Anthropological perspectives.   Columbia University Press, New York.
VALCÁRCEL, LUIS E.
1946.   Indian markets and fairs in Peru.   Vol. 2, pp. 477-482, in "Handbook of South American Indians," J. H. Steward, ed.   Smithsonian Institution, Washington, D. C.
VEGA, CARLOS
1966.   Mesomusic: An essay on the music of masses.   Ethnomusicology, vol. 10, pp. 1-17.
VOGT, EVON Z.
1965.   Structural and conceptual replication in Zincantan culture.   Amer. Anthropologist, vol. 67, pp. 342-353.

EDWIN E. ERICKSON

Systematics and Paleogeography of Some Fossil Salamanders and Frogs

Principal Investigator: Richard Dean Estes, Department of Zoology, San Diego State University, San Diego, California.

Grant No. 1185: In support of a study of the paleogeography of fossil salamanders and frogs.

Until recently, no systematic assessment of the fossil record of salamanders has been available. In correlation with my research on fossil herpetological faunas over the past ten years, however, I have been working on an annotated catalogue of fossil finds of this group, partially supported by the National Geographic Society, as well as a similar catalogue of fossil lizards supported in part by the National Science Foundation. Both of these catalogues will be published in the *Handbuch der Paläoherpetologie*.

Salamanders apparently have always been a Northern Hemisphere group, although other lower vertebrate groups that evolved during the Middle and later Mesozoic were able to disperse to both hemispheres (e.g., some dinosaurs and sphenodontids). Among the frogs, one group, the Pipidae, is now found in South America and Africa and appears to have always been a Southern Hemisphere group. Better knowledge of such distributions is significant to an understanding of lower vertebrate dispersal patterns. In this paper, I summarize some work on European fossil salamanders, particularly the Salamandridae and Prosirenidae, and briefly discuss studies of pipid frogs, in particular the Paleogene South African genus *Eoxenopoides.*

Problems in the Study of European Fossil Salamandrids

Special attention was paid in this study to a revision of European fossil salamanders, since my own previous work has helped to clarify the North American record (e.g., Estes, 1965, 1975a, 1976). The major problem associated with the European finds has been assessment of the validity of names applied by Herre (1939, 1949, 1955), and Herre and Lunau (1950) to Oligocene and Miocene specimens, primarily isolated vertebrae. Initial studies suggested that many of these names were based on minor vertebral variations or on vertebrae from different parts of the vertebral column of a single taxon. Studies on adequate samples of living forms (primarily Salamandridae, since

191

most European fossils are referable to this family) were made in order to test this hypothesis, and the results of the studies of intracolumnar variation were summarized by Estes and Hoffstetter (1976) and appear below with some revisions.

Intracolumnar Vertebral Variation in Salamanders

The following character states, for the most part correlated, are primarily qualitative features. They are valid for salamanders in general, but they apply best to the family Salamandridae. Individual variation is great, and one may find frequent exceptions to the generalities expressed here; nevertheless, they are useful in most cases. These data are based mainly on salamander skeletons in the Museum of Comparative Zoology, Harvard University; they complement the quantitative studies of Worthington (1971) and Worthington and Wake (1972).

1. The first vertebra (conventionally termed atlas, although from the embryological point of view, it is not the homologue of the mammalian atlas) is the shortest of the presacral vertebrae. It does not bear transverse processes, although small projections sometimes may be present. In most specimens, the neural arch of the atlas protrudes dorsally more than in any of the other vertebrae. The second and third vertebrae are in general longer than the axis, but shorter than the other presacrals. The longest centra are found in the posterior trunk region.

2. The subcentral foramina are in general smaller in the first two or three trunk vertebrae, in the sacrum, and in the first two or three caudal vertebrae.

3. The direction and size of the transverse processes are variable and difficult to describe with precision. In general, those of the anterior vertebrae are robust and almost perpendicular to the vertebral axis. Farther caudad, the angle between the process and the posterior centrum gradually decreases and the processes themselves diminish slightly in size. The transverse processes of the sacrum, however, are characteristically the largest and most ossified; they include the sacral ribs, fused to the vertebrae, and at their extremities bear enlarged articulation surfaces for the ilia. The transverse processes of the first two or three caudals again are perpendicular to the vertebral axis, but are unicipital, pointed, and do not bear ribs.

4. In general, the neural spines are higher in anterior vertebrae; they are less elevated in the posterior trunk region but increase again in height in the caudal region. This condition may be exaggerated or reduced according to the degree of dermal ossification on the tips of the neural spines.

5. The posterior border of the neural arch tends to be more vertically ori-

ented in anterior vertebrae, and thus the angle between this border and the axis of the centrum diminishes gradually toward the posterior trunk region.

6. Bifurcation of the posterior border of the neural arch (and that of the neural spine as well, if present) increases (or in some cases appears) posteriorly, and attains its maximum development posteriorly, correlated with the height of the neural spine. The angle subtended by this bifurcation is greatest anteriorly and diminishes posteriorly, becoming most acute in the caudal region. When dermal ossification is present on tips of neural spines, it is broad and short anteriorly and elongates posteriorly, correlated with the angle of bifurcation.

Other variations appear to be mainly intraspecific (or intrafamilial in the case of spinal nerve foramina; see Edwards, 1976), although some may result from particular adaptations in different genera or species.

These criteria should be used together in determining relative position within the column of isolated vertebrae, because the latter may show considerable variation in one or more of the character states.

Fossil Salamandridae and Prosirenidae from the Miocene of France

The above studies in intracolumnar variation have made possible extensive synonymy among names that have been given to European fossil salamander remains, and a summary of this follows (those not mentioned appear to be valid):

Salamandra sansaniensis Lartet, 1851
Salamandra laticeps von Meyer, 1858
Heteroclitotriton zitteli de Stefano, 1903
Salamandra broilii Schlosser, 1922
Palaeosalamandra kohlitzi Herre, 1949
Voigtiella ludwigi Herre, 1949
Dehmiella schindewolfi Herre and Lunau, 1950

Chelotriton paradoxus Pomel, 1853
Heliarchon furcillatus Meyer, 1860
Tylototriton primigenius Noble, 1928
Palaeosalamandrina dehmi Herre, 1949
Grippiella mohrae Herre, 1949
Tischleriella buddenbrocki Herre, 1949
Tischleriella langi Herre, 1949
Tischleriella remani Herre, 1949

Archaeotriton basalticus Meyer, 1859
Archaeotriton menzeli Laube, 1898

Triturus marmoratus (Latreille, 1800)
Triturus sansaniensis (Lartet, 1851)

Brachycormus noachius (Goldfuss, 1831)
Tylototriton kosswigi Herre, 1949
Oligosemia gerhardti Herre, 1949

A more detailed, annotated revision of all fossil salamanders is given in the *Handbuch der Paläoherpetologie* (Estes, 1981).

The studies of vertebral variation and consequent synonymies given above were essential to the preparation of a study on the salamanders from one Upper Miocene locality, La Grive-St. Alban, France (Estes and Hoffstetter, 1976). The fissures at this locality have yielded 130 species of vertebrates, including five species of salamanders, the latter represented by most of the major skeletal elements. These include four salamandrids: (1) *Salamandra sansaniensis* is an abundant species widely distributed in the Oligocene and Miocene of Europe and very close (perhaps ancestral) to the living species *S. salamandra*. (2) *Triturus* cf. *marmoratus* is a newt represented by abundant remains and hardly distinguishable from the Recent species. (3) *Chioglossa meini* is rarer and is related to the living species *C. lusitanica* from Spain and Portugal. (4) *Chelotriton paradoxus* is rare as well at La Grive, but the species is well known in other Oligocene and Miocene localities in France and Germany. *Chelotriton* is very close to (and perhaps synonymous with) the living Asian genus *Tylototriton*. The fifth salamander species belongs to the extinct family Prosirenidae, a family hitherto known from the Cretaceous of North America; other records of this family are now known from the Late Jurassic of Portugal, Late Cretaceous of Italy, and possibly the Late Cretaceous of Israel. *Albanerpeton inexpectatum* Estes and Hoffstetter (1976), the Miocene form from La Grive, is represented by excellent material of major skull bones, vertebrae, and proximal limb bones. It constitutes an astonishing late record of this group, otherwise known only from the Mesozoic. *Albanerpeton* is defined by an unusual specialization of the cervical vertebrae: the atlas has a complex posterior concavity with which the centrum of the second vertebra articulates; the second vertebra lacks any trace of neural arch and is either sutured or co-ossified with the centrum of the third vertebra; the neural arches of the first and third vertebrae meet over the centrum of the second. This remarkable specialization, which is analogous to the amniote atlas-axis complex in some regards, is a unique adaptation not approached by any other anamniote (fig. 1).

Other features of *Albanerpeton inexpectatum* are as follows: Vertebrae amphicoelous, rib articulation facets single-headed but elongate; weak anterior

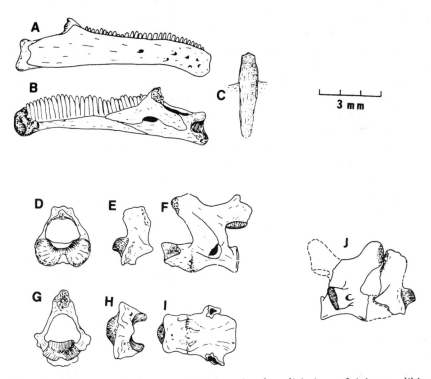

FIG. 1. *Albanerpeton inexpectatum*. A, B, lateral and medial views of right mandible; C. medial view of mandibular tooth (much enlarged, not to scale). D-J, the first three cervical vertebrae; D, E, H, anterior, left lateral and ventral views of atlas; F, G, I, left lateral, anterior and ventral views of fused second and third vertebrae; J. restoration of right lateral view of articulated first three cervical vertebrae. (From Estes and Hoffstetter, 1956.)

basapophyses present, posterior basapophyses weak or absent; zygapophyses hemicylindrical; anterior neural spines prominent, becoming sessile posteriorly; humerus well developed and strongly ossified, femur relatively thinner and less well ossified; dentary robust, 23-33 non-pedicellate teeth with faintly triconodont crowns; prearticular with strong projection for adductor muscles; articular and angular fused; mandibles meeting at the symphysis in a complex interdigitating suture; premaxillae paired; maxillae with 15-23 teeth; lacrymal large, two lacrymal foramina present; prefrontal strongly united with lacrymal; nasals apparently paired; frontal unpaired, triangular; parietals paired with strong postorbital projections; braincase bones fused; fenestra ovalis enormous, dumbbell-shaped; a pit-and-ridge dermal sculpture present on parietals, frontals, prefrontals, premaxillae, presumably also on the nasals (not preserved), weakly present on lacrymals and maxillae (fig. 2).

Dentaries, maxillae, premaxillae, and humeri of *Albanerpeton inexpectatum* are distinctive and closely resemble those of the North American Cretaceous genus *Prosiren* (Estes, 1969); thus no doubt exists as to the family reference of *Albanerpeton*. Similar elements were referred to the Cretaceous salamander *Prodesmodon* (Lance Formation, Wyoming) by Estes (1964), but Naylor (1979) has shown that vertebrae on which the latter are based are batrachosauroidid. The above-mentioned prosirenid skull elements can be referred to *Albanerpeton* on the basis of their general appearance. They can no longer be placed in *Prodesmodon copei* and are here placed in a new species, *Albanerpeton nexuosus* (Latin, interlaced, complicated; refers to the jaw symphysis), which differs from *A. inexpectatum* in lacking a large palatal shelf of the premaxilla and maxilla, having stronger heterodonty of anterior dentary and maxillary teeth, and lacking posterior expansion of the dentary. Figures of *A. nexuosus* are given in Estes (1964). Naylor (1979) has also identified *Albanerpeton*-like atlas vertebrae and skull elements from the Late Cretaceous Upper Milk River Formation of Alberta.

Still another Cretaceous prosirenid has been identified from the Lower Cretaceous deposits at Pietraroia, Italy. It is a nearly complete skeleton that was originally described by Costa (1864) as *Triton megacephalus* and later referred to *Triturus* by Kuhn (1938). It can now be referred provisionally to *Albanerpeton*. This nearly complete skeleton shows similarity to *A. inexpectatum* in general shape and detailed construction of the skull, in having the head relatively large with respect to the body, and in having the hind limbs more weakly developed than those of the front (Estes, 1981).

Prosirenids have been recorded from the Late Jurassic (Bajocian) of France by Seiffert (1969), who did not refer the specimens to species or family. These fossils show very well the specialized form of the atlas seen in *Albanerpeton* and can also be referred to that genus. Similar Late Jurassic (Kimmeridgian) records from Portugal are known, from localities worked by Kühne (1968).

The large, well-ossified head and forelimbs of *Albanerpeton,* as shown both by the complete Cretaceous specimen of *A. megacephalus* and the proportions of elements of the Miocene *A. inexpectatum,* suggest a possible burrowing habitus for *Albanerpeton.* Based on the bird fauna, one of the Miocene fissure fillings from which the specimens of the latter species were derived (Loc. M) suggests a rather humid climate with dense vegetation, and in this locality *Albanerpeton* is 85 percent of the salamander fauna. At another locality (L7) a dry climate has been interpreted, again based on birds, and here *Albanerpeton* forms only 5

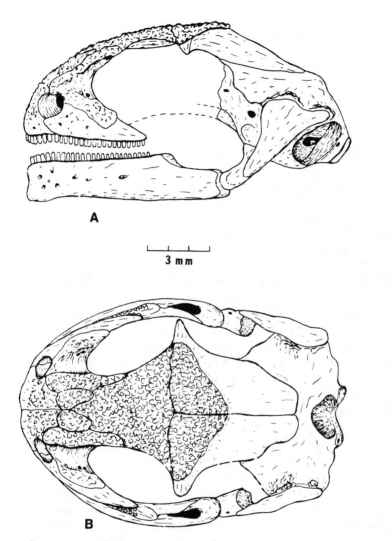

Fig. 2. *Albanerpeton inexpectatum.* Restoration of skull in lateral (A) and dorsal (B) views. (From Estes and Hoffstetter, 1956.)

percent of the salamander fauna, suggesting that it required a humid environment. Although this sort of environment would be presumed necessary for all salamanders, high numbers of individuals of nonburrowing salamandrids were preserved in the dry locality, indicating that sufficient moisture for salamanders was available. Thus, it can be hypothesized that the more humid environment may have been necessary to provide a substrate in which burrowing activities of *Albanerpeton* could take place.

A peculiar elongated salamander, *Ramonellus,* was described from the Early Cretaceous of Israel by Nevo and Estes (1969). It has vertebrae that are somewhat similar to those of *Albanerpeton,* and has a rather reduced humerus that resembles that element in prosirenids. The skull is somewhat different from that of *Albanerpeton* in being relatively longer (although this could be a concomitant of body elongation). For the present, it may be included provisionally in the Prosirenidae.

Valid Fossil Salamandrid Genera in Europe

Study of two important fossil salamandrid faunas from France, Coderet (Lower Miocene; undescribed) and La Grive-St. Alban (Upper Miocene; Estes and Hoffstetter, 1976), has permitted reevaluation of the fossil salamandrid fauna of Europe as a whole. Studies on intracolumnar variation summarized above have led to extensive synonymies among described forms. Most of the synonymies occur within two genera that are most common in Oligocene and Miocene European sites, *Salamandra* and *Chelotriton. Salamandra* is still widely distributed in Europe but seems never to have had a widespread Asian distribution. *Chelotriton* is closely related to the living Asian genus *Tylototriton.* The latter occurred in Europe in the Eocene but seems subsequently to have been replaced by *Chelotriton,* its probable derivative, which became extinct at the end of the Miocene. The basis for the synonymies is discussed below, with a brief review of valid forms. Documentation will appear in the *Handbuch der Paläoherpetologie* (Estes, 1981).

As noted above, *Salamandra sansaniensis,* the earliest named fossil species of the genus, is now based on abundant material from the Upper Miocene of France. Meyer (1859) named a species, *S. laticeps,* from the Lower Miocene of Czechoslovakia. This specimen is articulated and has a head length about one-fourth of snout-vent length rather than one-fifth as in extant species of *Salamandra.* Presacral vertebral number is the same as in the latter, but the vertebrae are relatively shorter and wider than in the living species, similar to conditions in *S. sansaniensis,* and *S. laticeps* is referred to the latter.

Schlosser (1922) described *Salamandra broilii* from the Lower Miocene of Germany; Herre (1949) referred additional specimens from the Middle and Upper Miocene of Germany to this species. Both Schlosser's and Herre's specimens are identical to those of *S. sansaniensis* from the Upper Miocene of France, and are here referred to that species.

Heteroclitotriton zitteli de Stefano (1903) was based on Upper Eocene or Lower Oligocene vertebrae from France; *Palaeosalamandra kohlitzi, P. renschi,* and *Voigtiella ludwigi* were described on Middle Miocene vertebrae from Germany by Herre (1949). Vertebrae of the first three species named are constricted behind the anterior zygapophyses, tend to have the posterodorsal surface of the neural arch flattened, and have a relatively small angle between transverse processes and axis of centrum. These are features often found in posterior trunk vertebrae of salamanders and occur in the sample of *Salamandra sansaniensis* from La Grive-St. Alban. While figured examples of these species are extreme for *S. sansaniensis,* intergrades between the latter and the German species occur in their type localities. *Voigtiella ludwigi,* on the other hand, was based on a vertebra with transverse processes nearly perpendicular to the vertebral axis and subequal length-width vertebral measurements, character states found in the second and third vertebrae of extant salamanders. In other features, all of these vertebrae resemble those of *S. sansaniensis.* These facts seem to demonstrate that *Voigtiella ludwigi, Palaeosalamandra kohlitzi, P. renschi,* and *Heteroclitotriton zitteli* are synonyms of *S. sansaniensis,* and thus Herre described anterior and posterior vertebrae of that species as different taxa.

Finally, Herre and Lunau (1950) described *Dehmiella schindewolfi* based on a tiny vertebra from the Middle Miocene of Germany; they referred it to the family Plethodontidae. This specimen is identical to larval specimens of *Salamandra sansaniensis* from the Miocene of France, and *Dehmiella schindewolfi* is here referred to that species.

Thus *Salamandra sansaniensis* is a very widely distributed species, based on the synonymies given here. It is the most common fossil species of the genus in the Tertiary of Europe; *S. salamandra* does not make its appearance until the Pliocene. The only other described species is *S. goussardiana* from the Upper Miocene of Sansan, France. It is a *nomen dubium,* because the specimen has been lost, but is likely to be a synonym of *S. sansaniensis,* since it comes from the same locality as the latter.

A fossil genus closely related to *Salamandra* is *Megalotriton,* represented by a single species, *M. filholi* Zittel (1890). *Megalotriton* specimens are all from Upper Eocene or Lower Oligocene deposits in France and Switzerland and thus are earlier than the vast majority of specimens of *Salamandra sansaniensis.* *Megalotriton* is represented only by vertebrae having a centrum length range of 7.9-12.5 millimeters, overlapping the range of 3.8-9.4 millimeters for *S. sansaniensis.* *Megalotriton* vertebrae seem to be characterized by a relatively greater width of the neural arch and greater diameter of rib-bearers than in vertebrae of equal size of *S. sansaniensis,* although the sample of Eocene vertebrae in smaller size ranges is inadequate to confirm this. Better samples of Eocene *Megalotriton* are needed to decide whether a generic difference from *Salamandra* is justified; it is possible that *M. filholi* (including *M. portisi* de Stefano, 1903) is no more than a large Eocene and Early Oligocene species of *Salamandra*.

Praesalamandra Brunner (1957) includes three species, *P. gossweinsteinia, P. pottensteinia,* and *P. sirenoides,* all from the Pleistocene of Germany. All three species are based on broken posterior ends of teleost parasphenoids, and *Praesalamandra* is thus not a salamander.

Another very common fossil European salamandrid is *Chelotriton paradoxus* Pomel (1853), which has been reported from various Oligocene localities in Germany and France, and Miocene localities in Germany, France, and Spain (Estes, 1981). The Pomel material has been lost, but the original description is adequate for identification of this distinctive form, and abundant, undescribed remains are known from the Lower Miocene of Coderet, France, so that vertebral variation can be assessed based on a good sample.

Although much of the known material of *Chelotriton* is disarticulated, a number of articulated specimens have been described. One was called *Heliarchon furcillatus* by Meyer (1860), based on a very faint imprint of a large larva from the Upper Oligocene of Germany. This specimen shows faint traces of the distinctive pustular sculpture found on the dermal bone of *C. paradoxus,* and in other ways is very similar to specimens of the latter. *Heliarchon furcillatus* is here placed in the synonymy of *Chelotriton paradoxus.* Noble (1928) described articulated specimens of *Tylototriton primigenius* from the Upper Miocene of Germany, and Westphal (1978) described additional material from the same locality. These specimens also show the characteristic pustular sculpture of dermal bone of *C. paradoxus,* as well as the large, distinctive, well-ossified quadratojugals of the latter. *Tylototriton,* a Holocene genus from Asia that is closely related to *Chelotriton,* has a pit-and-groove sculpture pattern and very small quadratojugals. *Tylototriton primigenius* is here placed in the synonymy of *Chelotriton paradoxus.*

Three genera based on isolated vertebrae were described by Herre (1949) from fissure fillings in Germany. These are *Palaeosalamandrina, Grippiella,* and *Tischleriella. Palaeosalamandrina dehmi* was based on Miocene vertebrae having rib-bearers close together, small neural canal, ventrally concave, strongly pitted centrum surface and narrow, thin cap of postular dermal bone on the neural spine. These features are characteristic of anterior caudal vertebrae of salamandrids, and the pustular sculpture indicates that *P. dehmi* is a synonym of *Chelotriton paradoxus. Grippiella mohrae* was based on Oligocene and Miocene vertebrae that have the anterior part of the neural spine and dermal bone broken off; this species is also a synonym of *Chelotriton paradoxus.*

Three species of *Tischleriella* were named: *T. remani* from the Oligocene, and *T. langi* and *T. buddenbrocki* from the Miocene. The type specimen of *T. remani* has lost its cap of dermal bone through breakage; it is close to the upper size range of *C. paradoxus*, but it is otherwise the same as in that species. The type specimen of *T. buddenbrocki* is at the lower size range of *C. paradoxus* and is probably an anterior caudal. The neural spine is relatively lower than in most *C. paradoxus*, and its dermal bone cap is of very limited extent. The type specimen of *T. langi* again has the dermal bone broken in part, but it is otherwise like vertebrae of *C. paradoxus*. Thus all three species of *Tischleriella* are based on specimens that have lost or reduced dermal bone through breakage; all species of *Tischleriella* are thus synonyms of *Chelotriton paradoxus*.

Epipolysemia ogygia is based on a Lower Miocene skeleton from Germany, from the same locality as the specimens of *Brachycormus* described below. Its larger size than the latter, as well as different body shape and cartilaginous carpals and tarsals, make it resemble *Chelotriton* specimens closely. Unfortunately the type specimen of *Epipolysemia* (originally described by Goldfuss, 1831) was not available for study. While its referral to *Chelotriton* is reasonable, I have not synonymized it with *C. paradoxus* since I have not seen the type specimen; it may remain for the present as *Chelotriton ogygius*.

Westphal (1979) described *Chelotriton robustus* from the Middle Eocene of Germany. Since both *Chelotriton* and *Tylototriton* occur in the Eocene and remain distinctive, both genera are probably valid, at least pending a more thorough study of the species of *Tylototriton*.

Tylototriton, a presently Asiatic salamandrid that is closely related to *Chelotriton*, has also been reported from the Eocene and Miocene of Europe. The specimens referred to *T. primigenius* by Noble (1928) and Westphal (1978) have been referred to *Chelotriton*, as noted above. *Tylototriton gerhardti* Herre (1949) was based on a specimen of *Brachycormus noachius*, discussed below, and there are thus no valid Miocene records of *Tylototriton*. Herre (1935) described *T. weigelti* from the Eocene of the German Democratic Republic (G.D.R.), however, and this appears to be the only authentic European record of the genus.

Brachycormus noachius was described by Goldfuss (1831) and revised by Meyer (1860) on the basis of five complete skeletons of Lower Miocene age from Germany and all from the same locality. Herre (1949) assigned two of these specimens to new species, *Tylototriton kosswigi* and *Oligosemia gerhardti*. Neither of these specimens differ in any substantial way from the other specimens of *Brachycormus*, but they were misinterpreted by Herre. The first of these assignments is reasonable in the sense that *Brachycormus* is a close relative of *Chelotriton*, and thus also of *Tylototriton*. The second bears no resemblance to

TABLE 1. Distribution in Time and Space for European Salamandrid Genera Represented as Fossils

NOTE: Use of the terms Miocene and Pliocene in Europe may be misleading since the beginning of the Pliocene may vary according to different workers from 4 million years B.P. to 12 million years B.P. All Pliocene occurrences given here are younger than 5 million years B.P.

	Greece	Spain	Italy	France	West Germany, G.D.R., Poland	Switzerland	Czechoslovakia	Russia
Pleistocene	*Triturus*	cf. *Euproctus*	*Salamandra*					
Pliocene			*Triturus*		*Salamandra* *Triturus* *Mertensiella*			†*Chelotriton*
Miocene	*Triturus*	cf. *Pleurodeles* *Salamandra* †*Chelotriton* *Triturus* †*Oligosemia*	*Salamandrina* (Sardinia)	*Chioglossa* *Salamandra* †*Chelotriton* *Triturus*	*Chioglossa* *Salamandra* †*Chelotriton* *Triturus* †*Brachycormus* *Mertensiella*		*Salamandra* *Triturus*	*Triturus*
Oligocene				*Salamandra* †*Chelotriton* *Triturus*	*Salamandra* †*Chelotriton* †*Palaeo- pleurodeles* *Tylototriton*		†*Archaeotriton*	
Eocene				†*Megalo- triton*		†*Megalotriton*		
Paleocene				†*Koalliella* †cf. *Sala- mandra*	†*Koalliella*			

† = Extinct genus.

the genus *Oligosemia*, a relative (or synonym) of *Triturus* from the Miocene of Spain (Navás, 1922). All of the specimens originally referred to *Brachycormus* are united in their possession of very small size, uniform skull shape, pustular sculpture of dermal bone, and other details. They differ from *Chelotriton* in their small size, full ossification of carpals and tarsals, and in having a skull slightly longer than wide. Skull ratios seem to demonstrate that they are on a different growth curve than is *Chelotriton*, and I have thus retained the use of the genus *Brachycormus*.

A discussion of other fossil forms is too extensive for the present paper, but synonymies are not so widespread, as the material has been less abundant. A number of fossil species of *Triturus* have been described, many of which are based on larval specimens, or on specimens collected in the 19th century and now lost. Several of the extant species groups are represented in the Oligocene and Miocene, but the majority of finds probably represents the living species *T. marmoratus* or a close relative. *Oligosemia*, from the Miocene of Spain (see above), is related to and perhaps synonymous with *Triturus*. The validity of the Miocene genera *Archaeotriton* from the Miocene of Czechoslovakia (Meyer, 1860) and *Palaeopleurodeles* from the Miocene of Germany (Herre, 1941) is in doubt; the first is probably related to some of the Asiatic newts such as *Pachytriton* or *Hypselotriton*. The second may be valid and related to *Chelotriton* and *Tylototriton*, but the material requires additional preparation to decide whether this is the case or whether it is in fact related more closely to the living *Pleurodeles*. *Koalliella*, from the Paleocene of France and Germany (Herre, 1950; Estes, Hecht, and Hoffstetter, 1967) is probably valid.

The synonymies above reduce the number of valid European salamandrid fossil taxa substantially. Table 1 gives the distribution in time and space for all genera of European fossil salamanders accepted as valid in this paper, as well as any fossil record of living genera not discussed above. The results discussed above are in general agreement with conclusions suggested by Sanchiz (1977a) in a comprehensive study of fossil amphibians from Spain; space limitations prevent comparisons of our results here, but they will be included in the catalogue for the *Handbuch der Paläoherpetologie* noted at the beginning of this paper. Additional data have been added from Sanchiz (1977b) and Sanchiz and Mlynarski (1979).

Paleogeography of Salamanders

The distribution of prosirenids was essentially a Mesozoic phenomenon. The Jurassic records of *Albanerpeton* from France and Portugal and the Early Cretaceous records of *Prosiren* from North America attest to an early dispersal of the group on a still-conjoined North American-Eurasian continent. A possible record of prosirenids from the Early Cretaceous of Israel (Nevo and Estes, 1969) is not compatible with this northern distribution as Israel was then part of the African plate, yet it was not far from Europe. The group appears not to have survived the end of the Mesozoic in North America, when *Albanerpeton* or a closely related form was common, but that genus survived in Europe until the Miocene.

Time of dispersal of the Prosirenidae is likely to have been in the Jurassic, since they first appear in the Late Jurassic of Europe. Although they have not yet been found before the Early Cretaceous in North America, they probably reached here at the Late Jurassic, a time of dispersal of some groups of fossil lizards that occur both in the Late Jurassic Morrison Formation of Wyoming, and the Late Jurassic Purbeck beds of England and localities of similar age in Portugal (Prothero and Estes, 1980). In the latter two localities, prosirenids occur together with some of the same lizards found in England and Wyoming, so that their absence in the Morrison Formation locality is likely to be a sampling error.

Among other salamander groups, the Salamandridae seem to have always been strongly limited to Eurasia, with only two genera gaining a foothold in North America. Ambystomatids and plethodontids on the other hand have remained essentially North American forms, although a few fossil ambystomatids seem to have occurred in the Early Tertiary of Europe, and a single plethodontid of strong North American affinities occurs in Europe today.

The primitive Cryptobranchidae occur today on both North American and Asian continents and are probably of Mesozoic origin, since the earliest records are in the Paleocene of North America (Naylor, 1981a).

No fossil record is known in Europe of the North American endemics, the elongated Sirenidae and Amphiumidae, nor of their fossil analogues, the extinct (and also endemic) Scapherpetontidae from the Cretaceous and Early Cenozoic of North America. The Batrachosauroididae, an extinct, primarily North American Family represented by four genera from the Cretaceous and Cenozoic, also has a single genus in Europe (Estes, 1981).

Proteid salamanders appear to be relatively primitive and are represented by a single living genus in Europe *(Proteus)* and one in North America *(Necturus)*. *Necturus* goes back to the Paleocene (Naylor, 1978); *Proteus* has only a Pleistocene record, but the group goes back to the Miocene in Eurasia (Estes and Darevsky, 1978).

The zoogeography of salamanders thus appears to be marked by continental endemism in both past and present, in spite of Mesozoic dispersal routes between the northern continents that do not appear to have become impassable until the early Eocene (e.g., Estes and Hutchison, 1980).

The majority of North American salamander fossils come from the Cretaceous and Paleocene, times poorly or not at all represented in Europe by terrestrial sediments. Nevertheless, there are sufficient Paleocene and Eocene localities in Europe to be reasonably certain that little similarity occurs in salamander faunas, and that both these regions had essentially endemic salamander faunas (see table 1 and Estes, 1970). Thus only the Prosirenidae seem to have achieved wide dispersal, while Ambystomatidae, Plethodontidae, and Salamandridae had only limited exchange, although the fossil record is not adequate to make general statements of high probability regarding these groups.

Naylor (1981c) suggested that North America was probably the major center for radiation of salamanders. In both Jurassic and Cretaceous, there was the possibility of dispersal between North America and Europe (Prothero and Estes, 1980), so that a North American center is not demonstrable. Probable salamanders from the Cretaceous of Niger suggest, in fact, that the early distribution of the group was more complex (de Broin et al., 1974; Estes and Reig, in prep.). Nevertheless, Africa was still close or connected to North America until the Middle Jurassic, and at that time Niger was apparently north of the Equator so that the then-distribution of salamanders may still have been essentially in the Northern Hemisphere.

If the Lissamphibia as proposed by Parsons and Williams (1963) is a valid concept, it is likely that the ancestral lissamphibian was a tropical group. Apodans probably diverged early and remained tropical. Salamanders, because of their historical association with the Northern Hemisphere, must have been derived from essentially northern populations, became heat-limited animals and were therefore seldom able to invade the tropical regions. Frogs must have been originally tropical, like apodans, but their broadly tropical adaptation permitted them to spread later both to Northern and Southern hemispheres.

The Fossil Record of the Frog Family Pipidae

In the Southern Hemisphere, the fossil record of salamanders is nonexistent and that for frogs limited primarily to South America (Estes and Reig, 1973). African frog fossils are rare, and the best represented group is the Pipidae, a group common there today as well as in South America. *Xenopus* is the most common living African genus, and its record there goes back to the Cretaceous (de Broin et al., 1974). South American records of this genus from the

Paleocene are now known and are close to the living species *Xenopus tropicalis* and *X. muelleri* (Estes, 1975b, c).

Xenopus romeri from the Paleocene of Brazil is related to the living African species *X. tropicalis,* while *X. pascuali* from the Paleocene of Argentina is more similar to living *X. muelleri.* These occurrences of a presently African genus in South America indicate evolution of the genus while Africa and South America were still part of Gondwanaland, i.e., 90 million years ago (Early Cretaceous); this is supported by the above-mentioned Late Cretaceous record of *Xenopus* from Africa.

Other records of pipids include other Late Cretaceous forms from Africa resembling living South American or African genera (de Broin et al., 1974), a Cretaceous genus from Argentina resembling *Xenopus* but more derived (*Saltenia;* Báez, 1980), and a *Xenopus*-like but more primitive genus from the Paleogene of South Africa, *Eoxenopoides* (Estes, 1977). The latter has sometimes been placed in its own family, but my study shows that it is pipid, as originally described, and that it has a remarkable mixture of primitive and derived character states. The anterior position of parietal foramen, length of scapula, unfused carpus and expanded transverse processes of posterior vertebrae indicate *Eoxenopoides* as more primitive than any living pipid. Highly specialized in lacking teeth, and particularly in reduction and fusion of centra in the vertebral column that results in possession of only six presacral vertebrae, it has nevertheless only one derived character state in common with the extant specialized *Hymenochirus* and South American pipids. Its greatest number of derived character states is in common with *Xenopus,* but *Eoxenopoides* appears to have diverged some time in the Cretaceous from an ancestor of the living genus.

Pipids are thus interpreted as a Southern Hemisphere (Gondwanan) group that has never had a distribution in the Northern Hemisphere. Although many Jurassic reptiles show North-South distribution (Colbert, 1973), others, such as Prosirenidae and the other salamanders, and the pipids among the frogs, did not surpass the equatorial barrier, so far as known.

REFERENCES

BAEZ, A.
1980. Redescription of *Sal-Tenia ibarrezi,* a late Cretaceous frog from northwestern Argentina. Unpubl. thesis, Univ. Buenos Aires.
BROIN, F. DE; BUFFETAUT, E.; KOENIGUER, J.; RAGE, J.; RUSSELL, D.; TAQUET, P.; VERGNAUD-GRAZZINI, C.; and WENZ, S.
1974. La faune de vertébrés continentaux du gisement d'In Beceten (Sénonien du Niger). Comptes Rendus Acad. Sci. Paris, vol. 279, pp. 469-472.

BRUNNER, G.
1957.   Die Breitenberghöhle bei Gössweinstein, eine Mindel-Riss und eine post-glaziale Mediterran-Fauna.   Neues Jahrb. Geol. Pal., Monatsh., vol. 1957, pp. 352-378, 385-403.
COLBERT, E.
1973.   Continental drift and the distributions of fossil reptiles.   Pp. 395-412 *in* "Implications of Continental Drift for the Earth Sciences," D. Tarling and S. Runcorn, eds., vol. 1.   Academic Press, London and New York.
COSTA, O.
1864.   Paleontologia del regno di Napoli contenente la descrizione e figura di tutti gli avanzi organici fossili racchiusi nel suolo di questo regno.   Atti Accad. Pont. Naples, vol. 8, pp. 1-198.
EDWARDS, J.
1976.   Spinal nerves and their bearing on salamander phylogeny.   Journ. Morphol., vol. 148, pp. 305-327.
ESTES, R.
1964.   Fossil vertebrates from the late Cretaceous Lance Formation, eastern Wyoming.   Univ. California Publ. Geol. Sci., vol. 49, pp. 1-180.
1965.   Fossil salamanders and salamander origins.   Amer. Zool., vol. 5, pp. 319-334.
1969.   Prosirenidae, a new family of fossil salamanders.   Nature, vol. 223, pp. 87-88.
1970.   Origin of the recent North American lower vertebrate fauna: an inquiry into the fossil record.   Forma et Functio, vol. 3, pp. 139-163.
1975a.   Lower vertebrates from the Fort Union Formation, Late Paleocene, Big Horn Basin, Wyoming.   Herpetologica, vol. 31, pp. 365-385.
1975b.   African frog *Xenopus* (Pipidae) from the Palaeocene of Brazil and its zoogeographic importance.   Nature, vol. 254, pp. 48-50.
1975c.   Fossil *Xenopus* from the Paleocene of South America and the zoogeography of pipid frogs.   Herpetologica, vol. 31, pp. 263-278.
1976.   Middle Paleocene lower vertebrates from the Tongue River Formation, southeastern Montana.   Journ. Paleont. vol. 50, pp. 500-520.
1977.   Relationships of the South African fossil frog *Eoxenopoides reuningi* (Anura, Pipidae).   Ann. South Afr. Mus., vol. 73, pp. 49-80.
1981.   *In* Handbuch der Paläoherpetologie, pt. II, Sauria, pp. 1-115.   Gustav Fischer Verlag, Stuttgart.
ESTES, R., and DAREVSKY, I.
1978.   Fossil amphibians from the Miocene of the North Caucasus, U.S.S.R.   Journ. Palaeont. Soc. India (Orlov Mem.), vol. 20, pp. 164-169.
ESTES, R.; HECHT, M.; and HOFFSTETTER, R.
1967.   Paleocene amphibians from Cernay, France.   Amer. Mus. Novitates, no. 2295, pp. 1-25.
ESTES, R., and HOFFSTETTER, R.
1976.   Les urodèles du Miocène de La Grive-St. Alban (Isère, France).   Bull. Mus. Nat. Hist. Nat., vol. 57, pp. 297-343.
ESTES, R., and HUTCHISON, J.
1980.   Eocene lower vertebrates from Ellesmere Island, Canadian Arctic Archi-

ESTES R., and HUTCHISON, J.—*Continued*
    pelago.　Palaeogeog., Palaeoclimatol., Palaeoecol., vol. 30, pp. 325-347.

ESTES, R., and REIG, O.
  1973.　The early fossil record of frogs: a review of the evidence. *In* "Evolutionary Biology of the Anurans," Vial, J., ed.　Univ. Missouri Press, Columbia, Missouri.

GOLDFUSS, G.
  1831.　Beiträge zur Kenntnis verschiedener Reptilien der Vorwelt.　Nova Acta Acad. Leop.-Carol., vol. 15, pp. 61-128.

HERRE, W.
  1935.　Die Schwanzlurche der mitteleocänen (oberlutetischen) Braunkohle des Geiseltales und die Phylogenie der Urodelen unter Einschluss der fossilen formen.　Zoologica, vol. 33, pp. 1-85.
  1939.　Über Urodelenreste von Walbeck.　Zeitschr. Naturwiss., vol. 93, pp. 117-120.
  1941.　*Palaeopleurodeles hauffi* nov. gen., nov. spec., ein fossiler Schwanzlurch aus dem Miozän Süddeutschlands.　Zool. Anz., vol. 134, pp. 1-17.
  1949.　Neue Tatsachen zur Stammesgeschichte der Schwanzlurche.　Zool. Jahrb. (Abt. Syst.), vol. 78, pp. 217-236.
  1950.　Schwanzlurche aus dem Paleocän von Walbeck.　Zool. Anz. (Klatt Festschr.), vol. 145, pp. 286-301.
  1955.　Die Fauna der Miozänen Spaltenfüllung von Neudorf a. d. March (Č.S.R.).　Sitz. Österr. Akad. Wiss. (M.-N.), Abt. 1, vol. 164, pp. 783-803.

HERRE, W., and LUNAU, H.
  1950.　Neue fossile Schwanzlurche aus dem Burdigalium.　Neues Jahrb. Geol. Pal., Monatsh., vol. 1950, pp. 247-259.

KUHN, O.
  1938.　Fossilium catalogus, 1: Animalia. Pars 84, Stegocephalia, Urodela, Anura.
  1960.　Fossilium Catalogus, 1:Animalia, pars 97, Amphibia.

KÜHNE, W.
  1968.　Kimmeridge mammals and their bearing on the phylogeny of the Mammalia. *In* "Evolution and Environment,"　E. Drake, ed.　Yale University Press, New Haven.

MEYER, H. VON
  1859.　[Letter on fossil vertebrates from Siebengebirge.]　Neues Jahrb. Min. Geol. Pal., vol. 1859, pp. 723-725.
  1860.　Salamandrinen aus der Braunkohle am Rhein und in Böhmen.　Palaeontographica, vol. 7, pp. 47-73.

NAVÁS, L.
  1922.　Algunos fosiles de Libros (Teruel).　Bol. Soc. Ibérica Cienc. Nat., vol. 21, pp. 52-61, 172-175.

NAYLOR, B. G.
  1978.　The earliest known *Necturus* (Amphibia, Urodela) from the Paleocene Ravenscrag Formation of Saskatchewan.　Journ. Herpetol., vol. 12, pp. 565-569.

1979.   The Cretaceous salamander *Prodesmodon* (Amphibia:Caudata).   Herpe-
           tologica, vol. 35, pp. 11-20.
1981a.   Cryptobranchid salamanders from the Paleocene and Miocene of Sas-
           katchewan.   Copeia, 1981, no. 1, pp. 76-86.
1981b.   A new salamander of the family Batrachosauroididae from the Pliocene
           of North America, with notes on other batrachosauroidids.   Paleobios,
           no. 39, pp. 1-8.
1981c.   Radiation of the Amphibia Caudata: Are we looking too far into the
           past?   Evol. Theory, vol. 5, no. 2, pp. 119-126.
NAYLOR, B. G., and KRAUSE, D. W.
1981.   Piceoerpeton, a giant early Tertiary salamander from western North
           America.   Journ. Paleont., vol. 55, pp. 507-523.
NEVO, E., and ESTES, R.
1969.   *Ramonellus longispinus,* an early Cretaceous salamander from Israel.   Co-
           peia, vol. 1969, no. 3, pp. 540-547.
NOBLE, G.
1928.   Two new fossil Amphibia of zoogeographic importance from the Mio-
           cene of Europe.   Amer. Mus. Novitates, vol. 308, pp. 1-13.
PARSONS, T., and WILLIAMS, E.
1963.   The relationships of the modern Amphibia.   Quart. Rev. Biol., vol.
           38, pp. 26-53.
POMEL, A.
1853.   Catalogue méthodique et descriptif des vertébrés fossiles découverts dans
           les bassins de la Loire et de l'Allier, 193 pp.   Paris.
PROTHERO, D., and ESTES, R.
1980.   Late Jurassic lizards from Como Bluff, Wyoming and their palaeobio-
           geographic significance.   Nature, vol. 286, pp. 484-486.
SANCHIZ, F.
1977a.   Neuvos anfibios del Neogeno y Cuaternario de Europa. Origen, desar-
           ollo y relaciones de la batracofauna española.   Ph.D. thesis, Universi-
           dad complutense de Madrid.
1977b.   Catálogo de los anfibios fósiles de España.   Acta Geol. Hispanica, vol.
           12, pp. 103-107.
SANCHIZ, F., and MLYNARSKI
1979.   Pliocene salamandrids (Amphibia, Caudata) from Poland.   Acta Zool.
           Cracov., vol. 24, pp. 175-188.
SCHLOSSER, M.
1922.   Untermiocäne Wirbeltierreste aus einer Spalte im Jurakalk von Oberko-
           chen in Württemberg.   Centr. Min. Geol. Pal., vol. 1922, pp. 57-60.
SEIFFERT, J.
1969.   Urodelen-atlas aus dem obersten Bajocien von SE-Aveyron (Südfrank-
           reich).   Paläont. Zeitschr., vol. 43, pp. 32-36.
STEFANO, G. DE
1903.   Sue batraci urodeli delle fosforiti del Quercy.   Boll. Soc. Geol. Ital.,
           vol. 22, pp. 40-50.

WESTPHAL, F.
1978. *Tylototriton* (Amphibia, Urodela) aus dem Obermiozän von Öhningen. Neues Jahrb. Geol. Pal., Monatshefte, vol. 1978, pp. 491-501.
1979. *Chelotriton robustus* ein Salamandride aus dem Eozän der Grube Messel bei Darmstadt. Senk. Leth., vol. 60, pp. 475-487.
WORTHINGTON, R.
1971. Postmetamorphic changes in the vertebrae of the marbled salamander *Ambystoma opacum* Gravenhorst (Amphibia, Caudata). Sci. Ser. Univ. Texas (El Paso), vol. 4, pp. 1-74.
WORTHINGTON, R., and WAKE, D.
1972. Patterns of regional variation in the vertebral column of terrestrial salamanders. Journ. Morph., vol. 137, pp. 257-278.
ZITTEL, K.
1890. Handbuch der Palaeontologie. Abt. I. Palaeozoologie. Band III. Vertebrata, xii + 900 pp. Munich and Leipzig.

RICHARD DEAN ESTES

Lithification of Internal Sediments in Modern Coral Reefs at the Discovery Bay Marine Laboratory, Jamaica

Principal Investigator: Robert L. Eutsler, George Washington University, Washington, D. C.[1]

Grant No. 1141: To study the interrelationships between internal sediments and submarine lithification.

The purpose of this research project was to study the internal structure and mineralogic changes in recent coral reefs. Previous published and unpublished work done mainly by dynamiting the edges of reefs indicated the possibility that the internal sediments of reefs would show a detectable progression from aragonite of the living coral to magnesium-rich calcite cement of the lithified reef rock. Well-lithified aragonite and high-magnesium calcite cemented reef rock had been exposed by dynamiting in several reefs around the world. I postulated that the physical act of blasting the reef down to the lithified rock must have removed the nonlithified sediment. The mineralogic transformations should theoretically be present in the nonlithified sediment. Therefore, I proposed to dig vertically into the top of a reef buttress, rather than blast horizontally into the side of a buttress as had been done before. I expected to find coral rubble and reef-derived sediments that would become progressively more cemented downward.

The reef at Discovery Bay, Jamaica, was selected for my research for several reasons. The reefs off the Marine Laboratory are the most extensively studied coral reefs in the world. One of the earliest studies of submarine lithification of internal sediments in reef-rock was done there by blasting (Land and Goreau, 1970; Land, 1971). Another reason for studying the Jamaican reefs was my familiarity with them, gained through a 5-week course there under the auspices of the Organization for Tropical Studies.

---

[1] I express my thanks and appreciation to the National Geographic Society, the Geologic Society of America, and the George Washington University for providing financial assistance for this project. Special thanks must be given also to the staff of the Discovery Bay Marine Laboratory for their help, as well as to the many visiting and resident scientists at the Marine Laboratory for their assistance under water and for many constructive discussions.

FIG. 1.   An oblique picture of the major excavation, DBML #1. The iron bar in the upper right corner is painted for 10 centimeters. Note that the rubble layers are visible but not well defined. The principal coral of the rubble, as of the terrace, is *Acropora cervicornis*. Here the calyxes are worn off to form elongate cylinders 1 to 3 centimeters in diameter.

Logistics

The logistics of doing research in a foreign country are as significant to a research proposal as are the scientific merits of the proposal. When I submitted the research proposal, I planned to reduce my living expenses in Jamaica by the expedient of sailing my 41-foot masthead cutter there, living aboard and using food and equipment brought from the U. S. This fine plan, however, did not materialize. The voyage ended in a 5-day tow by the U. S. Coast Guard in hurricane-force winds from a position 200 miles east-southeast of Cape Hatteras, during which the yacht nearly sank. Owing to my subsequent sale of the boat, and for other personal reasons, I had to abandon the original plan; but I did make it to Jamaica, though technical difficulties there further complicated the research.

Findings

When the excavations into the top of the reef terrace were begun, it was found that the reef structure bore no resemblance whatever to that suggested in the research proposal or for that matter by any previous work on the structure and lithification of modern coral reefs. Instead of an orderly progression from aragonite coral fragments, becoming increasingly more cemented by lithified internal sediments, a completely unexpected assemblage was found. The living *Acropora cervicornis* growing at −15 meters on the flat upper surface of the fore-reef terrace were growing directly on a hard layer. This layer was composed of *A. cervicornis* fragments bound and cemented by multiple layers of crustose coralline algae (composed of high magnesium calcite). There was virtually NO uncemented internal sediment between the coral rubble fragments in the hard layers. It was the postulated mineralogic changes in uncemented internal sediment that should have shown the mechanism for much of the reef lithification. Previous work with dynamited reefs had shown large amounts of well-lithified internal sediment deposited between coral fragments (Land, 1971; Land and Goreau, 1970; Ginsburg et al., 1971; Friedman et al., 1971, 1974). Further digging into the surface of the reef showed an internal structure and stratigraphy which was totally unexpected. Figures 1 and 2 are pictures of the deepest hole, DBML #1, 1.35 meters deep, which show that the excavation passed through four separate lithified layers, all apparently identical to the upper one on which coral is growing today.

Perhaps more significant than the layers themselves are the voids or cavities between the layers. Figures 1 and 2 show that between each cemented layer are more or less horizontal voids averaging about 5 centimeters thick.

FIG. 2.   A vertical picture of DBML #1. The hammer head is 8 centimeters long. This picture shows a partially removed layer of uncemented carbonate mud at the base of the hole.

Figures 3 and 4 show close-up pictures of the broken edges of individual lithified layers. An important feature of the internal structure of the reef is the presence of *unlithified* sediment on *top* of each lithified layer within the reef. The complete stratigraphy of DBML #1, therefore, is a cyclic sequence repeated at least four times and composed of the following "units": a lithified, bound coral rubble layer; a horizontal void; an unlithified layer of fine-grained carbonate mud composed predominately of high-magnesium calcite; and another rubble layer.

The principal significance of the cavities and horizontal voids is that they appear to be connected laterally to the reef surface. The existence of this connection was first suggested during work on the excavation. Work was begun on a day with unusually heavy swell (20-40 centimeters at the surface, 10-15 centimeters at −15 meters). The loose sediment layer on top of the lowermost cemented layer was undisturbed when I touched it to stir up a small cloud of sediment. Just at that moment a surge passed through the area, and I noticed that the sediment cloud moved laterally in pendulum fashion, into and out of view in the void at the bottom of the hole. As soon as this happened, I pulled my body out of the hole (into which it just fitted) and noticed that the surge of the sediment cloud was in-phase with the movement of a sea-fan (Gorgonian coral) nearby. Both were responding equally to the water movement. It is obvious that the water in the bottom of the hole could not move if the rock surrounding the hole were solid. Likewise, the in-phase movement of the sediment cloud and the sea-fan indicates that there was very little lag or internal friction to water movement within the reef. This indicates that the "solid" reef-rock is not solid at all, but rather appears to be essentially transparent to currents. The existence of currents deep within the reef would certainly supply an explanation for the transport of unlithified sediment and its deposition on top of the lithified layers.

Another feature of the rubble layers is an extremely thin brown film found only on the *underside* of the two lowest rubble layers. This film is about one micron thick and is developed on both coral fragments and crustose coralline algae. In rare instances the brown film was encrusted and overgrown by cryptic worm tubes following deposition. Preliminary X-ray fluorescence and diffraction of the brown film indicates that it contains a substantial amount of *manganese,* evidently amorphous. The presence of encrusting worm tubes not covered by the manganese film, and the position of the film only on the underside of rubble layers more than 0.50 meter below the present interface, both indicate that some unusual bio-geo-chemical process may have been present during its formation. It is interesting to note that this is the first reported occurrence of this type of manganese in recent sediments or coral reefs. It is unfortunate that the extreme thinness of the film makes analysis so difficult.

As mentioned above, the entire project was fraught with difficulties. The logistic problems precluded a stay in Jamaica long enough to collect enough

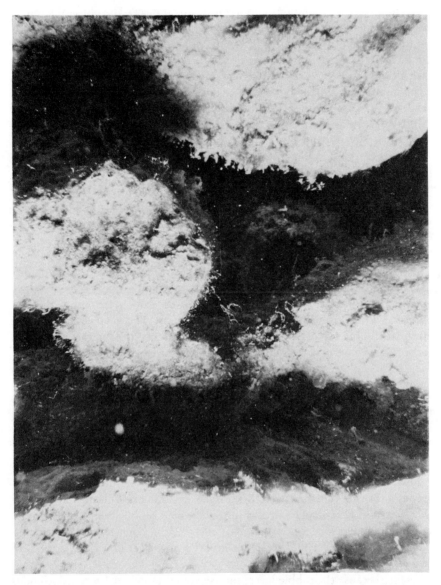

FIGS. 3 (left) and 4. Figures 3 and 4 were taken by D. Brad McCurda with an extreme close-up lens and show the broken edges of *A. cervicornis* fragments at about twice actual size. Both figures show horizontal layers of uncemented mud flooring the cavities. Note that the cavities are not empty, but contain rubble which appears to support the overlying lithified, bound rubble layer.

data to resolve the questions raised during the project. The physical strain of manually sledgehammering holes into the tightly cemented reef-rock, using SCUBA gear, meant that only one "deep" hole and two shallow holes could be dug. None of the holes penetrated into the type of tightly cemented reef rock which was exposed nearby by blasting (Land and Goreau, 1970; Land, 1971). The small number of holes precluded gathering enough samples to determine the origin of the lithified rubble layers, or the age of the sediment on top of the layers, or the origin of the manganese film on the bottom of the lowest layers. Both the scientific and logistic difficulties, and the problem of finding adequate further funding for the project caused me to drop it as the subject of my doctoral dissertation.

Without a great deal of additional data, any conclusions reached during the project must be considered rather tentative and speculative. The interpretations are presented as a guide for possible future work.

REEF GEOMETRY

Previous work on reef structure and geometry arising from dynamite blasting of recent reefs has presented a picture of coral rubble cemented by a matrix of lithified internal sediment. This is the same relationship that has been described from many uplifted ancient reefs. The geometry of discrete lithified rubble layers and cavities found off Discovery Bay poses a question about the geometry of reefs during growth and during subsequent deposition. The limited data found during the present study cannot suggest how all reefs grow, but they may provide a starting place for future work.

Coral reefs may grow concentrically, with more or less equal growth over the entire convex-upward surface. Occasional catastrophic events such as hurricanes or increased populations of reef grazers (such as the recent example of the crown-of-thorns starfish in the Great Barrier Reef off Australia) may cause widespread mass death of coral. This barren surface would be quickly overgrown by crustose coralline algae to form a new hard, lithified surface. Disgenesis of the crustose coralline algae would cause cementation and lithification of the coral fragments into a new hard rubble layer. Corals require a hard substrate for recolonization (Wells, 1957). Coral fragments sticking above the old layer would serve to support a new layer of rubble, creating a widespread cavity.

Just because the rubble layers intersected in DBML #1 were continuous over a horizontal distance of 40 centimeters does not mean that each layer is everywhere continuous. There are probably many gaps in the rubble layers. Figure 1 shows two rubble layers joining into one near the bottom of the hole. This indicates that the porosity of the layers is quite high. Figure 5 shows a

Sea Level

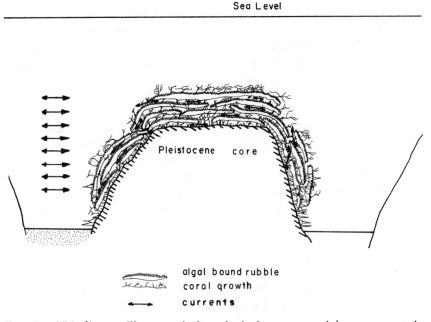

algal bound rubble
coral growth
currents

FIG. 5.   This diagram illustrates the hypothesis that overgrowth by crustose coral-line algae binds and lithifies the rubble layers. The rubble layers are made of random, unsorted large fragments of *A. cervicornis*. Each new growth layer of coral catches fragments that are then bound by encrusting coralline algae. The buried corals attached to the old hard layer (and now supporting a new hard layer) form large-scale porosity—a cavity perpendicular to coral growth-direction. Storm surges can penetrate into this porosity, carrying and depositing sediment. Where the cavities tend to the vertical, at the terrace edge, they are easily filled by sediment settling out of the water. Cavities near the edge are also much closer to the sediment source than those near the terrace center. This may explain why voids found in DBML #1 were only partly full of sediment.

hypothetical diagram of how the observed reef structure might be formed. Note that storm surges could easily transport sediment deep inside the reef. Note also that only on the top of the terrace would horizontal cavities be formed between rubble layers. At the edge of the terrace, the void (if formed) would be more vertical, and would be more easily filled by sediment. This would account for the dichotomy at DBML #1, where the vertical hole penetrated four layers, yet the dynamite excavation (Land and Goreau, 1970; Land, 1971) made only 25 meters away penetrated more than 2 meters into the side of the terrace with no sign of layering or of cavities.

If we were to examine a cross-section of the DMBL #1 terrace in, say, a few million years, we might find layers of coral rubble interbedded with fine-grained carbonate mudstone. Studies of Mesozoic reefs in the Alps (Zankl, 1968, 1971) have demonstrated that reef-building organisms such as calci-sponges and corals make up only about 10 percent of the total rock volume. Working in the Hoher Göll reef complex in the Dachstein (Upper Triassic— Norian/Rhaetian) Formation, Zankl (1968) concluded that such a low volume of reef-building organisms could not have produced a wave-resistant struc-ture. The reef-building organisms were bound and encrusted with several generations of crustose coralline algae, encrusting foraminifera and encrusting bryozoa. Zankl (1968, 1971) demonstrated that this faunal assemblage was interbedded with well bedded lime mudstone.

Fabricius (1968) studied in the Calcareous Alps, Rhaetian and Lower Ju-rassic hard grounds which are composed of reef rubble interbedded with lime mudstone. He concluded that rapid changes in depositional energy had taken place to form quiet-water deposits (lime mud) interbedded with agitated-water deposits (reef rubble). Shinn and others (1977) described a channel exca-vated in Holocene reef rocks off Miami, Florida, in which numerous horizon-tal cavities and voids were present, apparently identical to those found in DBML #1.

The end product of the reef stratigraphy in DBML #1 will almost cer-tainly be a sequence of interbedded lime mudstone and reef rubble. When all the available porosity is filled with lime mud, submarine cements, and epi-fauna, the reef at Discovery Bay should be identical in structure and texture with the Upper Triassic-Lower Jurassic reefs in the Alps. The presence of nu-merous horizontal voids within a wave-resistant growing reef suggests that ancient analogues which display interbedded reef rubble and lime mudstone were also wave-resistant. This conclusion alters our understanding of the pa-leogeography and paleoecology of reefs.

It is interesting to note that the sediment found on top of the rubble layers is very similar to that being formed today by certain reef burrowers and grazers. The grain size and mineralogy of the sediment on the rubble layers appear to be identical with that which may be found in niches and recesses un-der tabulate *Monastrea* sp. (a brain coral) growing at depths greater than 25 meters (personal observation). Exactly which faunal groups erode this sedi-ment is unknown—possibly boring clionid sponges. Both sediments, from DBML #1 and that from neat little piles under coral ledges, are predominate-ly high-magnesium calcite, with minor amounts of aragonite. This is a rather strange finding, as it suggests that either the burrowers are attacking only magnesium calcite, or that they are producing a mineralogic transformation

FIG. 6.   The upper surface of the terrace near where DBML #1 was chiseled into the reef. Note the large number of *A. cervicornis* colonies. Were these branches to break off and then be overgrown by crustose coralline algae, it is easy to visualize a dense layer of fragments being supported by a tangled network and creating large open cavities near the base. Note also that the surge caused by a wave passing overhead is visible in the motion of the Gorgonian coral in the background.

from original aragonite to high-magnesium calcite. If the sediment eroded from the reef by burrowing sponges is a main source for the sediment deposited on the rubble layers inside the reef, then the initial lithification of the reef may begin because of mineralogic changes caused by boring sponges. This possibility should be studied in detail in the future.

REEF CHEMISTRY

The recognition of a thin manganese-rich film on the underside of the two lowermost rubble layers poses many questions. This is the first reported occurrence of relatively concentrated manganese from shallow tropical water. The manganese is not highly concentrated in the sense of manganese nodules from the deep sea, but it appears to be more concentrated than is normal for reef limestones. The questions asked by this discovery are many: What is the origin of this film? Why is it found in such a peculiar manner, and does the mode of occurrence have anything to do with its origin? Was the film formed under some unique past condition, or is it still forming slowly today? The answers to these questions are important, as they may also provide answers to the broader, more important question of the origin of deep-sea manganese nodules. If additional work supports the preliminary finding of amorphous manganese on lithified rubble layers, future work on the geochemistry of manganese may be done in reefs, where it is certainly easier to make personal observations than in oceanic depths.

Significance

The study was unable to support many of the original working hypotheses. The small amount of data in both samples and excavations allows only preliminary inferences about reef geometry, reef porosity, the lithification of reef sediments, and possible manganese mineralization in the reef. The preliminary inferences are important only as they indicate suggestions for further work. For example, a thorough understanding of reef geometry and original porosity are vital for reservoir studies in lead-zinc mining districts and in oil-gas fields. It is my hope that the work begun in Jamaica under the auspices of the National Geographic Society will enable someone to undertake and solve the questions and relationships discovered during the project.

This project has shown that manual excavation of coral reefs is much too difficult, both physically and with regard to the amount of time spent for the knowledge gained. The use of dynamite for the excavations is ecologically unsound, unsafe, and may destroy much of the most important information. Future workers doing reef excavation would do well to investigate the feasibility of power tools. In areas lacking extensive surface support, the best power tool would probably be an air-hammer, powered by a SCUBA tank and a first stage diving regulator. The entire system should work well to −30 meters and cost less than $300. With good surface support, or more money, a hydraulic hammer would be the first choice. This system would require a hammer and tubing to the surface, as well as an engine and hydraulic pump. Either of these tools would be able to dig quick, clean holes into the reef. The holes cause no permanent degradation of the reef environment. In fact they are an aid to long-term study of reef growth, as they provide an excellent time-base for coral recolonization.

REFERENCES

FABRICIUS, FRANK H.
  1968.   Calcareous sea bottoms of the Rheatian and Lower Jurassic from the west part of the northern Calcareous Alps.   Pp. 240-249 *in* "Recent Developments in Carbonate Sedimentology in Central Europe," German Müller and Gerald M. Friedman, eds.   Springer-Verlag, New York.
FRIEDMAN, GERALD M.; AMIEL, A. J.; and SCHNEIDERMANN, NAHUM
  1974.   Submarine cementation in reefs, example from the Red Sea.   Journ. Sedimentary Petrol., vol. 44, no. 3, pp. 816-825.
FRIEDMAN, GERALD M.; SANDERS, JOHN H.; GAVISH, ELIEZER; and ALLEN, ROBERT C.
  1971.   Marine lithification mechanism yields rock resembling beachrock.   Pp. 50-53 *in* "Carbonate Cements," Owen P. Bricker, ed.   Johns Hopkins Univ. Stud. Geol., no. 19, illus.
GINSBURG, ROBERT N.; SCHROEDER, J. H.; and SHINN, EUGENE A.
  1971.   Recent synsedimentary cementation in subtidal Bermuda reefs.   Pp. 54-58 *in* "Carbonate Cements," Owen P. Bricker, ed.   Johns Hopkins Univ. Stud. Geol., no. 19, illus.
LAND, LYNTON S.
  1971.   Submarine lithification of Jamaican reefs.   Pp. 59-62 *in* "Carbonate Cements," Owen P. Bricker, ed.   Johns Hopkins Univ. Stud. Geol., no. 19, illus.
LAND, LYNTON S., and GOREAU, T. F.
  1970.   Submarine lithification of Jamaica reefs.   Journ. Sedimentary Petrol., vol. 40, no. 1, pp. 457-462.
SHINN, E. A.; HUDSON, J. H.; HALEY, R. B.; and LINZ, BARBARA
  1977.   Topographic control and accumulation rate of some Holocene coral reefs—South Florida and the Dry Tortugas.   Pp. 2-7 *in* "Proceedings, Third International Coral Reef Symposium," vol. 2.
WELLS, JOHN W.
  1957.   Coral reefs.   Pp. 609-631 *in* "Treatise on Marine Ecology and Paleoecology," Joel W. Hedgpeth, ed.   Geol. Soc. Amer. Mem. 67, vol. 1 (Ecology), illus.
ZANKL, HEINRICH
  1968.   Sedimentological and biological characteristics of a Dachstein reef complex in the Upper Triassic of the northern Calcareous Alps.   Pp. 215-218 *in* "Recent Developments in Carbonate Sedimentology in Central Europe." German Müller and Gerald M. Friedman, eds.   Springer-Verlag, New York.

ZANKL, HEINRICH—*Continued*
    1971.   A model of sedimentation and diagenesis in a Triassic reef.   *In* "Carbonate Cements," Owen P. Bricker, ed.   Johns Hopkins Univ. Studies Geol. no. 19.

ROBERT L. EUTSLER

Sedimentational Processes in the Delta Region, Southwestern Netherlands, with Emphasis on the Veerse Meer, a Nontidal Anoxic Basin

Principal Investigator: Richard W. Faas, Lafayette College, Easton, Pennsylvania.

Grant No. 1180:   In support of an in situ investigation of the turbidity maximum, Westerschelde Estuary, Netherlands.

The research summarized in this report was performed during the months of June-December 1973. As originally devised the research was to study the sedimentational processes occurring in the region of the turbidity maximum in the Westerschelde, the estuary lying between the Netherlands and Belgium. However, as it developed, a regional sedimentological survey of the Westerschelde, Oosterschelde, and an enclosed tideless basin, the Veerse Meer, was accomplished. In addition, special emphasis was placed upon the Veerse Meer because of its uniqueness and because the effects of man's alteration of this environment in 1961 had been insufficiently studied.

Background

Collaboration developed among myself (project leader); Dr. S. I. Wartel, sedimentologist of the Koninklijk Belgisch Instituut voor Natuurwetenschappen, Brussels; and Dr. K. F. Vaas, director, Instituut voor Hydrobiologisch Onderzoek, Yerseke, Netherlands. Dr. Wartel had recently completed his doctoral dissertation, which dealt with sedimentational problems of the river Schelde upstream of Antwerp. Our interests complemented each other and we began to examine the entire Schelde Basin. I made contact with Dr. Vaas at Yerseke and, after some discussion, was pleased to learn that he would provide ship time for Dr. Wartel and myself to sample systematically the bottom sediments of the above-mentioned water bodies (fig. 1).

Sediment Patterns

During our sampling in the Veerse Meer (fig. 1), a portion of the Oosterschelde that had been removed from tidal activity since 1961, we discovered that a number of changes had occurred in the composition of the bottom sediments. In particular, the sediments deposited since closure in 1961 consisted

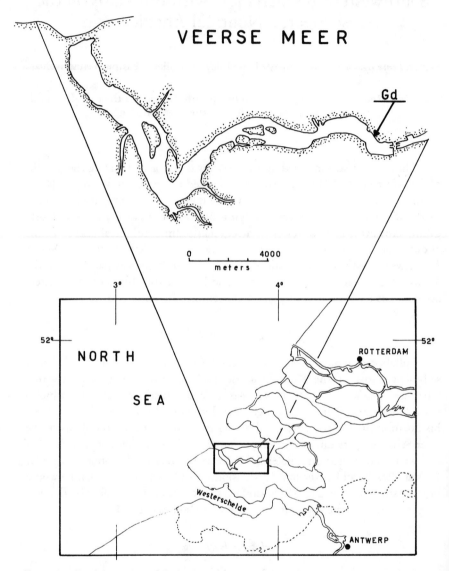

FIG. 1. Location map of Delta area showing Westerschelde, Oosterschelde, and Veerse Meer.

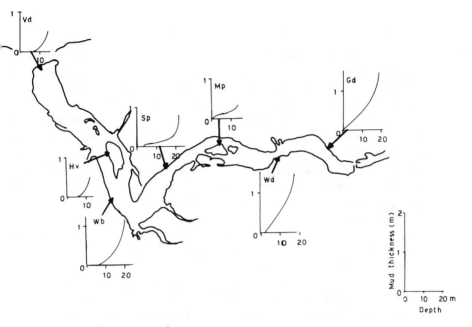

Fig. 2.   Mud accumulation map—Veerse Meer.

primarily of silt and clay-sized material, where previously they had been coarse sand. The Veerse Meer ceased being a conduit for the through-passing of sands from the Oosterschelde and the North Sea and became a self-contained basin whose fine-grained sediments are primarily derived from bioerosion of its confining slopes. Wind-driven surface currents tend to carry fine sediments from west to east, with the greatest accumulation (>2 meters) occurring at the base of slopes within the eastern part of the basin (fig. 2). In the western part of the basin fine-grained sediments are incorporated into the underlying sands through the activities of infaunal organisms. The homogenization of the old (pre-1961) deposits and the new (post-1961) silts and clays results from the mixing of oxygenated water throughout the entire water column. In the eastern part of the basin, anoxic bottom-water conditions were established early (sediment cores show a sharp interface between black muds and clean, coarse-grained sand at the base), and such conditions have a profound effect upon the depositional processes in those reaches. The general sediment distribution patterns in each of the water bodies studied are reported in Faas and Wartel (1976).

Underwater Slope Analysis

A detailed analysis of selected slopes in the anoxic reaches was performed at several localities in the eastern part of the Veerse Meer. This was done using SCUBA techniques. An underwater inclinometer was constructed and slopes measured whenever a change in slope occurred. The depths were recorded at each change in slope, using a precision depth recorder. Cores were taken from various levels along each slope and analyzed for their mass physical properties. Shear strength values of the surficial slope sediments were measured in situ, using a hand-held shear vane, following the procedure reported in Faas, 1972. A series of sediment cores was obtained from −11 meters at Gebroken Dijk in 1975 and was analyzed through one-dimensional consolidation techniques at the Laboratorium voor Grondmechanica, Universiteit Gent. The data so obtained indicated the sediments to be either "remolded in place" or "under-consolidated," having a high degree of compaction and negligible compressive strength (Faas and Wartel, 1977).

The data showed that fine-grained sediments being deposited in anoxic environments possess properties different from those of similar sediments deposited under oxidizing conditions. Methanogenesis, a process occurring in anoxic environments through the activities of anaerobic bacteria, inhibits normal consolidational behavior of the sediment and creates conditions at the base of the slopes leading to general slope instability.

A new form of underwater slope erosion was suggested from these studies (Faas, 1977). Figure 3 shows the process in detail. Profile A represents the pre-1961 slope at Gebroken Dijk. Upon closure of the estuarine segment, anoxic bottom water conditions developed, with anoxic sediment conditions migrating up the slope. Older interlaminated peats and clays are disrupted through methanogenesis and loss of shear strength due to breaking of geochemical bonds, and are transported basinward through geostatic forces. They accumulate within the region of anoxic water and are prevented from consolidating through the generation and ebullition of gases. Each successive profile (B-F) shows the position of the *redox* interface in the sediments and in the water column. Profile G shows the present Gebroken Dijk slope. The major sediment accumulation occurs below the redox interface in the water column and the region between the interface in the water column and in the sediment exhibits a change in slope associated with sediment removal and transportation. The ultimate slope to be achieved under these conditions will depend entirely upon the vertical position of the two redox interfaces. However, in the Gebroken Dijk example, a flattening of the original profile has resulted.

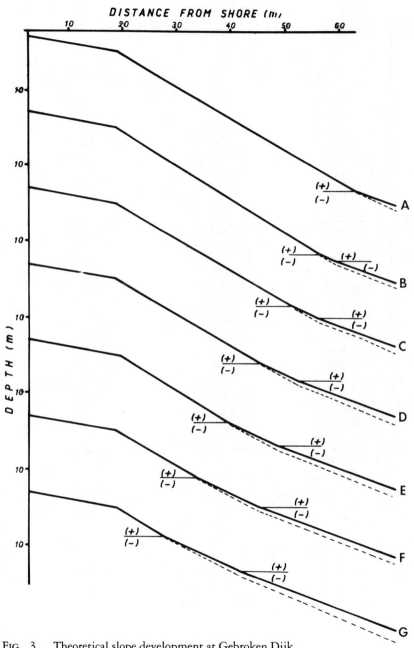

FIG. 3. Theoretical slope development at Gebroken Dijk.

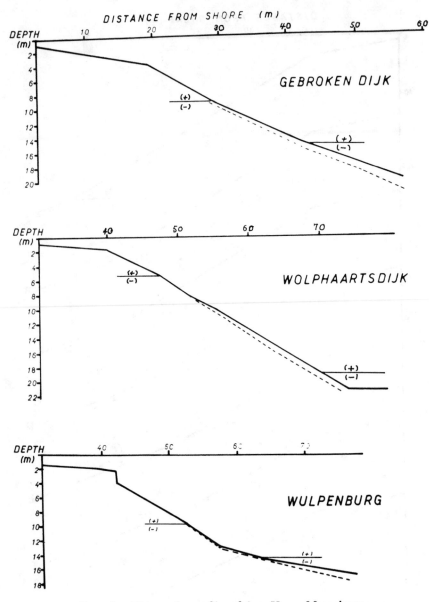

FIG. 4.   Time-series profiles of three Veerse Meer slopes.

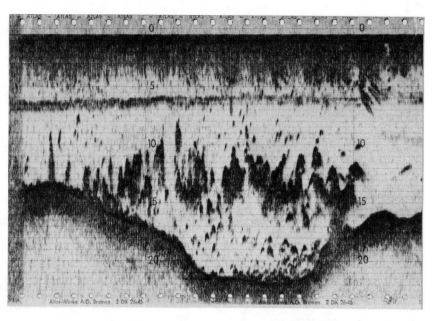

FIG. 5.   Echo-sounding over ship channel near Gebroken Dijk showing pycnocline
separating waters of different salinity at 7 meters.

Slope Evolution

A suggestion of the trend in anoxic slope development is seen in figure 4.
Three slopes are shown, the Gebroken Dijk slope being located farthest to the
east and Wulpenburg being farthest to the west. Anoxic conditions became
established shortly after closure in the eastern reaches of the Veerse Meer and
have progressed westward with time (Bakker, pers. comm., 1977). This may
be due to the fact that saline Oosterschelde water is periodically introduced
into the Veerse Meer from the Katseveer sluice, located at the easternmost end
of the lake. Figure 5 is an echo-sounding record that shows the density interface between water of 8.1 g/l salt above and 11.3 g/l salt below, with a
temperature difference of 0.5° between water masses. This leads to stable
water-mass conditions and contributes to oxygen depletion of the lower waters. Figure 4 therefore represents a time-series profile of successive stages of
underwater slope development. The slope at Wulpenburg shows the most recent effects of methanogenic erosion. Sharp knick points occur at −10 and −12
meters, associated with the position of the redox interface in the sediment and

in the water column, respectively. At Wohlphaarts Dijk, midway between the two, the redox interface in the sediment has climbed to −5 meters, with corresponding sediment accumulation beginning at −8 meters and extending down to the slope base. The most advanced profile, Gebroken Dijk, shows the sediment redox interface at −9 meters and sediment accumulating to more than a meter thick at −15 meters.

The significance of the anoxic environment in this situation is that it creates an unstable environment that will accelerate underwater slope erosion in such sediments until the condition itself changes or is changed, or until the slope reaches a stable angle of repose for such sediments, usually 5° or less. Terrestrial soil mechanics has long had as an axiom that if a landslide is to be stabilized one must stabilize the base of the slide. The same principle applies to underwater slopes, but in the case where anoxic water occupies the basal region of the slope, stabilization cannot easily be achieved. Methanogenesis will continue to inhibit normal consolidation of newly deposited sediments, owing to continual resupply of organic matter derived from higher up the slope through methanogenic erosion of peat units, and from material removed from shoal reaches by storms and boat wakes and transferred downward by gravitational processes.

The implications of the methanogenic process should be understood by estuarine managers when considering changes to estuarine ecosystems, either through dredging or other forms of channel maintenance. It may also be that methanogenic erosion is playing a role in deep-sea erosion at the present time and may have had a major role in deep-sea processes in the geological past (Schlanger and Jenkyns, 1976).

Much data concerning the size distributional parameters, clay mineral composition, calcium carbonate, organic matter contents, mass physical and engineering properties of the sediments, in addition to environmental parameters (pH, Eh, salinity, temperature, and interstitial water composition), are available and many have been reported (Faas, 1972, 1977; Faas and Wartel, 1976). They are not included in this report.

REFERENCES

FAAS, RICHARD W.
    1972.   Mass physical and engineering properties of some York River sediments.   Pp. 337-347 *in* "Environmental Framework of Coastal Plain Sediments." Geol. Soc. Amer. Mem. 133, B. W. Nelson, ed.
    1977.   Methanogenesis: An *in situ* remolding process.   P. 261 *in* "Program with Abstracts."   N. E. Geological Society of America meeting, Binghamton, New York, March 31-April 2, 1977.

FAAS, RICHARD W., and WARTEL, S. I.
  1976.   Sedimentology and channel slop morphology of an anoxic basin in southern Netherlands.   Pp. 136-149 *in* "Estuarine Processes," vol. 2, M. L. Wiley, ed.   Academic Press, New York.
  1977.   The effect of gas bubble formation on the physical and engineering properties of recently deposited fine-grained sediments.   Geol. en Mijnbouw, vol. 56, p. 3.
SCHLANGER, S. F., and JENKYNS, H. C.
  1976.   Cretaceous oceanic anoxic events: Causes and consequences.   Geol. en Mijnbouw, vol. 55, no. 3/4, pp. 179-184.

RICHARD W. FAAS

Exploration of Ice Caves in the Canadian Cordillera

Principal Investigator: Derek C. Ford, McMaster University, Hamilton, Ontario, Canada.

Grant No. 1176:   For the McMaster University 1973 expedition to the Nahanni North Karst, Mackenzie Mountains, Northwest Territories, Canada.

Geographical and Historical Background

The Mackenzie Mountains are one of the most remote and least-known parts of mainland Canada. They trend for 300 miles northwest from the 60th parallel and form the boundary between the Yukon and Northwest Territories. Their width is 120-150 miles; summit heights range 5,000-9,000 feet above sea level (a.s.l.) and trunk valley floors are at 800-2,000 feet a.s.l. Mean annual temperatures are below 32°F.; there are permanent glaciers on the highest mountains and discontinuous permafrost elsewhere. Treeline is at 4,000-4,500 feet.

The western ranges of the mountains, being highest and closest to Pacific sources of precipitation, were repeatedly glaciated by alpine glaciers and display characteristic alpine topography. The great Laurentide continental, or lowland, ice sheet, which submerged most of Canada 18,000 years ago and so moulded its modern landforms, encroached upon the most easterly ranges. In between are the Canyon Ranges, fold mountains that have either escaped glaciation altogether or have not been glaciated for more than 100,000 years. Their topography is more fluvial (river-built) than any other in Canada. The principal river is the South Nahanni which has carved three great canyons (named First, Second and Third) across these ranges.

In 1969 Parks Canada became interested in developing the South Nahanni canyon country as a National Park. The First Canyon is carved through 3,000 feet plus of dolomite rocks but displays at its crest a formation (Nahanni Formation) of the typical karst rock, limestone, that here is very massive and resistant in character and is 450-750 feet thick. Early travelers noted cave entrances in this rock, high in the Canyon walls. In 1970 and 1971 a Quebec adventure party began their exploration. In 1971, I was asked by Parks Canada to appraise the scientific significance of these caves. When this task was completed, I and my assistants flew air reconnaissance for 40 miles northeast of the Canyon, following the limestone outcrop. The result was the discovery of the most rugged and intensely developed karst (limestone solution) terrain known anywhere in Canada or the United States, "the North Karst." Preliminary studies commenced in 1972. A main expedition was launched in 1973 and is the subject of this report.

The North Karst is a belt of country measuring 30 by 20 miles and extending northeast from the north wall of the First Canyon. It is centered at latitude 61°28'N., longitude 124°05'W. It encompasses portions of two domal ranges, Nahanni Plateau and Ram Plateau, and a saddle in between them. Elevation ranges 2000-5000 feet a.s.l. The bedrock is the Nahanni limestone, fissured by the up-doming of the ranges. Shale rocks encroach from east and west, and supply runoff to the limestone, where it is absorbed underground. The country is uninhabited and trackless. Access is via chartered floatplane or helicopter from Fort Simpson, 100 miles to the east.

Aims of the Expedition

The expedition comprised eleven persons and was in the field for 45 days in the period June through August 1973. For the first 32 days it operated in two separate groups. Group 1 (leader, D. C. Ford) analyzed the South Nahanni landscape south and west of the karst. This was funded by Parks Canada. Group 2 (under Deputy Leader, G. A. Brook) studied the North Karst. For the last 13 days both groups combined in the North Karst. North Karst research was funded by Parks Canada, the National Research Council of Canada, and the National Geographic Society. Society funds were expended upon the costs of installing and maintaining two very experienced cave explorers and surveyors from Cincinnati, Ohio (Ralph O. Ewers and Larry S. Simpson), plus some of the general transportation costs involved in stocking and servicing the North Karst group. A base camp for this group was established by floatplane at Mosquito Lake in the northeast corner of the karst (the only suitable lake for fixed-wing aircraft) and a fly camp was set up by helicopter at Death Lake, 15 miles southwest.

The broad aim of the North Karst program was to delineate the physical geography, and the groundwater hydrology and hydrochemistry of the terrain. Surface karst morphology was mapped onto air photographs, with selected examples of each of the different landforms being accurately measured by line and Brunton compass. More than one hundred cave entrances were located and, where longer than a few tens of feet, the caves were mapped by line and compass. Groundwater flow between sink-points and springs was traced with Rhodamine WT and fluorescein dyes, collected on traps of activated charcoal. Concentrations of dissolved H, CO_2, $CaCO_3$, and $CaMg$ $2CO_3$ in the waters were fully analyzed in the field by standard potentiometric and colorimetric methods.

Results

The prime result of our work has been to obtain a description and analysis of one of the most remarkable (and unexpected) assemblages of karst land-forms that is known in the world. In the past, general theories of karst land-scape evolution have supposed that the most intensive and rugged development of the landforms will be found in wet tropical or sub-tropical climates (e.g., Puerto Rico), because here the rock solution processes operate fastest. In temperate climatic areas the karst topography becomes more sub-dued, as it is in the Sinkhole Plain of temperate Kentucky. In cold climates, development is subdued or almost entirely suppressed by the competing processes of glacier erosion and deposition, frost-shattering of rock, etc. The North Karst is among the very coldest of known karst lands (it has a Siberian-type climate with relatively little precipitation) and yet its ruggedness and density of development compares with the most accentuated tropical karst-lands. It contains particular karst landforms (towers, cenote sinkholes, poljes) hitherto supposed to be limited to tropical or warm temperate regions. We have established that the North Karst has been glaciated, but not for over 400,000 years. In contrast to most glacial karst terrains, where the ice receded only 10,000-15,000 years ago, there has been as a consequence a considerable span of post-glacial time at Nahanni for rock solution processes to mould the remarkable landforms. A second principal explanatory factor in this terrain is the massiveness of the host limestone and the exceptional depth of fissuration within it that is due to mountain uplifting (tectonic) processes. As a result of our findings, physical geographers and geologists specializing in karst studies the world over are placing increasing stress upon the roles of geology and available erosion time in explaining their findings, and less upon spatial variations of the modern global climate.

In more detail, the following are some of the principal categories of sur-face karst features discovered:

1. LIMESTONE PAVEMENT. In extensive tracts of these limestone pave-ments the ice-scoured bedrock surfaces are indented by interlocking patterns of small solutional channels. Limestone pavements are particularly common in recently glaciated terrains.

2. SINKHOLES. These are created by direct solution, by collapse into underlying solution caves, or by washing (suffosion) of unconsolidated glacial

drift into underlying solutional crevices. More than 400 examples were mapped. Most striking are the solution sinkholes; many of these are sheer-walled cylindrical shafts, filled with water to varying depths. Larger examples are 100 feet in length, 50 feet wide, 100 feet or more in depth. They are "ce-note-form" sinkholes, like the Mayan sacrificial cenotes (wells) of the Yucatán Peninsula, Mexico. At one place, 23 of these features are packed into a plat-form measuring 300 by 100 yards, a remarkably high density.

3.   LABYRINTH KARST. The most unusual surface karst forms are what we term "solution streets," straight, canyonlike features ranging from 300-600 feet long and 50 feet deep to $3\frac{1}{2}$ miles long and 600 feet deep. Their width varies from 15 to 150 feet. The streets are created by solution acting downwards, not by rivers flowing through their bottoms. Frost action has shattered the walls and partly filled the floors with debris, but relict caves are preserved in the walls and modern drainage seeps away into many small caves in the floors. Similar, but generally smaller streets, are reported in karsts of New Guinea and Western Australia.

The Nahanni streets intersect to form a natural labyrinth. At places of in-tersection, frost shatter and solution have caused the vertical walls to retreat, creating super-sinkholes that we have termed "karst platea"; these are up to one mile in diameter and 600 feet in depth. Like the streets, they drain through small, debris-clogged sinkholes in their bases.

The North Karst labyrinth appears to be the most extensive natural rock labyrinth known on Earth.

4.   POLJES. These are large closed basins with flat, alluvial floors. They are drained underground and may be seasonally inundated. They are solu-tional landforms. The finest examples are found in Yugoslavia; they are quite common in other warm temperate-tropical karstlands, and small, poorly de-veloped examples were known previously as far north as Ireland.

There are three small, but perfectly formed, poljes at the north end of the Nahanni karst, where the water table is nearer the surface than in most of the karst. The largest is $1\frac{1}{2}$ miles long, half a mile wide and its maximum depth is 230 feet. Base drainage is through alluvium at its lowest point; in response to occasional heavy summer rains it may flood up to a depth of 90 feet in 8 to 10 days, and water is discharged through small caves at the highwater line. Farther upstream there is a very large sinkhole, Raven Lake Depression, which is an incipient polje. Its water level fluctuates through a range of at least 200 feet.

5.   CLOSED CANYONS. These are semikarstic landforms found only at the northern and western extremities of the karst belt. They have the form of normal river canyons approaching the karst, but where they enter it at their

downstream extremities all drainage sinks through the bottoms of ponds into inaccessible caves. There are no surface channels at the canyon mouths, indicating that even in the wettest conditions all drainage is absorbed underground into the karst belt. Canal Canyon is the largest example; it is 19 miles in length and has a maximum depth of 3,000 feet.

Other canyons (e.g., Lafferty Canyon, a tributary of First Canyon) have regular canyon river beds but we have never observed water flowing in them. It is thought that there is surface flow during summer flash floods. At all other times, including the spring melt, drainage is underground into caves.

All waters sinking in the North Karst appear to drain to just two springs, one at the northern extremity, called Bubbling Spring, and one at the southern extremity that enters the South Nahanni River through its bed at a point in First Canyon. That such an extensive and rugged terrain is drained to merely two outlets indicates very well integrated underground drainage systems that must aggregate more than 100 miles of solution cave passages. During the 1973 expedition two successful dye traces were concluded. In the first, water from Mosquito Lake was shown to flow three miles underground to Bubbling Spring in 5 or 6 days. In the second, Death Lake, in the heart of the karst, was traced 11 miles to Bubbling Spring with a flow-through time estimated at 14 to 18 days. This test permitted the underground water divide between the two springs to be approximately positioned. Velocities of flow underground appear very similar to those measured in the Mammoth Cave area of Kentucky, i.e., the presence of discontinuous permafrost is not obstructing trunk groundwater flowpaths in the North Karst.

Before the 1973 expedition, approximately 12 natural caves were known in the north wall of First Canyon, their lengths ranging from 100 to 5,000 feet. All were of phreatic type (i.e., created under conditions of complete, permanent water-fill) but are now drained. They contain substantial deposits of stalactites and stalagmites, and of seasonal and permanent ice.

Working north of First Canyon, the 1973 expedition located more than 100 new cave entrances. But exploration results were very disappointing; only one cave could be explored for as much as 1,000 feet and most were completely obstructed within 100 feet of the entrance.

The cave finds divide into two classes, entry points to the modern groundwater-flow cave systems draining to the two springs, and relict caves. Invariably, the former are flooded to within a few feet of the entry point, i.e., the active groundwater circulation is through modern phreatic caves, so that exploration can only be by diving and, because water temperatures do not exceed 35°F., this will be a hard undertaking. The relict caves are fragments of older phreatic caves drained and abandoned in the walls of the karst streets and platea. Most are blocked by total seals of ice (permafrost) or of frozen silt. The greatest discovery was Raven Lake Cave, where an entrance shaft 240 feet deep entered a horizontal gallery 39 feet wide and up to 60 feet in height. At one end this terminated in an overlook in the vertical cliffs of the Raven Lake sinkhole. At the other end it was obstructed by boulders sealed in permanent ice.

Most relict caves that could be penetrated 50 feet or more before a terminal obstruction was reached displayed strong climatic zonation. An entrance zone, 10-500 feet in length, is sufficiently warmed in summer so that both rock and air temperatures are above the freezing point. Conventional stalactites and stalagmites of calcite precipitated from seepage water grow in the zone, though actively growing examples tended to be short and of simple cylindrical shape. A second zone, 20-1,000 feet in length, is enough cooler so that the bulk rock temperature is below the freezing point in summer, but liquid water can still seep through larger cracks. Upon emerging, it freezes to build large stalactites, stalagmites, and flowstones of ice. These are ablated by very cold, dry air during the winter and hence display curious erosional sculpture; but many evidently survive for tens of years. Most important, in this zone large, highly ornamented stalagmites, etc., of calcite could be found, often buried in the ice. They are not growing in the modern climate and evidently survive from warmer interglacial periods in the past. A third, innermost zone 10-2,000 feet in length is permafrozen. No seepage waters can enter from the rock overhead but warm summer air may penetrate and, upon cooling below the freezing point, deposits its water vapour as hexagonal platelet crystals of hoarfrost. All rock surfaces may be sheathed in millions of the crystals, a dazzling spectacle. In the North Karst, maximum crystal diameter was two inches. In one cave in First Canyon, it exceeded 15 inches, representing many tens of years of slow accumulation in a very stable thermal environment.

Our karst research group at McMaster University has specialized in Uranium series dating of calcite stalagmites and flowstones. Many stalagmite samples were taken from important stratigraphic sites in the North Karst in 1973 for analysis. A brief synopsis of conclusions to date is:

1. The one known incursion of glacial ice over the North Karst occurred before 350,000-400,000 years ago. The oldest caves of the region, now relict fragments, were fully enlarged before this ice came, so that a karst belt was already established. But the modern sinkhole and labyrinth assemblage has developed since the ice. A glacier margin approached the region some time after 350,000 years B.P., causing a lake to inundate it and fill the older caves with their typical silt chokes.

2. During the period 350,000+ to 280,000 years B.P. the climate for long spells was significantly warmer than present, permitting large stalagmites to grow in what are now the ice zones of the caves.

3. The mountain ranges of the region are probably still uplifting, thus fissuring the limestone and aiding further development of karst landforms. The rate of uplift at the center of First Canyon is approximately 2 meters per thousand years. As the rock is lifted, the River entrenches, creating the Canyon. First Canyon is estimated to be $1\frac{1}{2}$ million years old.

Work of the 1972 and 1973 expeditions to the North Karst was described in detail in a report to Parks Canada by Brook and Ford in 1974. A copy of this report has been deposited with the National Geographic Society.

REFERENCES

BROOK, G. A.
  1976.   Karst terrains of the South Nahanni area, Mackenzie Mountains, N.W.T., 566 pp.   Unpublished Ph.D. thesis, McMaster University.
          The full analytical account of the North Karst.
BROOK, G. A., and FORD, D. C.
  1974.   The Karstlands of the South Nahanni Region, N.W.T., 540 pp.   Report on Contract 72-32B, Parks Canada, Department of Indian Affairs and Northern Development, Ottawa.
          A full account of the karst and caves, groundwater hydrology and hydrochemistry of the North Karst, with many illustrations.
  1974.   Nahanni karst: unique northern landscape.   Canadian Geographic Journal, vol. 88, no. 6, pp. 36-43.
          A popular summary of the North Karst, with illustrations.
  1978.   The nature of labyrinth karst and its implications for climaspecific models of tower karst.   Nature, vol. 275, no. 5620, pp. 493-496.
          A formal summary of the North Karst labyrinth terrain in the foremost scientific serial.
  1979.   Hydrology of the Nahanni karst, northern Canada, and the importance of extreme summer storms.   Journal of Hydrology, vol. 46, pp. 103-121.
          The organization of groundwater systems in the North Karst, emphasizing the flooding induced by an exceptional summer storm.
FORD, D. C.
  1973.   Development of the canyons of the South Nahanni River, N.W.T.   Canadian Journal of Earth Sciences, vol. 10, no. 3, pp. 366-378.
          Summary of the geomorphology of the First, Second, and Third river canyons with estimates of their age derived from U-series dating.

1976.   Evidences of multiple glaciation in South Nahanni National Park, Mackenzie Mountains, N.W.T.   Canadian Journal of Earth Sciences, vol. 13, no. 10, pp. 1433-1445.

The history of glaciation of the South Nahanni region, emphasizing the application of U-series dates from the North Karst to establish the timing of glacial events.

HARMON, R. S.; FORD, D. C.; and SCHWARCZ, H. P.
1977.   Interglacial chronology of the Rocky and Mackenzie Mountains based upon ^{230}Th/^{234}U dating of calcite speleothems.   Canadian Journal of Earth Sciences, vol. 14, no. 11, pp. 2543-2552.

U-series dates from the North Karst and the Rocky Mountains are combined to estimate the ages of major interglacial periods in the western cordillera during the last 400,000 years.

DEREK C. FORD

Mountain Gorilla Research, 1974

Principal Investigator: Dian Fossey, Karisoke Research Centre, Ruhengeri, Rwanda, Africa.

Grant Nos. 1152a,   In support of the seventh year of research into the behavioral
1157a, 1262.   patterns and ecology of the free-ranging mountain gorillas
                  (*Gorilla gorilla beringei*) of the Virunga Mountains within the
                  Parc des Volcans, Rwanda.

The mountain gorilla research project, established under full grant by the National Geographic Society in 1968, began in the Parc des Virungas of Zaire in January 1967 under grants from the Wilkie Foundation, African Wildlife Leadership Foundation, and the New York Zoological Society. A political uprising terminated that study after $6\frac{1}{2}$ months. By September 1967 the research was able to continue on the Rwandan side of the Virunga Volcanoes within an area of the Parc des Volcans, 5 miles east of the original study site.

The Karisoke Research Centre, as the camp came to be known, lies at 10,000 feet adjacent to the base of Mt. Visoke and adjoins an extensive *Hagenia-Hypericum* forest terrain. There are only an estimated 214 mountain gorillas (*Gorilla gorilla beringei*) remaining in all the world, and they reside within the six dormant Virunga Volcanoes—Mikeno, Karisimbi, Visoke, Sabinio, Gahinga, and Muhavura. Two of the Virungas remain active and are not frequented by gorillas. The Karisoke study area, encompassing 25 square kilometers, initially contained four main study groups totaling 55 gorillas and several less-known fringe groups (those whose ranges abutted or were adjacent to the home ranges of the main study groups). By the end of 1974 there had been a considerable fluctuation in the composition of the main study groups because of births, deaths, and transfers of females between groups during intergroup interactions (see tables 1 and 2). The purpose of this report is to summarize briefly demographical data prior to 1974 and to detail the data resulting from 1974's observations.

By December 1974, 20 known births had occurred within Karisoke's main study groups, 2 occurring that year. Of this total 50 percent had lived, 30 percent had disappeared and were assumed dead, 10 percent had died of natural causes, and 10 percent had died from infanticide. All infants that disappeared did so within their first 18 months and were assumed dead because, even at that age, a gorilla is nearly totally dependent upon its mother for both travel and maintenance, and could not survive without her. All of the "lost" infants were assumed to have been healthy. The two that died of natural causes were stillborns, one of a primiparous and one of a multiparous mother. The two killed by infanticide were victims of intergroup interactions that involved the transfers of their mothers out of the groups into which they had been born but only following their deaths. Intergroup interactions, an important means by which group composition may be changed, will be discussed below.

By the end of 1974 and over a period of $7\frac{1}{2}$ years, 20 births had increased the population of the four main study groups by only 10 individuals. During that same time span, 18 deaths had occurred, 4 of these in 1974; 50 percent died of natural causes; 39 percent of the deaths were attributed to unknown causes and/or disappearances, and 11 percent to infanticide. The 9 deaths from natural causes included 2 infants (stillborn), 1 young adult (tree fall), and 6 adults, 4 of whom were considered aged. Pneumonia was the culminating cause of death in 4 cases and hepatitis in 2. The 7 unknown causes or disappearances included only 1 adult, an elderly silverback, Amok, whose dung had been abnormal for several years prior to his ultimate disappearance in 1974. In addition, his behavior had become increasingly erratic, so when no further trail or nesting signs could be found in the range area he had occupied consistently since 1967, it was assumed that he had died rather than that he had taken up residence elsewhere. In the 5 years since his disappearance, there has been no indication that he might still be alive.

Two of the most thoroughly documented and beloved individuals among the study groups died in 1974: Rafiki of pneumonia and complications of old age, and Old Goat of hepatitis. Rafiki was the dominant silverback of Group 8 when they were first encountered in 1967, and even at that time he was considered an aged animal. He was assumed to have sired at least 2 of the males in his small group of 5 animals, and roughly 19 months before his death he sired an infant by a primiparous female Macho, obtained during an interaction with Group 4. The birth of that infant, Thor, was of particular interest in that Rafiki was estimated to have been about 60 years old at the time and had not produced any other offspring for at least seven years prior to this birth. His health began to decline slightly in mid 1968, but he retained absolute authority within his group and also when confronting other silverbacks during interactions. Six days before his death, when his illness made it impossible for him to travel normally, he separated from his group of 3 (silverback son Peanuts, female Macho and their 11-month-old daughter Thor) to remain within a 50-by-80-meter area. He never moved more than 50 meters in any one day, fed little, and rested frequently. His group continued to circle within 150 meters of him and moved to 30 meters of his body the day following his death. They left the area 5 days later.

Rafiki's death provided the first proof of the assumption that a gorilla group cannot survive without a dominant and experienced leader. One of the many consequences of his death was the infanticide of his offspring Thor by Uncle Bert 28 days following Rafiki's death and 160 days before Macho, Thor's mother, transferred to Uncle Bert. Group 8 was then reduced to one member, Peanuts, who was to wander for another year before finding only another male to travel with. Throughout that time Peanuts had numerous interactions with other groups in the hopes of obtaining females of his own in order to start a new group, but he lacked the necessary experience to challenge successfully more dominant silverbacks. This was especially apparent after he lost Macho to Uncle Bert and he spent 14 successive days hounding Group 4 in futile efforts to regain her. Macho, 9 months after joining the group, gave birth to her second infant, a male sired by Uncle Bert within the first month of her transfer. Had she remained with Peanuts, she would have undoubtedly lost some 2 years before again giving birth, as Peanuts was estimated to be only 12 years of age when Rafiki died, or roughly 2 years away from sexual maturity.

Old Goat, deceased in October 1974, always had been recognized as the dominant female of Group 4 since it was first encountered in 1967. She was an unusual female in that she was masculine in appearance (angularity of body, pronounced brow ridge, short body hair yet long, luxuriant arm hair) and behavior (as the group's "watchdog" she was usually the first to spot the observer and displayed with male-type chestbeats, struts, and vegetation whacks in the years before they became habituated). Between 1967 and 1974 she had only two parturitions, one nonviable. Old Goat was an exemplary mother, consistent in her affection and protectiveness toward her son Tiger, destined to become the group's next dominant silverback because of her rank. Her unexpected death was noteworthy in that she was the second female known to have died from hepatitis following an intergroup interaction. Unlike the first female, Old Goat showed no external signs of illness before her death except for several heavily mucoid-covered dung deposits. During the course of the interaction, a violent one resulting in the transfer of Macho from Peanuts to Group 4, Old Goat kept up with her group along its flight route of some 6 kilometers before seeking the protective shelter of a large *Hagenia* tree adjacent to the group's night-nesting site. When her body was finally found, there was no trail-sign evidence to indicate that the group had remained around her for, at the time of her death, it was still in the process of fleeing to Visoke's slopes in advance of Peanuts. Surprisingly, in view of his unusually strong maternal attachment, Tiger, then nearly 7 years old, showed no "withdrawal

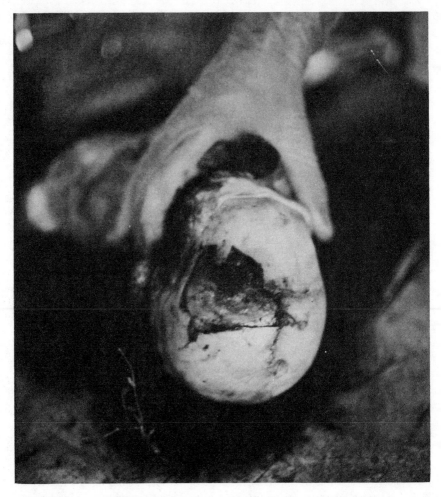

FIG. 1.   Typical infanticidal skull bite, inflicted on 11-month-old female Thor, of
Macho, by unrelated silverback Uncle Bert.

symptoms" following his mother's death. This was attributed to Tiger's concentration in supporting Uncle Bert and the blackback Digit with immature
male strutting and chestbeating displays toward Peanuts over a 2-week period. When Group 4 eventually resumed normal, uninterrupted ranging activities, Tiger then became engrossed in typical, vicarious sexual play with the
younger group members while Uncle Bert intensely copulated with the new
female, Macho. Subjectively, it appeared that Old Goat's death was responsible for a diminishment of intragroup cohesiveness, though that new aspect
might well have been due to the addition of Macho rather than the absence of

FIG. 2. Thor's mother, Macho, with second offspring, Kweli, born fourteen months after Thor's death and sired by the infanticidal male, Uncle Bert.

Old Goat's dominant personality. The individual most obviously affected by the matriarch's death was $9\frac{1}{2}$-year-old Digit. In the process of maturing as the second oldest male within the group, Digit increasingly shared the responsibility of "watchdog" with Old Goat. Her sudden absence left him alone to bring up the rear of the group when traveling, or alone in advance positions when most of the group was day-nesting. Despite his age and his assumed lack of blood ties with Old Goat, he consistently indicated, for about 8 weeks, a sense of deprivement, as shown by whining, morose facial expressions, re-

FIG. 3.   Dominant female Old Goat, of Group 4, carrying two-year-old son Tiger
dorsally.

duced feeding, and prolonged visual "searching" from treed positions toward
where her body lay, as yet undiscovered by observers.

Other than the obvious mechanisms of birth and death, the third means
by which group composition could be altered was by intergroup interactions;
61 were known to have occurred in 1974. An interaction is defined as any
communication between two distinct gorilla social units (either groups or
lone silverbacks), and there are three basic types: (1) auditory; (2) visual; (3)
physical.

An auditory intergroup interaction occurs when the vocalizations of one
social unit are heard by a second unit. The vocalizations need not have been

FIG. 4. The lone wanderer silverback, Nunkie, who came into the study area in November 1973 and acquired females from other groups to begin his own group.

purposely directed outside of the group but, if audible to another unit, they located the vocal group, thus constituting an auditory interaction. The most common example of the latter were intragroup outbreaks caused by friction within a group producing screams that could carry roughly 2 kilometers. The most common example of directed vocalizations were the hoot series, given with or without a terminating chestbeat, exchanged only between interacting silverbacks for identification purposes in communication over distance.

A visual interaction is one in which at least one member of two distinct social units is in sight of another beyond a distance of 15 feet. There is frequently a site-specificity to this type of interaction consisting of exposed ridges or slopes usually separated by ravines where silverback displays (chestbeats, struts and runs, vegetation whacking) are provided with a maximum visual setting.

A physical interaction occurs with either intermingling or approaches to within 15 feet between members of two distinct social units. Such encounters can include chasing, charging, biting, fighting, parallel displays, or mingled play and feeding between the individuals of two groups. Physical interactions

TABLE 1. Compositional Changes, 1974

CODE

— = Travel	B = Born	YA = Young adult stage (6-8 yrs.)	8T = Transfer from 8
L = Lone travel	D = Dead, died	A = Adult female (8 yrs. +)	T8 = Transfer to 8
{ = Mother and offspring	P = Poacher	TS = Transfer to Samson	4T = Transfer from 4
b = Birth	J = Juvenile stage (3-6 yrs.)	TN = Transfer to Nunkie	T4 = Transfer to 4

Stage and sex	Members	Jan.	Feb.	Mar.	Apr.	May	Jun.	Jul.	Aug.	Sep.	Oct.	Nov.	Dec.
GROUP 4													
Silverback	Uncle Bert	—	—	—	—	—	—	—	—	—	—	—	—
Blackback	Digit	—	—	—	—	—	—	—	—	—	—	—	—
Adult female	Flossie	—	—	—	—	—	—	—	b	—	—	—	—
Juvenile female (B Aug. 1971)	Cleo	—	—	—	—	—	—	—	J	—	—	—	—
Infant male (B Aug. 1974)	Titus								B				
Adult female (D Oct. 28)	Old Goat	—	—	—	—	—	—	—	—	—	D	—	—
Young adult male (B Nov. 1967)	Tiger	—	—	—	—	—	—	—	—	—	—	—	—
Young adult female (B Mar. 1969)	Simba II	—	—	—	—	YA	—	—	—	—	—	—	—
Adult female	Papoose						TN	TS	TN				
Adult female	Petula						TN	TS	TN				
Juvenile female (B Aug. 1970)	Augustus	—	—	—	—	—	—	—	—	—			
Adult female	Macho										8T		—

GROUP 5

Silverback	Beethoven	—	—	—	—	—	—	—	—	—	—	—	—
Blackback	Icarus	—	—	—	—	—	—	—	—	—	—	—	—
Adult female	Effie	—	—	—	—	—	—	—	—	—	—	—	—
Young adult female (B Dec. 1968)	Puck	—	—	—	—	—	—	—	—	—	—	—	YA
Infant female (B May 1972)	Tuck	—	—	—	—	—	—	—	—	—	—	—	—
Adult female	Marchessa	—	—	—	—	—	—	—	—	—	—	—	—
Adult female	Pantsy	—	—	A	—	—	—	—	—	—	—	—	—
Juvenile male (B Jan. 1971)	Ziz	J	—	—	—	—	—	—	—	—	—	—	—
Adult female	Liza	—	—	—	—	—	—	—	—	b	—	—	—
Juvenile female (B Jul. 1970)	Quince	—	—	—	—	—	—	—	—	—	—	—	—
Infant male (B Aug. 1974)	Pablo									B	—	—	—

GROUP 8

Silverback	Rafiki	—	—	D	—	—	—	—	—	—	—	—	—
Silverback	Peanuts	P	—	—	—	—	—	—	—	—	—	—	—
Adult female	Maisie	T⁴	—	—	—	4T	—	—	—	—	—	—	TS
Adult female	Macho	—	—	—	D	—	—	—	—	—	—	—	T⁴
Infant female (B Jun. 1973)	Thor	—	—	—	D	—	—	—	—	—	—	—	—

TABLE 2. Compositional Changes, Group 4, December 1977 through October 1978

CODE

— = Travel	(P) = Poacher	(BM) = Beestsme	T (K) = Karisimbi group
D = Dead	B = Born	T (N) = Nunkie's group	{ = Mother and offspring

Stage and sex	Members	Dec.	Jan.	Feb.	Mar.	Apr.	May	Jun.	Jul.	Aug.	Sep.	Oct.
Silverback male	Uncle Bert	—	—	—	—	—	—	—	D (P) 24th			
Silverback male	Digit	D (P) 31st										
Adult female	Flossie	—	—	—	—	—	—	—	—	T (N) 21st	T (K) 8th	—
Young adult female (B Aug. 1971)	Cleo	—	—	—	—	—	—	—	—	T (N) 21st	T (K) 8th	—
Juvenile male	Titus	—	—	—	—	—	—	—	—	—	—	—
Infant female (B Jun. 1978)	Frito						B 22nd		D (BM) 14th	—		
Adult female	Simba	—	—	—	—	—	—	—	—	—	—	—
Infant male (B Apr. 1978)	Mwelu[1]	—	—	—	B 6th	—	—	—	—	—	—	—
Adult female	Macho	—	—	—	—	—	—	—	D (P) 24th			
Juvenile male (B Jul. 1975)	Kweli	—	—	—	—	—	—	—	—	—	—	D (P) 26th
Blackback male	Tiger	—	—	—	—	—	—	—	—	—	—	—
Blackback male	Augustus	—	—	—	—	—	—	—	—	T (N) 21st	—	—
Silverback	Beetsme[2]	—	—	—	—	—	—	—	—	—	—	—

1 = Digit's only offspring   2 = Transferred to Group 4 Jan. 1976

can be calm, excitable, or violent. In 1974 there were 3 calm physical interactions resulting in no transfers, 4 excitable ones resulting in 4 transfers, and 4 violent physical interactions resulting in 2 transfers and 1 infanticide.

The infanticide of Thor was predictable, for without the protection of Rafiki, Macho automatically would be sought for breeding by the strongest surviving male, in this case Uncle Bert. In order to return the female to cyclicity, it is necessary that the infant be killed. The day before Thor's death a mutual approach was made between the two groups, and a calm visual type of interaction followed. Macho then mingled with Group 4, constituting a calm physical interaction, though Peanuts maintained a discreet distance. The following day, after some 5 hours of calm, Uncle Bert rapidly approached Macho, who retreated, carrying her infant ventrally. He was followed by several members of Group 4, causing Macho to retreat toward Peanuts even more hastily. A small pig-grunting outbreak was followed by a 75-second screaming outbreak accompanied by rapid movement partially obscured by foliage. At the end of the outbreak a small scream was heard from Thor and Peanuts came running belatedly toward Macho but retreated when chased by Group 4 members. An hour after the interaction Macho returned to Peanuts dragging Thor's body behind her. Both groups then began to feed with roughly 100 meters separating them initially. While Macho fed she alternately carried the body or placed it on the ground beside her before leaving it 10 meters from her night-nest site. For the next 10 days both groups had calm physical, visual, and auditory interactions unlike the violent physical interaction 160 days later when Uncle Bert took Macho for breeding purposes. The extended length of time that Macho remained with Peanuts following the death of her infant was the only unusual aspect to this otherwise typical infanticide.

The 6 transfers known to have occurred in 1974 involved only 3 other females in addition to Macho (Maisie, Petula, and Papoose) and 3 other silverbacks in addition to Uncle Bert and Peanuts (Samson, Rafiki, and Nunkie). All involved compositional changes in Group 4. The adult female Maisie made a total of 5 transfers, some of them very brief, in 1974. She moved from Group 8 to 4 (her original home group), to Samson (a lone silverback formerly of Group 8 and considered Rafiki's son), back to Group 4, to Peanuts and Macho, then again to Samson. When with Group 4 she never appeared to be an integral group member as, with the exception of Macho, she seemed resented by other females. By transfering to Samson, Maisie became his first acquired female. Since dominance order depends upon acquisition order among females, she will ultimately become the dominant female in his group. Unfortunately, her last transfer to Samson took her out of the main study area. The transfers of Petula and Papoose, both originally of Group 4, provided interesting data on the formation of a group. In June 1974 both were taken from Group 4 by a very mature lone silverback, Nunkie, who had only been within the study area for 20 months. During that time he was both known and suspected of having taken females from other groups, but none were with him when he took Petula and Papoose. His lone status was an enigma because of his age and obvious experience. Also unusual was the fact that he eventually succeeded in securing a range in terrain over which he had certainly never traveled during the previous 5 years, at least, and despite the presence of long-established resident groups. Shortly after acquiring Petula and Papoose, Nunkie briefly lost both to Samson before again regaining them permanently. This brought up the as-yet-unanswered question concerning the factors involved in the choice by a female of one male over another. It was felt that the less experienced male will not risk serious injury to hold a female he is bound to lose violently, and that the optimal breeding opportunities are provided by the more experienced silverback. In the above case, Nunkie was assumed the most experienced of the three silverbacks involved. With the start of what was going to grow into a successful group, Nunkie led his 2 females into more discreet terrain less frequented by other gorillas and sought no further interactions for over another year.

Petula's transfer marked the first time a mother with a young juvenile offspring (Augustus, 3 years and 10 months) had been involved in a transfer. When in Group 4 during 1974 Petula was known to have copulated with Uncle Bert 20 times. It is possible that lactation inhibits fertility. Petula was occasionally nursing Augustus. Her move to Nunkie's group terminated this and she produced an infant sired by him within one year. Suggestions of increased breeding success were not of similar importance in Papoose's case, as she had only just attained adulthood (8 years) and was not sexually mature. A possible reason for her transfer might have been related to her very close and long-term relationship with Petula having been more binding than those existing between her and other Group 4 members. A similar situation might have applied in the female-female association between Maisie and Macho when, in 1971, both left Group 4 together to transfer to Group 8 for the first time.

As graphically illustrated by Nunkie, a silverback in quest of females will trespass into the home ranges and core areas of other groups in order to obtain them. Home ranges (Burt, 1943) are those areas where animals sleep, travel, and feed. Within home ranges, there are certain core areas (Kaufmann, 1962) that are used extensively, while more peripheral areas may be visited only occasionally, often in connection with seasonal availability of food, i.e., bamboo zones. Home ranges may overlap (Fossey, 1974; Fossey and Harcourt, 1977),

FIG. 5.   Jay Matternes' charcoal drawing epitomizes the essence of the protection of
the silverback male, the maternal instincts of the female and the dependence of a
gorilla infant upon its parents.

and it is frequently in the overlap zones that interactions tend to occur more
often. Intergroup interactions had a strong bearing on both the size and the
direction of expansion of a group's range. Social units could move as far as 7
kilometers within 24 hours depending upon whether the individuals involved
were seeking or avoiding interaction probability. It was found that the study
groups were more inclined to withdraw with greater rapidity from interactions when farther away from their core areas and to behave more antagonisti-
cally in areas with which they were more familiar. Knowledge of different
areas was enhanced by yearly range changes that usually also involved shifts in
core areas. For example, in 1974 Group 4 dropped 23 percent of the squares
(.25-kilometer-sided sections used in range division) where interactions had
occurred in 1973 and 41 percent of their 1974 range consisted of new terrain,

though they retained the same core area. Simultaneously 56 percent of Group 5's 1974 range consisted of new terrain, and they shifted their core area by 1.25 kilometers between the two years. Between 1974 and 1975 the same trend continued for both groups, particularly as Group 4 acquired new range at a farther distance from the terrain being settled by Nunkie.

Most of this report deals with behavioral aspects and compositional fluctuations within Group 4 because of their considerable interactions with other groups. The same year was a relatively quiet one for Group 5 in that the group composition was altered by only 1 birth and was not affected by any of their 4 known intergroup interactions. Such periods of stability occur among all study groups but are nonetheless important in that there is a continuous development in the relationships between individuals brought about by such daily processes as maintenance interactions involving both affinitive or antagonistic behavior, maturation of young, and sexual cycling of females. It is such inevitable regulatory processes that help to mold the nature of a group's stability. Gorilla social organization, as clearly shown by this year's data, consists of the individual group or social unit as a part of a series of similar units, all of which interact, causing a "domino effect" over both space and time.

During 1974 the research was greatly facilitated by the following research assistants and students: A. H. Harcourt, Miss Kelly Stewart, Tim Caro, and Richard Rombach. Mr. Harcourt and Miss Stewart both worked on their Ph.D. projects—social relationships and social development, respectively—and in addition they worked toward maintaining general long-term records on individuals of the study area. Mr. Caro accomplished a 13-week study describing the size and differential use of the respective home ranges of two lone silverbacks. Considerable differences were found between the two males in the amount and the manner in which the animals utilized their core areas, and it was also found that neither traveled far outside his home-group range. Caro felt that ranging behavior was most likely related to food dispersion and that lone males did not travel farther nor more rapidly than groups. This contrasts with Schaller's (1963) and my own opinion that the ranging behavior of lone males relies more on opportunities to acquire females than food related motivations. Mr. Rombach did a nest-building study, essentially to determine what percentage of night nests were constructed from food-vegetation species. Of 598 nests examined, 585 were built of nonfood species. Of 196 built near a substantial number of food species, 185 were built of nonfood species. The cause of such selectivity was probably because food plants within the study area were unsuitable nest material. However, in Rio Muni, where food plants were suitable nest material, Jones and Sabater Pi (1971) found them extensively used.

Mr. Jay Matternes visited Karisoke Research Centre in 1974 and contributed invaluable information in analysis of a number of skeletal specimens, including Rafiki, Old Goat, and Thor, that were later sent to the Smithsonian. Mr. Matternes also drew some outstanding sketches and noseprint drawings of better-known gorillas and one of these was presented to the President of Rwanda, Juvenal Habyarimana, at a special showing of the National Geographic Society's 1973 lecture film, *The Mountain Gorillas.*

REFERENCES

Burt, W. H.
    1943.   Territorial and home range concepts as applied to mammals. Journ. Mammal., vol. 24, pp. 346-352.
Caro, T. M.
    1976.   Observations on the ranging behaviour and daily activity of lone silverback mountain gorillas (*Gorilla gorilla beringei*). Anim. Behav., vol. 24, pp. 889-897.
Fossey, D.
    1970.   Making friends with mountain gorillas. Nat. Geogr., vol. 137, pp. 48-68, illus.
    1971.   More years with mountain gorillas. Nat. Geogr., vol. 140, pp. 574-585, illus.
    1972a.   Living with mountain gorillas. Pp. 208-229 in "The Marvels of Animal Behavior." Nat. Geogr. Soc., Washington.
    1972b.   Vocalizations of the mountain gorilla (*Gorilla gorilla beringei*). Anim. Behav., vol. 20, pp. 36-53.
    1974.   Observations on the home range of one group of mountain gorillas (*Gorilla gorilla beringei*). Anim. Behav., vol. 22, pp. 568-581.
    1976.   The behaviour of the mountain gorilla. Ph.D. Thesis, University of Cambridge.
    1978.   Development of the mountain gorilla (*Gorilla gorilla beringei*) through the first thirty-six months. Pp. 138-184 *in* "The Behavior of Great Apes," D. A. Hamburg and R. McCown, eds. Addison Wesley, Menlo Park.
Fossey, D., and Harcourt, A. H.
    1977.   Feeding ecology of free-ranging mountain gorilla (*Gorilla gorilla beringei*). Pp. 415-447 *in* "Primate Ecology: Studies of Feeding and Ranging Behaviour in Lemurs, Monkeys and Apes," T. H. Clutton-Brock, ed. Academic Press, London, New York.
Harcourt, A. H., Stewart, K. J., and Fossey, D.
    1976.   Male emigration and female transfer in wild mountain gorilla. Nature, vol. 263, pp. 226-227. London.
Jones, C., and Sabater Pi, J.
    1971.   Comparative ecology of *Gorilla gorilla* (Savage and Wyman) and *Pan troglodytes* (Blumanbach) in Rio Muni, West Africa. Bibl. Primat., vol. 13, 1-96 pp., illus.

KAUFMANN, J. H.
  1962.   Ecology and social behavior of the coati, *Nasua narica,* on Barro Colorado
           Island, Panama.   Univ. Calif. Publ. in Zoology, vol. 60, pp. 95-222.
SCHALLER, G. B.
  1963.   The mountain gorilla: ecology and behavior.   University of Chicago
           Press, Chicago and London.

DIAN FOSSEY

Systematic Study of the Hesperiidae of Mexico

Principal Investigator: Hugh Avery Freeman, Hillcrest High School, Dallas, Texas.

Grant Nos. 1211,   For a distributional study of the hesperiid butterflies
1323, 1455.   (Lepidoptera) of Mexico.

I have been conducting scientific research on the American Hesperiidae since 1930. In 1965 I began careful collecting and study of the Hesperiidae of Mexico. Previous recorded evidence at that time listed 450 known species of Hesperiidae for Mexico. To date I have either collected or examined specimens that have increased that number to 688. The main purpose in conducting this research was to prepare a publication that would give complete data on the taxonomy, synonymy, and distribution of all the known species of Hesperiidae found to occur in Mexico. When this study is completed such a publication will be prepared.

Research conducted in Mexico in 1973-74, under grants 1211 and 1323, consisted of extensive collecting over various areas of Mexico, chiefly in the states of San Luis Potosí, Veracruz, and Chiapas, together with the examination of specimens from Yucatán, Quintana Roo, Tabasco, and Oaxaca received from other collectors. Scientific data were obtained on approximately 500 species, resulting in the discovery of 15 new species and 39 new records for Mexico. In order to make this study as complete as possible I made trips to Washington, D. C., to examine all the tropical American Hesperiidae in the National Museum of Natural History, to New York to spend some time in checking all the Mexican Hesperiidae in the American Museum of Natural History, and to other museums in the United States. In addition, complete data were obtained on all Mexican Hesperiidae from the British Museum. Thus the research covered the main collections of American Hesperiidae in the world. At present my collection of Mexican Hesperiidae is the most complete in existence.

Collecting methods consisted of first locating favorable areas in Mexico and then spending considerable time in obtaining as many specimens as possible during the summer months. Each specimen collected was placed in a triangular envelope with complete data placed on it. During the winter months these specimens were relaxed and mounted. When dry they were then classified and placed in my collection. When new species or records were found, various articles were written for publication describing the new species and listing the new records.

As a result of research in 1975, under grant 1455, nine more new species were discovered and seven more new records of hesperiids were found among specimens collected in the states of Veracruz and Oaxaca. These are treated in the articles cited in the References (Freeman, 1979 a and b).

Specimens are still being mounted and placed in my collection that were obtained during 1974 and 1975 to give more information on the distribution of the various species in Mexico. At the present time my records show over 700 species to be found in that country. In the near future sufficient information will have been obtained to prepare the finished publication on all of the Hesperiidae from Mexico.

REFERENCES

FREEMAN, HUGH AVERY
  1975. A new species of *Euphyes* Scudder from Texas. (Hesperiidae). Journ. Lepid. Soc., vol. 29, no. 4, pp. 227-229.
  1976. New Hesperiidae records for Mexico. Journ. Lepid. Soc., vol. 30, no. 1, pp. 62-67.
  1977. Six new species of Hesperiidae from Mexico. Journ. Lepid. Soc., vol. 31, no. 2, pp. 89-99.
  1979a. A review of the Mexican *Polythrix* Watson. Journ. Lepid. Soc., vol. 33, no. 2, pp. 124-128.
  1979b. Nine new species and seven new records of Mexican Hesperiidae. Bull. of the Allyn Mus., no. 52 (July 20, 1979), pp. 1-3, 29 figs.

HUGH AVERY FREEMAN

The Punic and Sister Ships, Sicily

Principal Investigator: Honor E. Frost, London, England.

Grant No. 1218:   In support of an excavation of a 3d-century, B.C., Punic ship off Marsala, Sicily.

The hitherto unique discovery of a warship of the Classical period resulted from a survey, begun in 1970, of a group of ancient wrecks lying off Isola Lunga to the north of Marsala. This modern town is built over the ruins of Lilybaeum, which, when it fell to the Romans after a long siege, brought the first Punic War to an end in 241 B.C. The wreck that became known as the "Punic Ship" was found in 1971; its stern and about one-third of its port side were in an exceptionally good state of preservation, but its prow was missing. Excavation continued for 4 years (from 1973 to 1977, with the help of the National Geographic Society). At the end of the final season, a sounding of a contiguous wreck known as the "Sister Ship" produced the missing structural information by revealing a contemporaneous prow complete with its ram (see fig. 1).

The Punic identity of both hulls is attested by the letters of the Phoenician alphabet that they bore. The study by William Johnstone (Department of Hebrew and Semitic Languages, Aberdeen University) of these signs and other carpenters' marks painted or scratched onto the hull of the Punic Ship has given: (*a*) a clearer understanding of the hitherto obscure technique of ancient "shell construction"; (*b*) an explanation of the seemingly incredible speed with which such warships had been copied by the Romans (as recorded by Polybius and Pliny); and (*c*) two philological "firsts," one of them concerning "the use of the Biblical Hebrew *wāwīm* in the light of new Phoenician evidence,"[1] which makes a small contribution to Scriptural interpretation.

That both wrecks represent warships is attested in the case of the Sister Ship by its ram and in the case of the Punic Ship by the long narrow shape of its hull, as well as by a mass of circumstantial evidence such as the absence of cargo and the presence of ballast stones. The lines of the Punic Ship have been established by calculation as well as by architectural deductions based on the

---

[1] William Johnstone, "Biblical Hebrew *Wāwīm* in the light of New Phoenician Evidence," Palestine Exploration Quarterly (London), 1977, pp. 96-105; "Cursive Phoenician and the Archaic Greek Alphabet," Kadmos (Berlin), vol. 12, no. 2, pp. 151-166; also chapter 12 of Frost et al., 1981 (see References).

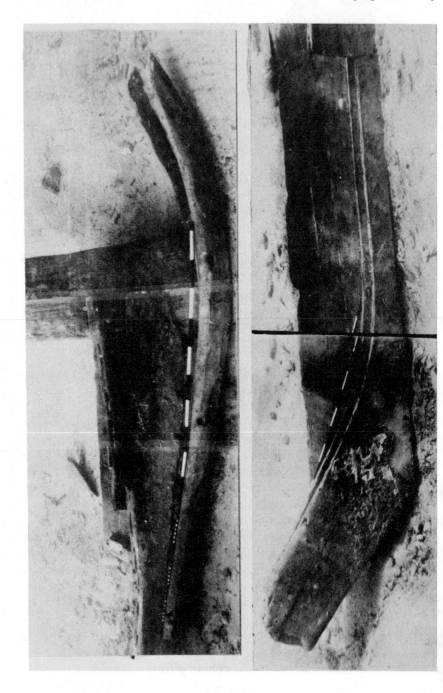

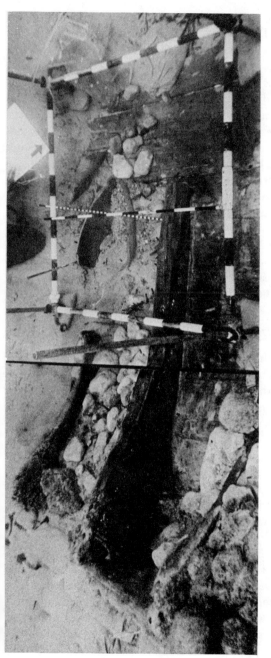

FIG. 1. Composite photographs of the Punic Ship showing (top) the prow, with ram structure of the "Sister Ship," on which was discovered (under the middle white division of the scale) a painted Phoenicio-Punic *waw;* (middle) the stern of the Punic Ship; and (bottom) a midship section. (All scales are in decimeters.)

excavation records of the wood. The work was carried out by three specialists working independently: Paul Adam, Austin Farrar, and Frank Howard. Calculation was possible because, very exceptionally, part of the stern had survived; without one of a ship's extremities it is impossible to project the shape of the hull with any degree of certainty (Adam, 1977).

After the end of the fieldwork, in 1974, research continued on every aspect of the ship and its contents. A mass of laboratory identifications has been carried out on the woods used in construction as well as the dunnage and other plant material, the ballast stones, metals, pottery, etc. Being in shallow water near the shore, the wreck had been salvaged, probably shortly after sinking, so that no valuables such as armaments had remained on board. The crew's crockery and their food (including butcher-trimmed meat bones, nuts, and two baskets of plant stalks, probably the hemp *Cannabis sativa*), together with all kinds of cordage and even a little brush for keeping things shipshape, had, however, remained untouched. They help to build up a vivid picture of life on board an oared fighting ship and indicate a high protein diet that contrasts with the eating habits on board contemporary merchantmen (to judge from the many known wrecks of these ships that have been investigated by divers).

Structural Characteristics

It is evident from both the carpenter's marks and the timbers themselves that this hull had been assembled from standardized parts. As soon as the keel had been laid, for instance, the placing of the internal cross timbers had been set out in an alphabetic sequence along its port face. Such a degree of pre-planning explains how the Romans (who at that period were not skilled shipbuilders) were able to mass-produce copies of the Carthaginian ships that they captured. The latter were, of course, highly superior since they embodied the accumulated skills of the Phoenician maritime tradition.

Both the relatively small size of the Punic Ship (its length is estimated at some 34 meters and its width 4.8 meters) and the appearance of the Sister Ship's ram evoke a liburnian with only one row of oars, rather than a trireme or quinquereme. Liburnians, a light, fast class of ship that originated among the Dalmatian pirates, had been introduced into the Phoenician, Greek, and Roman navies. Like most oared fighting ships, they could be sailed when the occasion demanded; it is therefore surprising that on the Punic Ship there was no trace of either a mast-step or any of the ubiquitous lead brailing-rings from sails that litter most wrecks. The Punic Ship may never have been rigged, since other evidence suggests that she was very new when she sank.

Quite the most surprising feature of this hull is, however, its spray deflectors. On the smooth, carvel-built shell, they have been achieved by sculpting a bevel onto the lower edges of the strakes spanning the waterline. This sophisticated device for keeping decks dry is still built onto fast-sailing ships, but it has never been found on any known wreck of an ancient merchantman. Its utility on a warship, where men with iron weapons lined the decks, is, however, apparent.

Dating

The dating of this wreck to the mid-3d century B.C. rests on four sets of evidence: Carbon-14 determinations, paleography, the possible historical context, and, finally, the pottery. Being, however, of a type that is not securely dated by archeological evidence on land, the pottery may eventually be dated by the other evidence from this wreck. The corrected calendar age of 235 ± 65 B.C. is an overall mean based on four carbon-14 tests on plant material.[2] The paleography of the alphabetic signs indicates a date between 300 and 250 B.C. The geographical position of the surrounding wrecks and the fact that, as a group, they appear to have been carrying ballast rather than cargo suggest that they sank as the result of a naval battle, the most likely being the Battle of the Egadi Islands in 241 B.C. at the end of the First Punic War.

Conservation and Reconstruction

The wood of the Punic Ship was conserved in treatment tanks in an expressly constructed laboratory at Marsala. The 5 tons of synthetic wax (polyethylene glycol) used for this purpose were purchased through the National Geographic Society's grant, from the stock left over after the conservation of the ancient merchantman at Kyrenia in Cyprus (see Katzev, 1970). Prof. Michael Katzev had been the first to carry a comparable excavation to its logical conclusion; he kindly came from Cyprus to give us the benefit of his experience in ship conservation; thus the 4th-century Greek merchantman and this Punic warship are linked through both sponsorship and technical collaboration.

At the time of writing (September 1978), the reconstruction (see fig. 2) of the remains of the Punic warship has virtually been completed in a beautiful building at Marsala. Standing on the extremity of Capo Boeo, the site of ancient Lilybaeum, this 19th-century wine establishment was acquired as a ship

---

[2] For full details see Frost et al. (1981) in References.

FIG. 2.   Reconstruction of the Punic Ship was largely accomplished by Vito Bonanno under the direction of the author.

museum by the Commune of Marsala in response to public pressure. Thus, the ancient warship will remain on the territory which it once defended and within sight of the battleground where it sank.

REFERENCES

ADAM, PAUL
    1977.   An attempted reconstruction of the Marsala Punic Ship.   Mariner's Mirror, vol. 63, no. 2, p. 35.
FROST, HONOR E.
    1972-1977.   Annual reports on the excavation have appeared as follows:
        Int. Journ. Nautical Archaeol., vol. 1, pp. 113-117, 1972; vol. 2, no. 1, pp. 33-49, 1973; vol. 3, no. 1, pp. 35-54, 1974; vol. 4, no. 1, pp. 150-153, 1975; vol. 4, no. 2, pp. 23-25, 1975.
        Mariner's Mirror, vol. 58, no. 3, pp. 348-349, 1972; vol. 60, no. 3, pp. 265-266, 1974; vol. 61, no. 1, pp. 23-25, 1975; vol. 63, no. 2, pp. 33-37, 1977.
        Notizie degli scavi.   Accad. Naz. Lincei Roma, vol. 36, pp. 651-673, 1977.

FROST, HONOR E., and others
1981.   The Punic Ship: Final excavation report, supplement to vol. xxx (1976), Notizie deglie Scavi.   Accademia Nazionale dei Lincei, Rome.
KATZEV, MICHAEL
1970.   Resurrecting the oldest known Greek ship.   Nat. Geogr. Mag., vol. 137, no. 6, pp. 841-857, illus.

HONOR E. FROST

Flora of the Bahamas, Turks, and Caicos Islands

Principal Investigator: William T. Gillis, Departments of Natural Sciences, Botany, and Plant Pathology, Michigan State University, East Lansing (formerly with Arnold Arboretum, Harvard University).

Grant No. 1257: For study of the flora of the Bahamas, Turks, and Caicos Islands.

Work on the subject of this grant continued from the time it became effective in October 1973 until the death of Dr. Gillis on June 20, 1979. The purpose of the research was to produce (1) a field guide to the flora of the Bahamas, (2) a complete flora of the islands, (3) a description of the vegetation of the islands, and (4) a compendium of local names of plants and plant uses by the inhabitants. The most recent flora of the Bahamas was published in 1920 by Britton and Millspaugh. It is estimated that 40 percent of the names for vascular plants in that flora are obsolete. The flora may also include 100-125 additional species not recognized by Britton and Millspaugh.

The project involved taxonomic research, exploration, and interaction with the local inhabitants. Two field trips to the Bahamas were specifically supported by this grant, but several additional subsequent trips were also made.

Because of the death of Dr. Gillis, this project will not be completed. However, considerable progress was made and a number of publications were produced. Between 1973 and 1977 Gillis and his collaborators, particularly George R. Proctor of the Science Museum, Institute of Jamaica, and Richard A. Howard of the Arnold Arboretum, Harvard University, published 21 papers on plants and natural history of the Bahamas. Of particular significance is the solution of many nomenclatural problems. On the basis of studies of specimens in U. S. and European herbaria, comparisons of living plant populations in the field, and critical examinations of type specimens, 6 papers were published concerning the nomenclature of Bahamian plants. Additionally, papers on the taxonomy of 5 plant groups and a 123-page bibliography of natural history of the Bahama Islands were published. Many herbarium specimens (probably more than 2,000) resulted from the field expeditions, and these have been deposited at several institutions, especially Harvard University, the Institute of Jamaica, the Field Museum, Chicago, and Michigan State University. Detailed line drawings for many specimens were prepared by a botanical artist.

REFERENCES

GILLIS, WILLIAM T.
1974.   Name changes for the seed plants in the Bahama flora.   Rhodora, vol. 76, pp. 67-138.
1974.   Phantoms in the flora of the Bahamas.   Phytologia, vol. 29, pp. 154-166.
1974.   The confused *Spermacoce*.   Phytologia, vol. 29, pp. 185-187.
1975.   Bahama Polygalaceae and their Greater Antillean affinities—a preliminary treatment.   Phytologia, vol. 32, pp. 35-44.
1976.   *Agave* in the Bahama Islands.   Phytologia, vol. 33, pp. 78-81.
1976.   The mistletoes of the Bahamas.   Phytologia. vol. 33, pp. 361-368.
1976.   Flora and vegetation of Cay Sal.   Bahamas Naturalist, vol. 2, pp. 36-41.
1977.   Additions and corrections to the Bahama flora—III.   Phytologia, vol. 35, pp. 79-100.
1977.   The royal palm of Little Inagua.   Explorers Journal, March 1977, pp. 12-13.
1977.   Unique setting of *Roystonea* in the Bahamas.   Principles, vol. 21, pp. 109-113.
1977.   Chapter 3, Biogeography and Vegetation. Pp. 13-15 *in* "Land Resources of the Bahamas: A summary (Land Resource Study 27)," by Little, B. G.; Buckley, D. K.; Cont, R.; Henry, P.W.T.; Jefferies, A.; Mather, J. D.; Stark, J.; and Young, R. N.   Land Resources Div., Ministry of Overseas Devt., Tolworth Tower, Surbiton, Surrey, England.
1977.   Remarks on the botany and statistics of the Bahama Islands.   Atoll Research Bull., vol. 219, pp. 12-16.
GILLIS, WILLIAM T.; BYRNE, ROGER; and HARRISON, WYMAN
1975.   Bibliography of natural history of the Bahama Islands.   Atoll Research Bull., vol. 191, pp. 1-123.
GILLIS, WILLIAM T.; HOWARD, RICHARD A.; and PROCTOR, GEORGE R.
1973.   Additions to the Bahama flora since Britton and Millspaugh—I.   Rhodora, vol. 75, pp. 411-425.
GILLIS, WILLIAM T., and PROCTOR, GEORGE R.
1974.   *Caesalpinia*, subgenus *Guilandina* in the Bahamas.   Journ. Arnold Arbor., vol. 55, pp. 425-430.
1975.   Additions and corrections to the Bahama flora—II.   Sida, vol. 6, pp. 52-62.
1975.   Bark characteristics of some Bahama trees and shrubs.   Phytologia, vol. 32, pp. 201-213.
GILLIS, WILLIAM T.; PROCTOR, GEORGE R.; and AVERY, GEORGE N.
1975.   Indigenous royal palms in the Bahamas.   Principles, vol. 19, pp. 104-105.

GILLIS, WILLIAM T., and STEARN, WILLIAM T.
  1974.   Typification of the names of the species of *Leucaena* and *Lysiloma* in the Bahamas.   Taxon., vol. 23, pp. 185-191.
GILLIS, WILLIAM T., and WARD, DANIEL B.
  1975.   The *Sisyrinchium* of the Bahamas.   Phytologia, vol. 31, pp. 241-245.
MEARS, JAMES A., and GILLIS, WILLIAM T.
  1977.   Gomphrenoideae (Amaranthaceae) of the Bahama Islands.   Journ. Arnold Arbor., vol. 58, pp. 60-66.

JOHN H. BEAMAN

Botanical Exploration in Madagascar

Principal Investigators: Peter Goldblatt, Missouri Botanical Garden, St. Louis, Missouri.

Grant No. 1259:   For botanical exploration and plant collecting in Madagascar.

The island of Madagascar, which lies off the southeast coast of Africa, has a very rich flora comprised of some 6,000 species, of which 85 percent are believed to be endemic, occurring nowhere else on earth. Madagascar has been isolated from the continent of Africa for a considerable time, probably since the Cretaceous, and thus its flora has evolved since that time in relative isolation. Madagascar lies in the tropics, but as it is such a large island a variety of climatic conditions occurs there. These range from rain forest in the north to semidesert in the southwest. As in most other tropical areas of the world, the native forests and other unique plant associations are being very rapidly destroyed, while the island's rich and interesting flora is relatively poorly known to science and seriously undercollected. It is thus likely that not only will many species be lost—some without ever having been collected or recorded by man—but also whole ecosystems are being destroyed with the loss not only of unique plants but of animals as well.

The high level of endemism found in the Madagascar flora is characteristic of many islands. This is because species evolve in situations protected from competition from larger mainland floras while at the same time many ancient and primitive forms are protected by this very isolation. The Madagascar flora is of particular botanical interest, as the island has remained under relatively equable climatic conditions since its separation from Africa, while Africa itself has been subjected to several very violent climate changes. This resulted, in Africa, in massive extinctions of species, especially in tropical rain forests that were most sensitive to climatic deterioration. During this time many primitive and interesting plants remained protected and still survive on Madagascar to this day, giving an indication of what the flora of Africa was like many millions of years ago.

This expedition was designed to collect as large a sample of Madagascar flora as possible to preserve in United States herbaria. Collections of Madagascar flora are mainly in European herbaria, notably at Paris and in Kew in England. Few duplicates of these important collections exist in the United

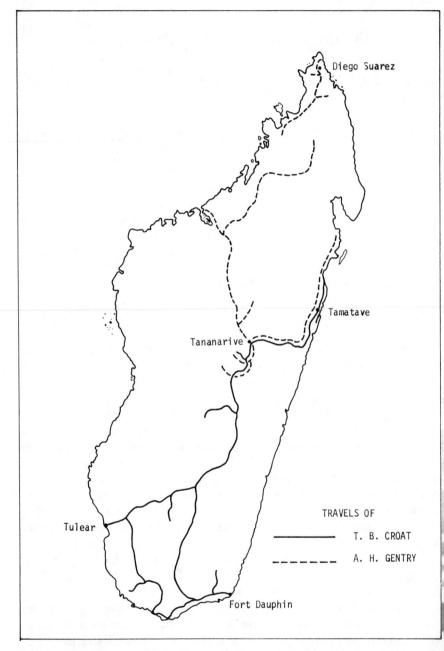

FIG. 1.   Travel routes of Drs. Croat and Gentry during botanical exploration of
Madagascar, 1974-1975.

States. The expedition thus aimed to collect as much of the rapidly vanishing flora as possible and also to establish and maintain collections in the United States for scientific study.

Owing to unforeseen last-minute circumstances, I as expedition leader was unable to work in Madagascar, but my colleagues Dr. Alwyn H. Gentry and Dr. Thomas B. Croat, both botanists at Missouri Botanical Garden, made separate trips to the island at different times of year and also visited different parts of Madagascar. Dr. Gentry's trip took place during May and June 1974 and covered parts of the central, north, and west of Madagascar, including the previously uncollected Tsaratana Massif (see map). Dr. Croat visited Madagascar in January and February 1975, traveling mainly in the center, south, and southwest. Both expeditions were successful from the botanical point of view, and approximately 5,000 specimens of the flora were collected. These collections, including many duplicates, represent a very substantial sample of the Madagascar flora of some 6,000 species. The primary aim of the project, to assemble in North America a collection of the plant species of the Madagascar region, was thus satisfactorily achieved.

The collection of Madagascar plants at Missouri Botanical Garden is now one of the more representative in the world and certainly the finest in North America. Collections of the unique flora are, in consequence of the National Geographic Society grant, readily available to North American scientists wishing to study the plants of Madagascar and to compare them with floras of other parts of the world.

A duplicate set of the collections has been deposited at Tsimboraza Herbarium, Madagascar, and a second set at the Laboratoire de Phanérogamie, Musée National d'Histoire Naturelle in Paris, the world center for the study of the flora of Madagascar. This latter collection is being sent to Paris in exchange partly for further specimens of Madagascar plants and also in return for names of some of the plants collected by Missouri Botanical Garden botanists. Remaining duplicates will be exchanged with botanical institutions with major interests in Madagascar as well as in African floras.

The discovery of several species new to science as well as a number of very rare species in more remote and inaccessible areas represents an immediate scientific contribution to the knowledge of Madagascar flora. In addition, to date one scientific paper by Dr. Gentry (1975) has been published as a result of his studies in Madagascar.

As a postscript I should like to record that all foreign scientific activities are becoming increasingly difficult in Madagascar, and authorities there have all but terminated research projects. It was only with special assistance from the U. S. Embassy that Dr. Croat's work was made possible. Future scientific studies in Madagascar will certainly encounter increasing obstacles and may not be feasible for some years. Exceptions as in Dr. Croat's case are always, of course, possible, but undertakings in Madagascar should be planned most carefully and only with full cooperation of Madagascar Government authorities.

REFERENCES

GENTRY, ALWYN H.
    1975.   *Kigelianthe:* A synonym of *Fernandoa* (Bignoniaceae).   Ann. Missouri
        Bot. Gard., vol. 62, pp. 480-483.

PETER GOLDBLATT

Microbial Ecology of Algal Mats and Recent Stromatolites in Shark Bay, Western Australia

Principal Investigator: Stjepko Golubic, Boston University, Boston, Massachusetts.

Grant No. 1207:   In aid of a study of the ecology of Recent stromatolites and algal carbonate structures in Shark Bay, Australia.

A four-week field research project on microbial communities of modern stromatolites in Shark Bay, Western Australia, was carried out in July and August 1973 (Australian winter).

Stromatolites are laminated organo-sedimentary structures built by various microorganisms, mostly blue-green algae (cyanophytes). When cemented by $CaCO_3$ these structures persist and may become fossilized. Stromatolites have been common throughout most of the early history of life; in fact, they represent the main documentation of life in the Precambrian (3×10^9 years ago), prior to the evolution of plants and skeleton-bearing animals (Walter, 1976). Toward the end of the Precambrian (0.6×10^9 years ago) stromatolite abundance and diversity declined (Awramik, 1971), probably because of destruction by grazing and burrowing Metazoa (Garrett, 1970) or because of competition by reef-building plants and animals (Monty, 1973). Since microorganisms that build stromatolites are very rarely preserved (Schopf, 1977), our understanding of their biology depends largely upon the study of their modern counterparts. However, very few modern environments permit stromatolite growth. The hypersaline Hamelin pool of Shark Bay in Western Australia is one of these unique habitats that harbor a variety of stromatolitic structures.

The research team, consisting of a biologist (S. Golubic, Boston University) and two geologists (S. Awramik and V. Koehler, Harvard University), assembled in Perth, Western Australia on July 14, 1973. Our objective was to study microbial ecology of Shark Bay stromatolites. The Geological Survey of Western Australia (P. Playford) was very helpful to us in providing field equipment and camping facilities as well as background information and advice. We rented a Jeep and SCUBA equipment and gathered supplies. Two days later the research party was heading north toward Shark Bay.

The climate of the Western Australian coastal region is mild. It ranges gradually from a mediterranean climate with moderate humidity (rainy win-

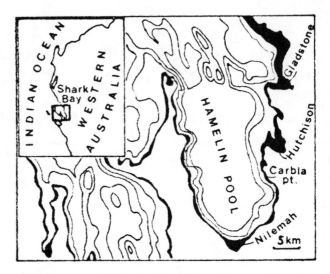

Fig. 1.   Map of the Hamelin Pool of Shark Bay, Western Australia. Inset, upper
left, locates the framed area. Black, areas with algal mats.

ters and dry summers) and increases in aridity along a south-north profile. The
landscape along this profile changes accordingly from open wooded areas,
with green pastures near Perth, to a semidesert that extends north of Carnar-
von. The Shark Bay area is between the mediterranean and semidesert regions.
The vegetation cover is a semiarid Australian bush. Fruticose perennial plants
grow as scattered low shrubs on high ground, while tall shrubs (2-3 meters)
occupy slightly moister valleys. Eucalyptus trees occur only around the few
rivers and springs in the area.

Our research team camped for three weeks at Carbla Point on the shore of
Hamelin Pool. Help and hospitality were provided by the Kopkes, who own
the grounds around Carbla Point. Other neighbors offered the use of their motorboat for our research.

Hamelin Pool (fig. 1) is a hypersaline basin (3 times normal sea-water
salinity) separated from the Indian Ocean by a shallow submerged sand bar.
The tides we monitored during the time of study showed erratic fluctuation
within a 1-meter range, depending more upon prevailing winds than on celestial causes. Yet, the assemblages of microorganisms along the coast show
marked zonal distribution corresponding to average conditions of water supply and air exposure. Between the land vegetation and the high-water mark is
a belt of white beaches composed of shells of a single endemic bivalve species,

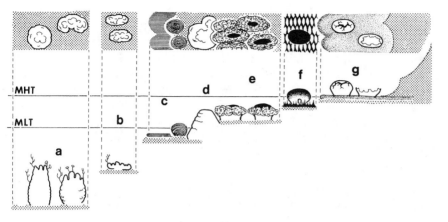

FIG. 2.   Sequence of algal mat and stromatolite types at the point north of Carbla, Hamelin Pool, Shark Bay, Western Australia. MHT, mean high tide; MLT, mean low tide; coarse dots, loose sand and beach; a, subtidal columnar and branched stromatolites; b, prostrate modification of a; c, finely laminated nonlithified stromatolites dominated by a *Schizothrix* sp.; d, nonlithified *Gardnerula corymbosa* stromatolites; e, stromatolites built by the pustular mat of *Entophysalis major;* black tops are lithified and covered by film mat; f, lithified stromatolites of e, covered by the epilithic and endolithic film mat; at the base between the stromatolites is the tufted mat of *Lyngbya aestuarii* that forms reticulate patterns; g, cracked and eroded stromatolites of e; at the base is beige flat mat of *Microcoleus tenerrimus*.

Phragum hamelinii. Beach rock forms along the shore, owing to carbonate cementation of *Phragum* shells and fragments, and is the source of the commercially used coquina rock. We did not find live *Phragum* during the time of our stay. Apparently this mollusk goes through periodic population explosions followed by massive mortality, whereupon enormous amounts of shells are washed out on local beaches.

The water in Shark Bay is clear and blue, owing to low plankton productivity. These conditions were favorable for an aerial survey that was needed to locate subtidal stromatolites. We rented a small Cessna airplane and documented the distribution of subtidal and intertidal stromatolites by aerial photographs and Super-8 movie sequences.

Large domal stromatolites are located in subtidal and intertidal ranges of wave-exposed points and headlands, while the protected embayments harbor extensive, zonally arranged, flat algal mats. Although localized lithification occurs throughout the range of stromatolite distribution, strongly lithified and hardened stromatolites are found in two distinct zones: (1) Large subtidal stromatolites (fig. 2a) are dominated by a highly diversified eukaryote-prokaryote (algae-cyanophytes) microbial community and show strong internal lithification; (2) intertidal elongated domal stromatolites are formed by the cyanophyte *Entophysalis major* and lithify progressively toward the upper range of their distribution; their hardening is external (fig. 2e-g). Lithified stromatolites remain in the environment long after the active accretion process has ceased; they also have the best chance to become fossils. We identified the microbiota and correlated their occurrence and species composition with the various stromatolitic structures. We have established the areas where the stromatolites grow, and distinguished the live structures from those that have formed in the past. These "subfossil" stromatolites are found in the upper intertidal zone. With the use of a small Nikon-H field microscope we have studied live microbial communities and established that various types of Shark Bay stromatolites are biologically different and have different genesis. Some domed stromatolites and algal mats (fig. 2c, d, f, and g base) do not lithify. Their preservation potential is probably smaller than that of the lithified ones. However, it is conceivable that minor changes in the chemistry of the ambient water may cause extensive $CaCO_3$ precipitation within the interstitial spaces and thus may harden all stromatolitic structures. Formation of coquina-beachrock indicates that such a possibility is real.

The terms "algal mats" and "Recent stromatolites" will not be used interchangeably in this report. The term "algal mat" refers to a living microbial community at the sediment-water interface; "Recent stromatolite" refers to the organo-sedimentary structure accumulated by "trapping and binding" activity of algal mats.

Zonation of stromatolitic structures and algal mats on a wave-exposed point north of Carbla is summarized in figure 2. According to their morphology these algal mats have been termed colloform, smooth, pustular, tufted, blister, and film (Hoffman, 1976). This terminology provides a useful orientation in recognizing stromatolite phenomena, and we will relate our findings to these divisions.

a. Subtidal stromatolites are produced by colloform mats that occur in irregular fields and semicircular ridges at a depth of 3-4 meters (fig. 2a). They are large, up to 60 (-100) centimeters high, firmly lithified, actively growing structures of characteristic morphology. They represent an autochthonous Recent phenomenon, distinct from the intertidal stromatolites of Shark Bay (Playford and Cockbain, 1976). The stromatolites are circular or slightly oval in vertical projection, without the pronounced elongation parallel to current and wave direction that is observed in the intertidal. In side projection they are steep (slope angle 60-80°, average 71°), conical in the upper half and bulbous in the lower. Their tops are either flat or branch into several smaller vertical columns. The surface has "contiguous convexities" arranged in labyrinthic fashion that resemble the surface of a human brain. These convexities are finer on the slopes (10-20 millimeters) than on the tops (30-50 millimeters). The columns on the top range from 150 to 250 millimeters in height. Smaller (up to 40 centimeters in diameter) stromatolite mounds appear to be established in loose sand rather than on hard bedrock.

b. Outside of stromatolite fields, colloform mats were found on oval and discoid crust fragments scattered over loose sand (fig. 2b).

c. Smooth, nonlithified, finely laminated domes and mats occur at the lower water mark. These structures are formed by a very small species of *Schizothrix* (fig. 2c).

d. A new stromatolite type was discovered betwen the ranges *c* (smooth mat) and *e* (pustular mat) in the midintertidal zone. It is biologically characterized by a distinct algal mat community whose dominant organism is *Gardnerula corymbosa* (Rivulariaceae, Cyanophyta) (fig. 2d). These stromatolites act as wave breakers at the outer edge of the intertidal stromatolite platform. They are higher and steeper sloped than the adjacent intertidal stromatolites. *Gardnerula* stromatolites create a steplike increase in the coastal profile, owing to very efficient sediment entrapment between vertically and radially growing algal filaments. Very little lithification was detected within these stromatolites during the time of the study.

e. Elongated domed stromatolites covered by a gelatinous pustular (mammillate) mat are the most prominent intertidal structure along wave-exposed coasts. They are formed by the coccoid blue-green alga *Entophysalis major*. Hard structures in the upper intertidal zone represent a lithified modification of this stromatolite type. Morphological continuity between the biologically active pustular mat and the lithified stromatolites is evident (fig. 2e).

f. top. The lithified stromatolites are secondarily covered by the film mat which is biologically distinct from the pustular mat and composed of coccoid epilithic and endolithic blue-green algae, which also cover the adjacent coquina crusts and loose shells (fig. 2f). These algae do not participate in accretion and stromatolite buildup; rather, they penetrate into hardened stromatolites and contribute to their destruction. The distribution range of the film mat in Shark Bay corresponds to the uppermost intertidal and supratidal zones and is comparable to similar endolith flora of carbonate rocky coasts. Lithification in the upper intertidal zone is relatively fast, and probably a seasonal, surface originating process, which results in external hardening of a stromatolitic structure leaving a soft or semisoft interior. As a consequence, older structures often crack and collapse, and their erosion leaves craterlike remnants with harder rims (fig. 3). Beige and rust-red crust surfaces of the uppermost stro-

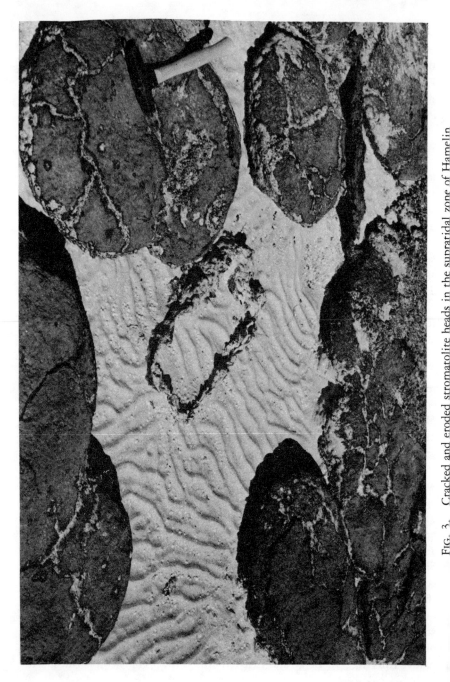

FIG. 3. Cracked and eroded stromatolite heads in the supratidal zone of Hamelin

matolites are not biological in origin and represent areas devoid of any algal vegetation.

According to these findings, hard upper intertidal and supratidal stromatolites can be considered "fossil" residues of structures once formed by sediment accretion of the pustular *(Entophysalis major)* mat at higher water levels. A microbial fossil *(Eoentophysalis belcherensis)*, morphologically indistinguishable from *Entophysalis,* has been discovered in silicified Precambrian stromatolites of the 2-billion (10^9)-year-old Belcher Island formation (Hofmann, 1976; Golubic and Hofmann, 1976).

f. base. Tufted mat forms ridges and network patterns in tidal pools and flats at the base of hardened stromatolites. Tufted mat is initiated by *Lyngbya aestuarii* but differentiates into a multilayered mat community. The surface layer is composed of *Lyngbya* and the underlying layers of *Schizothrix gracilis* and salmon-pink filamentous bacteria (fig. 2f). Although morphologically different, microbial composition of this mat is similar to the pinnacle mat of the Persian Gulf.

g. The upper margin of the algal mat sequence is occupied by a flat beige mat, built by *Microcoleus tenerrimus* (fig. 2g). This mat forms blisters in its upper range. Blistering of algal mats is a decomposition effect rather than a mat type. More than one type of mat can be subject to blistering, which usually occurs under conditions of prolonged air exposure. We found blistering modification of the pustular and the beige flat mat.

The zonation in sheltered areas is less regular, compared with the wave exposed coast. Smooth, pustular, tufted, and flat beige mats are all widely distributed over extremely mild slopes of protected embayments. These mats are arranged in the same sequence as those on exposed shores but promote only a low profile sediment accumulation (up to 2 centimeters). Associated with the smooth mat are flat ridges moderately encrusted with $CaCO_3$, that extend in a direction parallel to the coastline and incline seaward.

A new type of mat that forms thin pointed pinnacles was discovered in Gladstone embayment in the transitional zone between the smooth and tufted mats (fig. 4). This algal mat type is built exclusively by a small *Schizothrix* sp. and is not identical with the tufted mat of *Lyngbya*. Lithified structures in the upper intertidal zone of protected environments are flat, cracked crusts 20-30 millimeters thick that are often displaced. These crusts rest on loose sediment and their upper surface is covered by the film mat.

Preservation and accumulation (to form stromatolites) both of exposed and sheltered algal mats in Shark Bay are accomplished by periodic lithification rather than by formation of anaerobic algal peats as in the Persian Gulf. Intensive lithification occurs in two zones, the permanently submerged subti-

FIG. 4. Pointed pinnacle mat of *Schizothrix* sp., Gladstone embayment, intertidal zone.

dal and the periodically flooded upper intertidal. Structures with intermediate degrees of encrustation occur in all zones. During the winter, northerly winds bring large masses of oceanic water into Hamelin Pool. Water temperature ranges between 16° and 20°C. and the salinity is about 60 percent. Significantly higher temperatures, evaporation rates, and salinity values are associated with periods of prevailing southerly winds during the summer, when water exchange with the open ocean is restricted. We expect, therefore, that mineral precipitation and lithification periods occur mainly during the summer months.

In addition to our research in the field, we made collections for later laboratory study and supplied materials to other collaborating laboratories. Over 120 combined microbiological and sedimentological samples were preserved, 10 short sediment cores taken, and a series of algal mat specimens, including several large stromatolite heads, were collected. These are now exhibited in Harvard's natural history museum.

Upon conclusion of the fieldwork in Shark Bay, we returned to Perth. The flight connections to Australia and back to Boston allowed several stopovers. On my way to Australia I had spent four days in Abu Dhabi, United Arab Emirates, to sample algal mats of the Arabian (Persian) Gulf that are comparable to those in Shark Bay. Leaving Australia, I flew via India to Afghanistan where I visited the fresh-water carbonate deposits of the Band-I-Amir lakes. My last stop was in Piran, Yugoslavia. The marine saltworks of Piran are being studied microbiologically and geochemically by Dr. Juergen Schneider, Goettingen, West Germany. Together with Dr. Schneider and Dr. Therese LeCampion-Alsumard, Marseille, France, I collected and analyzed the algal mats that develop in a series of salt pans of increasing salinity. These mats, which are comparable to those of Shark Bay and Abu Dhabi, develop here under controlled conditions monitored by the saltworks and serve as an experimental setting to study algal mats and Recent stromatolites.

REFERENCES

AWRAMIK, STANLEY M.
    1971.   Precambrian columnar stromatolite diversity: Reflection of metazoan appearance.   Science, vol. 174, pp. 825-827.

GARRETT, PETER
    1970.   Phanerozoic stromatolites: Noncompetitive ecologic restriction by grazing and burrowing animals.   Science, vol. 169, pp. 171-173, illus.

GOLUBIC, STJEPKO
    1976a.   Organisms that build stromatolites.   Pp. 113-126 *in* Walter, 1976 (q.v.).

    1976b.   Taxonomy of extant stromatolite building cyanophytes.   Pp. 127-140 *in* Walter, 1976 (q.v.).

GOLUBIC, STJEPKO, and HOFMANN, H. J.
1976. Comparison of Holocene and mid-Precambrian Entophysalidaceae (Cyanophyta) in stromatolitic algal mats: Cell division and degradation. Journ. Pal., vol. 50, pp. 1074-1082.

HOFFMAN, PAUL F.
1976. Stromatolite morphogenesis in Shark Bay, Western Australia. Pp. 261-271 *in* Walter, 1976 (q.v.).

HOFFMAN, H. J.
1976. Precambrian microflora, Belcher Islands, Canada: Significance and systematics. Journ. Pal., vol. 50, pp. 1040-1073.

LOGAN, B. W.
1961. *Cryptozoon* and associated stromatolites from the Recent of Shark Bay, Western Australia. Journ. Geol., vol. 69, pp. 517-533.

MONTY, C.L.V.
1973. Precambrian background and phanerozoic history of stromatolite communities, an overview. Ann. Soc. Geol. Belg. Bull. 96, pp. 585-624.

PLAYFORD, P. E., and COCKBAIN, A. E.
1976. Modern algal stromatolites at Hamelin Pool, a hypersaline barred basin in Shark Bay, Western Australia. Pp. 389-411 *in* Walter, 1976 (q.v.).

SCHOPF, JAMES W.
1977. Biostratigraphic usefulness of stromatolitic Precambrian microbiotas: A preliminary analysis. Precambrian Res., vol. 5, pp. 143-173.

WALTER, M. R., ed.
1976. Developments in sedimentology, 20 (Stromatolites), 790 pp., illus. Elsevier Scientific Publishing Co., Amsterdam.

STJEPKO GOLUBIC

Botanical Expedition to Oaxaca and Chiapas, Mexico

Principal Investigator: Frank W. Gould and Stephan L. Hatch, Texas A&M University, College Station, Texas.

Grant No. 1242: In support of a biosystematic investigation of grasses of Oaxaca and Chiapas, Mexico.

The participants traveled by plane to Oaxaca on October 18, 1973, and then in seven days drove 2,240 kilometers in a rented car for plant collections and field observations at numerous localities in Oaxaca and Chiapas. On the return trip they stopped at Mexico City to study specimens in the herbarium of the University of Mexico and for conferences with the head of the botany department at that time, Dr. Gómez-Pompa, and other members of the botany department staff.

In addition to field notes and photos, some 256 sets of grass herbarium specimens, 14 packets of seeds, 39 bottles of grass bud materials for cytological studies, and 15 bottles of grass-shoot and spikelet material in FAA solution for anatomical studies were obtained. Despite some rain in the higher mountains, all target locations were reached, with fine results. Data obtained by Dr. Hatch contributed greatly to the quality of his Ph.D. dissertation entitled "A Biosystematic Study of the *Schizachyrium cirratum-Schizachyrium sanguineum* complex (Poaceae)," which is on file in the library of Texas A&M University.

Specimens and data obtained by Dr. Gould added significantly to the store of information concerning the grasses of southern Mexico. Dr. Gould currently is preparing a systematic treatment of the grasses of Chiapas for the projected Flora of Chiapas by Dr. Dennis Breedlove, California Academy of Sciences. At least two of the *Bothriochloa* collections may prove to be undescribed taxa. A collection of *Bothriochloa edwardsiana* (Gould) L. R. Parodi provides the first record of this species between the Edwards Plateau of Texas and locations in Uruguay.

FRANK W. GOULD

287

Recovery of Microvertebrates from the Miocene of South Dakota

Principal Investigator: Morton Green, Museum of Geology, South Dakota School of Mines and Technology, Rapid City, South Dakota

Grant No. 1183:   Search for Miocene and Pliocene microvertebrate faunas in South Dakota.

Washing and screening techniques for the recovery of small fossil vertebrates have been extraordinarily successful. In South Dakota, vertebrate fossil faunas of Oligocene, Miocene, and Pliocene ages have been known for many years. However, the majority of the species were those animals of large size, such as horses, camels, dogs, and cats. Small rodents and insectivores were poorly represented in museum collections.

The first effort to recover small vertebrates from Tertiary deposits in South Dakota by washing and screening techniques was that of Wilson (1971). His work was limited to the Oligocene. On a limited scale in 1967, I began washing and screening early Clarendonian beds in Bennett County, South Dakota. At the suggestion of J. C. Harksen of the South Dakota Geological Survey and J. R. MacDonald of Foothill College, we tested some matrix from a Batesland Formation (early Hemingfordian) locality, now called Black Bear Quarry I. This rock did not break down in water. A setup for treating the rock with mild acetic acid in the field was established (Green, 1970). This led to the accumulation of sufficient number of specimens which, together with specimens from two other localities in the Batesland Formation, has added significantly to the early Hemingfordian micromammalian faunas of South Dakota (Martin, 1976). Simultaneously, with the quarrying of Black Bear Quarry I, another quarry was begun in the underlying Rosebud Formation as Black Bear Quarry II (Green, 1972; Green and Martin, 1976; Green, 1977). This matrix also required acid treatment. Hundreds of isolated teeth and some jaw fragments were recovered from Black Bear Quarry II.

The success of these endeavors encouraged us to attempt further exploration for microvertebrates in localities known previously by megafaunas and to look for new localities. Funds to support this exploratory fieldwork were supplied by the National Geographic Society for the 1973 field season.

Skinner, Skinner, and Gooris (1968) described the stratigraphy of Turtle Butte in Gregory County, South Dakota, with faunas from the Turtle Butte

Formation and Burge member of the Valentine Formation of the Butte. The faunal lists were entirely of large-size taxa. Skinner, in his stratigraphic section, showed channel deposits with indications of bone chips. This resembled conditions under which we had achieved success at the Black Bear Quarries. Consequently, it was decided to begin our exploration at Turtle Butte. James E. Martin and Frank C. Campbell, graduate students in vertebrate paleontology at the South Dakota School of Mines and Technology, were the field assistants. Volunteer labor in collecting matrix and washing and screening was provided by members of the Donald W. Roosa family of Ideal, South Dakota, and by my daughter, Julia L. Green. Preliminary work had given us a lead, and a small quarry was opened. Several tons of matrix were collected and acid treated. Washing and screening were done in the nearby Keya Paha River. Although specimens were not abundant, our expectations were fulfilled, and a small microvertebrate fossil fauna was collected. Also, larger forms seen on the surface were collected. The microfauna will add materially to our knowledge of the Wewela local fauna of the Turtle Butte Formation. When the study is completed, it is expected that the new information will help refine stratigraphic correlation of the Turtle Butte Formation with deposits of the same age elsewhere. Since that time, other expeditions to Turtle Butte funded by the Museum of Geology, South Dakota School of Mines and Technology, have collected matrix from the Devil's Gulch and Burge members of the Valentine Formation and from the Cap Rock member of the Lower Ash Hollow Formation. Preliminary work indicates that microfaunas, though meager, are present in the Valentine Formation. The microfauna from the Cap Rock member seems to be a bit more abundant.

Matrix from the Devil's Gulch member is yet to be processed. Concentrate from the Cap Rock member has only recently been examined and picked for specimens. An important new locality was discovered also in 1973. Mr. Donald W. Roosa, who has worked with the Museum of Geology for many years, took us to an immense man-made road cut. The locality, Feyereisen Gap, in Gregory County, South Dakota, has yielded a fauna of Barstovian Age of both large and small animals, among them a new species of the zapodid jumping mouse *Megasminthus* (Green, 1977). Lizard, snake, and turtle are evident among the lower vertebrates. Insectivora, Lagomorpha, Rodentia other than zapodids, Equidae, Rhinocerotidae, and Artiodactyla are also present. The entire fauna is yet to be studied.

Another older locality to which we were able to go in 1973 was the Bijou Hills. The locality, on the eastern shore of the Missouri River, in Charles Mix County, South Dakota, was first explored by F. V. Hayden in 1853 (Skinner and Taylor, 1967). The Bijou Hills local fauna as revised by Skinner and Taylor included a small rodent. This indicated to us the possibility of obtaining microvertebrate specimens by washing and screening. During the season we spent only a little time at the locality because of its inaccessibility. However, we did open a small quarry and brought the matrix back to the laboratory for treatment. We soon learned that the fine silt would not wash in water nor would acid dissolve the cementing material. Fortunately, kerosene soaking of the rock followed by immersion in water successfully dissociated the rock, after which water washing with a little household dishwashing detergent reduced the rock to a concentrate. A concentrate of one cup of matrix was derived from a gunnysack full of rock. We returned to the Bijou Hills quarry during 1974 and 1975 and collected more matrix. Field assistants for 1974 were Allen J. Kihm and Michael F. Morea; for 1975, John L. Chaille. Only the zapodid rodents have been studied, to date. At the end of the 1974 season at South Bijou Hill, we discovered the remnant of a stream channel bed in which fossil bone was visible. Because it was our last day of the field season, we had little time and collected only a few sacks of matrix. When this material was prepared, it seemed of sufficient interest to study. The site, the Glenn Olson quarry, is named for the owner of the property. This small microfauna contains taxa similar to that of the larger quarry at South Bijou Hill and is of the same age, late Barstovian (Green and Holman, 1977). The fauna includes a new species of *Macrognathomys*.

Although the work at Feyereisen Gap and most of the work at the Bijou Hills was not supported by National Geographic Society, the impetus provided by the 1973 funding enabled us to continue exploration and collecting there and in other localities. All indications are that when the faunal studies at the several South Dakota sites are completed, we will be able to make a more refined and accurate correlation with deposits of similar age in Nebraska and elsewhere.

REFERENCES

GREEN, M.
   1970.   Recovering microvertebrates with acetic acid.   South Dakota Geol. Survey Circ. 40, pp. 1-11.
   1972.   Lagomorpha from the Rosebud Formation, South Dakota.   Journ. Paleont., vol. 46, pp. 377-385.
   1977.   Miocene and Pliocene Zapodidae from South Dakota.   Journ. Paleont., vol. 51, pp. 996-1015.
GREEN, M., and BJORK, P. R.
   1980.   On the genus *Dikkomys* (Geomyoidea, Mammalis).   Pp. 343-353 *in* "Palaeovertebrata, Montpellier, Mem. Jubil. R. Lavocot."

GREEN, M., and HOLMAN, J. A.
    1977.   A late Tertiary stream channel fauna from South Bijou Hill, South Dakota. Journ. Paleont., vol. 51, pp. 543-547.

GREEN, M., and MARTIN, J. E.
    1976.   Peratherium (Marsupialia: Didelphidae) from the Oligocene and Miocene of South Dakota. Athlon. Essays in Palaeontology in honour of Loris Shano Russell. Roy. Ontario Mus., Life Sci. Misc. Contr., pp. 155-168.

HOLMAN, J. A.
    1976.   Snakes from the Rosebud Formation (Middle Miocene) of South Dakota. Herpetologica, vol. 32, pp. 41-48.
    1979.   A new amphisbaenian of the genus *Rhineura* from the Middle Miocene of South Dakota. Herpetologica, vol. 35, pp. 383-386.

MARTIN, J. E.
    1976.   Small mammals from the Miocene Batesland formation of South Dakota. Univ. Wyoming Contr. Geol., vol. 14, pp. 69-98.

MARTIN, J. E., and GREEN, M.
    _____.   Insectivora, Sciuridae, and Cricetidae from the Early Miocene Rosebud Formation in South Dakota. Carnegie Mus. Nat. Hist. (In press.)

SKINNER, M. F.; SKINNER, S.; and GOORIS, R.
    1968.   Cenozoic rocks and faunas of Turtle Butte, southcentral South Dakota. Bull. Amer. Mus. Nat. Hist., vol. 38, pp. 381-436.

SKINNER, M. F., and TAYLOR, B. E.
    1967.   A revision of the geology and paleontology of the Bijou Hills, South Dakota. Amer. Mus. Novitates, no. 2300, pp. 1-53.

WILSON, R. W.
    1971.   Recovery of small mammals from the Oligocene of western South Dakota. National Geol. Soc. Res. Repts., 1965 Projects, pp. 279-287.

MORTON GREEN

Prehistoric Human Adaptation to the Central Arizona Environment

Principal Investigators: George J. Gumerman, Southern Illinois University, Carbondale, Illinois, and Patricia M. Spoerl, Central Arizona Ecotone Project, Southern Illinois University, Carbondale, Illinois.

Grant No. 1236: In support of a study of prehistoric human adaptation in an environmental transition zone of Central Arizona.

The Central Arizona Ecotone Project (CAEP) was conceived in 1971 as a multidisciplinary study of prehistoric human adaptation to an archeologically poorly known region in southcentral Arizona (fig. 1). Hydrologists, geologists, and biologists participated in this project along with archeologists, who integrated and synthesized the research results of the other disciplines. Initial aerial reconnaissance of the vast area, roughly between Phoenix and Prescott, Arizona, indicated the presence of large pueblolike sites in the northern plateau areas, and isolated hilltop "fortified" sites and extensive agricultural-water control systems in the transition area between the plateau country and the desert flats.

A study area that encompasses the environmental and cultural diversity observed from aerial reconnaissance was then defined for further examination. This area, bordered by Bloody Basin on the north, Lake Pleasant on the south, the Bradshaw Mountains on the west, and New River Mountains on the east, includes major portions of the Agua Fria and New River drainages.

Three principal physiographic zones are included in this study area. The mesa-canyon complex at the northern end is made up of plateaus cut by deep, narrow canyons whose streams are tributaries of the Agua Fria River. The transition zone includes gentle slopes and isolated buttes and mesas in its highly variable and dissected topography and is dissected by the Agua Fria and New River drainages. The basin and range complex in the southern portion of the test area consists of a flat desert region with isolated north-south mountain ranges and is drained by the Lower Agua Fria and New River. Elevations in the study area range from approximately 1,250 feet in the desert flats of the southern portion to 4,300 feet in the mesa-canyon complex at the northern end.

293

Three major environmental regions that correspond with the above physiographic zones are also represented in the study area. The Lower Sonoran Basin ãnd range area in the south consists of a desert scrub vegetation community with a large amount of creosote bush, bur sage, and many species of cacti. The northern mesa-canyon area has been described as Upper Sonoran Desert Grassland. The predominant plateau vegetation consists of various species of prickly pear and grasses with a scattering of chaparral shrubs, mesquite, piñon, and juniper.

A biological transition zone occurs between these two environmental zones. This area was initially described as an ecotone or edge-area (Odum, 1965) between the two major Sonoran environmental zones. It contains plant species common to the adjacent zones and some that reach their northern or southern limit in this area. The basic plant community consists of saguaro, paloverde, jojoba, cholla, and other cacti.

Preliminary exploration of the study area by the Central Arizona Ecotone Project (CAEP) indicated the remains of at least two different cultural groups, which appeared to be restricted to the different environmental areas (Gumerman and Johnson, 1971, p. 93). A major group of sites is located in the Upper Sonoran zone primarily on the Perry Mesa plateau along the rims of canyons. The majority of these sites are large (up to 100 rooms) and consist of pueblo-like contiguous masonry rooms. The ceramic assemblages contain a majority of locally manufactured plain brown wares such as Verde Brown and Tuzigoot Plain although redwares are dominated by Gila and Salt Red believed to have been imported from the Gila-Salt Valley. The few decorated wares present such as Gila and Tonto polychromes and Jeddito wares are representative of areas to the north and east of the study area.

The second grouping of sites occurs in the transition area and Lower Sonoran zone. Small, widely dispersed masonry room sites which tend to be more poorly constructed than in the north are typical of this area, along with sherd and lithic scatters that contain no evidence of subsurface structures. A number of extensive land management-agricultural systems including grid borders, linear borders, terraces, and check dams are also located near the small sites and artifact scatters. An exception to this pattern is the presence of a number of defensive "fortified" sites located on isolated buttes and mesas where access is extremely difficult. Virtually all of the ceramics encountered in this area are plainwares (Wingfield Plain and other brown wares).

It was deemed that the most profitable way of examining the environmental and cultural variability of such a diverse region as that encompassed by this study area was through the various methods of remote sensing.

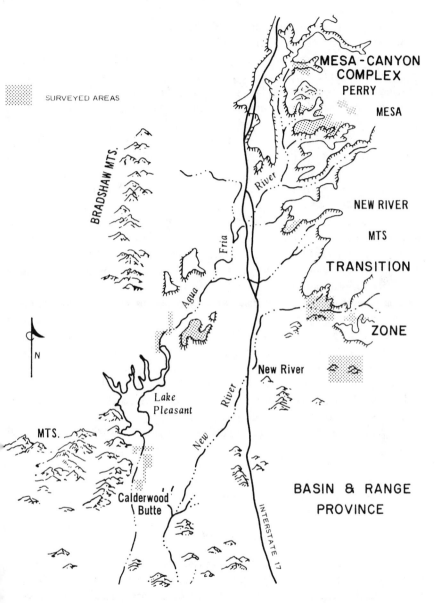

ADAPTED FROM ACME GRAPHICS

FIG. 1. Site of the Central Arizona Ecotone Project's multidisciplinary study of prehistoric human adaptation in southcentral Arizona.

In 1972 funds were provided by the National Aeronautics and Space Administration (NAS9-14610) and the National Geographic Society to test the applicability of remotely sensed data to archeological problems. Because of its apparent cultural and environmental diversity the study area provided an ideal location for this endeavor. The project investigators utilized a theoretical framework involving the nature of adjustments that human cultures undergo in adapting to a given environmental situation. Therefore, emphasis was placed on prehistoric land and water management methods in an attempt to understand prehistoric man-land and man-water relationships in varied environmental situations.

Remote-sensing data was supplied by the National Aeronautics and Space Administration (NASA) Skylab missions. High-altitude imagery from U-2 aircraft overflights and low-altitude fixed-wing aircraft coverage of the test area were used as a comparative format for the Skylab data. The various types of imagery were examined by the investigators in each of the disciplines involved, and the photographic formats were compared in order to determine their most appropriate usage. Although it was recognized that imagery derived from earth-orbiting satellites would not permit visual interpretation of prehistoric sites in the area, the other investigators on the project were able to use these data, particularly to delineate significant environmental and topographic features. All of the investigators concluded that color or color infrared Skylab coverage was the most appropriate for the project needs. The most useful photographic coverage over all, however, was the high-altitude U-2 black-and-white photographs. Lower altitude imagery aided the archeologists in terms of site location but was of little use in the other disciplinary studies.

A detailed evaluation of the remote sensing aspect of CAEP can be found in Gumerman et al., 1975. The following discussion provides a brief summary of the results obtained from the utilization of remote-sensing data in the CAEP study area, and of the subsequent ground truth surveys and archeological excavations which were conducted.

Geology-Hydrology Results

The identification of surficial geological types was carried out through the examination of Skylab coverage, ancillary ground truth studies, and U-2 imagery interpretation. Minor discrepancies were noted between the photographic interpretation and the ground truth results. These discrepancies generally were attributed to seasonal variations and the time of day during which the photos were taken. In addition, a problem of resolution in the Skylab imagery limited the possibilities of defining some of the finer geological structures from photographic interpretation alone. The U-2 imagery appears most successful for aerial mapping of geological features, particularly the finer structural units.

Definition of the geometric characteristics of selected small drainage basins in the study area was accomplished and mean annual runoff was determined for each test basin. It was calculated that the amount of water available far exceeded the *projected* needs of the estimated prehistoric population of any given basin. As with the surficial geologic mapping, the Skylab format was most informative, but the most successful analysis was conducted using U-2 imagery.

During ground truth surveys numerous water-management systems such as prehistorically constructed check dams and terraces were located. None of these systems could be identified utilizing either the Skylab or the U-2 imagery. It was possible, however, to predict with some accuracy those drainage basins that were most likely to contain water-management systems based upon the geometric characteristics of a drainage and its specific topographical situation.

Biology Results

The results of the biological studies indicated less usefulness for ultra-high-altitude imagery in the determination of Upper and Lower Sonoran plant communities and their distributions than those achieved in the geological and hydrological analyses. It was not possible, using any aerial photographic method, to clearly define the boundaries of the postulated ecotone. This transitional area is much less clearly defined than was originally anticipated, and does not represent a definitive belt between the Upper and Lower Sonoran vegetation zones.

Additional problems were created in the use of the Skylab data for biological purposes because the imagery was obtained during the dormant season which tended to obscure differences in vegetation.

Archeology Results

The project archeologists were familiar with many areas of archeological importance within the study region prior to the analysis of most of the Skylab imagery. Photographic analysis, therefore, was concentrated in localities where archeological sites or water management-land utilization systems were known to exist. It was apparent early in these analyses that, with the exception of the limited amount of low-altitude imagery, little direct data of an archeological nature could be detected. The remote-sensing data, however, did provide important information pertinent to archeological research. Orbital imagery from the Skylab and U-2 overflights was used in defining and mapping the major biological systems so that areas of potential resource exploitation could be further examined. The imagery delineated the nature of water sources which may have been used by the prehistoric inhabitants. Topographic features were also defined from the imagery, and these aided in the prediction of prehistoric settlement locations and supplemented the biological information regarding areas of potential resource exploitation.

The use of remote-sensing data during the first stage of CAEP's investigation of this archeologically unknown region enabled the acquisition of knowledge concerning biological, hydrological, geological, and general environmental conditions. It enabled the definition of a set of natural conditions in the test area from which a variety of hypotheses regarding the relationship between prehistoric adaptive strategies and specific environmental situations could be developed for archeological testing. A research design, focusing on the interrelationships between the above variables and the distinctive prehistoric cultural remains that had been located in the area, was then developed for intensive archeological investigations, which constituted the second stage of CAEP investigations.

Additional archeological surveys and limited excavations were carried out during 1974 and 1975, and final laboratory analysis and preparation of the research results for publication are being completed. This research has been funded by the National Science Foundation (Soc 75-03434 and Soc 6-21387). The CAEP research design employed an ecological approach as a framework for investigating the relationship between the natural environmental and prehistoric cultural development in the study area. The major hypothesis formulated was that the distribution of human populations is affected by biological transition zones and, therefore, biological transition zones are also cultural transition zones (Gumerman and Johnson, 1971, p. 83). The tendency for increased variety and diversity at the plant and animal junctures (transitional areas) may also apply at human community junctures. Therefore, the transitional area may have been one of contact between different cultural groups in the Southwest or may have served as a cultural boundary between these groups. A related goal of this research was to describe and interpret the character and variety of a culture contact or boundary situation in an area considered to have been culturally and environmentally marginal to areas of major prehistoric cultural development in the Southwest. An ancillary objective involved an understanding of the natural and social factors that affected settlement location and distribution. These factors are being considered by the Southwestern Anthropological Research Group (SARG) of which CAEP is a member. These Southwestern archeologists are coordinating their archeological data in order to examine basic questions regarding prehistoric settlement systems (Gumerman, 1971; Weed, 1978).

On the basis of the work accomplished to date, the hypothesis that the transition zone represents a definitive biological ecotone has not been substantiated, although the area does contain a more diversified floral community than the regions to the north and south. This diversity is partially due to the distinct and highly variable topographic nature of the area. The major hypothesis that the distribution of human populations is affected by environmental transition zones has been tested through archeological surveys and excavations, and preliminary use of ethnohistorical sources. It appears to be a valid hypothesis on a broad regional level. The size, distribution, and configuration of sites encountered in the mesa-canyon complex differ considerably from those of the transition zone and the basin and range area.

The cultural affiliation of the occupants of these areas has not been definitely determined. Artifactual and architectural traits are not clearly indicative of any of the major Southwestern cultural traditions (i.e., Hohokam, Anasazi, and Mogollon). The evident diversity of traits does indicate some type of cultural contact situation or a prehistoric boundary area between cultural groups.

It has also not been possible to develop a detailed chronology of prehistoric cultural development in the test area. The majority of the ceramics found have extremely long temporal spans and wide spatial distributions, and are thus poor chronological and cultural indicators; no datable species of wood for dendrochronological analysis were recovered from excavations; and only four samples of charred remains amenable to radiocarbon dating were secured. At this point, based upon artifactual comparisons with more securely dated areas of the Southwest and limited use of obsidian hydration analysis, it appears that intensive utilization and major occupation of the region did not occur until approximately A.D. 800. There appears to have been a northward movement from the Gila-Salt Valley along the Agua Fria River into the transition zone area at about this time. This occupation lasted until roughly A.D. 1200 when the area was abandoned. It was after this time that the large sites in the northern mesa-canyon area were constructed, possibly representing a blending of peoples from farther north and east moving into the area.

Evidence from archeological surveys of 10 square kilometers in the mesa-canyon area, the excavation of a 3-room site on the rim of a canyon, and of an 18-room site on an alluvial terrace at the bottom of a canyon led to the initial

consideration of the mesa-canyon region as part of the Salado cultural tradition. This hypothesis has been revised, however, owing to the generally disor-
dered state of what Southwestern archeologists call the "Salado Culture"
(Gumerman and Weed, 1976). Consideration of this area in terms of a Western Pueblo economic system is proving more viable as an explanation for the
culture history and exploitative system of the region (Reed, 1950). The large
pueblo sites on the canyon rims are located in an environmental situation
which is similar to other sites along the Mogollon Rim, such as Grasshopper,
Canyon Creek Ruin, and Tonto Ruin, and they appear to have had similar
adaptive strategies.

Small masonry room sites are located primarily on the sides of canyons
and on the interior of the mesa. Water control and agricultural systems, consisting mainly of rock terraces and cleared plots, are generally not extensive in
this area, particularly when compared with the transition zone. They tend to
be clustered near the canyon mouths and immediate rim localities near settlements and relatively stable water sources. Cross-cultural analysis of the few
decorated ceramics encountered indicate an occupation between A.D. 1200
and 1500 although there is also evidence for utilization of the canyon bottoms
in earlier times.

Great variability and an earlier occupation sequence are evident in the archeological remains of the transition zone and basin and range province. The
sites exhibit characteristics common to the Hakataya culture defined by
Schroder (1954) and to DiPeso's (1956) generalized Ootam culture. Approximately 20 kilometers of surveys and test excavations at four sites indicate,
however, that this region represents what was once an agricultural community or communities of Hohokam-related people. Certain aspects of their adaptation to this area differ from that of the Hohokam of the Gila and Salt River
valleys, but much of this variability may be explained in terms of responses to
local geological, topographical, and environmental conditions (Spoerl, n.d.).

Excavations included testing of a habitation site composed of 9 masonry-
footed rooms surrounding a plaza, and a pithouse site. The latter site represents a Hohokam Sedentary Period (A.D. 900-1110) occupation of the region.
It is located at the base of a large fortified hilltop site and between two extensive agricultural-water control systems.

The extensive and numerous agricultural-water control systems in the
area have been closely examined, but their function has still not been clearly
determined. The majority of evidence indicates that they were used to slow
and divert rainfall runoff to enable the cultivation of crops such as corn. Exploitation of native flora and fauna was also intensive in this area, and pollen
analysis indicates a heavy reliance on cholla and cheno-ams. There is no direct

evidence, however, to substantiate the idea that these field systems were used for horticultural purposes, i.e., the enhancement of growth of native plant species.

Two fortified hilltop sites were also partially excavated. One is a 9-room site completely encircled by a massive masonry wall, and is situated on a high (700 feet) isolated butte. The second site is located on an eroding volcanic plug which rises 400 feet above the desert floor. The 70-plus rooms at this site extend from a walled summit area down the least steep slope of the butte. Both sites, particularly the larger one, contain evidence of utilization for habitation purposes and the storage of gathered and cultivated resources.

Although numerous, such hilltop sites were identified from aerial photographs, only a few of these could be examined during ground surveys. They clearly exhibit defensive characteristics such as inaccessible location, masonry-constructed encircling walls, elaborate entryways, and loopholes possibly used as lookout points. The differences noted in size and accessibility indicate that these sites served different purposes, but the fortifications present at all of them suggest that the period between A.D. 1000 and 1100 was one of conflict in this northern periphery of Hohokam occupation.

In summary, CAEP during the last 6 years has conducted a wide-ranging interdisciplinary investigation in southcentral Arizona. Remote-sensing data were particularly useful in the early stages of investigation to adequately understand the physical nature of the test area and to serve as a base for further investigation of the adaptive strategies of the prehistoric cultures that occupied this portion of central Arizona.

REFERENCES

DiPeso, Charles C.
  1956. The Upper Pima of San Cayetano del Tumacacori: An ethnohistorical reconstruction of the Ootam of Pimeria Alta. Amerind Foundation, no. 7.
Gumerman, George J., ed.
  1971. The distribution of prehistoric population aggregates. Anthropology Reports, no. 1. Prescott College Press, Prescott.
Gumerman, George J.
  1978. Regional variation in the Southwest and the question of Meso-American relationships. Pp. 89-112 *in* "Across the Chichimec Sea," edited by C. Riley and B. Hedrick. Southern Illinois University Press, Carbondale.
Gumerman, George J., and Johnson, R. Roy
  1971. Prehistoric human population distribution in a biological transition zone. Pp. 64-81 *in* "The Distribution of Prehistoric Population Aggregates," edited by G. J. Gumerman. Anthropology Reports, no. 1. Prescott College Press, Prescott.

GUMERMAN, GEORGE J.; HANSON, JOHN A.; BREW, DOUGLAS; TOMOFF, KARL;
    and WEED, CAROL S.
1975.   The hydrology of prehistoric farming systems in a Central Arizona Eco-
        tone.   Prepared for L. B. Johnson Space Center, Final Report Project
        No. 9-14610. On file, Southern Illinois University Department of An-
        thropology, Carbondale.
GUMERMAN, GEORGE J.; and SPOERL, PATRICIA M., eds.
———   The prehistory of Central Arizona.   Southern Illinois University Press,
        Carbondale.
GUMERMAN, GEORGE J., and WEED, CAROL S.
1976.   The question of Salado in the Aqua Fria and New River drainages of Cen-
        tral Arizona.   The Kiva, vol. 42, no. 1, pp. 105-112.
GUMERMAN, GEORGE J.; WEED, CAROL S.; and HANSON, JOHN A.
1976.   Adaptive strategies in a biological and cultural transition zone: The Cen-
        tral Arizona Ecotone Project—an interim report.   University Museum
        Studies: Research Records, no. 6, Southern Illinois University, Carbon-
        dale.
ODUM, E. P.
1965.   Fundamentals of ecology.   W. B. Saunders Co., Philadelphia.
REED, ERIK K.
1950.   Eastern-central Arizona archaeology in relation to the western pueblos.
        Southwestern Journ. of Anthrop., vol. 6, pp. 120-138.
SCHROEDER, ALBERT H.
1954.   Four prehistoric sites near Mayer, Arizona, which suggest a new focus.
        Plateau, vol. 26, no. 3, Northern Arizona Society of Science and Art,
        Inc., Flagstaff.
SPOERL, PATRICIA M.
n.d.   Hohokam adaptation to a non-riverine environment in Central Arizona.
        Ph.D. dissertation, Southern Illinois University, Carbondale.
WEED, CAROL S.
1978.   The Central Arizona Ecotone Project and SARG.   Pp. 87-94 *in* "Inves-
        tigations of the Southwestern Anthropological Research Group: An Ex-
        periment in Archaeological Cooperation," edited by Robert C. Euler and
        George J. Gumerman.   Museum of Northern Arizona, Flagstaff.

GEORGE J. GUMERMAN
PATRICIA M. SPOERL

Archeological Investigations at the King Site, Floyd County, Georgia

Principal Investigator: David J. Hally, University of Georgia, Athens, Georgia.

Grant No. 1284:   In support of archeological investigations at the King site, Floyd County, Georgia.

The King site is located in the Piedmont of northwest Georgia approximately 25 miles west of the city of Rome. The site is situated in the alluvial floodplain of the Coosa River on the inside bank of a large meander loop known as Foster Bend. The approximately 2,000 acres of fertile bottomland surrounding the site constitute one of the largest tracts of alluvial land in the northwestern part of the state.

Scientific investigation of the King site began in the spring of 1971 when Patrick Garrow of Shorter College commenced weekend excavations with a volunteer crew. Excavations were continued intermittently by Garrow until the summer of 1973, when a formal 10-week field season was undertaken with financial support from Shorter College and the University of Georgia. At this time I became interested in the site and at Mr. Garrow's request agreed to seek financial support that would allow continuation of field investigations through the summer of 1975. In December 1973 I received a grant from the National Geographic Society for research at the site. These funds, along with generous contributions from local citizens and assistance from the University of Georgia, supported full-time excavation by a crew of five people under Garrow's direction until June 1974. At that time a research grant was received from the National Endowment for the Humanities,[1] and the crew was augmented by a University of Georgia summer field school class under my direction. Large-scale fieldwork was terminated on September 1, 1974.

The King site covers an area approximately 5 acres in extent. In all, 124,000 square feet, or nearly two-thirds of the site, have been excavated (fig. 1). The remainder has not been available for excavation. Stratigraphically, the site consists of a light-colored sandy loam subsoil and overlying plow zone. Occupation refuse and virtually all the aboriginal occupation surface have been destroyed by erosion and cultivation. Features such as burials and postholes, however, are preserved in the subsoil and are easily detected. Contours

---

[1] Grant no. (RO-20561-74-441).

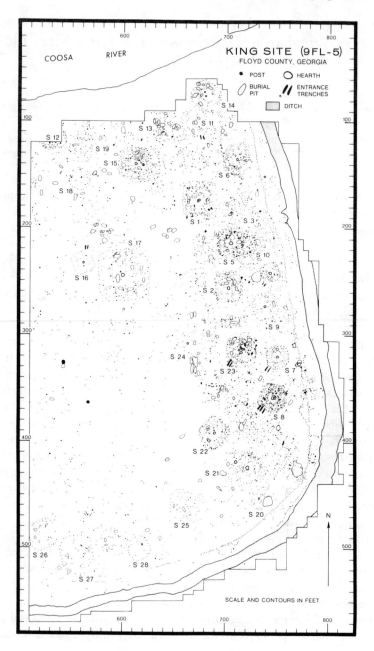

FIG. 1.   Map of King site archeological features.

of the subsoil surface and the relative absence of features along the southern periphery of the site (fig. 1) indicate that erosion damage is greatest in the southwest corner of the site.

Excavation of the site entailed first and foremost the removal of plow zone and exposure of subsoil surface. Heavy earth-moving equipment was used extensively in this operation. Features appearing on the exposed subsoil surface were mapped with plane table and alidade and, with the exception of postholes, were subsequently excavated by hand. Altogether, 222 burials, 7 intact house floors, and a small number of miscellaneous features were excavated.

The King site was occupied briefly during the early historic period. Four radiocarbon dates have been obtained, but they are of little value because of their combined range of 600 years. European artifacts—iron celts, knives, and rods with chisel-like points—present in a small number of burials, indicate an occupancy date in the 16th or early 17th century (Smith, 1975). Duration of site occupancy is estimated to have been less than 50 years, based on the existence of only one palisade line and the relatively low density of occupation features.

The King site has its closest cultural affiliation with the late prehistoric-early historic Lamar culture of north Georgia and the Dallas–Mouse Creek culture of eastern Tennessee. Identification of the historic ethnic or tribal affiliation of the site's inhabitants is difficult. The site is not historically documented, and its location is geographically intermediate to the known 18th-century location of Cherokee and Creek towns (Swanton, 1922). According to the United States DeSoto Commission report (1939), the DeSoto expedition passed within 50 miles of Foster Bend in 1540. Given the possibility that the King site was occupied as early as the second half of the 16th century, it is probably most meaningful to seek tribal affiliation with one of the towns or provinces—Chiaha, Coste, Tali, Tasqui, Cosa—encountered by DeSoto in the tristate area.

A recently conducted magnetometer survey of the unexcavated portion of the site has resulted in the location of the town's western perimeter. While verified by subsurface testing in only one location, it seems safe to conclude from this survey that the western ditch lies parallel to and approximately 460 feet from the eastern ditch. If the bank of the Coosa River formed the northern boundary of the site in aboriginal times, the town would have been roughly square in shape.

The basic elements of the King site settlement plan are: (1) a defensive perimeter consisting of ditch and palisade; (2) an inner zone of domestic structures; and (3) a large centrally located plaza containing buildings and other architectural features of a presumably public and ceremonial nature.

The ditch that encircles the entire excavated portion of the site had a depth of approximately 4-5 feet and a bottom width of 8-11 feet. The palisade is represented throughout most of its exposed length by a single line of posts. Architectural features such as bastions and entrances are difficult to recognize and may be absent in the area excavated. What may be a screened entrance and associated bastion are located east of Structure 21 (S390-420, E780-790). Small semicircular posthole arrangements occur at two points (S280 E770 and S495 E710) along the palisade and may represent bastions.

Within the palisade, 27 structures have been identified on the basis of posthole alignments and related architectural features.[2] Most of these occur in a relatively narrow zone adjacent to the palisade and are probably domestic in nature. The general characteristics of these structures include: (1) single-post wall construction, (2) wall trench entry passages located at building corners, (3) floor plans that are rectangular with rounded corners, (4) four interior supports, and (5) central hearths (fig. 2). The majority of these structures have been dismantled and rebuilt at least once during the period of site occupation.

Interior posts other than the four support posts are quite common in these structures. For the most part they occur outside the central floor area defined by the major support posts. They probably served at least two functions: bench or bed supports and studs for partition walls. Raised benches, placed against exterior walls, were a common feature of aboriginal houses throughout the Southeast in the historic period (Swanton, 1946, p.422). Evidence for the second identification is provided by preserved basal remnants of clay walls in Structures 4 and 7 (fig. 2).

Seven domestic structures had preserved floors at the time of site investigation. One of these was largely destroyed by vandals; the remainder were fully investigated through controlled excavation. Analysis of the occupation debris recovered in these excavations is far from complete, but already some interesting insights have been obtained into the functional nature of domestic structures.

By far the greatest quantity of occupation debris (broken pottery, animal bone, lithic *débitage*) occurs in the southern third of excavated structures, while the northern third almost invariably has little. This distribution contrasts with that of burials. Throughout the excavated site, subfloor burials occur almost entirely in the northern third of houses. Ethnohistoric evidence indicates that Southeastern Indians buried at least some of their dead beneath the beds of the living. Taken together, these three pieces of evidence suggest

---

[2] Structures 5 and 10 are counted as a single structure with two rebuilding stages.

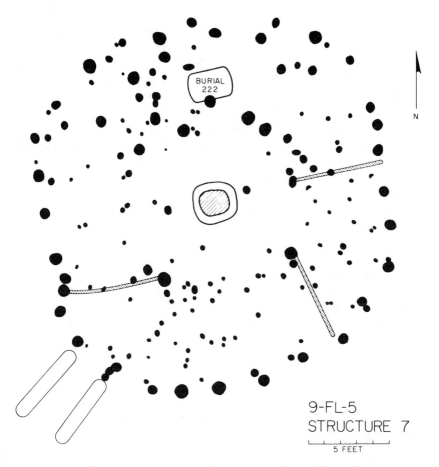

9-FL-5
STRUCTURE 7

5 FEET

Fig. 2.   Plan of Structure 7, King site, showing postholes, wall trench entrance passage, central hearth, and interior clay partitions.

that, at the King site, beds or benches were located primarily against walls in
the northern portion of domestic structures and that activities related to general household maintenance were usually performed in the southern portion.
    In the six excavated structures, lithic *débitage* is most heavily concentrated
in either the southcentral or southeast floor sectors. In three of these structures, lithic *débitage* was actually concentrated in a very restricted area. It
would appear then that some stages in flint knapping were carried out within
domestic structures and that there was a preferred location within these structures for this activity.

The large area in the center of the site, characterized by a low density of postholes, is identified as plaza. This area, as presently known, measures 150 feet east/west and 300 feet north/south. Notable features within the plaza are the two clusters of burials at the north end, the two structures (nos. 16 and 17) immediately to the south, and the two large postholes, Feature 11 (S365 E570) and Feature 45 (S325 E540) farther to the south.

Measuring 48 feet square, Structure 17 is by far the largest building encountered at the site. The central floor area of the structure, bounded by eight interior support posts, contains a hearth, two shallow pits, and a small number of postholes. Burials and numerous postholes fill the area between interior supports and exterior walls. The majority of postholes in this latter area form alignments that appear to divide each side of the structure into three or four compartments. Entrance to the structure was probably gained through an opening at the southeast corner.

It is probable that Structure 17 had public and ceremonial functions and that it can be equated with the Cherokee "town house" or Creek "hot house" of the early historic period. At least one 18th-century Creek hot house has been described as having a square floor plan with rounded corners (Swanton, 1928, p. 179). This shape matches that seen in Structure 17. The interior posthole alignments in the structure probably represent supports for platforms which are a common feature of historically documented structures of this kind.

Immediately adjacent to Structure 17 on the west is a building that in nearly all respects is similar to the domestic structures described above. It differs only in location, the absence of burials, and the occurrence of a small pit containing a pottery vessel immediately south of the hearth. The function of this structure is not known. Given its location, however, we can infer that it played a special role in community affairs.

Feature 45 is a large straight sided pit measuring 3.5 feet in diameter and 5 feet deep. Several large limestone slabs occurred in pit fill, and pit bottom was covered with a neatly arranged layer of similar slabs. Feature 11 is a narrower (1.5 feet diameter) but equally deep circular pit. Both features are unique on the site and, no doubt, are postholes. Given their size and location, it is possible that the posts they held can be identified with the "chunky" and "slave" posts that have been described for Creek towns since the late 18th century (Swanton, 1928, pp. 188-190). According to the late 18th-century naturalist William Bartram, both kinds of post stood in the town plaza or "chunky yard." "Chunky poles" were 30 to 40 feet tall, measured 2 to 3 feet across at the base, and were used in a ball game played between men and women.

"Slave posts" stood about 12 feet high and were used for the display of scalps and the torture of war captives.

Information obtained through field investigations at the King site is suitable for research in a variety of general problem areas including demography, subsistence patterns, settlement pattern, and social organization. Research in several of these areas is currently under way, and it is anticipated that the King site will emerge as one of the most thoroughly explored and completely understood aboriginal settlements in the Southeastern United States.

REFERENCES

SMITH, MARVIN T.
1975.   European materials from the King site.   Bull. Southeastern Archaeol. Conf., no. 18, pp. 63-67.
SWANTON, JOHN R.
1922.   Early history of the Creek Indians and their neighbors.   Bur. Amer. Ethnol. Bull. 73, 492 pp., illus.
1928.   Social organization and social usages of the Indians of the Creek Confederacy.   42d Ann. Rpt. Bur. Amer. Ethnol., pp. 23-472, illus.
1946.   The Indians of the Southeastern United States.   Bur. Amer. Ethnol. Bull. 137, 943 pp., illus.
UNITED STATES DESOTO EXPEDITION COMMISSION
1939.   Final report of the United States DeSoto Expedition Commission. 76th Congr., 1st sess., House Doc. 71, xvi + 400 pp., maps.

DAVID J. HALLY

Social and Reproductive Biology of the Yucatán Jay

Principal Investigators: John William Hardy, Florida State Museum, Gainesville, Florida; and Ralph J. Raitt, New Mexico State University, Las Cruces, New Mexico.[1]

Grant No. 1161:   For a study of the Yucatán jay *(Cyanocorax yucatanica).*

The aim of the present research was to reveal the social behavior and related ecology of the Yucatán jay, *C. yucatanica.* The study began in 1968 (non-breeding behavior in April), was resumed in June 1972 (early phases of breeding and vegetation analysis), continued in January 1973 (winter flocking) and completed, with the aid of the present grant, in July 1973 (communal care of the young).

Background and Aims of the Research

Four allopatric and closely related species of neotropical jays (genus *Cyanocorax,* subgenus *Cissilopha*) are found in Middle America. *C. beecheii* inhabits northwestern Mexico, *C. sanblasiana* southwestern Mexico, *C. melanocyanea,* highland northern Central America, and *C. yucatanica,* the Yucatán Peninsula of Mexico. The four have marked phenotypic similarity, being as adults largely blue (dorsum) and black (head and body). Each exhibits complex ontogenetic change from nestling to adulthood (Hardy, 1973) and is of highly social character, displaying communality including altruism in breeding ("helpers at the nest"). A comparative study to reveal the ecological basis and evolution of the sociality of these birds is the primary aim of this long-term project.

Social Behavior and Ecology

Large winter flocks (20-50 or more birds) of this species break up at least by April into the communal groups of 4 to 10 birds, typically consisting of

---

[1] Other scientific personnel involved in this study included Jorge Orejeula, New Mexico State University, Las Cruces, New Mexico; Thomas Webber, Glendale, California; and Bruce Edinger, Suffern, New York.

311

some individuals of various age classes (first-year to adult). The time of year is usually the height of the dry season, when most of the woodland has dropped its leaves, although in some winters (such as 1972-73) sufficient rain falls to cause the forest to retain leaves. The smaller groups move about through exclusive ranges, so far as we can tell, frequently attending army-ant swarms and otherwise foraging for fruits and insects.

The breeding season begins in late April or early May. After the severe dry winter of 1971-72, there was great synchrony of the commencement of breeding in the population under study. Ten nests that we discovered in the week of June 9-16 were all in early stages of incubation and there was no evidence that any groups anywhere in the area were in advance of the nests under study. After a wetter than normal season, in which the leaf canopy is retained and probably insect food remains at comparatively high levels, breeding begins earlier by between three and four weeks and is less synchronous in the population. Thus, after the wet winter of 1972-73 we discovered full-grown juveniles in late June and early July, as well as nests with young and a few with eggs.

Nests range in height from 14-32 feet (mean 20) and are usually a few feet beneath the crown of a tree 18-25 feet in height, usually within the forest but within 10 to 25 feet of the forest edge. Our studies were concentrated along a road extending for about 10 kilometers through preferred habitat, and all nests studied conformed to the above characterization. Building of the nest is undertaken almost completely by the nucleus female (our term for the presumed female parent), whose mate attends her closely and sometimes carries nest material. Other flock members can be found in the near vicinity but take no part in construction, although they visit the nest vicinity. At one nest where building was studied, construction took 5 to 7 days and the female began to sit (and presumably to lay) about 5 days after the nest was completed.

The clutch size ranges from 4 to 6, with a mean of 5. Only the nucleus female incubates, being fed on or near the nest by her putative mate and occasionally by other flock members. When the female leaves the nest, the male stands guard on the nest rim. The incubation period is approximately 18 days.

At first the young require little feeding and the participation of the communal group in their care is little in evidence. The female broods. The male brings food and distributes it to the young as well as to the female, who assists in feeding the young. After about 4 days the female also participates in acquiring food for the brood. It is at this time that the altruistic participation of other group members typically begins to occur. At one nest at least 5 adults provided food to the young, but the communal group was considerably larger and included juveniles of a first nesting that were not observed to visit the nest. The known feeders were the putative parents, 2 other adults (one of which failed to return after being netted and marked), and a first-year bird. At another nest regular feeders seemed to include 4 adults, with occasional visits by at least 3 first-year birds and rare visits by up to 4 juveniles.

Predators include snakes and probably squirrels. A snake removed a half-grown nestling without interference from adults. A squirrel visited a nest from which young had recently disappeared and another squirrel near a nest with young was mobbed and knocked from the tree.

Young seem to be fed largely insects, but berries were also fed to them. Young leave the nest a few days before being able to fly and within hours can climb several feet from the nest through the dense vegetation.

After the second nestings of the flocks nonbreeding or wintering flocks begin to take form. These must be composed of adjacent communal groups since they include up to 13 juveniles and a total of as many as 50 birds. Where nestlings are still being cared for such large groups are not in evidence. Where the latter are found, no remaining nesting activity was detected. The large flocks move long distances—up to a mile or more from feeding area to feeding area and resting areas. The area covered by these movements probably coincides with the combined home ranges of the smaller breeding communal groups. One bird marked in the breeding season of 1972 was found in the same area in 1973. Birds marked at the same general capture area in January 1973 were found together or in adjacent areas nearby in July 1973. These facts suggest the sedentary nature of the birds. Movements of up to 8 kilometers possibly occur, however, since one bird marked in June 1972 was thought to have been seen that distance away in January 1972.

Age composition of flocks varies greatly from year to year and provides an index of survival for at least the two previous breeding seasons. In June 1972, composition of groups was largely adults with most groups having 2-year-old birds and only a few having 1-year-olds. This indicated normal productivity and survival in breeding of 1970 and low productivity or survival in breeding of 1971. In 1973, further confirming the problems of 1971, and indicating good reproduction in 1972, most flocks had about half adults and half 1-year-olds, with no 2-year-olds being seen.

The foregoing abstract is based upon an overview of our data and field notes and not an in-depth analysis. Therefore characterizations made, correlations drawn, and conclusions reached are subject to revision. Other workers are therefore urged to use the information here only after referring to our comprehensive paper on the subject (Raitt and Hardy, 1976).

REFERENCES

HARDY, JOHN WILLIAM
   1973.   Age and sex differences in the black-and-blue jays of Middle America.
   Bird Banding, vol. 44, no. 2, pp. 81-90.
RAITT, RALPH J., and HARDY, JOHN WILLIAM
   1976.   Behavioral ecology of the Yucatán jay.   Wilson Bull., vol. 88, no. 4
   (December), pp. 529-554, illus.

JOHN WILLIAM HARDY

RALPH J. RAITT

Resource-use Knowledge Among the Otomí Indians of the Mezquital, Mexico

Principal Investigator: Kirsten Johnson Haring, Clark University, Worcester, Massachusetts.

Grant No. 1228:   In aid of a study of resource cognition among the Otomí Indians of Mexico.

The Otomí Indians of the Mezquital inhabit a series of valleys located in the central Mexican plateau approximately 100 miles north of the Valley of Mexico. The resource base of the Mezquital, with its rocky mountainous terrain, thin soils, overgrazed xerophytic vegetation, low unreliable rainfall (average 20 inches per year), and frequent droughts, affords the Indian population with a meager means of livelihood. Over the centuries the Otomí have managed to evolve a complex of resource-use strategies allowing them to subsist and persist in this inhospitable environment. Contemporary Otomí resource use reflects a sophisticated blend of pre-Columbian, Spanish colonial, and modern agricultural practices. Aside from their knowledge of desert resources and of the ways in which a limited and unpredictable moisture supply can be manipulated, an important feature of Otomí survival has been the very low level at which their needs are satisfied. The Mezquital is one of the poorest, most underdeveloped regions in the country, and its inhabitants are among the most marginalized of Mexico's Indian groups.

These circumstances are changing dramatically for a significant number of Otomí. Under government auspices an irrigation network is being extended to cover 47,000 hectares of Mezquital valley land. Irrigation creates a transformation of landscape and resource use in the communities encompassed by the network. Traditional moisture-management techniques, field systems, crop and animal complexes, and crafts manufacture give way to entirely new resource-use regimes and to the cultivation of cash crops for metropolitan wholesale markets. This agricultural transformation is accompanied by the capitalization of agriculture, the aggregation of large landholdings, and the disintegration of the peasantry, most of whom become wage workers and a few of whom become wealthy entrepreneurs.

Otomí are not the only ones with a stake in the development of irrigation in the Mezquital. The government expects that a dramatic increase in agricultural productivity will help offset its own heavy investment in the irrigation infrastructure. In addition, the government is counting on a strengthening of rural production systems to provide employment for the inhabitants of the countryside, and thereby to help stem the tide of migrants to Mexico's urban areas. These expectations arise from the government's own evaluation of the resources of the region and are embodied in the policies and ideology of the local development planners and agricultural extension agents (*técnicos*). This official evaluation of resources constitutes a body of theory and practice in much the same way as the Otomí farmer's does. Of course, *técnicos* and Otomí farmers view resources from widely separate vantage points. It is not surprising, therefore, that significant discrepancies exist between what each defines as an actual resource as well as what each considers to be the proper strategies of resource use.

Research Aims

The general aim of the research was to use ethnoscience theory and methods in order to examine and compare two bodies of resource knowledge within the context of rapid agricultural and social change. To accomplish this aim the ethnosemantic techniques developed in anthropological linguistics were modified and applied to an analysis of a body of traditional resource-use knowledge as well as to the new technological alternatives proffered by development agents. The study was primarily concerned with documenting the Otomí definition of resources and Otomí theories of proper agricultural practice. In addition, an attempt was made to record the official definition of the Mezquital's resources (which can also be regarded as an ethnoscience) contained in the views, knowledge, and practice of the local *técnicos*. Subsequently, the two ethnosciences were compared in order to determine areas of complementarity and contradiction.

A direct comparison of Otomí and *técnico* ethnosciences is both justifiable and important. The two can be regarded as equivalent cognitive systems on the grounds that both discriminate environmental phenomena, both organize and interrelate these discriminated categories on the basis of conceptual schemes, and both contain general principles that provide the system with coherence and integrity. It becomes important from a social point of view to establish the bases of formal comparability between the two ethnosciences since they will shortly come into conflict during the course of planned agricultural development. Viewed in a social context, each knowledge system represents a distinct resource assessment of the region that arises out of a distinct path of historical development relating to two different classes and systems of production.

Ethnosciences are bodies of knowledge as well as mechanisms for constructing this knowledge that all members of a reference group share. The degree and nature of this sharing cannot be stated in advance, but can only be hypothesized and then determined empirically. The following section deals with the methods and procedures developed during an 8-month field study in one community in the arid portion of the Mezquital that will shortly be irrigated. During this period Otomí ethnoscience was documented and structured in a comprehensive fashion and *técnico* ethnoscience in a partial one.

Field Methods and Procedures

To do ethnoscience fieldwork is to immerse oneself in an alien universe of knowledge and experience unarmed with the usual tools of the social-science research trade. Questionnaires, surveys, tests, and other techniques that define and organize data by means of imposed categories are declared out of bounds. In their place we have a handful of approaches derived mainly from anthropological linguistics enabling us to elicit what has been called "the inside view," which is generally taken to mean a definition of reality constituted by the categories, relations, and theories intrinsic to the cognitive system of the group under study.

Generally, ethnosciences are constructed on the basis of lengthy, structured interviews with a limited number of informants. Since one of the objectives of this study was to record shared knowledge, the standard approach had to be modified substantially. In the case of the Otomí, in-depth interviews were combined with informal conversations, observation, and gossip, and an attempt was made to cross-check all ethnoscience data on a community-wide basis. In the case of *técnicos*, lengthy structured interviews proved to be infeasible and were abandoned in favor of queries limited to specific spheres of resource knowledge. Subsequently, these interviews were supplemented with data gleaned from the available planning literature.

The field enquiry centered on the following key questions: (1) What are the principal categories of resource discrimination and what are the bases upon which these discriminations are made? (2) How are limited and unpredictable resources combined in such a manner as to make them less limited and more predictable? (3) What are the general premises that underpin this knowledge and allow the speakers to share similar sets of evaluations as well as comparable outlooks toward the future?

These questions were examined under three techniques: a construction of categories; a construction of relations; and a construction of proposition sets.

CATEGORIES

When people categorize they select and group events from the phenomenal world on the basis of invented criteria. These criteria are not invented over and over by each individual; they are constructed culturally and learned socially. The groups, or categories, of events formed in this manner constitute the basis of what a group knows about its environment. Categories are organized into classificatory systems known as *taxonomies*. The criteria determining these structures can be discovered by what is called *paradigmatic* analysis of taxonomies.

Categorical analysis will structure the bulk of what a group discriminates in the environment; subsequently, the investigator can infer which resources are central in the group's ethnoscience. Useful though it is, this is essentially a static analysis of events that have been reified into entities and structured into classifications of terms. If one is interested in the dynamic facets of an ethnoscience, then one must turn to two other approaches: relations and proposition sets.

RELATIONS

Terms acquire meaning not only from their inherent attributes but also from their ties to other terms. What is conceived of as an entity in the categorical approach is seen as an event in a stream of events in process in the relational approach. The interconnectivity of events is implicit in people's resource-use activities. It also exists as a covert "given" in their system of knowledge. The object of a relational analysis, therefore, is to abstract and reconstruct these implicit relations.

Two types of relational constructions were developed during the field research period: *taxonomy intersections* and *field relational chains*. In taxonomy intersections the original taxonomic matrix dissolves and terms are linked in a new web of associations. For example, maize intersects with certain field types, soil/water conditions, insect pests, etc. Different seasons intersect with the availability of different forage plants, diseases, etc. Thousands of these simple linkages constitute the building blocks of resource-use strategy. More complex networks of linkages indicate the ways in which resources are likely to be combined and timed. Field relational chains link a stream of events involved in a cycle of agricultural production. For example, when a certain category of landscape is appraised for a particular use (in this case agricultural) it becomes a category of terrain; and when a certain kind of human labor is performed on this terrain the result is a category of field; then, when certain other sequences of human labor are timed with the cycles of environmental process inherent in this field category, the result is a culturally anticipated crop potential. The chain linking landscape to crop potential is at the center of any society's agricultural system. The key operations linking the events in this chain are cognition (in the form of appraisals and expectations) and human labor. An ethnoscience usually contains several intersecting relational chains, a comprehension and application of which constitute part of a group's definition of proper agricultural practice.

PROPOSITION SETS

Categories and relations are analytical constructions abstracted from everyday discourse over which the investigator exerts a degree of control. This discourse is made up of the propositions and strings of propositions that form logical arguments. These arguments contain the whole of ethnoscientific explanation since they incorporate both the terms of taxonomies and the connections and interpenetrations of relations in a totality of judgments, assessments, and rules of thumb that articulate Otomí resource knowledge.

Some proposition sets relate only to very limited or specific domains of problem solving, while others are more general statements of belief that determine whole areas of understanding. One task of field investigation is to distinguish between particular propositions and general ones and to ground each in its own resource-use context. This can be accomplished by focusing dialogue on specific tasks that frame resource-use activity: e.g., building a terrace wall, hauling water from the well. Each activity frame contains its own microcosm of particular taxonomies (or partial taxonomies) and relations interwoven by explanatory proposition sets.

Findings

The field-research effort generated a very large body of data formulated in terms of the above-mentioned constructions. It is impossible adequately to summarize these data in this short survey. Instead, in the following pages are presented a series of general conclusions that are illustrated by selected examples from Otomí and *técnico* ethnosciences. These conclusions are presented in terms of the original key questions formulated at the outset of the field-research period.

CATEGORIES OF RESOURCE DISCRIMINATION

An examination of Otomí and *técnico* general landscape categorization and a comparison of the range of resources discriminated in each landscape type reveal that the Otomí discriminate the local (dry-land) microecology more highly than do *técnicos*. In addition (and with some reservations that will be discussed below) Otomí ethnoscience recognizes and makes use of a greater variety of soil/water conditions than does *técnico* ethnoscience.

The crucial difference between Otomí and *técnico* landscape categories is one of scale. Not surprisingly, *técnicos* think in regional terms while for the Otomí the meaningful scale is local. This, of course, does not mean that either is unable to conceptualize landscape at other scales; it means that the operative levels of landscape discrimination bring the Otomí much closer to a microecological frame of reference.

The implications of this disparity are borne out when one contrasts Otomí and *técnico* taxonomies of resources clustered by landscape type. Otomí recognize a substantially wider range (often twice or three times as large) of available resources in each of the three highest-level landscape contrast sets.

Entire Otomí resource categories, such as game and herbs, go unacknowledged in *técnico* ethnoscience. Others, such as construction materials and house sites, are acknowledged but given little importance. Some categories, such as animal forage plants and sources of firewood, involve resource-use practices that *técnicos* consider as contributing to ecological degradation. All local sources of water are judged by *técnicos* as inadequate and contaminated. Yet other Otomí resource categories, such as cerro maguey, pricklypear, and lechuguilla, are considered as being exploited in an economically irrational fashion. Perhaps most important, the gullies and depressions that constitute highly valued sites for Otomí field construction are virtually ignored (or else seen as evidence of severe erosion problems) in *técnico* ethnoscience. Otomí terracing on slopes is viewed as a beneficial erosion-control practice, but not as a mechanism to capture water, the primary concern of the local farmers. The propensity to devalue Otomí dry-land moisture-management strategies probably stems from the *técnico* regional landscape schema, which accords no agricultural potential (i.e., insofar as staple food crops such as maize are concerned) to the unirrigated portions of the Mezquital.

A comparison between *técnico* and Otomí domains of soil knowledge runs into one conspicuous difficulty from the outset. If a comparison is made between Otomí farmers and local extension agents, then it can be said that Otomí knowledge of soils is broader and more discriminative. However, extension agents also count on the services of soil scientists, and if their expertise is included in the *técnico* domain of soil knowledge, then it cannot be maintained that Otomí knowledge is more discriminative than the *técnico's*. Nevertheless, if the comparison is limited to soil knowledge that is applied, then it is probably fair to say that *técnico* practice is geared toward homogenizing local soil differences, while Otomí practice (having developed a greater number of discrete techniques to enhance different soil/water conditions) is more selective and adaptive to different soils.

Otomí soil knowledge cannot be interpreted in primarily categorical terms, since the fundamental concepts reside in the area of soil/water relations. It can be said that Otomí do not think in terms of soil; they think in terms of soil/water relations. The central concepts here are articulated as "water complicates" and "entrance of water." Water complicates soil in two ways, first in terms of increasing salinity. It is said that "water that has no exit complicates soil." The second way water complicates soil is along a dimension of increasing hardness. Otomí explain that *tepetates* and *canteras* are soils that have been complicated over long periods of time by water. They distinguish between "hollow" or soft *tepetate*, over which water has had a shorter time to work, and "hard" *tepetate*, which has taken a long time to form.

According to Otomí practice each type of soil requires a particular kind of labor or series of labors in order to enhance its qualities and overcome its limitations. Some need no special care beyond being fertilized when they are "tired." Others, like sandy or yellow soils, must be fertilized from the outset. In these cases fertilizer is used in order to improve water retention or to counter salinization. Hollow *tepetates* are also cultivable if the farmer is willing to labor with a pickax to smash and pulverize them. The most important process Otomí allow to work in their favor is what they term "entrance of water." Each series of gully or slope fields comprises a catchment with a certain potential to concentrate water and alluvium. "Entrance of water" is a measure of that potential. Almost all Otomí field systems incorporate mechanisms enabling topsoil buildup. These allow the farmer to overcome local site limitations of poor or even nonexistent soil. A common strategy used in order to deal with rocky or saline soils is simply to wait until layers of water-borne debris cover them.

Técnico ethnoscience adopts a completely different approach to the problem of the region's thin and inadequate soils. This approach applies uniformly to all soils and involves use of heavy equipment to remove all vegetation and then to break *tepetate* outcroppings and deep plow and mix the topsoil horizons. In addition, large quantities of organic or chemical fertilizer are applied in order to improve soil structure and fertility. Finally, terraces are built as an erosion-prevention measure on the slopes that need them.

COMBINATION OF LIMITED AND UNPREDICTABLE RESOURCES

An examination of field types illustrates how local farmers assemble their limited and unpredictable resources in such a manner as to make them less limited and more predictable. Moreover, a comparison between Otomí and *técnico* field taxonomies shows that the former transform local (dry-land) microecology into a greater variety of field types than do the latter.

Técnico options for dry-land agriculture are fairly limited. Maize is seen as uneconomical and destructive. Terraces for improved pasture are considered a distant possibility. The only crops that are viewed with any degree of enthusiasm are improved varieties of pricklypear and maguey. This low assessment of dry-land agricultural potential has a great deal to do with the limited number of possible field systems *técnicos* are able to envision for the arid portions of the region.

Otomí recognize four basic field types that relate to four different site and labor-input circumstances: gully fields (*atajadizos*), terraced or semiterraced slope fields (*bordos*), unterraced slope fields (*laderas*), and flat fields (*planes*). On the other hand, *técnicos* discriminate two basic field types: level fields and terraced fields. This leaves *atajadizos* and *laderas* unaccounted for in the *técnico* domain. These are important omissions, *atajadizos* being the most valued fields in the Otomí agricultural system, and *ladera* cultivation constituting a source of welcome catch crops during rainy years. The fourfold Otomí field system builds variety and flexibility into Otomí agriculture. *Técnico* ethnoscience views gullies as an erosion problem rather than the locus of important concentrations of water and topsoil.

A comparison of Otomí and *técnico* field relational chains points to some fundamentally different resource-use assumptions: (1) The *técnico* premise that dry-farm agriculture in the Mezquital must be defined in terms of high capital input, cash cropping, and long-term profit, compared to the Otomí premise that labor can yield short-term gain; (2) the *técnico* premise that all eventualities can be dealt with and that rain-fed agriculture can be profitable, compared to the Otomí premise that rain-fed farming is a gamble that must be taken but that is often lost. In this game the diversity of field systems and their different crop potentials are to the advantage of the Otomí farmer, whereas, in contrast, the standardization that *técnico* fields impose on the landscape relates to the standard agronomic formulas that guarantee control and success.

GENERAL PREMISES

Otomí and *técnico* ethnosciences are underpinned by two fundamentally different approaches to production and consumption. In terms of production, the aim of Otomí resource use is to maximize the use of household labor and of free locally available inputs; whereas *técnico* ethnoscience emphasizes the use of capital in order to purchase nonlocal inputs and hired labor. In terms of consumption, Otomí ethnoscience emphasizes production for the sake of household maintenance, while *técnico* ethnoscience stresses production for the sake of capital accumulation.

The Otomí approach to production revolves around the possibilities and limitations of the household labor unit and around a series of mechanisms that enable a flexible coordination of resources within the farm community. Different spheres of production possess their own specific proposition sets. Yet the possibilities and limitations intrinsic to the Otomí level of production organization determine that strong commonalities exist between the general principles underlying diverse spheres of resource use.

The underlying premises of Otomí resource use are manifest in specific activity frames. An apt illustration encapsulating the differences between Otomí and *técnico* production objectives can be seen in the case of livestock management. The stated objective of Otomí management is: "Animals are like a bank account that one has." The aim of Otomí efforts in this sphere is to keep this "bank balance" as high as possible with as little direct cash input as possible. Livestock is seen as a security cushion to be used by the family in case of an emergency. The Otomí approach to livestock management is encapsulated in decisions regarding feed and forage. Otomí divide the year into two periods: the first from about May to October, during which time "the animals fatten themselves," and the second period, between November and April, a time during which "animals maintain themselves," i.e., they starve. Unlike pastoralists, Otomí are tied to their village and fields and are unable to seek dry-season pasture. This means that their livestock must survive on what is available locally: chopped cacti and dwindling supplies of maize stalks. When these run out animals starve. The Otomí do not view this dilemma with equanimity and resort to various strategies in order to maintain their herds. The important fact to note is that hardly any of these strategies requires capital investment.

Técnico theories of "proper livestock management" center on the proposition that current Otomí practices are woefully inadequate and irrational and that a number of steps can be taken in order that animal husbandry enable "each peasant to become a rural entrepreneur." All except one of these steps involve capital investment, and their sum adds up to a heavily entrepreneurial approach. These techniques make less use of labor, or use labor in forms (such as wage labor) that render the family household labor unit obsolete. Moreover, the *técnico* approach to livestock management emphasizes integrated package solutions, making it difficult for the farmer to adopt one or two components of an innovation in isolation from the others. The general premises underlying *técnico* rationale for livestock management are paralleled in other spheres of production: cash tree crops and vegetable truck farming (for irrigation agriculture).

Otomí and *técnico* ethnosciences operate on fundamentally different principles: each defines different landscapes and within these landscapes different resources; each aims at different objectives, each assembles the factors of production according to different formulas, and each is constrained by different limitations. The root of these differences lies in the fact that each ethnoscience is based on distinct consumption imperatives: household maintenance and capital accumulation.

That Otomí emphasize production for the sake of household consumption and expect to continue to do so in the face of fundamental changes in their resource base is borne out by an examination of their assessment of the future irrigation landscape, its novel ways of assembling resources, and its potential problems. An analysis of Otomí proposition sets relating to these questions indicates that Otomí see irrigation as a means of increasing their security in maize and animals and of expanding their crop repertory. This does not mean that Otomí will not inch their way into more capital intensive production. They seem quite willing to contemplate expenditures on water, seed, and insecticides. Nevertheless, production for consumption and family maintenance is considered essential: "Maize comes first," Otomí state. This decision is graphically manifest in a projected irrigation field system where maize occupies most of the acreage and tree crops are kept to the margins.

While Otomí project a richer modified landscape where their needs will be met, *técnicos* envision a totally altered landscape with novel crops, field systems, productive arrangements, and tenure patterns, which is inhabited by a new breed of person, the rural entrepreneur. *Técnicos* bemoan Otomí's "psychological dependence on maize."

The two projections have little in common with each other, either in their fundamental assumptions or in their individual components. Each has the power to transform the landscape in its own image. The future irrigation landscape of the Mezquital will incorporate elements of both ethnosciences, along with other features as yet unforseen by either.

KIRSTEN JOHNSON

Archeological Investigations at the Lehner Site, Arizona, 1974-75

Principal Investigators: C. Vance Haynes, Jr., and Emil W. Haury, University of Arizona, Tucson, Arizona.

Grant Nos. 1261   For archeological investigations at the Lehner site, San
and 1492.   Pedro Valley, southern Arizona.

Introduction

The discovery of a mammoth skeleton and eight associated Clovis points at Naco, Arizona, in 1950 was the fourth known buried site of the Clovis Culture, the earliest clearly defined culture in the New World (Haury et al., 1953). While Emil Haury of the Arizona State Museum was excavating the Naco site in 1952, Edward Lehner reported the occurrence of more mammoth bones at his property on the San Pedro River 12 miles to the west. This eventually led to the excavation of the now famous Lehner Clovis site where the scientific results included the first Clovis fire hearths, the first radiocarbon dates for the culture, and the first possible association with extinct tapir, in addition to 13 Clovis points and eight other artifacts in association with bones of nine mammoths (Haury et al., 1959). The bones of horse *(Equus),* bison *(Bison),* and tapir *(Tapirus)* in addition to those of the mammoths were studied by John F. Lance (1959).

The early geological work was conducted by the late Ernst Antevs who described the detailed stratigraphy of the site and demonstrated that the kill had taken place in and along a small creek called Mammoth-Kill Creek, a tributary, now buried, of the San Pedro River (Antevs, 1959).

The deposit directly overlying the channel sands of Mammoth-Kill Creek and the adjacent banks is a black organic clay referred to as the "black mat" and probably representing a "fossil" soil formed in a wet meadow or cienega where the water table stood at the surface and supported a lush local flora.

In 1963, palynological and geochronological investigations at the site (Mehringer and Haynes, 1965) resulted in a better understanding of the paleo-environment of the past 11,000 years, and in one of our stratigraphic trenches another mammoth skeleton was revealed in the channel sands of Mammoth-Kill Creek. In subsequent years, two other Clovis sites, the Escapule and the Murray Springs sites, were discovered and excavated with sup-

325

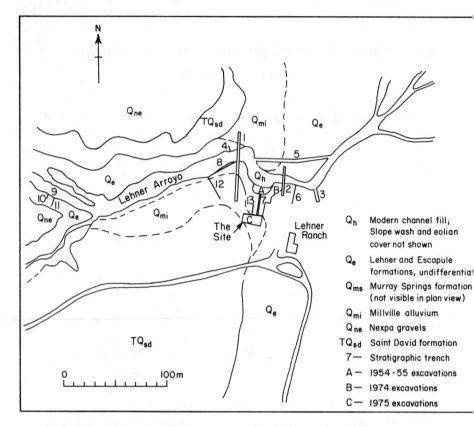

FIG. 1. Geologic map of Lehner Arroyo. Equivalent units of figure 2 are $Q_h = H_2$; $Q_e = F_1, F_2, F_2, F_3, G_1,$ and G_2; $Q_{ms} = E_1$; $Q_{mi} = Z$; $Q_{ne} = C$; and $TQ_{sd} = A + B$.

port of the National Geographic Society (Haynes, 1973, 1974, 1976; Haynes and Hemmings, 1969; Hemmings, 1970). The discovery of clearly defined kill, butchering and camping areas at the Murray Springs-Clovis site suggested that similar activity areas should also occur 12 miles to the south at the Lehner site, upslope from the buried channel of Mammoth-Kill Creek.

1974-1975 Excavations

With the objective of testing this possibility and excavating the mammoth found in 1963, new excavations were begun in 1974, and the Lehner Clovis site was reopened after 18 years of rest by removing up to 2 meters of culturally sterile overburden with mechanical equipment. The first area

South

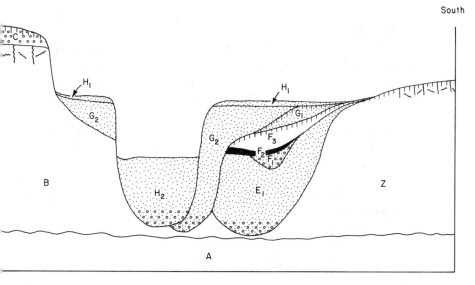

FIG. 2. Generalized geologic cross section of Lehner Arroyo. No scale. Width of modern channel is 10 to 20 meters and bank height is 2 to 3 meters.

cleared, Area B (fig. 1), was that west of the 1963 stratigraphic trench no. 2 and east of the 1954-55 excavations of Haury and others (1959) which will hereinafter be referred to as Area A. After careful exposure, the black mat (unit F_2, fig. 2) directly overlying the Clovis occupation surface was removed by hand with trowels, brushes, and dental picks.

Mammoth bones exposed by trench 2 in 1963 were the first paleontological specimens to be uncovered and were on and in the upper part of channel sands and gravels of Mammoth-Kill Creek (unit F_1, fig. 2). Ribs, leg bones, and mandibles representing two young mammoths were found in association with one chert flake and scattered lumps of charcoal.

Excavations to the south and west in Area B showed more evidence of human occupation of the south bank of the ancient creek. The ancient ground surface rises gently but irregularly to the south and contains several irregular depressions. Scattered over this surface were 2 unifacial tools, 2 fragments, a utilized flake, 27 flakes, numerous bone fragments, and charcoal lumps. An oval-shaped depression, the closed part of which measures 2 by 4 meters, in the middle of Area B contained a concentration of charcoal, charred and calcined bone fragments, and several flakes and tool fragments. Around this depression were numerous broken bones of a young mammoth, bison, jackrabbit, tortoise, and bear. The feature is obviously a hearth or roasting pit. Eighteen red and gray chert flakes concentrated at the western part of Area B are unifacial edge-sharpening flakes that very likely came from the large flake side scraper (no. 3) found farther west (Area A) in the 1954 excavations.

Trench 7, excavated with a backhoe to provide a stratigraphic profile, revealed the black mat to extend 37 meters farther south. To test the possibility that the occupation extended in this direction, a 6-meter-wide area was cleared eastward from the trench, thus extending Area B southward. Hand excavation of the black mat in the northern half of this area revealed scattered charcoal and bones (some charred) of bison, horse, camel, jackrabbit and garter snake. The split camel bones are the first evidence of Clovis utilization of this species, and the smaller animals have long been suspected of being a part of the Clovis diet, so this evidence is reassuring in that regard.

Several fragments, some matching, of fine-grained igneous rock came from near the center of Area B, but were found several centimeters above the Clovis occupation surface and at the base of the gray silt (unit F_3, fig. 2) that overlies the black mat. A concentration of charcoal occurred within the black mat in this area. This unexpected post-Clovis occupation may represent the Sulphur Spring phase of the Cochise culture and adds to the importance of the Lehner site. It suggests that the early Cochise stage is a different culture of later age.

Excavations in Area C were done in 1975 as a result of probing the strata with a soil auger and finding bone fragments in association with the buried black mat. While no definite artifacts were found in this area, there were a few bone and tooth fragments scattered on the Clovis occupational surface, the basal contact of unit F_2. Some of these proved to be teeth and jaw fragments of a juvenile mastodon *(Mammut americanum),* the first reported occurrence for Arizona. Further excavation revealed these remains to be a part of unit Z. They were exposed by erosion during the incision of the F_1 channel and, therefore, were undoubtedly exposed during occupation of the site by Clovis people (Mead et al., 1979).

A few meters west of the mastodon remains a cylindrical hole about 60 centimeters in diameter and 62 deep extended from unit F_3 through F_2 and into unit Z. It is probably a prehistoric well of the Cochise culture but associated artifacts were lacking. Similar wells were found at Murray Springs but of later Cochise age.

The preliminary results of radiocarbon dating 21 charcoal samples collected from the Clovis living floor indicate the occupation to have taken place 11,000 ± 100 years ago. Two dates of 9900 ± 80 B.P. (SMU-204) and 9860 ± 80 B.P. (SMU-197) indicate that the Cochise occupation took place about

1000 years later and is thus similar in age to the Sulphur Spring occupation at Double Adobe, Arizona (Whalen, 1971).

Geochronology

Geological investigations at Lehner Ranch arroyo (Antevs, 1959; Mehringer and Haynes, 1965) reveal that the alluvial deposits occupy an ancient channel cut into Blancan age valley-fill deposits of the Saint David Formation (Johnson et al., 1975), which, at the Lehner site, forms a 20-meter terrace of the San Pedro river (Q_{sd}, fig. 1; A and B, fig. 2). The earliest late Quaternary deposit filling the channel is a reddish brown, compact, poorly sorted alluvium consisting of clayey coarse sand intermixed with lenses of mudstone and clayey pebble to cobble gravel. Elsewhere in the upper San Pedro Valley, this unit (Z of Haynes, 1968, and fig. 2; and Q_{mi}, of fig. 1) is known to contain a Rancholabrean fauna (Lindsay and Tessman, 1974), but it is undoubtedly beyond the range of radiocarbon dating.

Unit Z is unconformably overlain by a similar, but less compact, alluvial fill (unit E_1, fig. 2) that may be an alluvial facies of a mudstone (unit D) and marl (unit E) that are exposed in many tributary arroyos along the west side of the upper San Pedro Valley (Haynes, 1968). At the Murray Springs Clovis site (Hemmings, 1970) radiocarbon dating of the marl indicates deposition between 30,000 and 12,000 years ago, or a late Wisconsin age. At the Lehner site, a small exposure of the mudstone and marl in trench 2 is unfortunately devoid of pollen, but the marl is clear evidence that the water table stood at the surface to form either a shallow pond or an area of low-gradient, seepy discharge during the last pluvial maximum.

An erosional unconformity separates unit E from the overlying F units (F_1, F_2, and F_3, fig. 2) bearing Clovis artifacts at the top of the lowest member (F_1) which is the fluvial sand occupying the relatively small channel referred to as Mammoth-Kill Creek (Haury et al., 1959). The F_1 channel sand is in part a lag deposit derived from the winnowing of older alluvium crossed by the ancient creek.

The microstratigraphy of the F_1 channel shows three regimes of discharge, the first of which is indicated by interbedded coarse sands and pebble gravels (F_{1a}) in a channel 5 to 7 meters wide and as much as a meter deep. A change to lesser discharge is indicated by 20 centimeters or less of medium to coarse sand (F_{1b}) which is the sedimentary matrix of the fossil bones. The random orientation of bones and the direct association with artifacts indicate that stream discharge during F_{1b}-time was inadequate to orient or sort these materials to any significant degree. Even less discharge is indicated by the overlying 2 to 3 centimeters of discontinuous, very calcareous fine sand (F_{1c}) which probably indicates little more than seepage along the bottom of Mammoth-Kill Creek.

The time duration of these events must have been relatively short because a radiocarbon date from the next older unit (E_1) of 11,600 ± 400 B.P. (A-478B, Haynes et al., 1966) is practically within a standard deviation (2σ) of the 21 dates from the Clovis level. And the overlying black mat (unit F_2) was dated 10,410 ± 190 B.P. (A-33, Damon and Long, 1962) and 10,550 ± 900 B.P. (A-746AB, Haynes et al., 1967). Because these are average ages of deposition of the interval sampled, the beginning of F_2 deposition was undoubtedly earlier; therefore, all of the time represented by unit F_1 is probably 500 years or less.

Unit F_2 is 15 centimeters or less thick and thins out away from the F_1 channel. In most places its upper contact with unit F_3 is conformable and gradational over 2 centimeters or less but in some low areas there is microstratigraphic evidence of erosion in the form of a small, shallow channel less than a meter wide and 5 to 10 centimeters deep at the most.

The overlying gray calcareous silt, unit F_3, is as much as a meter thick but shows no evidence of fluvial bedding. Aggradation appears to have been a combination of slope wash and aeolian deposition on the moist bottom of a shallow vegetated valley. A brown soil at the top of F_3, where exposed in trench 2, indicates that a period of stability occurred about 7,800 ± 420 years ago, according to the radiocarbon dating of the soil humins (A-715BBB, Haynes et al., 1967). Units F_2 and F_3 form an essentially unbroken stratigraphic record from 11,000 to 8,000 years ago, with maximum rates of sedimentation being approximately 0.01 millimeter per year for F_2 and 0.07 millimeter per year for F_3. Deposition of the upper portions of the channel sands (F_{1b} and F_{1c}) could have occurred in a few decades or, at most, a few centuries.

An interval of erosion of unknown duration followed the soil-forming period in evidence at the top of unit F_3 and was followed by the deposition of a grayish brown clayey sand alluvium, unit G_1, with a brown soil at the top. This unit pinches out westward, which is why the previous investigators did not encounter it, and thickens abruptly eastward where a buried head cut was discovered in a backhoe trench (6). This "fossil" head cut indicates that the arroyo-cutting episode represented by it was not as extensive as those that followed in Lehner Ranch Arroyo.

Unit G_1 is undated at the Lehner site, but elsewhere in the San Pedro Valley carbonized plant remains with radiocarbon dates ranging from 4,200 to 5,900 B.P. occur within unit G_1 (Haynes, 1968; Mehringer et al., 1967), of which the estimated average sedimentation rate is 1.3 millimeters per year.

TABLE 1. Lehner Site Fauna List as of 1975

(MNI: minimum number of individuals)

Fauna	New to fauna 1975	MNI of total fauna	Clovis occupational surface (lower F_2)	Unit F_2	Unit F_3	Holocene (general)	Mid-Wisconsinan
Mammuthus columbi		12	x				
Mammut americanum	x	1					x
Bison sp.		4	x	x	x		
Camelops cf. *hesternus*		3	x				
cf. *Hemiauchenia* sp.	x	1	x				
Equus sp.		1	x	x			
Tapirus sp.		1	x				
Ursus americanus		1	x				
Ursus cf. *arctos*		2	x		x		
Canis dirus	x	1	x	x			
Canis cf. *lupus*	x	1		x			
Canis latrans	x	1		x			
Thomomys sp.		1	x			x	
Perognathus sp.		1		?		x	
Ondatra sp.		1		?			
cf. *Microtus*		1	?	?			
Lepus sp.		2		x	x		
Sylvilagus sp.	x	1	x			x	
Scaphiopus cf. *couchi*	x	1				x	
Thamnophis sp.	x	1				x	
Crotalus cf. *atrox*	x	1				x	
Crotalus cf. *scutulatus*	x	1				x	
Crotalus cf. *willardi*	x	1				x	
Aves	x	1					

The brownish red alluvium of unit G_{2a} is clayey medium-to-coarse sand derived from slope washing of the uplands west of the site. The redness of the weak soil at the top of the unit is, therefore, mostly due to the displacement of an older paleosol. On the basis of radiocarbon dates from other localities in the area, unit G_{2a} is believed to be between 4,000 and 3,000 B.P. and the estimated minimum sedimentation rate is 2.4 millimeters per year. The ancient arroyo represented by G_{2a} is similar to the modern arroyo in size, and in some reaches the axes of the two coincide so that only small patches of unit G_{2a} remain along the sides of the modern wash.

Unit G_{2b} is another ancient arroyo fill similar lithologically to G_{2a}, and an erosional contact separates G_{2b} into upper (G_{2b2}) and lower (G_{2b1}) channel fills.

Without artifacts and radiocarbon dates the two are not distinguishable by themselves at the Lehner site. At trench 9, charcoal from a rock hearth provided a date of 2,550 ± 160 B.P. (A-450, Damon et al., 1964) near the middle of G_{2b}. At Fairbank, 23 miles downstream, the type site for the San Pedro phase of the Cochise culture occurs in alluvium of similar age (Antevs, 1955).

The modern episode of erosion at the Lehner site began in the 1920's (Haury et al., 1959) but within the last century, up to 50 centimeters of red slope washed sand (unit H) was deposited on top of unit G_{2b}. This medium-to-coarse sand was in part derived from thin patches of aeolian sand on the adjacent slopes and on the 20-meter terrace that is dissected by the Lehner Ranch arroyo.

Faunal Additions

The 1974-75 excavations resulted in substantial additions to the list of fauna from the Lehner site as first reported by Lance (1959). The more recent finds have been studied by Jeffrey J. Saunders and by James I. Mead, who has prepared a list of all fauna found at the site (Table 1).

Conclusions

From the 1974-75 excavations of the Lehner site it is apparent that (1) Clovis game processing and roasting areas extend southward from Mammoth-Kill Creek, (2) small vertebrates as well as large were utilized, (3) the Clovis occupation occurred at essentially the same time as at Murray Springs and elsewhere in southwestern North America, (4) Cochise people occupied the site approximately 9,700 years ago, and (5) mastodons lived in southeastern Arizona sometime before 30,000 B.P.

Acknowledgments

The 1974-75 excavations of the Lehner Clovis site were supported by grants, for which we are most grateful, from the National Geographic Society and the National Science Foundation (GA-35625). Equipment and administrative support were provided by the Arizona State Museum through Dr. R. H. Thompson. In addition to permitting the excavations, Mr. and Mrs. Edward Lehner have been gracious hosts throughout all phases of the scientific research conducted at the Lehner site over the past two decades. Furthermore, we have profited from discussions with them about Paleoindians in general and about Clovis occupation of the San Pedro Valley in particular.

The assistant director was Dr. Larry Agenbroad; Bruce Huckell was foreman; and crew members during one or both field seasons were Norma Ajeman, Bruce Bradley, Phil Chase, Peggy Corman, Alan Ferg, Lisa Huckell, Mary Ann Jones, Cheri Landrey, James I. Mead, Michael Morea, Nancy Neubert, E. Jane Rosenthal, Jeffrey J. Saunders, Wm. L. Singleton, and Michael Waters. Volunteer crew included Emily Dewitt, Jackie Escapule, Lisa Haynes, Jim Hewitt, Judy Kuncell, Peter Laudeman, and Pat Olsen. Louis Escapule collaborated with V. Haynes on the survey for other sites in the San Pedro Valley, and Herbert Haas, Southern Methodist University, undertook the radiocarbon dating for the 1974-75 excavations. Check samples were analyzed by Austin Long, University of Arizona, and Sam Valastro, University of Texas.

REFERENCES

ANTEVS, ERNST
  1955.   Geologic-climatic dating in the west.   Amer. Antiquity, vol. 20, no. 4, pt. 1, pp. 317-335.
  1959.   Geologic age of the Lehner mammoth site.   Amer. Antiquity, vol. 25, pp. 31-34.
DAMON, P. E.; HAYNES, C. V., JR.; and LONG, A.
  1964.   Arizona radiocarbon dates V.   Radiocarbon, vol. 6, p. 100.
DAMON, P. E., and LONG, A.
  1962.   Arizona radiocarbon dates, III.   Radiocarbon, vol. 4, p. 243.
DAMON, P. E.; LONG, AUSTIN; and SIGALOVE, J. J.
  1963.   Arizona radiocarbon dates IV.   Radiocarbon, vol. 5, pp. 283-301.
HAURY, EMIL W.; ANTEVS, ERNST; and LANCE, JOHN F.
  1953.   Artifacts with mammoth remains, Naco, Arizona.   Amer. Antiquity, vol. 19, pp. 1-24, illus.
HAURY, EMIL W.; SAYLES, EDWIN B.; and WASLEY, WILLIAM W.
  1959.   The Lehner mammoth site.   Amer. Antiquity, vol. 25, pp. 2-30, illus.
HAYNES, C. VANCE, JR.
  1968.   Preliminary report on the Late Quaternary geology of the San Pedro Valley, Arizona.   Arizona Geological Society, Southern Arizona Guidebook, vol. 3, pp. 79-96.
  1973.   Exploration of a mammoth-kill site in Arizona.   Nat. Geogr. Soc. Res. Rpts., 1966 Projects, pp. 125-126.
  1974.   Archeological excavations at the Clovis site at Murray Springs, Arizona, 1967.   Nat. Geogr. Soc. Res. Rpts., vol. 7 (1967 Projects), pp. 145-147.
  1976.   Archeological investigations at the Murray Springs site, Arizona, 1968.   Nat. Geogr. Soc. Res. Rpts., vol. 8 (1968 Projects), pp. 165-171.
HAYNES, C. VANCE, JR.; DAMON, PAUL E.; and GREY, DONALD C.
  1966.   Arizona radiocarbon dates VI.   Radiocarbon, vol. 8, pp. 1-21.

HAYNES, C. VANCE, JR.; GREY, DONALD C.; DAMON, PAUL E.; and BENNETT, R.
1967.   Arizona radiocarbon dates VII.   Radiocarbon, vol. 9. pp. 8 and 11.
HAYNES, C. VANCE, JR.; and HEMMINGS, E. THOMAS
1969.   The Escapule mammoth and associated projectile points, San Pedro Valley, Arizona.   Journ. Arizona Acad. Sci., vol. 5, pp. 184-188.
HEMMINGS, E. THOMAS.
1970.   Early man in the San Pedro Valley, Arizona, 236 pp.   Ph.D. dissertation, University of Arizona.
JOHNSON, N. M.; OPDYKE, N. D.; and LINDSAY, E. H.
1975.   Magnetic polarity stratigraphy of Pliocene-Pleistocene terrestrial deposits and vertebrate faunas, San Pedro Valley, Arizona.   Geol. Soc. Amer. Bull. vol. 86, pp. 5-12.
LANCE, J. F.
1959.   Faunal remains from the Lehner mammoth site.   Amer. Antiquity, vol. 25, pp. 35-42.
LINDSAY, E. H., and TESSMAN, N. T.
1974.   Cenozoic vertebrate localities and faunas in Arizona.   Journ. Arizona Acad. Sci., vol. 9, pp. 3-24.
MEAD, J.I.; HAYNES, C. V., JR.; and HUCKELL, B. B.
1979.   A Late Pleistocene mastodon (*Mammut americanum*) from the Lehner site, southeastern Arizona.   Southwestern Naturalist, vol. 24, pp. 231-238.
MEHRINGER, PETER J., JR., and HAYNES, C. VANCE, JR.
1965.   The pollen evidence for the environment of Early Man and extinct mammals at the Lehner mammoth site, southeastern Arizona.   Amer. Antiquity, vol. 31, pp. 17-23, illus.
MEHRINGER, PETER J., JR.; MARTIN, PAUL S.; and HAYNES, C. VANCE, JR.
1967.   Murray Springs, a mid-post glacial pollen record from southern Arizona.   Amer. Journ. Sci., vol. 265, pp. 788-797.
WHALEN, N. M.
1971.   Cochise culture sites in the central San Pedro drainage, Arizona.   Ph.D. dissertation, University of Arizona.

C. VANCE HAYNES, JR.

Mass Migrations of the Spiny Lobster

Principal Investigator: William F. Herrnkind, Florida State University, Tallahassee, Florida.[1]

Grant No. 1251:   For in situ investigations on mass migrations of the spiny lobster (*Panulirus argus*).

Mass movements of the spiny lobster occur primarily in autumn in the Bahamas but are reported for the winter in the Caribbean and in association with severe storms (e.g., hurricanes, tropical storms) at various times. The events are known from virtually the entire range of the species extending from Bermuda to Brazil in the western Atlantic. In all known cases the migratory pathways lie adjacent to extensive shallow waters (3-10 meters depth) serving as nursery areas for relatively dense populations of juveniles and young mature lobsters.

The number of lobsters involved in mass migration is unknown, although we estimate 200,000 for a 1969 movement near Bimini, and 100,000 migrants were estimated by others for a movement off Grand Bahama Island the same year. This number compares to a standing crop of 20,000 lobsters and a total estimated population of 200,000 at St. John, U. S. Virgin Islands. Such phenomena when discovered are heavily attended by commercial and sport lobstermen. We witnessed catches of 500 to 1000 lobsters per day per bully-netter off Bimini. This represents a five- to six-fold increase in their daily catch rate and, with lobster bringing from $2 per pound whole, represents a sizable economic gain. Of course, migrations may occur unnoticed in sparsely populated areas. Suffice it to say that mass movements involve a significant proportion of any local spiny-lobster population.

The most striking aspects of mass movement, aside from sheer numbers, are the single-file formations, or queues, of migrants and their precise migratory pathway and bearings. None of the dozens of other species of spiny lobster or any other benthic crustacean is yet known to migrate in formation. Queues consist of 2 to 60 lobsters, each individual (except the leader) directly over the extended abdomen of the one ahead. Physical contact is maintained, permitting maintenance of the queue in darkness or turbid water. Nearly all

---

[1] I am indebted to my research assistant, Joseph G. Halusky, for valuable help in this research.

queues travel in parallel headings, maintaining them within a narrow corridor. When a queue stops, the leader begins to spin in a tight circle, causing the followers to wind up in an ever-widening spiral. We have observed the resultant pod to unwind in somewhat of a reverse fashion as other individuals assume leadership and move off.

The precise bearings of migrants raise new questions as to the mechanism of orientation. The patent means suggested to guide migratory birds, fishes, or sea turtles, such as sun or star compass and current-odor orientation, are not appropriate. The lobsters are confined to the bottom, often in turbid waters or at night, eliminating visualizing celestial objects. In addition, currents in the migratory pathway are variable. We are presently testing a hypothesis that the hydrodynamic oscillation caused by passing swells, detectable at considerable depths and consistent in direction over large areas, represents one useful guidepost.

Mass migrations are probably caused by the synergistic effect of certain environmental events and the lobsters' internal physiology. Our studies show that migratory restlessness in midautumn may be induced by the decreasing photoperiod and, perhaps, a waning of the reproductive urge associated with the hormonal system. The lobsters exhibit this initial restlessness, or Zugunruhe, by increased activity and queuing in laboratory pools and by the movements resulting in pre-mass-migration buildup of numbers in areas usually devoid of lobsters. At this time, a violent autumnal storm causing a sharp drop in temperature, increased turbulence, and turbidity "triggers" the population to move en masse. At present we are becoming more certain of the location of source populations; hence the value of the research supported by the present grant.

The biological "reason" or selective advantage of mass migration is still unclear. Certainly the population is redistributed and perhaps attains new regions for feeding, shelter, and reproduction. Reproduction per se is not a direct consequence of the migrations, since it occurs primarily in spring and summer. Another intriguing possibility derives from the geological history of the area. Autumn migrations of young lobsters may once have served to bring them into deeper, more thermostable, waters from the Bahama Bank in ages when the region was much cooler. Even now, the shallower waters cool severely, causing kills of resident fishes and invertebrates.

Research Results

Our research team studied the behavioral ecology of spiny lobsters near Bimini, Bahamas, for approximately 5 weeks during the fall of 1973, including 10 days operating from the R/V *Tursiops* (Florida State University) and the remaining time at the Lerner Marine Laboratory on Bimini. We intended to examine the population dynamics and behavior of the lobsters in order to document further the biological events surrounding the autumnal mass migrations. Three major developments occurred involving establishment of a new hypothesis to explain the source of mass migrants, the first detailed observations of spontaneous formation of migratory "queues" or single-file lines of lobsters, and, serendipitously, the first detailed documentation of a symbiotic association between lobster phyllosoma larvae and the cnidarian *Aurelia* (moon jellyfish). (See Herrnkind, 1975, for photographic documentation of these phenomena.)

Because mass migrations are typically triggered by a severe autumnal storm generating widespread turbidity, the source of migrants cannot be determined by backtracking. Therefore, we have been forced to employ inferential methods based on comparative correlation of populational features such as size (age) frequency, sex ratio, sexual condition, molt state, etc., between the migrants and populations of lobsters in various habitats surrounding the migratory pathway (the latter an area with few lobsters prior to a movement). Populations on the shallow habitats on the Great Bahama Bank and those on the deep, Bank-edge reefs are distinctly different. The former show a mean size of approximately 80 millimeters in carapace length, with few gravid females and a size range mainly from 60 to 100 millimeters in carapace length. The latter show a mean size of nearly 90 millimeters in carapace length, 40 to 60 percent gravid females, and a size range mainly 75 to 110 millimeters in carapace length, with some large males exceeding 140 millimeters. By comparison the mass migrants show a very low incidence of gravid females (less than 1 percent) and a mean size of approximately 85 millimeters in carapace length, with a range mainly from 70 to 105 millimeters in carapace length. Hence the migrants are somewhat intermediate in size. Our working hypothesis until this past year, based on the absence of gravid females, was that migrants were virtually all shallow-habitat animals, excluding very young lobsters unable to walk as fast or as far as older individuals.

Based on data from 1971, 1972, and particularly 1973 we now believe that a significant proportion of migrants actually derive from the deep-reef populations after the reproductive period.

Many Bahamian lobsters appear to move offshore in spring-summer and mate on the deep reefs well into autumn. In midautumn, starting around the first of October, reproduction declines (observable as a reduced proportion of gravid females), and many young lobsters return inshore. At this time we observe a buildup of large numbers in the migratory pathway, prior to any storms, and occasional queues moving in alongshore and inshore bearings during the crepuscular and nocturnal periods. In some years such as 1972 and 1973 no movement occurred except that associated with this buildup population of lobsters which eventually disperses.

The deep-source hypothesis better accounts for our observations of migrants too large to have come from the shallow waters and better explains the presence of occasional queues moving toward shore during midautumn just prior to mass migration. We planned to re-examine the deep-reef population during migration time. By the new hypothesis, we should find a marked decrease in gravid females and a general reduction of population density. Very large (old) lobsters, which evidently do not migrate, should still be present in the deep areas.

We remain convinced, however, that the bulk of migrants during mass movements, such as occurred in 1963, 1969, and 1971, derive from shallow habitats. The deep population is simply too small to generate the large numbers, whereas the Bahama Bank can, since it sustains an enormous and, thus, heavily fished population. In fact, some 6 to 7 million pounds of lobsters marketed each year in Florida are caught on the Great Bahama Bank while an unknown quantity is marketed in Cuba.

Queuing, the formation of single-file lines of lobsters head to tail in lockstep formation, is the typical mode of travel by mass migrants. Although we were the first scientists to describe and document this unique phenomenon, we had not previously witnessed the spontaneous formation of queues in the field. During our period of support by the National Geographic Society we observed the event numerous times and were able to record the associated temporal, spatial, and behavioral components.

Lobsters were typically crowded into crevices during daylight hours—normal behavior except that up to 200 lobsters occupied dens where only several dozen resided one week earlier. Only the antennae protruded and individuals pushed outward by the crowd immediately attempted to retreat back under the ledge. Several times this led to apparent agonistic interactions between the displaced lobster and another blocking its retreat.

At dusk, with the sun low on the horizon, the lobsters gradually moved outward and lined up just in front of the ledge. When the sun reached the horizon, some individuals began to walk slowly away from the ledge and were followed and usually touched by the antennules of several others. Each such group meandered about in a circuitous path for several minutes and then began to form a queue as the lead lobster increased walking speed. Thereafter the paths straightened and the queue moved rapidly several hundred meters and ultimately beyond our visual range.

The time from first emergence to queue formation was approximately 1 hour. By half an hour after sunset only 10-15 lobsters remained in the dens formerly holding between 100 and 200 individuals. The largest queues observed consisted of 22 and 17 lobsters, with a mean of 8 (21 queues) queue members. This compares to a mean of 7 recorded during a mass movement in 1969 (246 queues).

Formation and maintenance of queues in nature was identical to that we observed in laboratory pools and that observed when we "forced" lobsters out of dens during the day for photographic purposes. Those lobsters initiating movement are approached within a distance of several meters by others, which then make antennal or antennular contact with the initiator or other nearby lobster. Individuals occasionally prod and push as the group moves about until one, usually the initiator in those cases observed, begins to move faster and more linearly. Thereafter each follower maintains physical contact with the lobster ahead by constant flicking of the tactile sensitive antennules or by grasping with the forward pair of walking legs. As speed increases the antennae initially perpendicular to the body are brought closer together and become nearly parallel at top speed, approximately 1 kilometer per hour. We believe this antennal adjustment reduces drag and allows more efficient locomotion.

Both the behavior of queues and some drag measurements lead us to believe that queuing behavior is primarily an adaptation to increase locomotor efficiency and conserve energy. Our first crude measurements reveal that 5 queued lobsters present the same amount of drag as two lobsters moving separately at equivalent velocity. Energy savings are certainly significant during migrations covering 20 or more kilometers over several days. This may constitute one of the few clear demonstrations of fluid dynamic efficiency gained by formation movement; a point of theory for fish schools and bird flocks.

While ascending from a free dive, I chanced to see a larval lobster, or phyllosoma, attached to the aboral (convex) surface of an *Aurelia* jellyfish. This association has been described only twice before in the literature, and these from Pacific species, based on only a few specimens. Since *Aurelia* are very numerous off Bimini in early fall, we examined a large number to determine whether the association was merely a chance occurrence. Of 402 *Aurelia* observed, 80 carried a single phyllosoma and 1 carried two larvae, suggesting that jellyfish-riding is a significant aspect of phyllosoma behavior.

Further study revealed that the phyllosomas were late-stage larvae, which in two cases molted overnight at the lab into the puerulus, or settling stage, of the shovel-nosed or Spanish lobster, *Scyllarus*. Scyllarid expert William Lyons of the State of Florida Department of Natural Resources has determined it to be either *S. americanus* or *S. chacei*.

We observed that the phyllosomas hold securely to the jellyfish bell by the posterior appendages while holding the anterior setose appendages into the water column. In 11 cases a tiny medusa adhered to the latter appendages, suggesting the possibility that the phyllosomas feed on small jellyfish captured from the zooplankton passing near the *Aurelia*. This discovery, if confirmed, may be extremely helpful to mariculturists attempting to rear phyllosoma larvae of various lobster species. Thus far, experts on larval Crustacea attribute their poor success at rearing spiny lobsters to lack of nutritional knowledge.

At least four pieces of evidence support the contention that the phyllosoma-*Aurelia* association is in fact a true symbiosis and not a casual occurrence. First, a 20-percent frequency of occurrence indicates that many millions of *Aurelia* must carry phyllosomas. Second, the phyllosomas appeared only on *Aurelia* and not on any of the other three common drifting cnidaria or ctenophores. Indeed, only those *Aurelia* having a bell diameter of between 20 and 35 millimeters carried scyllarid larvae, although they ranged from 15 to 135 millimeters. Third, the phyllosomas attached so securely to the jellyfish that they could be dislodged only by pulling or scraping them off. Fourth, the phyllosomas appear to be immune from the nematocyst sting of the *Aurelia*.

We cannot yet offer a certain explanation for the adaptiveness of the symbiosis although several possibilities exist. Certainly the larvae conserve energy in maintaining depth levels and are additionally transported both vertically and horizontally by their host. In addition, the *Aurelia* probably afford protection from predation by phyllosoma predators.

A review of updated findings can be found in Herrnkind (1980).

REFERENCE

HERRNKIND, WILLIAM F.
1975.   Strange march of the spiny lobster.   Nat. Geogr. Mag., vol. 147, no. 6, pp. 819-831, illus. (Photographs by Rick Frehsee and Bruce Mounier.)
1980.   Spiny lobsters: Patterns of movement.   Pp. 349-407 *in* "Biology and Management of Lobsters," vol. 1, Cobb and Phillips, eds.   Academic Press, New York.

WILLIAM F. HERRNKIND

Ecology of the Wolverine in Northwestern Montana

Principal Investigator: Maurice G. Hornocker, Idaho Cooperative Wildlife Research Unit, University of Idaho, Moscow, Idaho.[1]

Grant Nos. 1237,   For a continuing study of the wolverine in northwestern
1402, and 1549.   Montana.

Little is known of the population ecology of the largest terrestrial mustelid, the wolverine (*Gulo gulo*). Although the species has a vast circumpolar range, few scientists have attempted to study wolverines in their natural habitat. Van Zyll de Jong (1975) states that the reason for this is that the species is uncommon, highly mobile, and restricted to the more remote and inaccessible parts of the country. Some studies, mainly utilizing snow tracking, have been carried out in Europe (Teplov, 1955; Krott, 1959; Haglund, 1966; Pulliainen, 1968; Myrberget, 1970). Most wolverine studies in North America have dealt with the species' breeding biology and other information gained from carcasses (Kurtén and Rausch, 1959; Rausch and Pearson, 1972; Wright and Rausch, 1955; Wright, 1963), but prior to this research no intensive field study has ever been undertaken.

The U. S. Fish and Wildlife Service, in a wolverine status report in 1974, stated, "There has never been a scientific study carried out on a wild wolverine population (in North America). The information available comes from examination of carcasses and reproductive tracts, trapping and bounty records, limited snow tracking studies, subjective observations made by trappers, and from often exaggerated folklore. This information provides a general description of wolverine habits, but contributes little to our understanding of the ecology of wolverine populations."

The report goes on: "Research on wolverine populations is sorely lacking. Inventory methods are limited because of low population densities and the remoteness of the habitat. Track counts alone is a questionable method. There is, however, a need to attempt to assess numbers throughout its range. More

[1] Idaho Cooperative Wildlife Research Unit, U. S. Fish and Wildlife Service, University of Idaho, Idaho Department of Fish and Game, and the Wildlife Management Institute, cooperating.

important is the need to document the biology and ecology of a viable wolverine population. There is need for information on range and space requirements, on food habits both winter and summer, and on wolverine relationships with other species. There is need to assess the habitat, in all respects, with an eye toward enhancing wolverine populations elsewhere in the future. We need to know more about wolverine movements and how these movements are affected by man's activities."

Authors of recent papers dealing with the wolverine's status and distribution all have pointed out the dearth of information in the literature (van Zyll de Jong, 1975; Dagg and Campbell, 1974; U. S. Fish and Wildlife Service, 1974; Nowak, 1973). All urge the inception of ecological research. Dagg and Campbell (1975) state that "almost nothing is known about the density of wolverine populations in North America or about their exact distribution." They recommend extensive research be initiated on wolverines in their native habitat. Radiotelemetric tracking should enable biologists to determine the territorial needs of individuals. A method should be set up whereby the density of a population can be determined from wolverine tracks observed in the winter.

The 1973 edition of "Threatened Wildlife of the United States" lists the wolverine under "Status-undetermined Mammals." A status-undetermined species or subspecies is "one that has been suggested as possibly threatened with extinction but about which there is not enough information to determine its status. More information is needed . . ." (U. S. Department of the Interior, 1973). Clearly there is need for intensive research on this species.

Our research, now (1976) in its third year, is the first intensive ecological study of this species attempted in North America. Major aims have been (1) to investigate the dynamics of a population of wolverines in a semiwilderness and a wilderness environment, (2) to evaluate the role of the wolverine as a predator, and (3) to investigate the wolverine's relationship to other predatory species.

A great deal of data has been obtained and a fund of information is accumulating. We have quantitative information on the population's size, density, and structure. Data obtained from radiotracking have established daily and seasonal movement patterns, habitat selection, and home-range size and utilization. Relationships to other species are being investigated by means of snow tracking and radiotelemetry. Scat analysis and snow tracking are providing data on food habits. Behavior of wolverines is being studied and further research in this area is planned.

Within the contiguous United States, wolverines occur only in a few States. Montana appears to have the largest populations; within the past 30 years there is evidence that wolverines have increased in numbers in the western, mountainous region of the State (Newby and Wright, 1955; Newby and McDougal, 1964). It is believed that these wolverines initially came from Canada and Glacier National Park. The northwestern region of Montana therefore appeared to offer the greatest potential for studying wolverines in the continental United States.

The area selected for this study is in the Flathead National Forest south and west of Glacier National Park. It is in the South Fork of the Flathead River drainage, including a portion of the Bob Marshall Wilderness Area. The area is dominated by high mountain peaks and ridges with elevations ranging from 3,560 to 8,700 feet. Approximately half the area is relatively remote, primarily used for logging and recreational purposes; the other is wilderness.

During the course of the study trapping was carried on from early December each year through late April. During the 1975-76 season, 45 live traps were set on two separate lines in the semiwilderness area. These lines totaled approximately 100 miles in length and were operated throughout the season. A 25-mile line, utilizing 20 live traps, was operated for the first time in the Bob Marshall Wilderness Area. This expanded effort was initiated for two reasons: (1) to maintain contact with wolverines that were captured outside the Wilderness Area and that radiotracking showed were ranging deep into the wilderness, and (2) to compare wolverine population density in the wilderness habitat to that in an area managed for multiple use.

The U. S. Forest Service provided a headquarters building near Hungry Horse on the edge of the study area, as well as three cabins in the Bob Marshall Wilderness Area. We established a permanent camp at Spotted Bear, in the middle of the study area, and a semipermanent camp at Bunker Creek. These camps permit full coverage of the entire area. Winter travel is by snowmobiles in the semiwilderness area, by cross-country skis in the wilderness.

In all, 21 wolverines have been captured and marked since the study began. Nine of these were males, 12 were females. Eight individuals were recaptured 57 times, making 78 the total number of initial captures and recaptures.

Seventeen wolverines were fitted with radio transmitters, and 413 radio locations were made on these individuals, spanning varying periods of time. Four different wolverines, an adult male and three adult females, were tracked in consecutive years. Data were obtained on the male over three winters, on the females for a period spanning two winters.

Wolverines may depend on other predators to provide them with food in the form of carrion. Different authors allude to the possible relationship of wolverines to more skilled predators such as wolves, cougars, and man. With this potential relationship in mind we kept records on the number of trails left by other predators on the study area.

Major predatory species are coyotes (*Canis latrans*), cougars (*Felis concolor*), lynx (*Lynx canadensis*), bobcats (*Lynx rufus*), and fisher (*Martes pennanti*). Grizzly bears (*Ursus arctos*) and black bears (*Ursus americanus*) are present but are inactive during late fall and winter months. Lesser predators such as marten (*Martes americanus*), mink (*Mustela vison*), and weasels (*Mustela* spp.) occur in numbers on the study area. Wolves (*Canis lupus*) and wolf sign have been reported by experienced observers. If wolves do occur here, and it appears they at least frequent the area, it remains to be seen how many there are and if they merely travel through or are full-time residents.

We planned to instrument with radio transmitters, during the 1976-77 season, a limited number of other predators to determine if a relationship between wolverines and other predators exists. Expanded trapping effort for wolverines precluded marking cougars and lynxes during the 1975 trapping season. To date (December 1976), four male fishers have been captured, instrumented, and released. One of these, No. 1, was initially captured in April 1975 and was recaptured and reinstrumented the following season; later we monitored three instrumented fishers.

An absolute determination of population size for the entire area remains difficult to establish. Wolverines travel great distances complicating population estimates. Five individuals were known lost to the population this past winter (2 died, 3 were removed by fur trappers in adjacent drainages). At the same time, we captured seven new wolverines for the first time. Because they do travel extensively, wolverines are susceptible to trapping mortality, but on our study area (which is closed to trapping) it appears that this mortality is compensated for by emigration—6 of the 7 new individuals were mature adults.

Radiotracking data show that some wolverines appear to be "homeless"— they wander throughout the study area, never remaining in one general area for any length of time. On the other hand, a number of individuals do confine themselves for most of the year to a specific area, although this area is quite large. Periodically, however, even these animals strike out on forays of many miles, but always return to the same general area. Whether this behavior is a normal function of the life-style of the species—a scavenging species at least seasonally—or whether the population is in a state of flux remains to be seen. We know that a minimum of 23 wolverines has been removed from the population since 1972. This could be an important factor affecting the population in a number of ways.

Whatever the case, population size is remaining stable, if not increasing.

Our original estimate of 20 animals on the study area appears to be holding. Last year we knew of 18 individuals—this year 13 marked wolverines were known to be present, plus two that escaped capture in the Bob Marshall. Two females captured in the 1974-75 season were radiotracked throughout the summer and fall of 1975; radio contact was last made on December 24, 1975. They were not recaptured but we believe they were present. Therefore, a minimum of 17 adults was on the study area the past season.

We have not been able to obtain, with our capture-recapture methodology, quantitative information on reproduction. Wolverines give birth to young in late winter and early spring—about the time our trapping methods become ineffective. By the following winter the young have left the mother and are completely independent. These subadults are recognizable, but we have no way of knowing if they were reared on the study area or have emigrated from adjacent areas.

We expect to gain adequate quantitative data on reproduction from analysis of specimens collected from this area by the Montana Fish and Game Department. Trapping of wolverines is permitted outside our study area but the carcass must be turned over to the Department. These specimens are being analyzed by K. Greer of the Department and Dr. P. L. Wright of the University of Montana, and the results will be available to us. Only those specimens from northwest Montana from areas ecologically similar to our study area will be utilized.

Carrion appears to be quite important in the winter diet of wolverines. Analysis of 56 scats collected in winter shows that food items taken as carrion occur more frequently than those presumably taken as live prey. We believe most elk and deer are taken as carrion—these occurred in 27 percent of the scats. Domestic cow and horse occurred in 27 and 18 percent of the scats, respectively. We do not know where the domestic cow was obtained, for most of the scats containing this item were collected deep in the Bob Marshall Wilderness Area. It is possible the wolverines obtained this either in the Swan drainage to the west or east in the Sun River country. Undoubtedly the horse was obtained from our baits. The important fact is that wolverines do scavenge and, particularly in winter, carrion appears to make up a significant part of their diet.

The occurrence of marmots in 11 percent of the scats is interesting. To kill marmots in winter, wolverines necessarily must dig them from their hibernating dens. We have made speculation on this, based on wolverine movements and behavior, concerning not only marmots but other hibernating small mammals. It now appears that this does occur, but to what extent we do not know.

We still lack quantitative data on summer food habits. Different authors allude to the suspected varied diet of wolverines in summer. An omnivore, the wolverine probably takes a variety of berries, fruits, and other vegetable matter when available. We believe that rodents are of more importance in summer than in winter. They are then more available, and our impression from radiotracking is that wolverines utilize areas of relatively high rodent densities.

The study area supports an unusually complex and dense population of predatory species. Whether or not this is a factor in the dynamics of the wolverine population is unknown. The fact remains that all these species must have an adequate prey base. Small mammals are known to comprise a large percentage of the diet of most of these predatory species. In an attempt to determine the extent of this prey base we studied the density and species diversity of small mammals in different vegetative types. These different types were created by different aged clearcuts. The work was carried out in the Sullivan and Quintonkin drainages, typical of the whole study area outside the Bob Marshall Wilderness Area. Objectives were (1) to estimate the species diversity and density of small mammals in the different vegetative types created by known-age clearcuts as well as in uncut mature timber stands, and (2) to determine which vegetative types support the most diverse and dense populations of small mammals. The work was done in the summer and fall of 1975 and the spring and early summer of 1976.

Clearcutting, like naturally occurring fire or outbreaks of disease, removes the tree canopy and results in changes in the vegetation. This in turn creates different habitat for rodents and other small mammals. Some species occur in relatively uniform densities throughout all types; others do not.

At this point in our research, it appears that wolverines depend upon carrion to a large extent in winter. The availability of this carrion depends largely on the status and condition of populations of large ungulates inhabiting the area, principally elk (*Cervus canadensis*) and deer (*Odocoileus hemionus*). Data on elk populations in our study area are currently being collected by the Montana Fish and Game Department and the University of Montana. These data will be available to us. In summer, wolverines probably depend on small mammals and vegetative matter and to a much lesser extent on carrion. Our work with small mammals is designed to aid in arriving at sound interpretations of seasonal prey utilization by wolverines and other predatory species.

Final interpretation of all these data on ungulates and small mammals and how they relate to predator populations, and specifically the wolverine, must await further data collection and analysis.

Movement data are being collected largely by radiotracking from a light fixed-wing airplane. The rough terrain, despite the fact that a good system of roads exists, makes tracking on the ground very difficult and inefficient. The airplane permits "line of sight" radio contact and has proved to be an efficient technique. Normally, two flights a week are made if the weather permits. If a wolverine exhibits unusual movement, then additional flights are made in order to keep in touch.

Through July 1976, we have made 413 radio locations of 17 different individuals. These locations, made from season to season and for some individuals from year to year, enable us to map the home range for these wolverines. Males No. 5, 9, and 16 and females No. 7, 8, 12, 14, 18, and 21 have provided quantitative data on home-range utilization. All have shown continued use of a relatively specific area, although as previously stated this area is quite large, particularly for males. Male No. 13 and female No. 11 have wandered a great deal and show no real attachment to any area.

In general all wolverines inhabit the high country during spring, summer, and fall, although they may cross river valleys in moving from one area to another. In winter, they move to lower elevations where food is more available. They do, however, make forays in midwinter to some of the highest ridges.

The distances traveled by some individuals are startling. In a 24-hour period 15 airline miles is not an uncommon movement for males. Some wolverines, including females, have made movements of 60-70 airline miles over extremely rough terrain. These movements appear excessive from an energy conservation standpoint, but, again, may be "normal" for an animal dependent at least in part, upon scavenging.

All wolverines were active both day and night in winter. In summer most movements of any distance were made at night when temperatures are cooler. It is obvious that our baiting and trapping in winter is influencing the movements of some individuals. Some go from trap site to trap site eating the attractant baits hung outside the traps. We have tracked some wolverines that have traveled several miles directly to our baits, fed, then returned on the same trail. These wolverines had traveled from high rocky areas bordering the river bottom. In all cases it appeared the wolverines knew exactly where they were going.

Our impression, after three seasons of work and extensive radiotracking of 17 individuals, is that relative to other species we are dealing with a regional population rather than a local one. Some wolverines confine themselves to the South Fork of the Flathead drainage, but many roam the adjacent Middle Fork and Swan River drainages, some cross the Continental Divide eastward to the Sun River country, and others travel north into Glacier National Park. We believe that large home ranges and long movements are probably normal for this species, but the structure and characteristics of the population may be a factor.

Studying such a population of wide-ranging animals without radio-telemetry would be hopeless in such mountainous terrain. This technique has shown home-range use and habitat preference but neither the radiotracking nor the capture-recapture methodology has revealed any form of territorialism. We have, however, recorded what appears to be territorial behavior by snow tracking. Some individuals have marked trees by scratching the base, others have climbed trees a few feet and marked them by biting or scratching. In one case in the Bob Marshall different individuals marked the same tree, the same wolverines returning on different occasions. We have observed also where wolverines have scent marked. This has been done by males but females may also mark in this manner. This behavior is similar to that reported by some European authors, but we have not observed, either by snow tracking or radiotracking, evidence of intraspecific aggressive behavior or territory defense reported by those same authors.

Wolverines possess an exceptionally keen sense of smell. They come directly to baits from great distances and are able to locate food buried under deep snow. This, again, is characteristic of species dependent, at least seasonally in the case of wolverines, upon scavenging for survival. Some European authors describe the caching of food by wolverines and their subsequent feeding at these caches throughout the winter. We have observed no such behavior. Wolverines do carry away small parts of baits and have been seen by others carrying bones and scraps. In most cases, wolverines ate our baits on the spot, occasionally carrying away a small scrap. Caching any quantity of meat in this area would not be efficient—it would quickly be consumed by numerous other species.

From my experience, I believe the species' reputation for malicious cunning and intelligence and for feats of strength is the result of lack of sound information. The animal is "mysterious" and lends itself to exaggeration. Wolverines are reasonably intelligent, they are very agile and possess tremendous strength for an animal this size, but many tales describing their feats are grossly exaggerated. They behave much as some other members of the family Mustelidae, while possessing their own individuality as a species.

REFERENCES

DAGG, A. I., and CAMPBELL, C. A.
   1975.   Historic changes in the distribution and numbers of wolverine in Canada and northern United States.   Can. Wildl. Serv. MS. Rpt., 22 pp.

HAGLUND, B.
  1966.   De stora rovdjurens vintervanor. [Winter habits of the lynx (*Lynx lynx* L.) and wolverine (*Gulo gulo* L.) as revealed by tracking in the snow.] Viltrevy, vol. 4, no. 3, pp. 81-299. (Summary in English.)
KROTT, PETER
  1959.   Demon of the north, 259 pp., illus. Alfred A. Knopf, New York. (Translated from German by Edward Fitzgerald.)
KURTÉN, B., and RAUSCH, R.
  1959.   Biometric comparisons between North American and European mammals.   Acta Arctica, vol. 11, 44 pp.
MYRBERGET, S.
  1970.   The Norwegian populations of wolverine, *Gulo gulo* (L.) and *Lynx lynx* (L).   Pap. Norwegian State Game Res. Inst., ser. 2, 33 pp. (Summary in English.)
NEWBY, F. E., and MCDOUGAL, J. J.
  1964.   Range extension of the wolverine in Montana.   Journ. Mamm., vol. 43, no. 3, pp. 485-487.
NEWBY, F. E., and WRIGHT, PHILIP L.
  1955.   Distribution and status of the wolverine in Montana.   Journ. Mamm., vol. 45, no. 3, pp. 485-487.
NOWAK, RONALD M.
  1973.   Return of the wolverine.   Nat. Parks and Cons. Mag., vol. 47, no. 2, pp. 20-23, illus.
PULLIAINEN, E.
  1968.   Breeding biology of the wolverine (*Gula gula* L.) in Finland.   Ann. Zool. Fenn., vol. 5, pp. 338-344.
QUICK, HORACE F.
  1933.   Wolverine, fisher, and marten studies in a wilderness region.   Trans. North Amer. Wildl. Conf., vol. 18, pp. 513-533.
RAUSCH, R. A., and PEARSON, A. M.
  1972.   Notes on the wolverine in Alaska and the Yukon Territory.   Journ. Wildl. Manag., vol. 36, no. 2, pp. 249-268.
TEPLOV, V. P.
  1955.   On the winter ecology of the glutton in the Pechora Nature Preserve. Byull. Mosk. Obshch. Ispyt. Prir., biol. sect., vol. 60, no. 1, pp. 1-11. (Original not seen.)
UNITED STATES DEPARTMENT OF THE INTERIOR
  1973.   Threatened wildlife of the United States.   U. S. Bur. Sport Fish. and Wildl. Publ. 114, 289 pp.
  1974.   Wolverine status 1974, 13 pp.   Office of Endangered Species and International Activities, U. S. Fish and Wildlife Service.
VAN ZYLL DE JONG, C. G.
  1962.   The distribution and abundance of the wolverine (*Gulo gulo*) in Canada. Can. Field-Nat., vol. 89, pp. 431-437.

WRIGHT, PHILIP L.
    1962.   Variations in reproductive cycles in North American mustelids.   Pp.
             77-97 *in* "Delayed Implantation," Allen C. Enders, ed., 318 pp., illus.
             University of Chicago Press.
WRIGHT, PHILIP L., and RAUSCH, R. A.
    1955.   Reproduction in the wolverine.   Journ. Mamm., vol. 36, no. 3, pp.
             346-355.

MAURICE G. HORNOCKER

Limnological Studies of Flamingo Diets and Distributions

Principal Investigator: Stuart H. Hurlbert, San Diego State University, San Diego, California.

Grant Nos. 1271, 1540. For limnological studies of flamingo diets and distributions in the high plains of Chile, Bolivia, and Peru.

The goal of this research program is to analyze the feeding ecology of the three species of flamingos (*Phoenicopterus chilensis, Phoenicoparrus andinus,* and *Phoenicoparrus jamesi*) found in the altiplano region of the central Andes. Specific objectives have included (1) determination of the diets and patterns of feeding selectivity of the three species; (2) analysis of the macro- and microgeographic distributions of the flamingos, especially in relation to the distributions of their prey species; and (3) correlation of distributions of prey species with chemical composition of lake waters.

The little information available on the diets of these flamingos is summarized in Jenkin (1957) and Patrick (1961). Aside from general information on their geographic distributions and on timing of reproduction, the biology of these birds, especially the two *Phoenicoparrus* species, is unstudied. Best recent sources of information on flamingos in general are Allen (1956), Rooth (1965), and Kear and Duplaix-Hall (1975).

Two trips were made to the altiplano region to carry out this work. The first was made during the period November 26-December 16, 1974. Accompanied by professors (Daniel Torres, Matilde Lopez, Ibcia Santibañez) and students (Raul Lopez, Andres Scherson) from the University of Chile, I visited Laguna Lejia, Salar de Aguas Calientes, and Salar de Atacama in northern Chile and Laguna Colorada and Laguna Hedionda in southern Bolivia. Samples of water, surface sediments, plankton, and flamingo excrement were collected at each lake visited and general observations of feeding behavior were made. One specimen of *Phoenicoparrus andinus* (at Laguna Lejia) was shot for study of stomach contents.

The second trip took place during the period November 15-December 21, 1975. Supplemental funds from the Society permitted James O. Keith of the U. S. Fish and Wildlife Service to participate in this period of fieldwork, so that we could assess the feasibility of banding and color-marking flamingos

351

for study of population movements. Prof. Luis Peña and his assistant, José Escobar, formed the remainder of the team. On this expedition we visited 27 bodies of water in northern Chile and southern Peru. At each we censused the flamingo populations, made detailed observations on their behavior, and collected samples of water, surface sediments, plankton, and flamingo excrement. We collected 5 flamingos (3 *Phoenicoparrus andinus,* 1 *P. jamesi,* 1 *Phoenicopterus chilensis*) for study of their stomach contents. At Laguna Lejia and Salar de Atacama, Chile, we employed two snaring techniques to capture birds for banding and color-marking, but these proved much less effective than expected. Only three birds were snared. One of these was found dead in the early morning and the other two struggled free and escaped when we approached them.

Research on these flamingos and lakes is being continued with the support of the National Science Foundation. In 1976 two further trips (June, November) were made to the altiplano and the region of study was extended to the northern end of the altiplano, just south of Cuzco, Peru. With a few exceptions, the following summary pertains only to the results of the two trips financed by the National Geographic Society.

Range Extensions. The rarest of the world's six species of flamingos is *Phoenicoparrus jamesi.* Our fieldwork extended its known geographic range and located another breeding colony. On November 24, 1975, we observed 14 *P. jamesi* feeding in very shallow channels along the western margin of Salar de Pedernales, Chile; this is about 300 kilometers farther south than this species has been found previously, except for the very unusual sighting of two individuals in Patagonia more recently (Muñoz and Muñoz, 1975). Accompanying the *P. jamesi* in Salar de Pedernales were 12 *P. chilensis* and 12 *P. andinus.*

On December 14, 1975, we observed a few dozen *P. jamesi* engaged in nest construction and egg incubation in Salar de Chalviri, Bolivia. At least 1,500 *P. jamesi* were present. This salar is only about 50 kilometers south of Laguna Colorada, apparently the only other place where nesting of *P. jamesi* has been confirmed. At least 300 *P. chilensis* and 1,000 *P. andinus* were also present in Salar de Chalviri, but no evidence of nesting by these two species was observed.

On June 28, 1976, 80 *P. jamesi* were observed feeding in Laguna Parinacochas, Peru, 300 kilometers farther west in the Peruvian Andes than it had been known to occur. On the same lake were observed 1,600 *P. chilensis* and approximately 3,000 flamingos too far away from us for identification.

These observations and those of Muñoz and Muñoz (1975) suggest that *P. jamesi* has a wider geographic distribution, at least latitudinally, than does the more abundant and better-known *P. andinus.*

Censuses. A summary of the census data obtained between November 22 and December 17, 1975, is presented in table 1. These lakes were all in northern Chile and southern Bolivia; they ranged in surface area from 0.1 to 50 square kilometers and in total salinity from about 5 grams/liter to >300 grams/liter. Some had dense zooplankton populations and others were completely lacking in zooplankton. Analyses of sediment, plankton, and water samples are not yet completed, and so we will discuss only general aspects of distribution here.

All three species were present on the great majority of lakes, suggesting that differences in their microgeographic distributions and in their ecological requirement are subtle. *P. jamesi* was the most abundant over-all, but the figures for this species are largely determined by a single lake—Laguna Colorada, Bolivia, where we estimated 24,000 *P. jamesi* to be present. The fact that *P. jamesi* occurred on three fewer lakes than did the other two species seems not to be significant: *P. jamesi* was found to be present on two of those lakes when they were more thoroughly explored in December 1976.

The variance/mean ratios calculated from density data provided an index of the degree to which each species tends to concentrate its population on specific lakes as opposed to distributing its population more or less evenly over all available lakes. If for a given species the number of individuals present on a lake is proportional, allowing for sampling error, to the size of the lake, this variance: mean ratio should equal unity. The calculated values indicate that *P. chilensis* shows only a weak tendency to concentrate its population on specific lakes, whereas *P. jamesi* has a very strong tendency to do so, *P. andinus* being intermediate in this respect.

The data indicate that *P. jamesi* occurs at slightly higher elevations, on average, than does *P. andinus*. The difference reflects the concentration of *P. jamesi* at Laguna Colorada (elevation 4,278 meters). However, excluding the data from this lake increases the mean elevation for *P. jamesi* by more than a hundred meters but leaves the mean elevation for *P. andinus* unaffected. Comparisons with *P. chilensis* are less interesting as a large number of that species occurs in lowland regions outside the altiplano, and so the lakes censused cannot in any way be considered a representative sampling for the species.

Diet and Feeding Behavior. Diets of the three species are being assessed on the basis of analysis of gut contents of several specimens of each flamingo and of excrement samples collected from lake shorelines. Most of the samples are not yet analyzed, but preliminary results are quite interesting. Large numbers of diatom frustules are found in samples from *P. andinus* and *P. jamesi,* and diatoms appear to be the principal food of these species. *P. andinus* filters primarily the larger (> 80 μm long) diatoms while *P. jamesi* filtered primarily smaller (< 60 μm long) ones. *P. chilensis* feeds on invertebrates in a probably opportunistic fashion. Indirect evidence indicates that brine shrimp, chironomid larvae, amphipods, and corixids are their most important food in the altiplano. Copepods are often abundant in altiplano lakes, but their good swimming and escape abilities may give them some protection from *P. chilensis*, which as often as not is scarce on lakes with high densities of copepods and few other invertebrates.

Feeding behaviors of the three species show notable similarities and differences. All three almost always feed at the sediment-water interface; very rarely have individuals been observed filtering organisms from the upper portion of the water column. Only in the case of *P. chilensis* have *groups* of birds been observed filtering planktonic organisms; in some small Peruvian lakes rich with planktonic cladocerans, the flamingos swam about filtering right at the water surface. Only rare isolated individuals of *P. andinus* and *P. jamesi* have been observed to feed in this way.

Feeding at the sediment-water interface, the flamingos are generally restricted to water somewhat less than a meter deep, or, more specifically, to water no deeper than their necks are long. All three species will dabble upended, submerging their entire head and neck, and pedal with their feet while moving their beak along the lake bottom. However, this type of behavior is common only in *P. andinus*. It has been observed only once in *P. jamesi;* several dozen individuals were observed feeding in this manner in the center of Laguna Colorada in December 1975. *P. chilensis* does not hesitate to submerge its entire neck while feeding, but it usually keeps its feet on the "ground," perhaps because it cannot move quickly enough to catch its prey otherwise.

The principal feeding mode for all three species is to walk along with the beak, beak and head, or beak, head, and neck submerged, the beak moving from side to side and leaving a feeding track of greater or lesser sinuosity. However, the species differ in the rate at which they walk while feeding in this manner. *P. jamesi* typically averages 10-15 steps/minute, *P. andinus* 20-30, and *P. chilensis* 40-60. *P. jamesi* steps slowly, follows an irregular path, and spends a relatively long time "working" the surface sediments in each spot. At the other extreme *P. chilensis* may be said to stride along, often in a fairly straight line. *P. andinus* is intermediate in its behavior. There is, of course, marked behavioral variation within each species, between lakes, and between areas. For example, both *P. jamesi* and *P. andinus* walk more slowly when feeding in very shallow water than they do when feeding in deeper water.

The faster walking rate of *P. chilensis* may be accounted for by the mobility of its prey. We do not understand at present why *P. andinus* should walk more rapidly while feeding than does *P. jamesi*. Completion of analyses of gut contents and lake sediments may suggest some explanations.

P. chilensis, like other species of *Phoenicopterus*, exhibits another feeding mode, stomping or treading. The bird remains in one spot, rapidly stomping its feet and turning in a circle at the same time. Usually at least the head is submerged, and this describes a tight circle about the spot where the bird stomps. The rate of stomping is great, usually 130-200 steps/minute. This feeding mode is never observed on some lakes and is the dominant one on others. It appears most commonly employed where the aquatic plant *Ruppia* forms a sparse carpet on the lake bottom. It must be a very effective way of dislodging such invertebrates from their refuges.

TABLE 1. Summary of Census Data

(For the three flamingos, genus *Phoenicopterus*, on 24 waterbodies between Laguna Santa Rosa, Chile (27° 30' lat., S.) and Laguna Cañapa, Bolivia (21° 30' lat. S.), November-December 1975.)

Species	No. lakes occupied	Total no. present	Mean no.[a] per lake	s/m^2 ratio	Mean[b] elevation (meters)
Phoenicopterus chilensis	19/24	2359	98	1.5	4,141
Phoenicoparrus andinus	19/24	4882	203	8.6	3,955
Phoenicoparrus jamesi	16/24	31062	1294	19	4,295

[a] These variance:mean ratios have been calculated from the densities (number/hectare) and not from the absolute numbers.

[b] Each bird is given equal weight in this calculation.

REFERENCES

ALLEN, ROBERT P.
  1956.   The flamingos: Their life history and survival.   Nat. Audubon Soc. Res. Rep. no. 5, 285 pp.
HURLBERT, STUART H.
  1978.   The measurement of niche overlap and some relatives.   Ecology, vol. 59, no. 1, pp. 67-77.
HURLBERT, STUART H., and CHANG, CECILY C. Y.
  1981.   Ornitholimnology: Effects of grazing by the Andean flamingo (*Phoenicoparrus andinus*).   (In manuscript.)
HURLBERT, STUART H., and KEITH, JAMES O.
  1979.   Distribution and spatial patterning of flamingos in the Andean Altiplano.   The Auk, vol. 96, pp. 328-342.

HURLBERT, STUART H.; LOPEZ, MATILDE; and STEIN, ROSALYN
———.	The diets and feeding behaviors of three South American flamingos. (In preparation.)
JENKIN, P. M.
1957.	The filter-feeding and food of flamingoes (Phoenicopteri).	Philos. Trans. Roy. Soc. London, ser. B., vol. 240, pp. 401-493.
KEAR, JANET, and DUPLAIX-HALL, NICOLE, eds.
1975.	Flamingos, 246 pp., illus.	T. & A. D. Poyser, Ltd., Berkhamsted, England.	(Proceedings of the International Flamingo Symposium held at the Wildfowl Trust, Slimbridge, England, July 1973.)
MUÑOZ, J., and MUÑOZ, CARMECITA
1975.	Chubut Province, Argentina.	Pp. 91-92 *in* Kear and Duplaix-Hall, 1975.
PATRICK, RUTH
1961.	Results of researches in the Antofagasta ranges of Chile and Bolivia, II: Diatoms (Bacillariophyceae) from the alimentary tract of *Phoenicoparrus jamesi* (Sclater).	Postilla (Yale Peabody Museum), no. 49, pp. 43-57.
ROOTH, J.
1965.	The flamingos on Bonaire.	Natuurw. Stud. Suriname en de Ned. Antilles, no. 41, 151 pp.	Utrecht, Netherlands.

STUART H. HURLBERT

Physiological Ecology of the Telmatobiid Frogs of Lake Titicaca

Principal Investigator: Victor H. Hutchison, Department of Zoology, University of
                            Oklahoma, Norman, Oklahoma.

Grant No. 1231:   For field collection and laboratory studies on the aquatic
                            frogs of Lake Titicaca (*Telmatobius culeus*).

The aquatic frogs of Lake Titicaca have interested biologists and natural historians for many years. Although these amphibians possess very small lungs, they have not been seen to breathe air. They occur at depths of several hundred feet (Allen, 1922; Parker, 1940; Schmidt, 1954; Vellard, 1954; Diaz y Gomez, 1965). The largest high altitude lake in the world, Lake Titicaca has a surface area of 7,800 square kilometers and an elevation at the surface of 3,812 meters. The waters of the lake are cool and vary from about 15.7°C at the surface in summer to 11.1°C through the water column in midwinter. The hypolimnion is close to 10°C (Richerson et al., 1975). Although the anatomy of the Titicaca frog had been described in detail (Macedo, 1960), almost nothing was known about the adaptations of this species for survival under the relatively hypoxic conditions of high altitude and aquatic existence in the absence of an aerial gas exchange with the lungs.

In addition to the principal investigator, the other personnel of the expedition were Howard B. Haines, Professor of Zoology, and graduate students Gustav Engbretson and Donald Howard, all of the University of Oklahoma. The following persons and organizations contributed greatly to our efforts: Mildred Fung; Drs. Alfonso Criales Q., Enrico Linares, Jean Coudert, Jorge Rioja Roca, Hugo Villegas, Lydia Ruiz, Luis Hartmann; Drs. Mario Diaz M., Juan Nogales O.; Director General de Agricultura Gover Barja B., Vicealmirante Xavier Pinto T., Lt. Kelly Hughes, USN; Universidad Mayor de San Andres, Ministerio de Agricultura y Ganaderia, Instituto Boliviano de Biologia de Altura, Fuerza Naval Boliviana.

Field Studies

The expedition to Bolivia was made in December 1973 and in January 1974. Collections of the Titicaca Frog (*Telmatobius culeus*) were made along the shoreline and in shallow waters of Lago Pequeño, in the vicinity of Copacabana and, especially, along the bases of rocky cliffs in the Estrecho de Tiquina near San Pablo and San Pedro. The frogs were taken by snorkeling at depths of about 2 meters. Other anurans, especially *Telmatobius marmoratus,* were collected from streams in the area. About 800 *T. culeus* were collected and returned to the laboratory for subsequent use. About 300 of these were shipped to the University of Oklahoma for a continuation of research on respiratory gas exchange.

We had the opportunity to visit the Ulla Ulla Game Preserve in northwestern Bolivia in the Cordillera Apalobamba to investigate the reported occurrence of frogs in a glacial lake (Lago Nube) at approximately 4,700 meters. Although no frogs were seen in the lake, lizards (*Liolaemus multiformis*) were collected from dry pampas areas for later study (Engbretson and Hutchison, 1976). We also were able to observe and photograph behavioral interactions between family groups and a bachelor herd of vicuña. The Ulla Ulla Reserve was established by the Bolivian government to preserve this endangered mammal.

Laboratory Studies

Investigations on the respiratory adaptations of the Lake Titicaca frog (fig. 1) were conducted in La Paz, Bolivia, and at the University of Oklahoma. This unique species has a remarkable combination of behavioral, morphological, and physiological adaptations which allows an aquatic life in cool (10°C to 15°C) O_2-saturated (at 100 mm Hg) waters at high altitude (3,812 meters). The skin surface area is increased by pronounced folds and the cutaneous capillaries penetrate to the outer layers of the skin. The erythrocyte volume (394 μ^3) is the smallest reported for amphibians. The P_{50} (15.6 at pH 7.65 and 10°C) is the lowest, and the erythrocyte count (729 · $10^3/mm^3$) the highest for an anuran. The O_2 capacity (11.7 vol%), hemoglobin (8.1g/100 ml), hemoglobin concentration (0.281 pg/μ^3) and hematocrit (27.9%) measured at 18°C and 3,800 meters are all elevated in comparison with most amphibians. The O_2 dissociation curve is sigmoid (n=2), the Bohr factor is small ($\Delta logP_{50}/\Delta pH=-0.30$) and the buffering capacity (-8.9mM HCO_3^- · l^{-1} · ΔpH^{-1}) is typical for an aquatic amphibian. The metabolic rate (14.1 $\mu l · g^{-1}$ · h^{-1}) is the lowest reported for a frog and among amphibians only the giant salamanders (*Amphiuma, Necturus* and *Siren*) have lower values. If prevented from surfacing in hypoxic waters, the frogs ventilate the skin by "bobbing" behavior; if allowed to surface, they will ventilate the small lungs and the metabolic rate increases to 23 $\mu l · g^{-1} · h^{-1}$. A detailed report of these studies has been published (Hutchison, Haines, and Engbretson, 1976). Motion pic-

FIG. 1. The Lake Titicaca frog *Telmatobius culeus*. As individuals grow there is an allometric increase in the surface area of the skin such that large adults present a very "baggy" appearance. These folds are richly vascularized with capillaries which penetrate to just below the outer layers of the skin (*stratum corneum*). The skin has thus become the major respiratory organ for this totally aquatic anuran.

tures of the "bobbing" behavior of *Telmatobius* and of a similar "rocking" behavior in the hellbender, *Cryptobranchus*, were made for detailed analysis; these films are now used in lectures.

Lizards (*Liolaemus multiformis multiformis*) collected from scattered rocks and burrows in a fluvioglacial area near Ulla Ulla, Departamento de La Paz at altitudes between 4,500 and 4,800 meters were used to measure erythrocyte count (124×10^4 mm^3), hematocrit (34.3%) and hemoglobin content (10.1 g%). Although there is no widespread evidence that with increased altitude lizards alter erythrocyte numbers, hematocrit and hemoglobin content, our findings indicate that *L. m. multiformis* have higher values than many other lizards and suggest that more thorough investigations on the physiological adaptation to high altitude in lizards are needed (Engbretson and Hutchison, 1976).

The thermal tolerance of the Titicaca frog was studied with the critical thermal maximum (CTM) as the end point. The CTM is the temperature at which locomotory activity becomes disorganized and the animal loses its ability to escape from conditions that will promptly lead to its death. Details of the method were previously described (Hutchison, 1961). The frogs were acclimated in early January at 5°C and 15°C and the natural photoperiod for several days in La Paz after capture and determinations made between 1,000 and 1,200 hours to avoid possible daily cycles in thermal tolerance. There was no significant difference between the two acclimation temperatures: 5°C, x̄ = 32.6 ± 0.60°C, N = 11; 15°C, x̄ = 32.38 ± 1.21°C, N = 26). Although these data are preliminary, they suggest that the evolution of this species at a fairly constant temperature has resulted in the loss of the ability to acclimate to different thermal environments. The CTM of the Titicaca frog is similar to those of two species of Colombian frogs from high altitude, *Eleuthrodactylus bogotensis* (33.8-34.5°C) and *Phyllobates subpunctatus* (31.1-32.6°C), both acclimated at 15°C and various photoperiods (Hutchison, 1971).

REFERENCES

ALLEN, W. R.
  1922.   Notes on the Andean frog *Telmatobius culeus* (Garman).   Copeia, pp. 52-54.
DIAZ y GOMEZ, E.
  1976.   La respiracion en un anuro del altiplano andino (*Telmatobius culi escomeli* Angel).   Bol. Soc. Esp. Hist. Nat. Secc. Biol., vol. 63, pp. 265-269.
ENGBRETSON, G., and HUTCHISON, V. H.
  1976.   Erythrocyte count, hematocrit and hemoglobin content in the lizard *Liolaemus multiformis*.   Copeia, p. 186.
HUTCHISON, V. H.
  1961.   Critical thermal maxima in salamanders.   Physiol. Zool., vol. 34, pp. 92-125.
  1971.   Herpetological expedition to Colombia.   Nat. Geog. Soc. Res. Rep., vol. 6 (1965 Projects), pp. 113-122.
HUTCHISON, V. H.; HAINES, H. B.; and ENGBRETSON, G.
  1976.   Aquatic life at high altitude: Respiratory adaptations in the Lake Titicaca frog, *Telmatobius culeus*.   Resp. Physiol., vol. 27, pp. 115-129.
MACEDO, H. de.
  1960.   Vergleichende Untersuchungen an Arten der Gattung *Telmatobius* (Amphibia, Anura).   Zeit. Wiss. Zool., vol. 163, pp. 355-396.
PARKER, H. W.
  1940.   The Percy Sladen Trust Expedition to Lake Titicaca in 1937. XII. Amphibia.   Trans. Linn. Soc. London, series 3, vol. 1, pp. 203-216.
RICHERSON, P. J.; WIDMER, C.; KITTEL, T.; and LANDA C., A.
  1975.   A survey of the physical and chemical limnology of Lake Titicaca.   Verh. Internat. Verein. Limnol., vol. 19, pp. 1498-1503.

SCHMIDT, K. P.
1954.   Notes on frogs of the genus *Telmatobius* with descriptions of two new Peruvian species.   Fieldiana, vol. 34, pp. 277-287.
VELLARD, J.
1954.   Etudes sur le Lac Titicaca. V. Les *Telmatobius* du haut-plateau Interandin.   Trav. Inst. Franc. Etudes Andines, vol. 4, pp. 1-57.

VICTOR H. HUTCHISON

The Submerged Sanctuary of Apollo at Halieis in the Argolid of Greece

Principal Investigator: Michael H. Jameson, Stanford University, Stanford, California.

Grant Nos. 1201, 1339.   For excavation and study of the submerged sanctuary of Apollo at Halieis in the Argolid of Greece.

In the summer of 1973 the excavation program for the Sanctuary of Apollo was brought to completion, and in the following summer a team of reduced size conducted research on the results of the three previous seasons and returned briefly to the submerged site for verification of details. Although work in the sea was somewhat curtailed by an international and national crisis, significant new information was acquired. Since then research has continued in preparation for a final publication as the second volume in the projected series on Halieis. The report that follows summarizes results of the expedition as a whole and the state of our knowledge as of May 1978.

Excavation of the sanctuary was conducted on behalf of the University of Pennsylvania and Indiana University, specifically the departments of classical studies of the two universities and the University Museum of the University of Pennsylvania, with financial support from these institutions, the National Endowment for the Humanities, the Ford Foundation, the National Geographic Society, and private benefactors. Work in the Sanctuary of Apollo is part of a larger project in this area of the Argolid that is under the auspices of the American School of Classical Studies at Athens and the Archaeological Service of the Republic of Greece.

Shallow-water archeology requires a large technical and general staff. For the last two seasons and for the preparations for publication we are conspicuously in debt to Dr. Frederick A. Cooper (architecture and surveying), Christina M. Dengate (pottery), Nancy K. Cooper (roof-tiles), Dr. Nancy Bookides (sculpture), Lucy Weier Krystalli (conservation), Mr. and Mrs. Julian Whittlesey (balloon photography), Stephen Hallin and John Wollerton (chief mechanics and divers), Virginia Jameson and Anne Kilinski (records), and Dr. and Mrs. Wilson Myers in a great variety of capacities. Dr. James A. Dengate of the Department of Classics of the University of Illinois, Urbana, was associate director; and the author of this report, currently research associate of the

University Museum of the University of Pennsylvania and Crossett Professor of Humanistic Studies, Stanford University, directed the project.

In the Classical period Halieis was a fortified town on a sheltered harbor at the entrance of the Argolic Gulf. It existed as a more or less independent city-state from around 700 to 300 B.C., when the site was abandoned after violent destruction on its acropolis. The north side of the town, facing the harbor, has gradually been submerged to a depth of more than 3 meters. Excavation in five seasons between 1962 and 1968 had been concerned with the town site, both on land and in the sea, and methods for reconnaissance and excavation in the sea had been developed. Extensive remains outside of the town, in the northeast part of the present harbor, were located and photographed in 1968 by means of a balloon-supported camera (Jameson, 1969). Cleaning and excavation were begun in 1970. By 1971 the remains could be identified as the chief cult center of the Greek city, sacred to the god Apollo, on the basis of the god's name inscribed on a large, iron temple key. The building in which the key was found, along with the god's statue in marble, was a temple facing south to a large altar. Other buildings in the sanctuary included what was probably another temple (Building 2), parallel to the first and at its closest no more than 1 meter away from it, and a complex consisting of a number of rooms with a rectangular well-head nearby, all no doubt for the use of visitors to the sanctuary. Only the Temple of Apollo has provided us with sufficient information for detailed reconstruction. The heart of the precinct covered an area of some 100 by 50 meters, but to this must be added a stadium 167 meters long, with associated structures. The whole sanctuary in its most developed form in the later 4th century B.C. is an excellent example of an extramural cult center. For this report, a few aspects of the varied research set in motion by the discovery of the site are selected for comment. (For a more general discussion with plans and photographs, see Jameson, 1974.)

Study of the architecture of the Temple of Apollo by Dr. F. A. Cooper, of the Department of Art History of the University of Minnesota, has been particularly revealing. Its walls were of mud-brick on a foundation of hard, dark-gray limestone slabs, a material not found in the immediate vicinity of Halieis. These stones were laid in two rows to form the two faces of each wall. Only the outside face of each stone was dressed straight. Each course was laid separately, in perfectly level planes, with four courses above ground on the west, seaward side of the temple and three on the east. The resulting masonry was isodomic but not ashlar. Doorways were reinforced with stone piers on each side, of longer, more fully dressed blocks. A central row of wooden columns in at least the two rear rooms of the building and of half columns along the interiors of walls rested on roughly circular and semicircular bases of the same limestone; the half-column bases in turn were set on a narrow ledge projecting from the base of the walls. Sometime after the original construction the central row of column bases was replaced in part by squared bases of a softer limestone surmounted by circular plinths, and a threshhold of ashlar blocks of the same material was inserted between the Entrance Hall *(prothyron)* at the south and the Front Chamber. The floor was at least partly paved with irregular slabs of a greenish sandstone, still used for this purpose in the region, set in a bed of crushed white limestone ("poros"). Traces have been found of a white, painted plaster, decorated with brown bands, used on the walls of the Front Chamber.

Two rooms were entered from the south, where lay the altar—the Entrance Hall and the Front Chamber. A Middle and Rear Chamber were each entered through separate doorways on the west side. All construction was remarkably precise. The side walls of the temple are parallel in their whole course with a variation of no more than 1:3000 (1 centimeter). The Entrance Hall and Front Chamber, which no doubt contained the original statue of the god as well as its later marble replacement, are of standard plan, but the two separate rear chambers with their lateral entrances are unusual, reflecting presumably their cult functions. We are, however, at a relatively early stage in the development of Greek religious architecture and should not expect a high degree of uniformity. There was no exterior colonnade.

The roofing systems of the temple and Building 2, to its east, have been the subject of research by Nancy K. Cooper. The central and engaged columns of the temple were required to support rafters underlying heavy terra-cotta tiles of Corinthian type: flat pan tiles fitting tightly against each other were covered at their joints by narrow, angular cover tiles. The ridge of the roof was capped by separate, double-pan and double-cover tiles that hung over the ridge and overlapped pan and cover tiles, respectively, on both sides. The front and rear ends of the temple were gabled. No decorative elements, sculptured, molded, or painted, have been detected, except that the lower end of the cover tiles, at the eaves, rises in three peaks, thus serving the function of antefixes. The evidence from Halieis permits the most detailed reconstruction so far of a type of roof known from elsewhere in the Argolid, on the island of Aigina and at Delphi, where it may be explained by the activity of a city of this region. Decoratively it was extremely simple but technically very efficient. Comparison with other roofs points to a date in the later 7th century B.C.

The larger structure, Building 2, to the east of the Temple of Apollo, survives only in its foundations and in fragments of its roofing. Its dimensions, 28.16 by 6.45 meters (compared to 27.30 by 4.46 meters of the Temple of

Apollo), suggested another "100-foot" building with a foot of 0.28 meter. The roofing is of purely Laconian type with concave pan tiles and convex cover tiles. An arched, tubular series of kalypters lay along the roof ridge, terminating at the south end in an akroterion consisting of two terra-cotta disks with molded (and probably painted) decoration, connected to each other by struts. Reconstruction of the roofing has determined the southern orientation and the probability that Building 2, in view of its size and decoration, was also a temple. Previously a stoa had also been considered possible. Since disk akroteria are not thought to have been used much after 600 B.C., we would seem to have two temples, side by side, facing the same altar for most of the life of the sanctuary.

The existence of more than one temple in a sanctuary is by no means uncommon. It is tempting to assign the different temples to different gods although we rarely have evidence that permits us to do so, and in some cases, as at Delos or on the Acropolis of Athens, it is certain that the same god possessed more than one temple. The problem is linked to that of the various epithets of a single god and to the multiple statues of a god in a single sanctuary, as well as to that of multiple sanctuaries of the same god. For Halieis even our scanty evidence points unquestionably to the dominant position of the cult of Apollo for the state. His son, Asklepios, was also worshiped at Halieis (*IG* IV². 1. 122, 69 ff.), but that cult can hardly have been established before the 5th century B.C. Silence about Apollo's sister and mother, Artemis and Leto, is not in itself significant, but it is extremely improbable that any other god would have possessed a larger temple than that of Apollo in his own sanctuary. We should therefore consider the historical circumstances that may have led in a matter of decades to the building of two temples to the one god.

Excavation on the acropolis of Halieis has shown a strong Laconian presence in the form of a garrison in the period between about 640 and 590 B.C. (The evidence will be set out by Charles K. Williams II, in the forthcoming full publication of the acropolis as *Halieis,* vol. 1.) Prior to this time, and indeed through and beyond the years of Laconian presence, there also existed a local community. Tentatively we may suggest that the roofing system of the Temple of Apollo, of a type characteristic of this region, is to be associated with the local community, whereas the Laconian system of the other temple, Building 2, is a product of the Spartan presence. While the system is not confined to Lakedaimon or to Spartan activity elsewhere it was certainly the dominant system in areas under their influence in the early Archaic period.

It should be noted that Laconian influence did not cease after about 500 B.C. though it no longer involved the presence of a Spartan garrison. Laconian interest in a cult on the acropolis and in the Sanctuary of Apollo is shown by lead votive offerings and pottery of the 6th century. But at present, because of the dating of other examples of disk akroteria, Building 2 seems to belong in or near the 7th century and thus very likely to the period of Spartan occupation. For the Temple of Apollo, on the other hand, a date prior to ca. 640 B.C., and thus prior to the Spartan occupation, would better suit the earliest pottery (from the Front Chamber) and the radiocarbon dates of wood (from the Middle and Rear Chambers), which point to the first half of the 7th century. If that proves to be irreconcilable with the architecture, we will need to posit an earlier, local shrine on the same spot some of whose dedications, and perhaps timber, were incorporated in its successor.

The later history of the site is still unclear. It seems unlikely that athletic festivals or calendrically regular sacrifices were celebrated after the abandonment of the city. Inundation of the sanctuary began sometime after ca. A.D. 400, some 700 years later, to judge from the radiocarbon date of a wooden post found in place in the Front Chamber of the, by then, long ruinous Temple of Apollo.

REFERENCES

JAMESON, MICHAEL H.
1969.   Excavations at Porto Cheli and vicinity, a preliminary report, I: Halieis, 1962-68.   Hesperia, vol. 38, pp. 311-342.
1974.   The excavation of a drowned Greek temple.   Sci. Amer., vol. 231, no. 4, pp. 110-119, illus.
1979.   Excavations at Halieis, 1973-1974.   Archaiologikon Deltion, vol. 29 (1973-1974), Chronika, pp. 261-264.

MICHAEL H. JAMESON

The Geology of Marble Canyon Quadrangle, Death Valley, California

Principal Investigator: Edward A. Johnson, Geologic Division, U. S. Department of the Interior, Denver, Colorado.

Grant No. 1179:   In support of a study of the geology of Marble Canyon Quadrangle, Death Valley, California.

The first reported geologic investigation involving the Marble Canyon Quadrangle was the reconnaissance mapping conducted by Ball (1907) and his geologic interpretation of the area appears on the Geologic Map of California Death Valley Sheet compiled by Jennings (1958) as an oversimplification of the facts. A small portion of the extreme northwest corner of the area was covered by McAllister (1952) in his report on the geology of the Quartz Spring area. Also, a substantial part of the western side of the area was studied by Stadler (1968), resulting in an unpublished master's thesis from the University of Oregon.

During the period 1968 through 1971, I prepared a detailed study of the geology of the eastern half of the quadrangle. An unpublished Ph.D. thesis (Johnson, 1971a) resulted from this project. One month of fieldwork was conducted during the summer of 1972 in an effort to acquire additional information on the unmapped portion of the quadrangle.

Continuing this effort to compile a complete geologic map of the 15-minute Marble Canyon Quadrangle, a 250-mile area located in the northern Panamint Range which makes up the west side of Death Valley in southeastern California, I established a base camp at Hunter Springs on May 27, 1973, actual fieldwork was initiated the following day. Excluding several days which were used to obtain needed supplies in nearby Lone Pine, California, a total of 37 days were spent in the field before the extreme heat forced an end to activities on July 4. During this time approximately 25 square miles were mapped in detail at a scale of 1:31,000.

Research covered all geologic aspects of the area including the stratigraphy, geologic structure, and economic geology. This area contains some of the roughest terrain in the Monument as well as some of the most complex geologic structure. Specific disclosures made during the 1973 field season include detailed structures in the upper plate of the Marble Canyon thrust fault in regard to Late Tertiary block faulting and information concerning the Rest Springs Shale-Lee Flat Limestone facies change.

I would like to express my sincere thanks to the National Geographic Society for the granting of funds in support of my research.

REFERENCES

BALL, S. H.
  1907.   A geologic reconnaissance in southwestern Nevada and eastern Califor-
           nia.   U. S. Geol. Survey Bull. 308, 218 pp.
JENNINGS, C. W.
  1958.   Geologic map of California, Death Valley sheet.   Calif. Div. Mines and
           Geol.
JOHNSON, E. A.
  1971a.   The geology of a part of the southeastern side of the Cottonwood Moun-
           tains, Death Valley, California.   Rice University, Ph.D. thesis,
           81 pp.
  1971b.   Thrust faulting in the eastern Cottonwood Mountains, Death Valley,
           California.   Geol. Soc. Amer., abstracts with programs, vol. 3, no. 2.
McALLISTER, J. F.
  1952.   Rocks and structure of the Quartz Spring area, northern Panamint
           Range, California.   Calif. Div. Mines and Geol., Spec. Rept. 25,
           38 pp.
STADLER, C. A.
  1968.   The geology of the Goldbelt Springs area, northern Panamint Range,
           Inyo County, California.   University of Oregon, M.S. thesis, 78 pp.

EDWARD A. JOHNSON

Ecology of Small Mammals on Iron and Titanium Open-pit Mine Wastes in the Central Adirondack Mountains, New York

Principal Investigator: Gordon L. Kirkland, Jr., Shippensburg State College, Shippensburg, Pennsylvania.

Grant No. 1205:   For a study of mammal ecology on open-pit mine-waste dumps.

The sparsely vegetated mine-waste disposal areas of the MacIntyre Development of N L Industries, Inc., at Tahawus, Essex County, New York, constitute an ecological island surrounded by mature mixed deciduous-coniferous Adirondack Mountain forests. The physical and biological environments on the mine wastes differ markedly from those in the neighboring natural communities. As such, the isolated mine provides a natural laboratory on which to study the exploitation of this disturbed area by small mammals.

In 1972 research was initiated to study the small mammals inhabiting the mine wastes and to answer two major questions. Are there any differences between the small mammal communities on the mine wastes and in the surrounding natural forests? Which species are most successful in invading and establishing populations on the mine wastes? This paper presents the results of research conducted from 1972 to 1975 and describes the success of small mammals in invading and occupying the lands of the MacIntyre Development.

Personnel and Acknowledgments

Sampling during the four years was conducted by students in the Field Research in Biology course from Shippensburg State College, Pennsylvania. Rebecca J. Griffin was student coordinator of research in 1972.

Work on the mine wastes would not have been possible without the cooperation and generous assistance of Walter M. Chapman, manager, and Robert Hampson, lands manager, of the MacIntyre Development of N L Industries, Inc. In addition to providing access to mine lands, N L Industries, Inc., supplied housing and laboratory space during the study period.

This project was supported by a research grant from the National Geographic Society in 1973. The support of Shippensburg State College throughout the four years is acknowledged.

Site Description

The research was conducted at the MacIntyre Development of N L Industries, Inc., an open-pit mining operation in the central Adirondack Mountains, Essex County, New York. The Tahawus mine is located 5.7 miles north, 5.2 miles east, of Newcomb (U.S.G.S. Santanoni Quadrangle). Extraction and refinement of the ilmenite-magnetite ore during the past quarter century have resulted in the creation of extensive terraces of overburden and crushed rock from the mining and milling operations. Waste-disposal areas cover about 400 acres of former forest land. When active dumping ceases, these sites begin to undergo ecological succession; however, the severe environmental conditions and poor soils of the waste areas retard the rate of succession compared to that which occurs on sites disturbed by lumbering and fires.

The vegetation on the mine wastes consists of a mosaic of clumps of sapling hardwoods, herbaceous cover, and bare rock. The dominant trees, quaking aspen *(Populus tremuloides)*, fire cherry *(Prunus pensylvanica)*, and white birch *(Betula papyrifera)*, grow on sites having sufficient soil to support them. Herbaceous cover is dominated by introduced white sweet clover *(Melilotus*

TABLE 1.   Trapnight Sampling Effort on Mine Wastes and in Surrounding Forests, 1972-1975

Year	Mine wastes		Forests*	
	Live	Snap	Live	Snap
1972	____	1,037	1,170	1,908
1973	3,042	563	____	450
1974	805	380	____	
1975	1,275	____	180	540
Totals	5,122	1,980	1,350	2,898

*Forest mammal data for 1974 used in this paper are from 1,865 trapnights of snap-trap effort at two sites in Schroon and Minerva Townships, Essex County, approximately 20 miles south of Tahawus.

alba). Other important species are St. John's wort *(Hypericum perforatum),* goldenrods *(Solidago* sp.*),* pearly-everlasting *(Anaphalis margaritacea),* rattle-snake weed *(Hieracium venosum),* poverty grass *(Danthonia spicata),* evening primrose *(Oenothera biennis),* and strawberry *(Fragaria virginiana).* Depending upon the age of the site, the percentage of living ground cover varies from 0-90+ percent.

TABLE 2. Abundances and Diversity of Small Mammals Sampled on the Tahawus Mine Wastes as Compared to Those from Surrounding Forests

Species	Mine Wastes		Forests		Difference	
	No.	Pct.	No.	Pct.	Pct.	Z value[a]
Sorex cinereus Kerr	—	—	17	4.6	4.6	3.26[b]
Sorex fumeus Miller	1	0.3	3	0.8	0.5	0.96
Sorex dispar Batchelder	2	0.5	1	0.3	0.2	0.45
Blarina brevicauda Say	2	0.5	55	14.8	14.3	7.60[c]
Tamias striatus (Linnaeus)	26	6.5	15	4.0	2.5	1.55
Tamiasciurus hudsonicus (Erxleben)	1	0.3	2	0.5	0.2	0.45
Glaucomys sabrinus (Shaw)	—	—	1	0.3	0.3	1.22
Peromyscus leucopus (Rafinesque)	4	1.0	—	—	1.0	1.96
Peromyscus maniculatus (Wagner)	235	58.5	69	18.6	39.9	11.34[c]
Microtus pennsylvanicus (Ord)	83	20.7	5	1.4	19.3	8.44[c]
Microtus chrotorrhinus (Miller)	—	—	2	0.5	0.5	1.39
Clethrionomys gapperi (Vigors)	29	7.2	134	36.1	28.9	9.83[c]
Zapus hudsonius (Zimmerman)	7	1.7	—	—	1.7	2.51[b]
Napaeozapus insignis (Miller)	12	3.0	67	18.1	15.1	6.77[c]
Total Individuals	402		274			
Total trapnights sampling effort	7,102		4,248			
Catch/100 trapnights	5.66		6.45			
Number of species	11		12			
Species/100 individuals	2.74		4.38			
Shannon Diversity Index	1.89		2.50			
Equitability	.55		.70			

[a]Z test of differences between proportions (Zarr, 1974) [b]$P < .01$ [c]$P < .001$

The physical environment of the mine wastes is severe. Portions not supporting woody or dense herbaceous cover exhibit extremes of temperature and moisture. In the absence of shade, the dark rocky soils reach surface temperatures in excess of 37.8° C. during the summer. High evaporative rates produce pronounced surface drying by midafternoon, in spite of frequent heavy evening dews.

Methods and Materials

During the four years, live- and snap-trap sampling was conducted on the mine wastes and in the surrounding natural forest habitats. The sampling was designed to yield data on the presence, distribution, and relative abundance of small mammals in both ecological zones. Systematic sampling with grids and lines of traps, as described in Kirkland and Griffin (1973) and Kirkland (1976), was augmented by nonsystematic trapping of a variety of microhabitats on the mine wastes. Sampling effort during the four years totaled 11,342 trapnights (table 1).

Results and Discussion

COMMUNITY COMPOSITION.

Data collected from 1972 to 1975 reveal small-mammal community differences between the mine wastes and surrounding forests. Of the 14 species trapped in the two areas, 11 were on the mine wastes and 12 in the forest habitats (table 2), and only 9 were common to both ecological zones. A Coefficient of Community analysis (Hagmaier and Stults, 1964) of the two mammal communities produced a Coefficient of Community (CC) of 64.3 percent. This value falls within the range of CCs (60.30 - 64.60 percent) used to determine North American mammal provinces (Hagmaier, 1966). Thus the differences between the small-mammal species compositions of the mine waste and forest habitats approximate those that distinguish mammal provinces.

The relative abundances of the species in the mine waste and forest mammal communities also differed. Spearman Rank Correlation analysis (Siegel, 1956) of the rankings of the species in the two communities revealed no significant correlation at the 0.05 level ($r_s = .42$).

The abundances of seven species differed significantly (table 2). The masked shrew, *Sorex cinereus* Kerr, the short-tailed shrew, *Blarina brevicauda* Say, the red-backed vole, *Clethrionomys gapperi* (Vigors), and the woodland jumping mouse, *Napaeozapus insignis* (Miller), were more abundant in the forests. The deer mouse, *Peromyscus maniculatus* (Wagner), the meadow vole, *Mi-*

crotus pennsylvanicus (Ord), and the meadow jumping mouse, *Zapus hudsonius* (Zimmerman), were significantly more abundant on the mine wastes. The species differences illustrate the grassland characteristics of the mine waste mammal community.

A similar comparison of the two mammal communities on the basis of the five families/subfamilies represented also revealed the distinctive characteristics of the two communities. The percentage representation of four of the five families/subfamilies differed significantly (table 3). Shrews (Soricidae), voles (Microtinae), and jumping mice (Zapodidae) were less abundant on the mine wastes. Squirrels (Sciuridae) had comparable abundance in the two ecological zones.

ABUNDANCE AND DIVERSITY

During the four-year study period, the forest small mammals exhibited greater community species diversity and were slightly more abundant than mammals on the mine wastes (table 2). These differences may reflect a negative impact of the severe mine-waste environment on resident small mammals. The lower Shannon diversity indices (Shannon and Weaver, 1963) and Shannon evenness component for the mine-waste mammals are attributable to the overwhelming abundance of a single species, *Peromyscus maniculatus,* which

TABLE 3. Comparisons of the Abundance of Families or Subfamilies of Small Mammals on the Mine Wastes and in the Forests with Z Test of Differences in Proportions (Zarr, 1974)

Family or subfamily	Mine Wastes		Forests		Pct. diff.	Z value
	No.	Pct.	No.	Pct.		
Soricidae (shrews) 4 species	5	1.2	76	20.5	19.3	8.65[a]
Sciuridae (squirrels) 3 species	27	6.7	18	4.9	1.8	1.27
Cricetinae (mice) 2 species	239	59.5	69	18.6	40.9	11.82[a]
Microtinae (voles) 3 species	112	27.9	141	38.0	10.1	2.51[b]
Zapodidae (jumping mice) 2 species	19	4.7	67	18.1	13.4	6.01[a]

[a]P < .001   [b]P < .005

accounted for 58.5 percent of the individuals trapped on the mine wastes. It should be noted that during the four summers 1972-1975, the relative abundance of mine-waste mammals mirrored that of forest mammals as follows:

| | Catch per 100 trapnights | |
Year	Mine wastes	Forests
1972	7.2	7.8
1973	3.0	4.0
1974	5.7	4.2
1975	12.9	15.6

Species Accounts by Family/Subfamily

SHREWS (SORICIDAE)

Only five shrews were captured on the mine wastes in four years. Three specimens, 2 *Sorex dispar* and 1 *Blarina brevicauda,* were trapped in an isolated forest remnant. This cool, moist, boulder-strewn habitat is typical for *Sorex dispar* (Jackson, 1928; Richmond and Grimm, 1950). An additional *Blarina* was captured on an open, rocky terrace within 100 feet of the above-mentioned forest remnant. The limited distribution of *Blarina* may be related to its high moisture and humidity requirements (Getz, 1961) and avoidance of temperature extremes (Pruitt, 1959). A single *Sorex fumeus* was captured in dense grass on a terrace slope. Although *S. fumeus* is generally considered a resident of northern forests (Hamilton, 1963), I have trapped it on recent clearcuts, including grassy sites in West Virginia (Kirkland, 1974; and unpublished data).

SQUIRRELS (SCIURIDAE)

Of the two species of sciurids captured on the mine wastes, *Tamiasciurus hudsonicus* was represented by a single individual, presumably a transient. Although *Tamias striatus* was more abundant, only seven specimens were trapped from 1972 to 1974, primarily near forest remnants and at the edge of the mine wastes. In 1975, *Tamias* was conspicuously more abundant. The 19 specimens trapped comprised 12 percent of the total 1975 small-mammal catch on the mine wastes. The reason for this increase is not evident. All the 1975 *Tamias* were captured in the interior of the mine wastes on sites that had exhibited conspicuous tree growth in the four years. It is unlikely that the increase in *Tamias* abundance was due to an influx from the surrounding forests, since *Tamias* comprised only 4 percent of the 1975 forest mammals sampled.

VOLES (MICROTINAE)

In 1973-74 *Microtus pennsylvanicus* was the only microtine on the mine wastes. However, in 1972 and 1975 *Clethrionomys gapperi* was also present. The joint occurrence of these two microtines is noteworthy because of their normal competitive relationships and ecological segregation (Grant, 1969, 1970; Morris and Grant, 1972). The presence on the mine wastes of the forest-dwelling *C. gapperi* is attributed to small-mammal population pressure in surrounding forests. In 1972 and 1975, forest small-mammal populations were relatively high (see above), with *C. gapperi* the most abundant species (42 and 28 percent of the small mammals caught). *Clethrionomys* was absent from the mine wastes during the two years of low forest small-mammal populations (see above), years when *C. gapperi* represented only 6 and 8 percent of the small mammals captured.

The distribution and abundance of *M. pennsylvanicus* on the mine wastes appeared to be dependent upon the amount of herbaceous cover. This species was most abundant on heavily seeded terrace slopes with dense grass cover. Although it was the second-most abundant species on the mine wastes during the four-year study period, *M. pennsylvanicus* was not as widespread as the ubiquitous *Peromyscus maniculatus*.

MICE (CRICETINAE)

The woodland deer mouse, *Peromyscus maniculatus gracilis* (LeConte), was the most abundant and widespread small mammal on the mine wastes throughout the four-year study period. Mine-waste populations resembled those in the surrounding forests for the population parameters of age distribution, density, home range, and sex ratio (Kirkland, 1976).

Although *P.m. gracilis* is normally a forest-dweller, its successful invasion of the Tahawus mine wastes conformed to a pattern of exploitation of non-forested habitats recorded from three other localities (Hatt et al., 1948; Ozoga and Phillips, 1964; and Fitch, J. H., personal communication). In each case, the potentially competitive northern white-footed mouse, *Peromyscus leucopus noveboracensis* (Fischer), was absent. This condition was approximated at Tahawus where only four *P.l. noveboracensis* were trapped on the mine wastes and none in the surrounding forests in four years.

JUMPING MICE (ZAPODIDAE)

The two zapodids, *Zapus hudsonius* and *Napaeozapus insignis,* had a complementary pattern of capture on the mine wastes, with the former trapped in 1972 and 1974 and the latter taken in 1973 and 1975. The low abundance of zapodids in all years precluded a meaningful analysis of the alternating pattern of capture of the two species. Whitaker and Wrigley (1972) note that these two zapodids tend to segregate ecologically in the different seral stages of plant succession, with *Zapus* primarily in meadows and *Napaeozapus* in woods.

Conclusion

The results of the four-year study of small mammals at Tahawus reveal the distinctive character of the small-mammal community on the mine wastes as compared to that inhabiting the surrounding forests. Small mammals on the mine wastes are less diverse and in general less abundant than in the forests. The mine-waste small-mammal community is characterized by the presence of grassland species and very few soricids. The woodland deer mouse is the most successful invader of the mine wastes. Its exploitation of the isolated mine site is at least partly related to the near absence of the potentially competitive white-footed mouse.

The species composition, abundance, and distribution of the mine-waste small mammals varied during the four-year study. Prime factors regulating such changes appear to be plant successional changes on the mine wastes and variation in abundance of small mammals in the surrounding forests. The small-mammal populations in the forests and on the mine wastes will be monitored in the future to establish more clearly the relationship between changes in small mammal populations in the forests and those observed in the mine-waste community.

REFERENCES

GETZ, LOWELL L.
  1961.   Factors influencing the local distribution of shrews.   Amer. Midl. Nat., vol. 55, pp. 67-88.
GRANT, P. R.
  1969.   Experimental studies of competitive interaction in a two-species system, I: *Microtus* and *Clethrionomys* species in enclosures.   Can. Journ. Zool., vol. 47, pp. 1059-1082.
  1970.   Experimental studies of competitive interaction in a two-species system, II: The behaviour of *Microtus, Peromyscus* and *Clethrionomys* species. Animal Behav., vol. 18, pp. 411-426.

HAGMAIER, Edwin M.
1966.   A numerical analysis of the distributional patterns of North American mammals, II: Re-evaluation of the provinces.   Syst. Zool., vol. 15, pp. 279-299.
HAGMAIER, EDWIN M., and STULTS, C. D.
1964.   A numerical analysis of the distributional patterns of North American mammals.   Syst. Zool., vol. 13, pp. 125-155.
HAMILTON, WILLIAM J., JR.
1963.   The mammals of Eastern United States, 432 pp. Hafner Publishing Co., New York.
HATT, ROBERT T.; VAN TYNE, JOSSELYN; STUART, L. C.; POPE, CLIFFORD H.; and GROBMAN, ARNOLD B.
1948.   Island life: A study of the land vertebrates of the islands of eastern Lake Michigan.   Cranbrook Inst. Sci. Bull 27, 179 pp.
JACKSON, HARTLEY H. T.
1928.   A taxonomic review of the American long-tailed shrews (genera *Sorex* and *Microsorex*).   North Amer. Fauna 51, vi + 238 pp.
KIRKLAND, GORDON L., JR.
1974.   Preliminary sampling of small mammals on clearcut and uncut red spruce stands in West Virginia.   Proc. West Virginia Acad. Sci., vol. 46, no. 2, pp. 150-154.
1976.   Small mammals of a mine waste situation in the central Adirondacks, New York: A case for opportunism by *Peromyscus maniculatus*.   Amer. Midl. Nat., vol. 95, pp. 103-110.
KIRKLAND, GORDON L., JR., and GRIFFIN, REBECCA J.
1973.   Microdistribution of small mammals at the coniferous-deciduous forest ecotone in northern New York.   Journ. Mamm., vol. 55, pp. 417-427.
MORRIS, RALPH D., and GRANT, P. R.
1972.   Experimental studies of competitive interaction in a two-species system, IV: *Microtus* and *Clethrionomys* species in a single enclosure.   Journ. Animal Ecol., vol. 41, pp. 275-290.
OZOGA, J. J., and PHILLIPS, CARLETON J.
1964.   Mammals of Beaver Island, Michigan.   Publ. Mus. Michigan State Univ., biol. ser., vol. 2, pp. 307-347.
PRUITT, W. O., JR.
1959.   Microclimates and local distribution of small mammals on the George Reserve, Michigan.   Misc. Publ. Mus. Zool. Univ. Michigan, no. 109, 27 pp.
RICHMOND, N. D., and GRIMM, WILLIAM C.
1950.   Ecology and distribution of the shrew *Sorex dispar* in Pennsylvania.   Ecology, vol. 31, pp. 279-282.
SHANNON, CLAUDE E., and WEAVER, WARREN
1963.   The mathematical theory of communication, 117 pp.   University of Illinois Press, Urbana.

SIEGEL, SAMUEL
  1956.   Nonparametric statistics for the behavioral sciences, 312 pp.
          McGraw-Hill Book Co., New York.
WHITAKER, JOHN O., JR., and WRIGLEY, ROBERT E.
  1972.   *Napaeozapus insignis.*   Mammalian Species no. 14, 6 pp.
ZARR, JERROLD H.
  1974.   Biostatistical analysis, 620 pp.   Prentice-Hall Inc., Englewood Cliffs,
          New Jersey.

GORDON L. KIRKLAND, JR.

Field Observations of the Splashing Characid, *Copeina arnoldi,* in Guyana

Principal Investigator: C. O'Neil Krekorian, California State University, San Diego, California.

Grant No. 1142:   For a field study of reproductive and parental behavior of the splashing characid in Guyana.

The splashing characid, *Copeina arnoldi,* has a mode of reproduction and parental care that is unique among living fishes. Complex courtship brings a male and female together side by side at the surface of the water. From this position they jump simultaneously out of the water and cling to the underside of an emergent leaf or other surface. The eggs are deposited and fertilized while the pair adhere side by side to the spawning surface through the surface tension of their wet bodies and outspread fins. After several seconds the pair fall back into the water and prepare for another jump. Many jumps may occur before spawning is completed. Upon termination of spawning the male uses its tail to splash the eggs repeatedly with water, keeping them wet until they hatch on the second or third day and the fry fall into the water.

Although some aspects of *C. arnoldi*'s reproductive and parental behavior are well known as a result of laboratory studies (Krekorian and Dunham, 1972a, b; 1973), there have been no published scientific accounts of its general biology and ethology in the field. During August 1973, I went to Guyana with the hope of finding the splashing characid so that its reproductive and parental behavior in the wild could be studied. My specific objectives were: (1) to find out when spawning occurs in the wild, (2) to discover what plants or other substrates are used for spawning, (3) to study the social and physical conditions associated with spawning, and (4) to compare and check previous laboratory findings with field observations.

Shortly after my arrival in Guyana I met with Harry Rambarran, proprietor of Guyana Aquarium Traders. He introduced me to one of his collectors, who was to serve as my guide. After discussing my objectives we met the following day and traveled approximately 5 miles by boat from the Timerhi Highway up the Lamaha Canal, to an isolated "creek" where the splashing characid occurs in great numbers. The study area was approximately 40 miles from the city of Georgetown.

The "creek" at the study area was approximately 18 meters wide and extended 3-4 meters into the dense jungle vegetation on each side. The water was stagnant and coffee colored. An 8-centimeter white Plexiglas disk disappeared from view at a depth of 46 to 61 centimeters. Water samples taken from the "creek" showed that the water was very soft (DH = 1/4-1/2) and acidic (pH = 4.5-4.8). The great disparity between the water hardness and pH found in the field and that suggested by aquarist literature (DH = 5 and pH = 7) indicates how little was known about the natural environment of *C. arnoldi* prior to this study.

I believe that the splashing characid spawns primarily during the summer rainy season (May, June, and July) as soon as the "creek" fills up. This belief is supported by three pieces of evidence. First, 84 percent of the fish we collected by means of dip nets in August were subadults and uniform in size. Second, Mr. Rambarran and Mr. Defreitas have stated that the splashing characid occurs in great quantities following the summer rainy season. The fish are not collected during May, June, and July because they are difficult to catch (they move into the dense jungle vegetation to breed when the "creek" widens owing to the rain) and too small for export. Third, spawns have not been found during the dry months. Some spawning, however, may occur also during the winter rainy season although I have no data to support this allegation. Fortunately, when I arrived in August, the splashing characid was still breeding in this "creek" in small numbers.

Spawns were found on three species of aquatic plants and five species of terrestrial plants. The sizes and shapes of the plants varied greatly. The largest number of spawns were found on the aquatic plants *Montricardia arborescens,* which has arrow-tipped-form leaves; *Sacciolepis striata,* a small slender-bladed bamboo grass, and *Nymphoides humboldtianum,* which has water-lily-shaped leaves. There were no rocks overhanging the creek in this area that could be used as a spawning substrate. Whether they are used in other areas is still unknown.

The spawns I found tended to be in clusters rather than being uniformly distributed along the "creek." In some locations the density of spawns was quite high, and as many as 7 spawns within a radius of 0.8 meter were found.

Generally, field measurements of spawn size, the ranges of minimum and maximum spawn heights, the location of spawns on plants, and the splashing frequencies of males were very similar to equivalent data collected in the laboratory in previous work. As in the laboratory, field spawns were always found on the undersides of leaves and were invariably located immediately adjacent to the side edge or lower tip of the leaf and extended medially (Krekorian and Dunham, 1972a). Placement of spawns adjacent to or near the edge of leaves is important to the remarkable splashing accuracy males exhibit during parental care (Krekorian and Dunham, 1972b).

There were, however, some differences between laboratory and field observations indicating the caution that must be used in interpreting laboratory data. For example, although the ranges of minimum and maximum spawn heights in the field were similar to equivalent measures in the laboratory, the distributions of minimum and maximum spawn heights in the field were significantly higher than those in the laboratory. Whether the higher field spawn heights indicate a preference for higher spawning surfaces or are merely a reflection of higher spawning substrates is not yet known. Also, in contrast to the clear transparent spawns obtained in the laboratory, field spawns had a yellow cast due to the coffee-colored water.

The parental splashing of males in the field appeared to be influenced by environmental conditions. During the rain parental splashing does not occur, and for several hours following the rain the parental splashing frequency of males (N = 3) was substantially lower than pre-rain splashing frequencies. Following rain, the humidity is extremely high and the foliage and plants remain wet for several hours.

Ten spawns were placed in the "creek" water. The eggs appeared to develop normally but hatching was not confirmed. Predation on the eggs was not observed when they were in the "creek" water or when they were on emergent leaves. Snails, which have been observed to feed on eggs in the laboratory, were practically absent from the study area. The absence of snails may be due to the small amounts of $CaCO_3$ in the water, which some feel is necessary for shell construction (Klein and Traut, 1961). Three spawns that were placed in a hatching can partially filled with "creek" water developed normally and resulted in healthy fry.

Since the eggs will develop and hatch in the "creek" water and predation on eggs in the water by snails does not appear to be of any consequence at this time, one is led to ask, What other factor(s) could have been operative in the evolution of this unique mode of reproduction? We may never know the answer to this question. Perhaps, however, it was not the disadvantage of spawning in the water as much as it was the avantages of spawning out of the water that promoted this behavior. Pairing out of the water would eliminate predation and interspecific competition for spawning substrates and also greatly increase the number of available spawning substrates to the species since both terrestrial and aquatic plants could be used. This latter factor would especially be true if spawning occurred during the rainy season when flooding is extensive. In addition, pairing above the water on emergent vegetation confines the eggs and sperm to a thin film of water and thus increases the probability of fertilization of eggs. Once pairing on emergent vegetation evolved, any one of these advantages would be sufficient to promote the continuance of *C. arnoldi*'s unique behavior.

REFERENCES

KLEIN, U., and TRAUT, W.
   1961.   Zur Herkunft der Schalenkalkes bei Süsswassermollusken.   Int. Rev. Gesamt. Hydrobiol., vol. 46, pp. 434-440.
KREKORIAN, C. O'NEIL
   1976.   Field observations in Guyana on the reproductive biology of the spraying characid, *Copeina arnoldi* Regan.   Amer. Midl. Nat., vol. 96, pp. 88-97.
KREKORIAN, C. O'NEIL, and DUNHAM, D. W.
   1972a.   Preliminary observations on the reproductive and parental behavior of the spraying characid, *Copeina arnoldi* Regan.   Zeitschr. für Tierpsychol., vol. 31, pp. 419-437.
   1972b.   Parental egg care in the spraying characid, *Copeina arnoldi* Regan: Role of the spawning surface.   Animal Behav., vol. 20, pp. 355-359.
   1973.   Visual discrimination by the spraying characid, *Copeina arnoldi* Regan. Animal Behav., vol. 21, pp. 741-748.
NELSON, STEPHEN G., and KREKORIAN, C. O'NEIL
   1976.   The dynamics of parental care of *Copeina arnoldi* (Pisces, Characidae). Behavioral Biology, vol. 17, pp. 507-518.

C. O'NEIL KREKORIAN

Survey of Manuscript Collections in Nepal

Principal Investigators: Lewis R. Lancaster and J. Frits Staal, University of California, Berkeley, California.

Grant No. 1221:   For a survey of manuscript collections in Nepal, Sikkim, and Bhutan.

The University of California at Berkeley has been engaged for several years in a project that aims at a survey of manuscript collections in Nepal, Sikkim, and Bhutan. Most of these are housed in Buddhist monasteries and private homes. They are written in Tibetan and Sanskrit, and there are also rare xylographed books. The subjects dealt with include Buddhist religion, philosophy, history, geography, biography, and medicine.

Where possible, the project calls for the microfilming of important or rare materials, so that they will be accessible to scholars and students. Since Berkeley has several units of movable microfilming equipment, the manuscripts are copied in the places where they are kept, avoiding the risks of dislocation. Such documentation is supplemented with photographs, films, and tape recordings of art, ritual, recitation, initiation, and similar manifestations and expressions of monastic life. Similar work has been undertaken in the past by Tucci (e.g., Tucci, 1953, 1956) and Snellgrove (e.g., Snellgrove, 1957, 1961, 1967). The Berkeley project seeks to continue these earlier investigations and aims at greater comprehensiveness.

The first phase of the project dealt with Nepal and was initiated in the spring of 1972, when two research assistants from Berkeley made a survey of the collection of the Teng-bo Che monastery in Solu-Kumbhu and photographed 48 texts. The team compiled some lists of books in other monasteries. It was found that many of the chief lamas and other Buddhist dignitaries were much interested in the project and were very cooperative. This is partly explained by the fact that our teams comprised Tibetan speakers, that the manuscripts did not have to be dislocated, and that many Tibetan scholars were concerned about their preservation since many collections have been destroyed by fire.

In 1972 an agreement was made with Dr. Raj Prayag Sharma, dean of the Institute of Nepal and Asian Studies at Tribhuvan University, Kathmandu. Following this agreement, copies of the 5,000 frames of microfilm made in Solu-Kumbhu were deposited in the library of Tribhuvan University as well as in the Asiatic Library at Berkeley.

Personnel

Project leaders of the 1973 expedition were Lewis R. Lancaster, associate professor of Oriental languages, and J. Frits Staal, professor of philosophy and South Asian languages, both at the University of California at Berkeley.

Associate members were Michael Aris, Carl and Fumiko Bielefeldt, John Cepelak, Joe Clack, James G. Ebin, Janet Frank, Prof. P. S. Jaini, Matthew Kapstein, Robert F. Kritzer, Kunga Lama, Kai Man Lee, John Mokotoff, William Powell, and Tom Trabin.

Negotiations with H. M. Government of Nepal

The first two expedition members, Michael Aris and J. F. Staal, arrived in Kathmandu on August 5, 1973. They had gone on the strength of our agreement and correspondence with Dean Sharma of Tribhuvan University. We had also enlisted the cooperation of two Indian scholars: Dr. Lokesh Chandra of the International Academy of Indian Culture, New Delhi, and Prof. E. R. Sreekrishna Sharma of the Department of Sanskrit at Shri Venkateshwara University, Tirupati. Prior to arrival we had written to the U. S. Ambassador to Nepal, asking his assistance and support. We anticipated that it would take some time to obtain the necessary trekking permits for the regions of Mustang, Dolpo, and Humla-Jumla (Solu-Kumbhu posing no problem). Hence the other team members were scheduled to arrive a few weeks later. Little did we know, at that time, that the ensuing two months would be mostly taken up with negotiations between ourselves and H. M. Government of Nepal. During this period we received no assistance from the U. S. Embassy, which later issued a partially misleading report to the Department of State. We received much help, however, from Kent Obee, director of the U.S.I.S.

Since the success of our survey depended largely on the outcome of these negotiations, a sketch of the underlying issues is in order. The trekking permits we needed were to be issued by the Ministry of Home and Panchayat Affairs through its Department of Immigration. These permits were written out for us, waiting to be signed as soon as positive advice would be received from the Ministry of Education. In the latter ministry, opposing forces were at work. Tribhuvan University and its Vice-Chancellor strongly supported our project. The University was criticized, however, for having entered into an agreement of its own without consulting other departments of the Education Ministry. Within this Ministry, the agreement between us and the University was attacked by the Department of Archaeology, which had earlier entered into an agreement with the *Deutsche morgenländische Gesellschaft,* the German counterpart of the American Oriental Society. After many years of negotiation, that agreement had been signed in 1970. It entitled a German team to make microfilm copies of the manuscript collection of the National Archives, located in Kathmandu. It did not give the Germans any rights to go out into the field, and it did not allow them to make any use of the microfilms without specific approval of the Department of Archaeology. In the cases where such approval was requested, it had not been forthcoming.

The "German" agreement—referred to as if it were an agreement between two governments—resulted in the manuscripts being even more inaccessible than they had been before. It was clear to our Berkeley team that to agree to such terms would be doing a disservice to scholarship. The Germans themselves hoped that Berkeley would be able to obtain better terms. This would enable them to reopen discussion on the terms of their own agreement, which by that time they had come to recognize as a bad mistake. Basically these issues remained unresolved throughout our stay in Nepal.

Fieldwork

During these lengthy negotiations our team members were getting restive and all were eager to start on the treks. We modified our aims, dropped Mustang and Dolpo when it became clear that permits for these areas were unlikely to be obtained, and constituted four teams for the following four areas: Rolwaling-Kumbhu (Lancaster with the Bielefeldts, Kapstein, Powell, and Trabin); Kutang-Nubri (Aris with Cepelak and Clack); Jomossom (Jaini with Kunga Lama, Frank, and Mokotoff); and Jumla-Humla (Staal with Ebin, Kritzer, and Lee). A brief description of their fieldwork follows.

ROLWALING-KUMBHU (see map A)

The team reached the Solu-Kumbhu area via the Rolwaling Valley by crossing the Traslu Lopche Pass (about 19,100 feet), and returned via the ordinary route. The Rolwaling Valley is still entirely Tibetan in culture and character and yielded much new information. In all, this team visited 18 gompas and inventoried their collections of books. At the Thakshing Du Monastery, 28 volumes were examined dealing with doctrinal, ritual, historical, and medical texts of the Nyingma tradition, including biographies of lamas. At Silbut, near the Tisang Pass, a recent gompa, constructed 21 years ago, was visited, but it was found that it had only well-known canonical

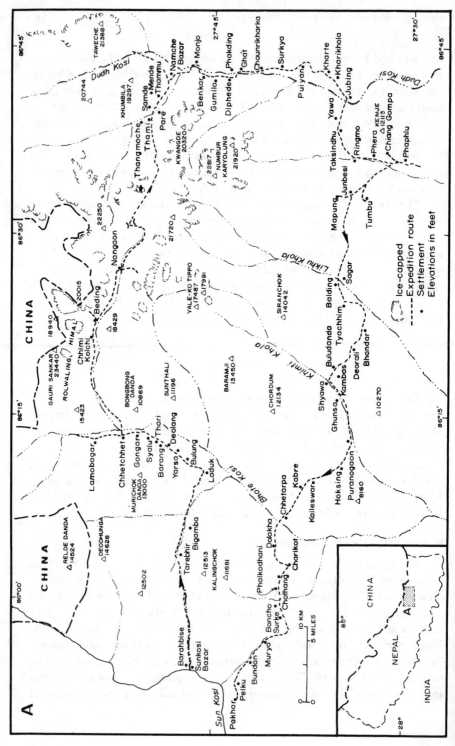

MAP A

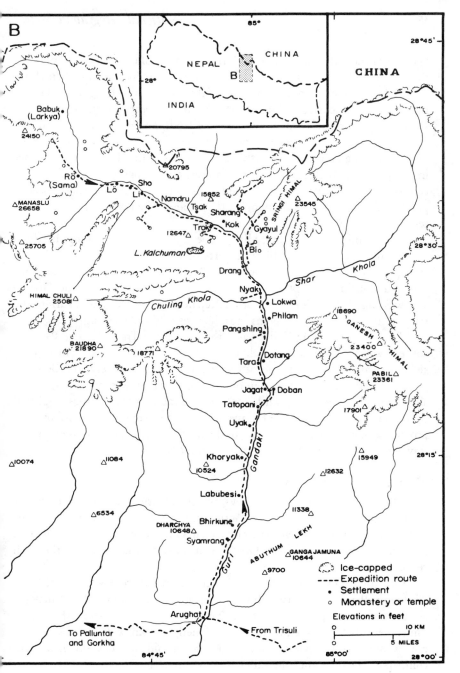

B

28°45'

85°

CHINA

NEPAL

B

28°

INDIA

CHINA

28°30'

28°15'

Babuk
(Larkya)
△24150

Rō
(Sama)
Lō
Sho
Li
Namdru
△20795

△MANASLU
26658

△25705

Tsak
Sharang
Trok
Kok
Gyayul

15852

23545

SRINGI HIMAL

12647△

L. Kalchuman

Bio

Drang

Shar   Khola

Nyak

Lokwa

Philam

△18690

Pangshing

GANESH HIMAL

HIMAL CHULI
25081△

Chuling Khola

BAUDHA△
21890

1877△

Tara

Dotang

23400△

PABIL△
23361

Jagat Doban

Tatopani

17901△

Uyak

△10074

△11084

Khoryak
10524

△12632

15949△

Labubesi

△6534

Bhirkune

DHARCHYA
10648△

Syamrang

11338
△

GANGA JAMUNA
10644

ABUTHUM LEKH

△9700

Guri Gandaki

  Ice-capped
---- Expedition route
• Settlement
○ Monastery or temple
Elevations in feet

0   10 KM
0   5 MILES

Arughat

To Palluntar
and Gorkha

From Trisuli

84°45'

85°00'

28°00'

MAP B

books. On the other hand, much information was collected at the nunnery of the Shes-bu Thang, which houses 30 nuns from the local area and an abbot from Tibet. The surrounding lands are in the possession of the gompa. Half of the crop (mainly barley and potatoes) goes to the gompa for its support, and the other half to the farmers who use the land. The nunnery acts also as a money-lending institution (an ancient function of Buddhist monasteries). One interesting point was the discovery of the prevailing Bhutanese influence in this particular region, the results of an earlier missionary activity from that country. In addition to the monk and nuns in the monastery, there was one painter of religious thankas living in the village. The team carried on an extensive interview with him.

The famous monastery of Beding—one of the reasons for taking this difficult route—houses a large library, parts of which were inventoried by the team. The abbot had in the past visited Tibet yearly for further studies but had to discontinue this practice in 1960 when the monastery on the Tibetan side was closed. He, along with other Nepalese lamas, has had to turn to the refugee communities of Tibetans in India for study and training.

After the Rolwaling Valley came the crossing of Trashi Lopche Pass. Of concern was the fact that two trekkers in other groups had died from altitude sickness while making the journey over the pass. Fortunately, the Berkeley team did well; only one Sherpa guide from Kathmandu was affected by edema and required medication. While they were climbing over the pass, nightfall came and the group was forced to make camp on top of the 19,100-foot pass, providing them with an experience of the harshness of the environment which travelers must face in these high mountain regions.

KUTANG-NUBRI (see map B)

This team penetrated into valleys, which are largely unknown and where strong Tibetan influence persists. Actually, some areas are so remote that the people seem to have managed their own affairs independently of governments. Nominally, Nubri was under Tibetan control until the middle of the 19th century.

One highlight of the trek was the unexpected discovery of one of those "hidden valleys" of Padmasambhava, mentioned throughout the Himalayas as places of refuge, peace, and plenty. This "Valley of Happiness" (sKyid.mo. lung), never before visited by foreigners (Snellgrove knew of its existence but not its location), was pointed out by the 19-year-old lama of Gyayul, who accompanied the team into the valley up to the temple of Sharang.

Arrangements were made for the copying of five autobiographical works pertaining to the lineages of Kutang and dating from the period from the mid-17th to the mid-18th century. These works describe the lamas' travels, adventures, philosophico-religious discussions, visions, and dreams. The authors were all inveterate travelers, making arduous pilgrimages throughout Tibet and to parts of Nepal and Sikkim. Some of these journeys were undertaken for their own sake. As Aris describes it, the journey is regarded as of equal importance as its goal, which reflects the Mahāyāna philosophy, "which tends to reduce the inherent duality between the path of enlightenment and its ultimate realisation" (Aris, 1975, p. 60).

At Drang, the first village of Kutang, a word list was made of the rare Ku.skad dialect of Tibetan. At Bi, painted wooden panels were found to consist of as many as four sets of painting, superimposed upon each other. At Rö, an exhaustive study was made of local rituals and festivals, which combine with the major festivals of the Buddhist calendar.

The expedition of Kutang and Nubri is described in greater detail in Aris (1975), which also lists the works that were located and copied.

JOMOSSOM (see map C)

The trek from Pokhara to Jomossom covers well-known ground. The prevalent Buddhist sects are Nyingma and Saskya. General monastic festivals were witnessed. The Saskya monasteries were well kept; their paintings have been renovated and new paintings are being commissioned. It was difficult to get access to the libraries, which contrasted with the situation found in other areas. However, the team did complete some inventory work, though limited by the attitudes of the lamas, probably due to the unscrupulousness of many of the tourists who frequent this area.

JUMLA-HUMLA (see map D)

The team's goal was Limi, a large monastery in the extreme northwest of Nepal with a reportedly rich library, never surveyed or studied. The Limi region was not reached because of delays due not only to the negotiations (from which all teams suffered) but also to the extraordinary lateness of the monsoon. This resulted in another 3-week period of waiting for a plane, which finally transported the team from Kathmandu to Jumla on October 14. The trek from Jumla in a northwestern direction, while incredibly beautiful, did not reach the predominantly Tibetan areas. Concern about rapidly dwindling food supplies in an area where no food could be obtained, and about high passes which might be snowbound on the way back, led to numerous discussions. Finally, at Darma, the majority of the team members cast their vote in favor of return.

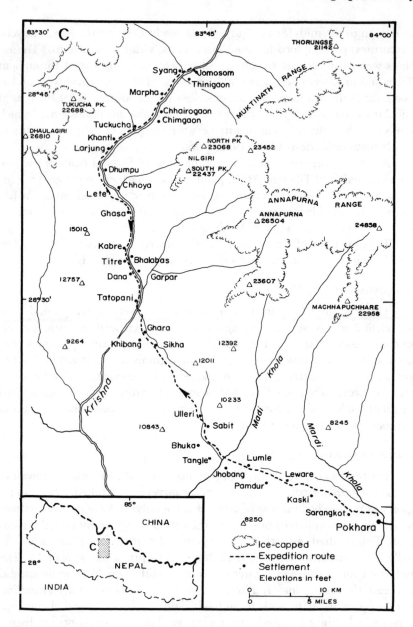

Map C

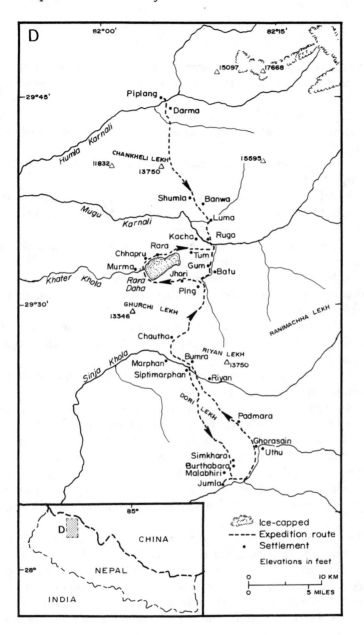

MAP D

Results

All members of the teams returned with a vast store of incredibly rich experiences. Apart from these, the main results of the expedition are the following:

1. A catalog of all the Tibetan material at Berkeley, including the microfilms taken in Nepal, is being prepared and will be published when completed.

2. A report of the Kutang-Nubri trek has been published by Michael Aris (Aris, 1975).

3. Aris is making use of some of the materials he has gathered in preparing a Ph.D. thesis for the University of London (School of Oriental and African Studies), supervised by Snellgrove.

4. Lewis Lancaster is preparing an edition of the *Vajracchedikā*, using the only existing copy from Nepal.

5. Michael Kapstein stayed on from 1973 through 1975 and made a complete inventory of the collection of about 250 xylographed volumes of the Serlo monastery near Jumbesi.

6. Lama Koncchok from Takshing Du monastery came to Berkeley to study public health, comparative religion, and English; he also taught the Sherpa language.

7. Numerous slide shows and lectures were given on campuses across the country, on television and on radio.

8. Chancellor Bowker of the University of California at Berkeley has continued to address letters to the Minister of Education of H. M. Government of Nepal, seeking to reach an agreement acceptable to both parties.

9. Contacts with Bhutan are slowly progressing in cooperation with the Institute for Advanced Studies of World Religions (New York). The librarian of the National Library of Bhutan visited Berkeley for five weeks and familiarized himself with our library and cataloguing and microfilming techniques.

Our combined experiences have strengthened our conviction that the aims of the Berkeley manuscript survey can be achieved only in one of two ways: either with official support at a very high level, or through the private activity of individual scholars who visit the Himalayan countries as tourists, visitors, or mountaineers. In the meantime, we derive satisfaction from Michael Aris's observation on the philosophical overtones of his lamas' voyages: the path is as important as the goal.

REFERENCES

ARIS, MICHAEL
1975.   Report on the University of California expedition to Kutang and Nubri in northern Nepal in autumn 1973.   Contributions to Nepalese Studies, Journ. Inst. Nepal and Asian Stud. Tribhuvan Univ., vol. 2, pp. 45-87.

BERNBAUM, EDWARD
1974.   The way of symbols: Use of symbols in Tibetan mysticism.   Journ. of Trans-Personal Psychol. 6, no. 2, pp. 93-110.
1975.   The Sherpa view of mountains.   Harvard Mountaineering, no. 20, pp. 37-39.
1979.   The prisoners. *In* "Search," J. Salzberger, ed.   Harper & Row.
1980.   The way to Shambala, 316 pp.   Anchor/Doubleday, Garden City, New York.

KAPSTEIN, MATTHEW
1979.   The four-themed precious garland.   Library of Tibetan Works and Archives, Dharmsala.
1980.   *An Uninvited Guest Has Arrived,* and *A Joyous and Pure Upland Ridge.*   Pp. 21, 169-170 *in* "Rhythms of a Himalayan Village," by Hugh R. Downs, Harper and Row, San Francisco.
1981a.   The Shang-pa Dkar'rgyud: Unknown tradition of Tibetan Buddhism.   Hugh Richardson Felicitation Volume.
1981b.   Remarks on the *Mani Bka'bum* and the cult of Avalokiteśvara in Tibet, Ron Davidson, ed.   Wind Horse, vol. 2, Asian Humanities Press, Berkeley.   (In Press.).

SNELLGROVE, DAVID L.
1957.   Buddhist Himalaya: Travels and studies in quest of the origins and nature of Tibetan religion, 324 pp., illus.   Bruno Cassirer, Oxford.
1961.   Himalayan pilgrimage, 304 pp., illus.   Bruno Cassirer, Oxford.
1967.   Four lamas of Dolpo, 302 pp., illus.   Bruno Cassirer, Oxford.

TUCCI, GIUSEPPE
1953.   Tra giungle e pagode, 139 pp., illus.   Libreria dello Stato, Rome.
1956.   Preliminary report on two scientific expeditions in Nepal.   Pp. 1-156 *in* "Materials for a Study of Nepalese History and Culture, Part 1."   Serie Orientale Roma, vol. 10, Istituto Italiano per il Medio ed Estremo Oriente, Roma.

LEWIS R. LANCASTER
J. FRITS STAAL

Research at Olduvai Gorge, 1973

Principal Investigator: Mary D. Leakey, Nairobi, Kenya.

Grant Nos. 1141a,   For continued investigations at Olduvai Gorge, Tanzania.
1154, 1156.

Considerable progress was made during the year in studying and analyzing specimens excavated from Beds III and IV. Analysis of the faunal material was nearly completed and promised to give results very different from those from Beds I and II (see accounts of these studies in previous volumes of these *Reports*). Preliminary identifications were also carried out by Dr. J. Harris, paleontologist at the National Museum, Nairobi.

Geology.   Dr. Richard L. Hay of the University of California, Berkeley, revisited Olduvai in September and again in December. These two visits enabled him to finalize some problems still outstanding from 1972. He planned to complete his volume on the geology of the gorge in 1974.[1]

Dating by Paleomagnetism and Racemization.   As a result of further studies by Prof. Allan Cox of the Department of Geophysics, Stanford University, it was discovered that Bed IV is older than formerly believed. A sample with reversed polarity was recovered from the lower part of the bed, indicating that when this deposit was laid down the Mutayama Reversed Epoch had not yet come to an end. A date of not less than 700,000 years B.P. is therefore inferred. Previously, the boundary between the Mutayama Reversed Epoch and Brunhes Normal Epoch was thought to be at the junction of Beds III and IV.

Prof. Jeffrey L. Bada of the Scripps Institution of Oceanography, University of California, San Diego, visited Olduvai in June 1973 in order to collect further samples for amino- and aspartic-acid dating. Preliminary results are most promising. It is possible that this method of dating will eventually fill the gap between the potassium-argon and radiocarbon methods of dating.

Palynology.   Dr. Raymonde Bonnefille spent three weeks at Olduvai in 1973, accompanied by a student. She collected 50 samples for fossil-pollen analysis as well as 10 samples of present-day lake sediments for comparison. This series of samples was obtained in collaboration with Dr. R. L. Hay.

---

[1] Dr. Hay's book *Geology of the Olduvai Gorge; A Study of Sedimentation in Semiarid Basin,* 203 pages, was published by the University of California, Berkeley, in 1976.

With the information that he was able to supply concerning the paleogeography of the Olduvai region it will be possible to identify the samples with various vegetational areas, i.e., lake margin, gallery forest, savannah, etc.

Results from the 11 samples collected in 1972 proved very promising. Several hundred pollen grains are estimated to be contained in 4 of the samples, and smaller numbers in 5 others. Only 2 samples proved negative.

Pits and Channels at Site JK. R.I.M. Campbell completed stereophotography of the pits complex uncovered in 1972. Dr. Celia Kamau began a large-scale contoured plan of the area but was unable to finish it in the time available. Funds were made available by Gordon Hanes to erect a permanent stone building at the site.

Camp Water Supply. Geologists from the Geological Survey of Tanzania surveyed the Olduvai area with a view to drilling for water. Their report was wholly unfavorable. It was therefore decided to enlarge the existing area of roofs and collect rain water in underground tanks. Gordon Hanes generously financed this operation, and George Dove of Ndutu Safari Lodge kindly supervised the building. These storage tanks in conjunction with the eight 1,000-gallon tanks already installed greatly reduced water haulage, although they were insufficient for a whole year's supply.

Visitors. More scientists connected with paleoanthropology and related interdisciplinary subjects visited Olduvai for varying periods during 1973 than in any previous year. Fourteen college and student groups booked lecture tours of the gorge with me.

The figure for tourists was lower this year than for 1972—20,406 as against 23,340. I understand that game lodges in Tanzania showed a similar falling-off in the latter part of the year, although figures for January to July were higher than in 1972.

Sales of books, postcards, slides, etc. were very satisfactory and contributed substantially to the research funds.

MARY D. LEAKEY

Continuing Research East of Lake Turkana in Northern Kenya, 1973-1976

Principal Investigator: Richard E. F. Leakey, National Museums of Kenya, Nairobi, Kenya.

Grant Nos. 1153,   For continuing paleontological and archeological research
1155, 1299, 1320,   in the vicinity of Lake Turkana, Kenya.[1]
1446, and 1590.

The years 1973-1976 have resulted not only in further important hominid discoveries east of Lake Turkana (formerly Lake Rudolf) but also in a considerable advance in our understanding of the geology, geomorphology, paleontology of the area, and many related topics. Research reported in *National Geographic Society Research Reports* for 1969 and 1970 (vols. 10 and 11), has extended from the initial area of richly fossiliferous Plio-Pleistocene deposits to include the Miocene deposits to the north and south. It is clear that the Turkana Basin offers a unique opportunity to study a series of fossiliferous strata covering a very long period of time, and to find the answers to many outstanding geological, anthropological, and paleontological problems.

The extensive Plio-Pleistocene deposits east of Lake Turkana cover an area of over 800 square kilometers. The exposures are discontinuous, however, being restricted laterally by extensive bush cover. For convenience the region has therefore been divided into a number of areas. Each area has been numbered and is bounded either by natural vegetation cover or by easily recognizable topographic features (fig. 1). Where possible local names have been used for geographic features and for the naming of geological marker horizons such as tuffs. The former name for the lake, given by Count Teleki in 1888 after the Crown Prince of Austria, Prince Rudolf, was officially changed in 1975 when the Kenya Government decreed that the lake should be called Lake Turkana.

[1] The continuing program of research at Lake Turkana has been supported by many organizations, but in particular by the National Geographic Society, the National Science Foundation, the William H. Donner Foundation (through NGS grant 1369), the Vincent Astor Foundation (through NGS grant 1383), the National Museums of Kenya, and others, who wish to remain unnamed (through NGS grants 1294a and 1509a).

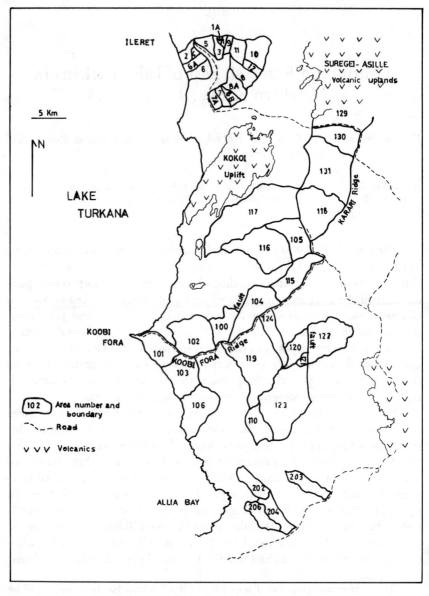

Fig. 1.   Map of the region east of Lake Turkana showing main geographical features
and the locations of the paleontological collecting areas.

Fieldwork Undertaken in 1973

During 1973, the East Rudolf Research Project completed its sixth year. Several new scientists joined the project with a view to concentrating on more detailed investigations of several aspects of the research. Emphasis was placed on the study of the microstratigraphy and paleoenvironmental reconstruction. A detailed survey of the upper and lower members of areas 130 and 131 was undertaken by students from Iowa State University under the supervision of B. Bowen, and the complete geological section of the Koobi Fora Formation exposed in area 102 was studied by a group from Dartmouth College, New Hampshire, under G. Johnson. A. K. Behrensmeyer completed a preliminary investigation of the hominid sites and an interpretation of the environments of deposition of the sediments in which the fossil hominids were buried. P. G. Williamson began an analysis of the molluscan assemblages common throughout the succession, as these seemed promising indicators of changing water chemistry and lake levels. R. Bonnefille initiated a palynological study as an indicator of paleoenvironments.

I. C. Findlater continued mapping the tuffaceous horizons to the south of Koobi Fora in order to provide correlations between areas, and he also continued collecting samples for isotopic dating. Paleomagnetic studies were initiated to assess the age of those strata where other means of dating were somewhat insecure. Paleontological exploration to the south of Koobi Fora, begun in 1972, was continued under J. M. Harris, while a further 20 hominid specimens were collected from the Koobi Fora Formation. Archeological investigation was extended under the direction of Dr. G. L. Isaac with J.W.K. Harris conducting major excavations at several sites in the upper member of areas 130 and 131. Paleontological surveys of the Miocene deposits to the south at Kajong were conducted by R. E. Leakey and to the north at Buluk by J. M. Harris and R. Watkins.

Symposium

In September 1973, a symposium on the stratigraphy, paleoecology and evolution in the East Rudolf Basin was organized between members of the Koobi Fora Research Project and the Omo International Expedition to discuss research activities and problems arising out of the research in the two areas. The symposium, which involved some 38 participants, included 4 days of discussions at the Kenya National Museum, Nairobi, based on preprinted and circulated papers. These were followed by 4 days of field excursions to East Rudolf and an additional day in the Shungura area of the Omo Valley, after

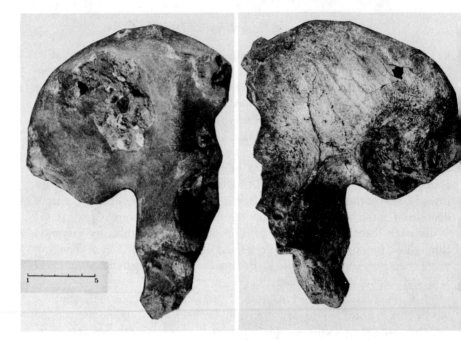

FIG. 2.   Innominate bone, KNM-ER 3228; *left,* lateral view, and *right,* medial
view.

which a final day of general discussion concluded the conference.

The conference was highly successful; it provided not only an opportunity
for open discussion between members of the two research projects, but also
clarified several areas of disagreement. One of the main problems to emerge
centered on the apparent discordance between the faunal successions of the
two areas with the currently recognized radiometric dates. It became clear
that the considerable periods of time represented in the two areas and the potential for cross checks provided remarkable opportunity for evaluating faunal
evolution generally and hominid evolution in particular in the period 4–1
million years ago. The conference was a milestone in paleo-anthropological research in that it brought together scientists from many disciplines and clearly
demonstrated the benefits of multidisciplinary teams. Details of the 41 papers
presented are published in Coppens et al. (1976).

Research 1974-1975

In 1974, the research team was considerably enlarged, with additional
scientists joining the various ongoing studies and other teams initiating new

studies. A group from the Carnegie Museum, Pittsburgh, began a study of the microfauna, and a geomagnetic survey was initiated by N. J. Skinner and N. V. Bhatt of Nairobi University. Samples of volcanic tuff were collected by A. Hurford (London University) for fission-track dating, in an effort to check the dates already obtained by K/Ar dating. D. Gifford began a study of the camp sites and living quarters of the local people inhabiting the area, in order to provide a basis for comparison with the ancient archeological sites.

The paleontological collecting was increased, with special emphasis on the fossil suids. The suids underwent considerable evolutionary change over the time period under study and were therefore considered a particularly suitable group to use in solving the problem of the apparent discordance in the faunal successions of the Omo and East Turkana.

A few fossil hominids were collected, the most noteworthy being a mandible of a robust australopithecine, KNM-ER 3230, which was recovered in an archeological excavation by J.W.K. Harris. This was the first hominid to be recovered from an excavation at East Turkana. The laboratory preparation and description of the fossil hominids continued, and by the end of 1974, nine papers containing detailed descriptions of the fossil hominids had been published in the American Journal of Physical Anthropology (Leakey et al., 1971; Leakey et al., 1972; Leakey and Wood, 1973; Day and Leakey, 1973; Leakey and Walker, 1973; Day and Leakey, 1974; Day et al., 1974; and Leakey and Wood, 1974a and 1974b) and one further manuscript was in press (Day et al., 1976). This brought the description of the fossil hominids almost up to date.

By the end of 1974, the volume of data accumulated during the previous seven field seasons was such that it was considered unreasonable to continue to collect more information without first assessing the field data in the laboratory and writing up the results. In addition the logistical and financial problems faced in supplying such large numbers of personnel in the field were immense. A geological and archeological moratorium was therefore called in 1975, and this is considered to mark the end of Phase I of the research project. Phase II is intended to include more detailed studies of specific aspects and problems realized in Phase I.

Paleontological collecting was intensified in 1975, with almost 1,500 specimens collected. Special emphasis was given to the suids. A detailed study of this group by J. M. Harris and T. White followed; it resulted in the publication of a comprehensive monograph covering all the Plio-Pleistocene African suids (Harris and White, 1979). Eleven more hominid specimens were collected: these included an innominate bone, KNM-ER 3228 (see fig. 2), discovered below the KBS Tuff in area 102 (Leakey, 1976a) by Bernard Ngeneo, and an almost complete cranium of *Homo erectus*, KNM-ER 3733 (see fig. 3).

Interim Informal Scheme for Labeling Marker Horizons

At the end of 1975, it was evident that there were several outstanding problems which urgently required serious discussion among the key scientists in the project. The suid and mollusk studies in particular indicated discrepancies in the stratigraphic correlation of the deposits in certain areas. T. Cerling's study of the chemical and morphological properties of the layers of volcanic ash also indicated that several tuffs which had been given one name, although possibly very close in age, were unlikely to be from a single eruptive event. In addition Curtis et al. (1975) had found that samples of the KBS tuff from two localities gave differing ages of 1.6 and 1.82 million years, neither of which were in agreement with that of Fitch and Miller (1970), of 2.6 million years (myr.). The current system, whereby a restricted set of names was applied to marker horizons derived from a type outcrop, clearly required revision.

In August 1976, therefore, a small group, including geologists and paleontologists, spent two weeks at the Koobi Fora base camp, visiting areas where contradictions appeared to exist and considering the geological evidence in the field. It was finally agreed that while many of the mapped tuffs and their projected horizons appeared to define valid stratigraphic intervals over wide areas, and the evidence from fossil vertebrate and invertebrate assemblages appeared to substantiate the correlations, major discordance occurred in some areas. Since discontinuous tuffaceous outcrops could not be unequivocally matched, it was misleading to imply certain correlations where no such certainty existed. There was thus a need for a system of labels for the local marker beds currently in use that did not prejudge correlations being tested.

Consequently, an index was prepared in which each known tuff occurrence in each area was assigned a serial number from the lowest to the highest. For example in area 102, the previously labeled "KBS" tuff which was the sixth tuff up from the base of the section became 102/T VI. Only tuffs in the type areas retained the original names. This system was designed as a temporary working device which was to facilitate studies of biostratigraphy on a basis that was independent of previous correlations (Harris, 1978).

Fieldwork 1976

While archeological and geological studies continued during 1976, very few paleontological specimens were collected, as it was realized that there was a backlog of laboratory work to be completed before acquiring further material. Ten hominid specimens, however, were recovered, including a cranium of *Homo erectus,* KNM-ER 3833, discovered at Ileret.

Summary of the Results of the 1973-1976 Fieldwork

Much of the information gained over these years is summarized in Leakey and Leakey (1978). A brief résumé of the major topics of study is given below.

GEOLOGY

In 1973 a formal stratigraphic nomenclature (Bowen and Vondra, 1973) was erected for the stratigraphic correlation of the sediments east of Lake Turkana based on four laterally extensive tuffaceous horizons—the Suregei, Tulu Bor, KBS, and Chari tuffs (fig. 4). A further three—the Okote, Hasuma, and Allia—were named informally. These provided a basis for correlation between areas, but because the tuff outcrops are generally of restricted lateral extent, the possibility of miscorrelation is always present. Three formations—the Kubi Algi, the Koobi Fora, and the Guomde—were recognized. The Holocene Galana Boi beds overlay the Guomde in some areas.

The history of the lake is a complex one of changing lake levels reflecting transgressive and regressive stages. Various long term trends determined by either climatic or tectonic conditions were interrupted by shorter term changes in lake level (Vondra and Bowen, 1976, 1978).

Sediments of the Kubi Algi Formation are derived from the south and are almost totally of volcanic origin. Those of the Koobi Fora Formation are derived from a catchment to the east and are dominated by material from the metamorphic rocks of the regional basement complex. During deposition of the Kubi Algi Formation, an initial regression, which reached its maximum around Hasuma tuff times, was followed by a transgression that by Suregei tuff times had extended the shoreline far inland to the present-day boundary between the sediments and volcanics to the east. An initial regression in the Lower Member of the Koobi Fora Formation was followed by a major transgression that continued until deposition of the KBS tuff, when a climatic change (Cerling et al., 1977) induced a further regression. During deposition of the Upper Member, a number of short-term regressions and transgressions appear to have taken place until after deposition of the Chari tuff, when a period of erosion followed. Renewed sedimentation gave rise to the Guomde Formation most of which has been subsequently eroded. The capping Galana Boi beds, which have been dated to a period between 10,000 and 4,000 B.P., represent the most recent period of high lake level (Findlater, 1978).

DATING

Consistent dates for the major tuffaceous horizons have been obtained by Fitch and Miller (1976) in a major dating program, but the age of the KBS tuff continues to be a source of controversy. The suid evidence in particular (Cooke and Maglio, 1972) indicates some discordance. In 1975 Curtis et al. dated samples of the KBS tuff by the conventional K-Ar method from areas 10, 105, and 131. Three different pumice clasts from the KBS tuff in areas 10 and 105 gave an average age of 1.6 ± 0.05 myr. while two separate pumice clasts from the tuff in area 131 gave an average age of 1.82 ± 0.04 myr. This suggested that not only was the original date of 2.6 myr. in error, but also that the KBS tuff in the three areas was inaccurately correlated.

The controversy continued when Fitch et al. (1976) recomputed their 1969 data and suggested that an age of 2.42 ± 0.01 myr. for the KBS tuff was probably more accurate but they found no evidence for there being more than one tuff. This was followed by further evidence from fission-track dating (Hurford et al., 1976) which gave an age of 2.44 ± 0.08 myr. for the KBS tuff in area 131. Interpretation of the magnetostratigraphy, although initially promising (Brock and Isaac, 1974), was not helpful in resolving this problem (Hillhouse et al., 1977), since it offered two possible alternatives, each fitting one or another of the radiometric dates obtained. Resolution of the controversy will have to await dating of further samples by several different methods.[2]

GEOCHEMISTRY

Geochemical studies (Cerling et al., 1977) indicate a marked increase in value of the oxygen isotope δ^{18} in carbonates laid down after deposition of the KBS tuff. This suggests a drastic decrease in rainfall at about this time and corresponds with a major regression detected in the geological strata, and a major extinction event documented in the mollusk faunas (see below).

MOLLUSK ASSEMBLAGES

The Koobi Algi and Koobi Fora Formation have yielded the best preserved, the most numerous and one of the longest series of lacustrine mollusk assemblages known from the Tertiary of Africa. These faunas provide data pertinent to several major fields of inquiry: (1) They provide a basis for biostratigraphic correlation, (2) they act as paleoenvironmental indicators, and (3) the evolutionary events documented in certain molluscan lineages contribute to our understanding of more general evolutionary processes.

---

[2] This has recently been accomplished and the KBS tuff is now firmly dated at 1.8 myr. (Cerling et al., 1979; Drake et al., 1980; McDougal et al., 1980).

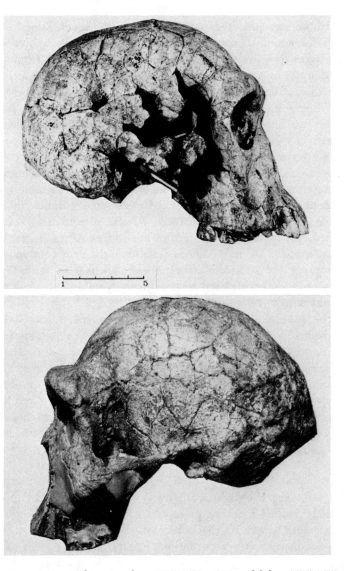

FIG. 3. Lateral views of crania; *above*, KNM-ER 1813 and *below*, KNM-ER 3733.

P. G. Williamson (University of Bristol) has identified 18 genera and 35 species of mollusks. *Etheria* reefs occur in fluviatile facies but the majority of the molluscan taxa are from lacustrine sediments. Out of a sample of more than one million mollusks only 2 terrestrial species have so far been identified.

Williamson recognizes seven distinct molluscan zones. Zone 1 comprises some half-dozen mollusk species which are widespread geographically and indistinguishable from extant species. Williamson terms these "Cosmopolitan" species. Zone 2, in contrast, consists solely of species endemic to Lake Turkana which are clearly derived from cosmopolitan species. These species, which Williamson terms "phyletic endemics," suggest long-term stability of the lake in late Kubi Algi Formation times, with geographic isolation from other lakes.

Zone 3 begins at the base of the Koobi Fora Formation, when cosmopolitan species reinvaded the lake and replaced all the phyletic endemics of Zone 2. This suggests that the lake was no longer isolated from surrounding inland waters. Zone 3 also includes a species of *Valvata,* an essentially Holarctic genus, while Zone 4 includes the bivalve *Pliodon,* a primarily West African form. These species, not commonly known from East African lakes, Williamson terms "exotics." Zones 4, 5, and 6 maintain the same cosmopolitan species present in the subjacent zones; these, Williamson terms "radiative endemics," suggest a fairly deep, environmentally stable lake with a variety of facies exploitable by Mollusca.

All the radiative endemics which evolved in Zones 4, 5, and 6 become extinct at the beginning of Zone 7. This major extinction event, apparently related to the major regression occurring a short stratigraphic distance above the KBS tuff, reflects the development of inimicable water chemistry, such as high salinities or alkalinities, consequent on a lowering of water levels. The exclusively cosmopolitan forms of Zone 7 are those available to recolonize the lake following establishment of tolerable water chemistry, and they suggest a relatively shallow, environmentally unstable lake that was affected by fluctuations in salinity or alkalinity (Williamson, in prep.).

VERTEBRATE FAUNAS

The sediments from which the fossil vertebrates were obtained reflect only periods conducive to bone preservation and fossilization. Those parts of the sedimentary succession that represent major transgressions of the lake were not conducive to the preservation of terrestrial faunas, and such lacustrine episodes are virtually barren of mammalian fossil material. The majority of specimens collected have been the result of surface prospecting; few paleontological excavations have been undertaken. A total of well over 4,000 mammalian fossils has been collected, enough to permit detailed investigation of most mammalian groups represented in the faunas. The well-preserved and complete nature of much of the material is striking, and is important in the correct identification of more fragmentary material from other East African

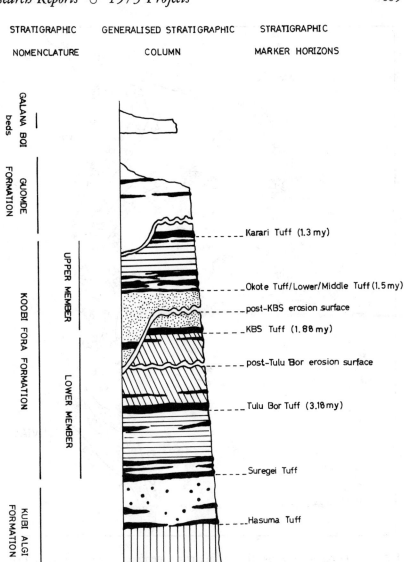

STRATIGRAPHIC NOMENCLATURE

GENERALISED STRATIGRAPHIC COLUMN

STRATIGRAPHIC MARKER HORIZONS

GALANA BOI beds

GUOMDE FORMATION

KOOBI FORA FORMATION

UPPER MEMBER

LOWER MEMBER

KUBI ALGI FORMATION

Karari Tuff (1.3 my)

Okote Tuff/Lower/Middle Tuff (1.5 my)

post-KBS erosion surface

KBS Tuff (1.88 my)

post-Tulu Bor erosion surface

Tulu Bor Tuff (3.18 my)

Suregei Tuff

Hasuma Tuff

Allia Tuff

FIG. 4. A generalized stratigraphic column showing stratigraphic nomenclature (after Bowen and Vondra, 1973).

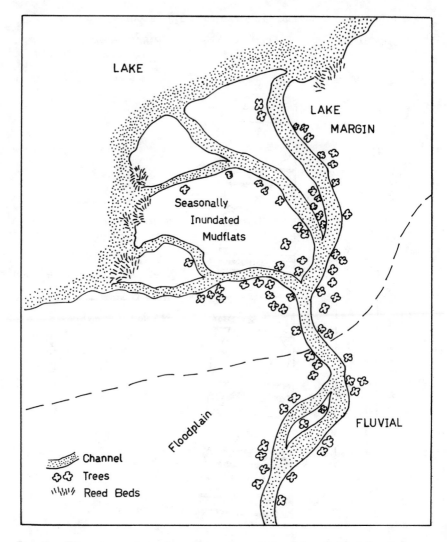

Fig. 5.   Diagram to show the main environments of deposition (after Behrensmeyer, 1978).

Plio-Pleistocene localities. Studies of the major groups represented are underway and will undoubtedly play a vital role in the comprehension of evolutionary and environmental changes in the late Pliocene and early Pleistocene.

    From the Koobi Fora Formation 75 extinct mammalian species (exclusive
of micromammals) and 12 extant species are known. The bovids are the most

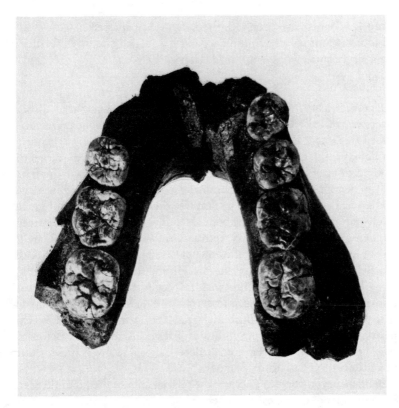

FIG. 6.   Mandible, KNM-ER 1802, occlusal view.

prominent group in terms of both number of species and total number of specimens, but primates, carnivores, and suids are also numerous and diverse. Many of the mammalian families were represented by a greater number of geologically synchronous species than are known in the region today. This may be due to the fact that surface collecting, while sampling fauna from a geologically short span of time, may nevertheless reflect a number of seasonal or short-term climatic changes. Thus the resultant assemblage contains taxa with a variety of different habitat preferences. The faunal evidence indicates that the environment was largely wooded or bush grassland with well-vegetated lake margins and perennial and ephemeral rivers fringed by gallery forest.

Preliminary washing and screening of samples of the sediments from selected localities for microfaunal remains showed this fauna to be rare. Representatives of three insectivorous families and several species of thryonomid and murid rodents have been recovered. Microfaunal assemblages act as very good indicators of paleoenvironment, and it is hoped that with further sampling a larger fauna will be obtained (Harris, 1978).

PALEOECOLOGY

The studies of A. K. Behrensmeyer (1975) have shown that fossil-bearing deposits east of Lake Turkana reveal sedimentation with bone preservation in at least three major depositional environments—delta margin, channel, and floodplain (fig. 5). Different sedimentary environments preserve rather different proportions of the parts of the animal's skeletons. On low-lying flats of a delta the bones remain relatively undisturbed and are preserved in much the same frequency as they occur in a complete skeleton. In sands and gravels of river channel deposits, where the bone assemblages are disturbed by river currents, dense skeletal parts such as teeth and limb-bone articular ends are much more common, while the lighter elements have been swept away. In addition A. K. Behrensmeyer found that lake-margin and fluvial depositional environments preserve faunas that differ with respect to the proportions of various mammalian groups. In general, more grassland mammals are associated with fluvial deposits, while both bush and grassland forms occur in lake-margin deposits. Taphonomic evidence indicates that this is not due to factors of differential preservation, but that some paleoecological record is preserved in the distribution of the East Rudolf faunas.

Behrensmeyer went on to study the relationship of the hominid fossils to the environments of deposition (Behrensmeyer, 1978). She found that approximately equal numbers of hominids were buried in each environment, but that while *Homo* and *Australopithecus* were buried in comparable numbers in lake margin environments, *Australopithecus* was significantly more abundant in fluvial environments. As might therefore be predicted, *Australopithecus* was more common in the Upper Member of the Koobi Fora Formation, where there is an increase in fluvial deposits compared with the Lower Member.

PALYNOLOGY

Of the 27 initial samples collected from different localities in the Koobi Fora Formation for pollen analysis, only one was found to contain pollen in sufficient quantity to justify study and interpretation. This sample from a stratigraphic level between the KBS tuff and the Lower/Middle tuff in area 12 indicated more humid conditions than those prevailing in the area today. The vegetation in the vicinity of the sample site was dominated by Gramineae and Chenopodiacae appropriate to the margins of a slightly saline or alkaline lake, while the good representation of *Acacia, Commiphora,* and *Salvadora* implies a shrub and tree cover more dense than that prevalent in the basin today. The prominence of montane forest elements is particularly striking, and indicates that vegetation of highland forest type existed closer to the basin margins than is presently the case (Bonnefille, 1976).

GALANA BOI BEDS

The Galana Boi beds represent the most recent transgression of the lake, and have been dated between about 10,000 and 4,000 B.P. J. W. Barthelme (University of California) found these beds to be extremely rich in archeological remains. He reported over 35 sites containing bone harpoons, and fish remains with microlithic stone tools. Domestic animals, various forms of decorated pottery and stone bowls were recovered from the later sites (Barthelme, 1977).

Numerous hominid remains have also been noted in the Galana Boi beds, some very complete. These are the subject of an investigation by K. Bell, who is currently recovering as many specimens as is feasible. The extensive late Holocene beds of East Turkana represent an important phase in our recent past and should yield much valuable information.

MIOCENE DEPOSITS

Two important sites of Miocene fossiliferous deposits were investigated. In 1973, the author led an expedition to the Kajong area to the south of Allia Bay and northeast of Loiengalani. The sediments were found to contain fossils of Miocene age, including *Gomphotherium, Prodeinotherium,* and a primitive suid. In view of the obvious importance of the site R.J.G. Savage and P. G. Williamson subsequently spent two seasons mapping the area and collecting a limited number of fossils (Savage and Williamson, 1978).

The second Miocene site to be investigated is located to the north of Koobi Fora and south of Lake Stephanie. R. Watkins (Birkbeck College, London University), who is currently mapping the area for a Ph.D. topic, discovered volcaniclastic sediments with a mammalian fauna. In 1973, J. M. Harris joined Watkins to carry out a preliminary survey of the fossiliferous deposits. Several pockets of fossiliferous sediment were discovered on the flank of the Suregai-Assile plateau. The sediments are capped by a basalt flow dated at 17.3 ± 1.4 myr. Most of the fossils were found to comprise rhinocerotid and proboscidean postcranial elements, but enamel and bone fragments indicated the presence of medium to small mammals. The preliminary survey suggested this to be an important early Miocene site warranting further investigation (Harris and Watkins, 1974).

ARCHEOLOGY

Two series of archeological occurrences have been recognized in the Koobi Fora Formation. The older series, which occurs chiefly in the KBS tuff, was the subject of initial excavations and surveys (M. D. Leakey, 1970; Isaac et al., 1971 and 1976), and the artifacts recovered have been referred to as the KBS Industry. The younger series, discovered in the Upper Member and the subject of more recent investigations, has been termed the Karari Industry (Harris and Isaac, 1976).

The Karari Industry sites are particularly abundant in the strata associated with the Okote tuff in the Karari area, but two are also known from Ileret in low-energy river floodplain deposits at the same stratigraphic level. The whole series of sites of the Karari Industry derive from the fluviatile deposits

TABLE 1. Catalogued Archeological Sites in the Koobi Fora and Guomde Formations

Reference no.	Other labels	Area	Stratigraphic position	Archeological classification
FwJi 1	GFS	6A	Guomde Formation	Undetermined
FwJi 1	NAS	8	Lower/Middle tuff	? Karari Industry
FxJj 1	KBS	105	KBS tuff	KBS Industry
FxJj 2	–	105	Surface and superficial Pleistocene beds	Includes MSA element
FxJj 3	HAS	105	KBS tuff	KBS Industry
FxJj 4	PBS	105		
5	–	105		
6	–	105	Surface indications of site in KBS tuff	KBS Industry
7	–	105		
8	–	105		
9	–	105		
FxJj 10	NMS	118	Tuff 118/T II or a tuffaceous sand above it	KBS Industry
FxJj 11	BBS	130	Just below base of Okote tuff	Karari Industry
FxJj 13	CPH	105	KBS tuff	KBS Industry
FxJj 14	–	130	Surface indications of site in tuff 130/T1	? KBS Industry
FxJj 15	–	130	Channel cutting into tuff 130/T1 and was filled with tuffaceous silt	Undetermined
FxJj 16	–	130	Channel within Okote tuff beds	
171	–	130	Okote tuff beds	

Reference no.	Other labels	Area	Stratigraphic position	Archeological classification
18	GS Lower Horizon	130	Channel at base of Okote tuff beds	Karari Industry
18	GS Upper Horizon	130	Channel at base of Okote tuff beds	
18	NS North site	130	Sand/silt interface at base of Okote tuff beds	
FxJj 18 IHS	–	130	Okote tuff	
19	–	130	Surface indications of site in channel lateral to Okote tuff beds	
20M	Main site	131	Okote tuff beds	
20E	East site	131	Okote tuff beds	
20AB	–	131	Okote tuff beds	
21	–	131	Surface indications of site in Okote tuff beds	?Acheulian
23	–	East of 131	Okote tuff beds	Karari Industry
24	–	East of 130		
25		"	Surface indications of site in sands thought to be laterally equivalent to Okote tuff beds	Karari Industry
26	–	"		
27	–	"		
28	–	"		
29	–	"		
FxJj 30	–	129		
31	–	129		
32	–	129	Surface indications of site in Okote tuff beds	Karari Industry
34	–	129		
35	–	129		
FxJj 38NW	North west	130	Between 130/T II and Okote tuff	KBS Industry
38E	East site	130	Between 130/T II and Okote tuff	Indeterminate
38SE	Southeast site	130	Between 130/T II and Okote tuff	Indeterminate
FxJj 40	–	130	Surface indications of site in Okote tuff beds	Karari Industry
41	–	130		
FxJj 44	–	118	Surface indications of site in sands/gravels, lateral equivalent to Okote tuff	Karari Industry
45	–	118		
46	–	118		
FxJj 50	–	131	Surface indications of site in Okote tuff beds	Karari Industry

in the stratigraphic interval between the KBS tuff and the Chari tuff. Lake margin deposits correlating with this interval have not yielded artifacts.

More than 50 sites have been located (table 1) and, with the exception of 2 near the lake margin at Ileret, they all occur 15 to 25 kilometers inland from the ancient shoreline, either in stream channels or river floodplains. Tree and bushlined stream channels probably provided shade, shelter, and a source of nuts and berries, as well as ready access to raw materials, and were thus attractive places for a home base.

The stone artifacts of the Karari Industry indicate opportunistic flaking techniques, rather than a fixed highly organized pattern of core preparation. Choppers, polyhedrons, and discoids are important components, but handaxes and cleavers seem to have been rare. The inclusion of a conspicuous series of core-scrapers makes the Karari Industry distinctive.

The distribution of the Karari archeological sites, together with studies of the spatial arrangement of the tools, the associated bone remains, and the materials from which the tools were made, provide clues to the life of our ancestors between 1.8 and 1.2 myr. B.P. Small groups appear to have shared food. Meat was eaten and at times transported to a home base. Raw materials for the manufacture of tools were carried for significant distances and a considerable variety of tool types were made, presumably intended for a variety of functions.

TABLE 2. Hominid Specimens Collected from the Koobi Fora Formation, 1973-1976

Year	Area	KNM-ER no.	Details of specimens
1973	130	1800	Cranial fragments
1973	131	1801	Left mandible, P_4, M_1, M_3
1973	131	1802	Mandible, left and right P_4-M_2, right P_3
1973	131	1803	Right mandible fragment
1973	104	1804	Right maxilla, P^3-M^2
1973	130	1805	Cranium and mandible with dentition
1973	130	1806	Edentulous mandible
1973	103	1807	Right femur shaft
1973	103	1808	Associated skeletal and cranial fragments
1973	121	1809	Right femur shaft
1973	123	1810	Proximal left tibia
1973	123	1811	Mandibular fragments
1973	123	1812	Right mandible fragment and left 1_1 and M_1
1973	123	1813	Cranium with dentition
1973	127	1814	Associated elements of upper dentition
1973	6A	1816	Fragments of juvenile mandible

Year	Area	KNM-ER No.	Details of specimens
1973	1	1817	Left mandible
1973	6A	1818	1^1
1973	3	1819	M_3
1973	103	1820	Left mandible, dm_2, M_1
1973	123	1821	Parietal fragment
1973	123	1822	Femur shaft
1974	6	2592	Parietal fragment
1974	6	2593	Molar fragment
1974	1A	2595	Parietal fragment
1974	15	2596	Distal left tibia
1974	15	2597	Lower left molar
1974	15	2598	Occipital fragment
1974	15	2599	Lower premolar fragment
1974	130	2600	Lower molar fragment
1974	130	2601	Right lower $dm-_2$
1974	117	2602	Cranial fragments
1974	117	2603	Molar fragment
1974	117	2604	Premolar fragment
1974	117	2605	Tooth fragment
1974	117	2606	Tooth fragment
1975	102	3228	Right innominate
1975	103	3229	Mandible, right and left P_4
1975	130	3230	Mandible with complete dentition
1975	100	3728	Left femur
1975	102	3729	Left edentulous mandible
1975	105	3731	Fragments left edentulous mandible
1975	105	3732	Partial cranium and natural endocast
1975	104	3733	Cranium with partial dentition
1975	105	3734	Left mandible, $C-M_2$
1975	116	3735	Cranial fragments, distal right humerus, proximal radius, partial sacrum, and fragments tibia, 3 phalanges, and distal femur shaft
1975	105	3736	Proximal two thirds radius
1976	1	3883	Calvaria
1976	5	3884	Cranium and palate, almost complete dentition
1976	104	3885	Lower premolar crown
1976	104	3886	Premolar and left $dm-^2$
1976	1	3887	Partial lower molar crown
1976	1	3888	Proximal radius
1976	1	3889	Fragment right mandible
1976	6A	3890	Lower molar crown
1976	105	3891	Cranial fragments
1976	105	3892	Left frontal fragments

Although the archeological sites at East Turkana are often small and restricted compared with those from other sites such as Olduvai Gorge, this has great advantage in terms of interpretation. Too many artifacts obscure much of the information, while a small assemblage of fragments yields a great deal of information. Interpretation of a discrete cluster of artifacts struck from only one or two cobbles is relatively easy, whereas interpretation of a larger area with thousands of artifacts is difficult.

FOSSIL HOMINIDS

The team of Kenyans responsible for the discovery of the fossil hominids has now developed an expertise unequaled anywhere in the world. Each year they search as much of the area as time allows, but pay particular attention to localities felt to be important for one reason or another. While the whole area has now been intensively searched several times it continues to yield important finds each year. Table 2 lists the specimens discovered between 1973 and 1976.

The 1973 collection includes three specimens of particular importance. A well-preserved mandible, KNM-ER 1802 (see fig. 6), was discovered in situ by Dr. J. M. Harris below the KBS tuff in area 131. The dentition is only slightly worn, and fragments of both M_3 crowns suggest that death occurred before these teeth were fully erupted. The canines and incisors are represented by roots and by alveoli filled with matrix. The mandible is moderately robust, with fairly large teeth, and shows similarities with OH 7, the type specimen of *Homo habilis* from Olduvai Gorge. It clearly differs from the typical robust mandibles of *Australopithecus boisei* and, like the cranium KNM-ER 1470, it is assigned to *Homo habilis*.

A skull and mandible, KNM-ER 1805, were discovered by Dr. P. Abell in situ in the Okote tuff in area 130. The cranium is unusual in that it has a moderately large cranial capacity, 582 cubic centimeters, and well-developed parasagittal crests, nuchal crests, and mastoid crests. The calvaria is broken through the orbital cavities, but the palate and part of the facial region are preserved, as is the mandible. The taxonomic interpretation of the skull remains enigmatic.

The third specimen, a cranium KNM-ER 1813 (see fig. 3), was discovered in situ by Kamoya Kimeu in area 123. The specimen was fragmented but has been reconstructed, so that only part of the left side of the face, much of the sphenoid, and part of the left occipital is missing. The skull is small and lightly built, with an estimated cranial volume of 505-510 cubic centimeters. The supraorbital tori are not particularly salient, and the glabella is not prominent. There is a slight postglabella sulcus and the frontal bone then rises gently in the midline in a convex curve to bregma. The postorbital constriction is moderate, and the temporal lines remain far apart and can be traced posteriorly. The nuchal crests are weak and the mastoid process small. These new discoveries led us to re-evaluate our interpretation of hominid evolution in East Africa. Prior to this, a relatively simple evolutionary picture had emerged, including only two lineages, the robust australopithecines which became extinct, and the *Homo* lineage leading to modern man. The discovery of KNM-ER 1813, suggested a more complex history with at least three lineages represented. It also became clear that two gracile specimens from Olduvai Gorge (OH 13 and OH 24), previously assigned to *Homo habilis,* closely resembled KNM-ER 1813. A third hominid thus appears to be represented at both sites. It appears to be the equivalent of *Australopithecus africanus* in South Africa although, like *A. robustus* and *A. boisei,* it shows significant geographical variation (Leakey, 1974 and 1976b).

In 1975, the brow ridges of a hominid skull were discovered by B. Ngeneo, just protruding above the surface of the sediment in area 105. Careful excavation of this specimen revealed a complete calvaria of *Homo erectus;* after reconstruction in the laboratory by Dr. A. Walker (Harvard University), the face and palate were reassembled, making this specimen the most complete *Homo erectus* ever found. This skull, KNM-ER 3733 (see fig. 3), is from deposits 1.5 myr. old and establishes the presence of *Homo erectus* in Africa at this early date. Although the dates for this species in Java and China are insecure, it seems likely that *H. erectus* was in Africa at least half a million years earlier than in Eurasia (Walker and Leakey, 1978).

In 1976, a second, slightly younger cranium of *H. erectus,* KNM-ER 3883, was also discovered at Ileret in area I, above the Lower/Middle tuff. Although this skull is less complete than that found the previous year, many details of the basicranium are preserved, including the styloid process, a bone rarely preserved in fossil hominids.

In 1976, the cranium of an early *Homo sapiens* was also found in the Guomde Formation. The skull unfortunately was very squashed, but it has been partially reconstructed by Dr. A. Walker. It is important, as it represents a stage in the development of *H. sapiens* not well documented in Africa.

Conclusions

The continuing research, east of Lake Turkana, is contributing much to our knowledge of our past in the period between 1 and 3 million years ago.

The research brings scientists together from many disciplines, with each line of inquiry dependent in varying degrees on many others. Gradually a detailed picture is being pieced together, but there is still much to be done.

REFERENCES

BARTHELME, J.
  1977.   Holocene sites north-east of Lake Turkana: A preliminary report. Azania, vol. 12, pp. 33-41.
BEHRENSMEYER, A. K.
  1975.   The taphonomy and palaeoecology of Plio-Pleistocene vertebrate assemblages east of Lake Rudolf, Kenya.   Bull. Mus. Comp. Zool., vol. 146, pp. 473-578.
  1978.   The habitat of Plio-Pleistocene hominids in East Africa; taphonomic and microstratigraphic evidence.   Pp. 165-189 *in* "African Hominidae of the Flio-Pleistocene: Evidence Problems and Strategies," C. J. Jolly, ed. Duckworth, New York.
BONNEFILLE, R.
  1976.   Implications of pollen assemblages from the Koobi Fora Formation, East Rudolf, Kenya.   Nature, vol. 264, pp. 403-407.
BOWEN, B. E., and VONDRA, C. F.
  1973.   Stratigraphical relationships of the Plio-Pleistocene deposits, East Rudolf, Kenya.   Nature, vol. 242, pp. 391-393.
BROCK, A., and ISAAC, G. Ll.
  1974.   Palaeomagnetic stratigraphy and chronology of hominid bearing sediments east of Lake Rudolf, Kenya.   Nature, vol. 247, pp. 344-348.
CERLING, T. E.; BROWN, F. H.; CERLING, B. W.; CURTIS, G. H.; and DRAKE, R. E.
  1979.   Preliminary correlations between the Koobi Fora and Shungura Formations, East Africa.   Nature, vol. 279, pp. 118-121.
CERLING, T. E.; HAY, E. L.; and O'NEIL, J. R.
  1977.   Isotopic evidence for dramatic climatic changes in East Africa during the Pleistocene.   Nature, vol. 267, pp. 137-138.
COOKE, H.B.S., and MAGLIO, V. J.
  1972.   Plio-Pleistocene stratigraphy in East Africa in relation to proboscidean and suid evolution.   Pp. 303-329 *in* "Calibration of Hominoid Evolution," W. W. Bishop and J. A. Miller, eds.   Scottish Academic Press, Edinburgh; University of Toronto Press.
COPPENS Y.; HOWELL, F. C.; ISAAC, G. Ll.; and LEAKEY, R.E.F., eds.
  1976.   Earliest man and environments in the Lake Rudolf basin: Stratigraphy, palaeoecology, and evolution, 615 pp.   University of Chicago Press.
CURTIS, G. H.; DRAKE, R.; CERLING, T. E.; and HAMPEL, J. H.
  1975.   Age of KBS tuff in Koobi Fora Formation, East Rudolf, Kenya.   Nature, vol. 358, pp. 395-398.
DAY, M. H., and LEAKEY, R.E.F.
  1973.   New evidence for the genus *Homo* from East Rudolf, Kenya (I).   Amer. Journ. Phys. Anthrop., vol. 39, pp. 341-354.

1974.   New evidence for the genus *Homo* from East Rudolf, Kenya (III).   Amer. Journ. Phys. Anthrop., vol. 41, pp. 367-380.

DAY, M. H.; LEAKEY, R.E.F.; WALKER, A. C.; and WOOD, B. A.
1974.   New hominids from East Rudolf, Kenya (1).   American Journ. Phys. Anthrop., vol. 42, pp. 461-476.
1976.   New hominids from East Turkana, Kenya.   Amer. Journ. Phys. Anthrop., vol. 45, pp. 369-436.

DRAKE, R. E.; CURTIS, G. H.; CERLING, T. E.; CERLING, B. W.; and HAMPEL, J.
1980.   KBS tuff dating and geochronology of tuffaceous sediments in the Koobi Fora and Shungura Formations, East Africa.   Nature, vol. 283, pp. 368-372.

FINDLATER, I. C.
1978.   Stratigraphy.   Pp. 14-31 *in* "Koobi Fora Research Project, Vol. 1. The Fossil Hominids and an Introduction to Their Contexts, 1968-1974," M. G. Leakey and R.E.F. Leakey, eds.   Clarendon Press, Oxford.

FITCH, F. J., and MILLER, J. A.
1970.   Radioisotopic age determinations of Lake Rudolf artefact site.   Nature, vol. 226, pp. 226-228.
1976.   Conventional K-Ar and ^{40}Ar/^{39}Ar dating of volcanic rocks from East Rudolf.   Pp. 123-147 *in* "Earliest Man and Environments in the Lake Rudolf Basin. Stratigraphy, Palaeoecology, and Evolution." Y. Coppens, F. C. Howell, G. Ll. Isaac, and R.E.F. Leakey, eds.   University of Chicago Press.

FITCH, F. J.; HOOKER, P. J.; and MILLER, J. A.
1976. ^{40}Ar/^{39}Ar dating of the KBS tuff in the Koobi Fora Formation, East Rudolf, Kenya.   Nature, vol. 263, pp. 740-744.

GLEADOW, A.J.W.
1980.   Fission track age of the KBS tuff and associated hominid remains in northern Kenya.   Nature, vol. 284, pp. 225-230.

HARRIS, J. M.
1978.   Palaeontology.   Pp. 32-53 *in* "Koobi Fora Research Project, Vol 1, The Fossil Hominids and an Introduction to Their Context, 1968-1974," M. G. Leakey and R.E.F. Leakey, eds.   Clarendon Press, Oxford.

HARRIS, J. M., and WATKINS, R. T.
1974.   A new early Miocene fossil mammal locality near Lake Rudolf, Kenya.   Nature, vol. 252, pp. 576-577.

HARRIS, J. M., and WHITE, T. D.
1979.   Evolution of the Plio-Pleistocene African Suidae.   Trans. Amer. Phil. Soc., vol. 2, pp. 1-128.

HARRIS, J.W.K., and ISAAC, G. Ll.
1976.   The Karari Industry: Early Pleistocene archaeological evidence from the terrain east of Lake Turkana, Kenya.   Nature, vol. 262, pp. 102-107.

HILLHOUSE, J. W.; NDOMBI, J.W.M.; COX, A.
1977.   Additional results on palaeomagnetic stratigraphy of the Koobi Fora Formation, east of Lake Turkana (Lake Rudolf), Kenya.   Nature, vol. 265, pp. 411-415.

HURFORD, A. J.; GLEADOW, A.J.W.; and NAESER, C. W.
1976.   Fission track dating of pumice from the KBS tuff, East Rudolf, Kenya.
         Nature, vol. 263, pp. 738-740.
ISAAC, G. Ll.; HARRIS, J.W.K.; and CRADER, D.
1976.   Archaeological evidence from the Koobi Fora Formation. Pp. 533-564
         in "Earliest Man and Environments, East Rudolf, Kenya in the Lake Ru-
         dolf basin: Stratigraphy, Palaeoecology, and Evolution," Y. Coppens,
         F. C. Howell, G. Ll. Isaac, and R.E.F. Leakey, eds.   University of
         Chicago Press.
ISAAC, G. Ll.; LEAKEY, R.E.F.; and BEHRENSMEYER, A. K.
1971.   Archaeological traces of early hominid activities, east of Lake Rudolf,
         Kenya.   Science, vol. 173, pp. 1129-1134.
LEAKEY, M. D.
1970.   Early artifacts from the Koobi Fora area.   Nature, vol. 226, pp. 228-
         230.
LEAKEY, M. D., and LEAKEY, R. E., eds.
1978.   Koobi Fora Research Project, Vol. 1., The fossil hominids and an intro-
         duction to their context, 191 pp.   Clarendon Press, Oxford.
LEAKEY, R.E.F.
1974.   Further evidence of Lower Pleistocene hominids from East Rudolf,
         North Kenya, 1973.   Nature, vol. 248, pp. 653-656.
1976a.   New hominid fossils from the Koobi Fora Formation in northern Kenya.
         Nature, vol. 261, pp. 574-576.
1976b.   Hominids in Africa.   American Scientist, vol. 64, pp. 174-178.
LEAKEY, R.E.F., and WALKER, A. C.
1973.   New australopithecines from East Rudolf, Kenya (III).   Amer. Journ.
         Phys. Anthrop., vol. 39, pp. 205-222.
LEAKEY, R.E.F., and WOOD, B. A.
1974a.   New evidence for the genus Homo from East Rudolf, Kenya
         (IV).   Amer. Journ. Phys. Anthrop., vol. 41, pp. 237-244.
1974b.   A hominid mandible from East Rudolf, Kenya.   Amer. Journ. Phys.
         Anthrop., vol. 41, pp. 245-250.
LEAKEY, R.E.F.; MUNGAI, J. M.; and WALKER, A. C.
1971.   New australopithecines from East Rudolf, Kenya.   Amer. Journ. Phys.
         Anthrop., vol. 35, pp. 175-186.
1972.   New australopithecines from East Rudolf, Kenya.   Amer. Journ. Phys.
         Anthrop., vol. 36, pp. 235-251.
MCDOUGALL, I.; MAIER, R.; SUTHERLAND-HAWKES, P.; and GLEADOW, A.J.W.
1980.   K-Ar age estimate for the KBS tuff, East Turkana, Kenya.   Nature,
         vol. 284, pp. 230-234.
SAVAGE, R.J.G., and WILLIAMSON, P. G.
1978.   The early history of the Turkana depression.   Pp. 375-394 in "Geologi-
         cal Background to Fossil Man," W. W. Bishop, ed.   Scottish Academ-
         ic Press, Edinburgh; University of Toronto Press.
VONDRA, C. F., and BOWEN, B. E.
1976.   Plio-Pleistocene deposits and environments, East Rudolf, Kenya.   Pp.
         79-93 in "Earliest Man and Environments in the Lake Rudolf Basin." Y.
         Coppens, F. C. Howell, G. Ll. Isaac, and R. E. Leakey, eds.   Univer-
         sity of Chicago Press.

1978.   Stratigraphy, sedimentary facies and palaeoenvironments, East Lake Turkana, Kenya.   Pp. 395-414 *in* "Geological Background to Fossil Man," W. W. Bishop and J. A. Miller, eds.   Scottish Academic Press, Edinburgh.

WALKER, A. C., and LEAKEY, R.E.F.
1978.   The hominids of East Turkana.   Scientific American, vol. 239, pp. 54-66.

RICHARD E. F. LEAKEY

The Fulani and Their Cattle: Applied Behavioral Technology in a Nomadic Cattle Culture and its Psychological Consequences

Principal Investigators: Dale F. Lott, Department of Wildlife and Fisheries Biology and Department of Psychology, University of California, Davis, and Benjamin L. Hart, Department of Physiological Sciences, School of Veterinary Medicine, University of California, Davis.

Grant No. 1195:   In support of a study of the Fulani and their cattle as a two-species social system.

The Fulani are nomadic cattle herders who range across subsaharan Africa, north of tsetse fly infestation, from the Atlantic to the Nile. They are a small, wiry people with a reputation for physical beauty and success in war (Johnson, 1967). Many features of their culture have been described (Hopen, 1958; Stenning, 1959) and some features of their cattle husbandry as well (St. Croix, 1945). The current study concentrated on the behavioral aspects of their cattle-husbandry techniques, and the impact of those husbandry techniques on the socialization and personality of the people.

The study was conducted in the general region of Zaria, in Northern Nigeria, an area of major Fulani concentration. Fieldwork was conducted in late spring and early summer of 1973. We visited Fulani camps, spent days with Fulani herdsmen, and interviewed Fulani that we met along trails and in markets. Our interpreters were veterinary students whose first language was Fulani and who were very fluent in English. The combination of their sophistication in Fulani culture and language and our connection to the veterinary college in Zaria yielded a high level of cooperation from our contacts.

Fulani Cattle and Their Husbandry

The Fulani cattle are a mixture of *Bos indicus* and *Bos taurus* (Epstein, 1971). They are rangy and have long sharp horns. Their milk yield is very low, but they are disease and drought resistant. The Fulani maintain them as separate herds owned and managed by a nuclear family. Families often coordinate the activities of their herd with those belonging to close relatives who

425

travel together as a clan. A typical herd contains 20 to 30 cows, 10 to 15 calves and juveniles, 1 senior (4-year) bull, a few immature bulls, and often 3 or 4 castrated males (oxen).

A striking constraint on Fulani cattle husbandry is the almost complete lack of means of physical restraint. There are no mechanical squeezes, no tranquilizers, no corrals and no fences; moreover, the Fulani use neither horses nor dogs to help control the cattle. Yet they must achieve a high level of control. The cattle graze to the very edge of unfenced fields of tempting green farm crops but must not be allowed to enter the fields. The herd must be moved to new camps and grazing areas several times a month, they must be kept at the campsites overnight, and they must be handled so that they can be milked, their ticks removed, etc.

The only physical tools the Fulani use are herding sticks about two meters long and three to four centimeters in diameter, and ropes braided from the bark of local trees and bushes. The achievement of such demanding tasks with such limited tools is made possible by a thorough understanding and exploitation of the behavioral properties of the cattle (Lott and Hart, 1979).

Behavioral Control Through Exploitation of Innate Aversions of Cattle

Some of the behavioral techniques for managing these herds use innate aversions of cattle. Natural selection has produced behaviors that help avoid parasites and disease in all animals. The Fulani exploit two such behaviors in cattle: (1) aversion to their own feces and (2) aversion to flies; both potential sources of parasites and disease.

The aversion to feces is exploited to keep the cattle out of the crops by smearing fresh cow dung on the leaves of some of the plants at the edges of the fields. The odor repels the cows from these plants. Similarly, the family's milk supply is protected in the cow's udders by smearing fresh dung on the udders of cows with nursing calves before the herd is taken out to feed for the day. The calves are repelled by the odor, so there is still milk in the udder at the end of the day. Fresh feces and the knowledge of cattle's reaction to them substitute for both fences and nursing muzzles.

Fulani give their cattle relief from flies by building a smoke fire with green leaves at dusk. The cattle crowd into the smoke. While they stand there the herdsmen exploit the aversion to flies that brought them there by tying the left forelegs of matched pairs together with about half a meter of rope. This secures the animals for the night and thus substitutes for a corral.

Behavioral Control Through Exploitation of Social Predispositions of Cattle

Like other group-living species, cattle have many patterns of social behavior and behavioral predispositions that make group living possible. Fulani cattle husbandry exploits a number of these.

Cattle herds have a natural leader (rarely if ever the dominant) which the others follow. Fulani exploit this following tendency by taking the role of leader to move the herd. When campsites are being changed the cattle may be led as much as 30 kilometers in a day by a herdsman walking from the front and giving the unique leadership call. The cattle follow single file or two abreast. They are moved farther, faster, and with less stress than would be possible by driving them with horses.

The maintenance of a social organization requires a certain amount of friendly interaction (Schloeth, 1958). Adult cattle lick one another and mothers lick their nursing calves. The Fulani must be able to approach and physically touch their animals in order to milk them, to place ropes on them, remove ticks, etc. The herders appear to achieve this through exploitation of the tendency of cattle to enter into friendly relationships characterized by touching and mutual grooming. Many of their approaches to the cattle are to stroke or groom them. The cattle stand quietly at their approach, often stretching their head and neck upward to be groomed under the neck and jaw, just as they do to conspecifics. Cows often lick the inner surface of the rear legs of their nursing calves. Adult cattle will interrupt walking, grazing, or any other activity when a herdsman pets them there, and stand apparently transfixed until he stops. These friendly relationships are to a degree reciprocal, with the cattle sometimes approaching the Fulani to lick them as though they were a friendly conspecific.

Not all interactions among members of the herd are friendly. The natural social organization of a cattle herd involves dominance of some individuals by others, with a fairly linear hierarchy leading to the most dominant individual at the top (Hafez et al., 1972). The Fulani exploit the readiness of cattle to enter into a subordinate status by asserting dominance over them through aggressive behavior, including striking them with sticks and threatening them with shouts. The dominance status thus achieved gives the Fulani safety among potentially dangerous animals and at the same time permits them to control the location and activity of members of the herd just as a dominant is able to do. The Fulani exploit this status mainly to keep cattle from entering crops, to prevent attacks on themselves or others, and to break up fights within the herd.

Cultural Consequences of Husbandry Through Social Domination

There is good reason to believe that the social domination aspect of cattle husbandry has influenced the socialization and personality of the Fulani (Lott and Hart, 1977). Asserting dominance over large, potentially dangerous animals like the Fulani cattle requires courage and a good deal of aggressive behavior. The socialization of Fulani men emphasizes the importance of courage and self assertion above all other virtues. The Fulani consider these to be their defining attributes.

The social ideal of aggressive assertiveness and retaliatory response to aggression is not confined to interactions with cattle. Fulani boys are encouraged to show these traits in every aspect of their lives. Failure to do so is severely punished. The resulting Fulani personality is much like that of other pastoralists, whose exceptional agressiveness among themselves and toward more sedentary neighbors is an important issue in cultural anthropology (Edgerton, 1971). A number of factors have been advanced to account for this phenomenon. Our evidence suggests that one important factor is the socialization process that produces the aggressive assertive personality needed for many kinds of animal husbandry. Thus one of the determinants of the relationship of pastoralists to their neighbors is their relationship with their animals.

Control of Behavior Through Magic

When more mundane measures fail to achieve behavioral control the Fulani turn to magic (St. Croix, 1945). Some of their magical "controls" seem founded on superstition alone. For example, some Fulani contend that it is possible to make a herd theft-proof by adding the leaves of certain plants to the evening smoke fire. Cattle bathed in this smoke will be ready to fight off strangers or thieves. Three or four smoke treatments are alleged to produce this behavioral effect for a year. We never saw this demonstrated, and there is no reason to suppose it works.

But some magical practices seem likely to have a basis in fact. One such practice involves the adoption of calves by cows. If a cow rejects her calf at birth the Fulani may put soup stock (or some other salty substance) on the calf's back, then blow into the cow's vulva while she is licking it. They report that the cow will then adopt the calf. While we never saw this widely reported procedure demonstrated, there is a very real possibility that it could work through a known physiological mechanism.

Blowing into the vulva of cows is known to stimulate the release of the hormone oxytocin. Oxytocin is known to stimulate milk ejection during nursing and has been hypothesized to motivate mammalian mothers with pre-cocial young to bond with their offspring. Therefore it is quite possible that the Fulani are achieving behavioral control by manipulating the hormonal state of the mother.

Concluding Remarks

The Fulani are keenly aware of the behavioral properties of their cattle and are very ingenious in the use of that awareness in their cattle-husbandry tech-niques. Much of the cattle's behavior is determined by the Fulani. Close study of such materially simple but behaviorally sophisticated husbandry systems can both teach us a good deal about animal behavior, and offer some proven alternatives to the cattle-husbandry techniques now in use in Europe and North America.

At the same time, the behavior of the people is in part a product of the behavioral properties of the cattle. The adaptive value of an aggressive person-ality in cattle husbandry has led to socialization emphasizing aggression and self-assertion as a cultural ideal that determines the behavior of Fulani men in every aspect of their lives.

Cultural ideals can persist after the conditions that made them adaptive have passed. Cultural ideals established during a period that placed a premi-um on the handling of the domestic horse, for example, may mark the cul-tures that did so, as ours did, for many generations. Perhaps this helps us to understand the origin and impact of the cowboy as a cultural ideal in our own society. If so, the study of the Fulani-cattle system has also taught us some-thing about our own behavior.

Acknowledgments

We gratefully acknowledge the support of the National Institute of Men-tal Health, Grant MH-24767, the National Geographic Society, and the University of California Committee on Research.

Space limitations prevent our acknowledging all the many people whose help was essential to the successful conduct of our research, but we cannot neglect to mention Usman Ardo, Ronald Cohen, and Mohammed Jingi of Zaria, Nigeria, and Stanley Dennis of Manhattan, Kansas.

REFERENCES
EDGERTON, R. B.
    1971.   The individual in cultural adaptation, 351 pp.   University of Califor-nia Press, Berkeley.

EPSTEIN, H.
1971. The origin of the domestic animals of Africa, vol. 1, 573 pp. African Publishing Corporation, New York.
HAFEZ, E. S. E.; SCHEIN, M. W.; and EWBANK, R.
1972. The behavior of cattle. Pp. 235-295 *in* "The Behavior of Domestic Animals," E. S. E. Hafez, ed. Williams and Wilkins, Baltimore.
HOPEN, C. E.
1958. The pastoral Fulbe family in Gwanda, 165 pp. Oxford University Press, London.
JOHNSON, H. A. S.
1967. The Fulani empire of Sokoto, 312 pp. Oxford University Press, London.
LOTT, D. F., and HART, B. L.
1977. Aggressive domination of cattle by Fulani herdsmen and its relation to aggression in Fulani culture and personality. Ethos, vol. 5, no. 2, pp. 174-186.
1979. Applied ethology in a nomadic cattle culture. Appl. Anim. Ethol., vol. 5, pp. 309-319.
ST. CROIX, F. W.
1945. The Fulani of Northern Nigeria, 74 pp. Gregg International, Westmead, England. (Republished in 1972).
SCHLOETH, R.
1958. Cycle annuel et comportment social du Taureau de Camargue. Mammalia, vol. 22, pp. 121-139.
STENNING, D. J.
1959. Savannah Nomads, 266 pp. Oxford University Press, London.

DALE F. LOTT
BENJAMIN L. HART

The Colombian Llanos in the 19th Century: A Tropical Plains Frontier

Principal Investigator: Jane M. Loy, University of Massachusetts, Amherst, Massachusetts.

Grant No. 1265:   In support of archival research in Bogotá to study the history of the Colombian Llanos from 1810 to 1910.

Historians have long been concerned about the role of frontiers in national development. Stimulated by the writings of Frederick Jackson Turner, many North American scholars have debated the significance of the "moving western frontier" in United States history (Taylor, 1972). In contrast, no continuous wave of pioneers moved into the empty tropical grasslands, or Llanos, lying east of the Colombian Andes. Since the 19th century, the Llanos have formed a "permanent" frontier[1]—symbolizing from earliest times a potentially rich region but never effectively exploited or integrated with the core highland settlements.

Constituting one-third of the territory of the Republic of Colombia, the Llanos slope eastward from the eastern Andean Cordillera to merge imperceptibly with the Llanos of Venezuela. Their southern limit is the Guaviare River at the edge of the Amazon jungle. Of the many rivers that cut through the region, the largest is the Meta, which can be navigated to its confluence with the Orinoco (fig. 1). Along the rivers are strips of rain forest, but the predominant vegetation is tall, tropical bunch grass.

The Llanos are scarcely 80 surface miles from Bogotá, but since they are 18,000 feet lower in altitude, the tortuous descent down the mountainside has isolated them for centuries (fig. 2). The severe tropical climate has further limited their development. Influenced by the nearness of the Equator, the pattern of trade winds, and the mountain barrier to the west, the temperatures on the plains range between 70° and 110°F. The rainy season lasts from April until November with annual accumulations of up to 160 inches of precipitation. For 8 months the flooding rivers create vast seas, and animals must seek refuge on the little islands of dry ground that remain. During the dry season

---

[1] The term frontier is used throughout this report to indicate an elastic geographical zone which consists of both the fringes of European settlement and the wilderness beyond occupied solely by Indians.

Fig. 1. Map of the Llanos region of Colombia showing the highway from Bogotá to Villavicencio and the location of cities and towns mentioned in the report. (Drawn by John E. Marti.)

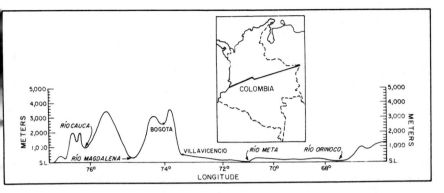

Fɪɢ. 2.   Cross section of Colombia from the Pacific coast to the Orinoco Plains showing the drop in altitude between the core highland area and the Llanos. (Drawn by John E. Marti.)

from December to March, the hot sun returns, reducing the rivers to tiny streams and leaving the land cracked as if there had been an earthquake (West, 1962). In this environment of violent extremes, man and animal must struggle constantly for survival.

Spanish and German conquistadors first explored the Llanos in the early 16th century. Despite the rugged climate, cattle and horses multiplied on the natural grassland so that ranching soon became an important economic activity. The Jesuits established one of their largest mission and hacienda systems among the nomadic Indians. Miscegenation between Spanish, Indians, and blacks produced a cowboy subculture called the Llaneros, who later in the Wars of Independence formed the nucleus of Simón Bolívar's victorious army. The impact of this long struggle was especially harsh in the plains, and the population declined steadily after 1824.

As in other Colombian regions in the 19th century, those who continued to live in the Llanos provinces were quite isolated, adapting to a way of life distinct from that of the rest of the republic. Efforts by the national governments to revive the missions or to discover new tropical products were unsuccessful for the most part. It was not until the 1930's, with the completion of a paved highway from Bogotá to Villavicencio, the "gateway to the Llanos," and the control of deadly tropical diseases through improved medical technology, that sustained colonization could be launched (Crist and Guhl, 1957). Between 1957 and 1967 the population of the southern region of Meta, formerly known as San Martín, tripled to surpass 200,000 (Brunnschweiler, 1973). Writing in 1973, Brunnschweiler regarded the Llanos as among the most active pioneer settlement zones in Latin America. Nevertheless he cautioned that the few hundred thousand settlers who had crossed the Andes would not be the avant-garde of millions of migrants and concluded, "Colombia does not move eastward behind her eastern frontier."

Objectives and Methodology

The purpose of this investigation was to reconstruct the history of the Llanos between 1810 and 1910 and to analyze the interaction of the region with the highland population centers in the interior. The research was conducted as part of a larger project to review the evolution of the Llanos as a geographical unit from colonial times to the present, to compare the attempts of Colombia and Venezuela to develop the area, and to construct a model that would posit the characteristics of a "permanent" or "static" historical frontier.

Archival research provided the bulk of the data collected. Primary sources for the 19th century include the records of the provinces of Casanare, Bogotá and Boyacá, missionary reports, census data, reports prepared by national ministers and special investigators, accounts by travelers and scientists, congressional debates, law codes, and articles in official and nonofficial periodicals. These sources were consulted in Bogotá at the Archivo Nacional, the Archivo del Congreso, the Biblioteca Luis Ángel Arango, the Biblioteca del Ministerio de Gobierno, and the Biblioteca de la Academia de Historia during the summer of 1974. Summaries or xeroxed copies were made of the relevant manuscript material. These notes were supplemented by first-hand observations taken during two field trips to *hatos,* or ranches, in the Department of Meta and the Intendency of Casanare.

The project was modified in two ways during early stages of the research. First, the starting point for the study was pushed back from 1830 to 1810 when it became evident that the decade of the 1830's could not be understood without considering the fate of the Llanos during the Wars of Independence (1810-1824) and the Gran Colombia era (1819-1830). Second, the sources revealed many variations among subregions within the Llanos. The experience of Casanare and Arauca to the north proved to be very different from that of Meta in the south. Thus an effort was made to gather material equally for the three areas to permit comparisons on an intraregional basis.

Conclusions

Although much of the data requires further analysis, some preliminary conclusions may be offered. Within the Llanos, the most notable economic trend was the catastrophic decline in cattle ranching. Animals not confiscated in the war were killed by a variety of diseases. After a few years tame cattle and horses virtually disappeared, leaving only a small number of wild beasts roaming the plains. The depletion of formerly immense herds was noted by missionaries and landowners (AN-GC, 1837). The only section that continued to enjoy some prosperity was Arauca where cattle herding was stimulated by easier access to Venezuelan markets via the Arauca River and a vigorous contraband trade.

No new export emerged to replace hides and beef. The depressed economy was broken sporadically in the last half of the century by attempts to harvest tropical forest products. The demand for quinine in the 1870's and for rubber in the 1890's spurred exploration in Meta for stands of the valuable trees. The resulting exploitation took the form of miniature "boom and bust" cycles, which brought limited growth to certain localities and drained laborers from others (Martin, 1929).

Tied in part to these cycles was the fleeting existence of many Llano towns. By mid-19th century, the colonial mission towns were in ruins. Pore, General Santander's capital in Casanare in 1817, was already a ghost town. The Archivo Nacional contains numerous *solicitudes* or petitions from town councils requesting permission to move their *municipios* because of unhealthy climate, isolation, economic necessity or Indian attacks (AN-GC, 1847). New settlements were founded but few achieved permanence. Begun in 1842, Villavicencio was an exception. It survived a devastating fire in 1890 and repeated epidemics of malaria to become the most important outpost in the south by 1910 (Ortega Ricaurte, 1943).

Indian depredations increased the high white mortality rate. Unlike their ancestors who submitted to the ministrations of the colonial missionaries, the 19th-century Indians took the offensive. They stole horses and arms from the whites and waged implacable attacks against them. The Guahibos of Casanare were notorious for their ferocity. After completing a geographic survey of Colombia in 1856, Agustín Codazzi recommended that Casanare be reduced from province to territory, citing the erosion of civilized activity by the murderous climate and the Indian menace (Codazzi, 1856). Missionary activity continued throughout the century but on a limited scale. Occasionally, the priests would persuade an Indian group to organize a town in exchange for receiving the comforts of the Christian religion, Colombian protection, and tools for agriculture. Such agreements were short-lived. The Indians soon returned to their nomadic ways, and their towns exhibited the same lack of permanency as those of the whites.

Venezuela rather than the Colombian highlands was the source for most of the migrants to the Llanos. Almost constant civil war in that country pro-

FIG. 3.   The Llanos of Casanare, August 1974. (Photo by John W. Loy, Jr.)

duced a stream of refugees who fled to the relative peace of the Colombian plains. The border between Arauca and Venezuelan Apure was a zone of constant tensions. *Caudillos* on both sides crossed the line with impunity to conscript cattle and men. In many towns, Venezuelans outnumbered the Colombians, and at least twice, in 1830 and 1901, local groups in Casanare voted to secede from Colombia to join Venezuela (Moreno, 1832; Hernández C., 1904). Strangely enough, it was not until the end of the 19th century that the Colombian government regarded Venezuelan encroachment with alarm and took steps to protect the border. Other critical issues between the two countries included negotiating the exact location of their mutual boundary and Colombia's demand for free navigation on the Orinoco.

During the 19th century the Llanos were administered under many political arrangements. At the end of the Wars of Independence, Meta consisted of little more than the mission town of San Martín, which was attached to the Province of Bogotá. On the other hand, Casanare, including Arauca, was a large and still populous territory enjoying provincial status. The latter's steady decline brought about its incorporation into the neighboring Andean province of Boyacá in 1857. With the establishment of the United States of Colombia in 1863 both Meta and Casanare were declared national territories under direct federal control, but after some initial success this experiment failed. In 1886 the territories were returned to Boyacá and Cundinamarca only to be reestablished as national intendencies in 1897 (Plazas Olarte, 1944). These changes created new bureaucracies and sometimes new capitals but brought no far-reaching reforms. The true wielders of authority were the regional *caudillos,* whose role remains to be investigated further. The decline of the north and the modest growth of the south have continued into the 20th century and may be measured today by the fact that Meta is a self-governing department while Casanare and Arauca are still special territories (fig. 3).

It is more difficult to assess the impact of the Llanos frontier on the interior of Colombia than to outline developments within the region. Only once after the Wars of Independence did the Llaneros invade the highlands, and that was in 1830 when an army led by Juan Nepomuceno Moreno marched from Pore to Bogotá via Tunja to topple the dictatorship of Rafael Urdaneta (Groot, 1870). Civil wars in the interior after 1830 sparked disturbances in the Llanos, and the plains served as a sanctuary for exiles and fugitives of all political colors, but never again did the "barbarous" plainsmen seriously challenge rule by the *"cachacos,"* or gentlemen, of Bogotá.

Perhaps the most significant effect of the Llanos was that their continued unfulfilled potential as an expanding frontier encouraged among national leaders a political syndrome that might be dubbed the "El Dorado Complex."

From the days of Santander to those of Reyes, governments in Bogotá stead-
fastly proclaimed that the Llanos was a region of untold wealth that within a
few short years would become the heartland of Colombia. Representative of
this attitude is the following statement taken from an 1892 Senate report (*Anales del Senado,* 1892):

> The vast and rich eastern region of the Republic known by the name of the
> Llanos of Casanare and San Martín, by its topography, by the fertility of its
> soil, and by the abundance and wealth of its natural products is called to be
> in the more or less distant future, the center of a civilization more advanced
> perhaps than that which the now occupied interior regions will reach.

The most striking impression left by a review of the 19th-century sources is
the contrast between the rhetoric of Congress and the desperate reports from
local Llanero officials, the *municipios* and missionaries who observed the decay
of civilization around them and cried out for assistance.

It is not that the national governments failed to produce plans for development. Nearly every administration endorsed some program. A favored solution was to send priests to reestablish the missions and to pacify the Indians.
Other strategies included building roads, facilitating navigation on the Meta
River, sponsoring immigration from Europe, and introducing new products
such as tobacco and silk. With monotonous regularity laws were passed to implement these plans, only to be shelved within a few years. The laws failed because the obstacles of a small population, limited resources, and civil strife
made it impossible for the governments to enforce them. They failed because
it was more essential to national interest to use what meager resources there
were to develop the interior. They failed, finally, because the "El Dorado
Complex" in furnishing the illusion of the fabulous wealth of the Llanos obscured entirely the geographic realities of the region and encouraged the fabrication of schemes that were both unsuitable and unworkable in this area so
different from highland Colombia.

Despite the considerable growth of Meta since World War II, the "El
Dorado Complex" is still functioning to the detriment of the Llanos. For example, on June 29, 1974, a landslide at Quebradablanca on the Bogotá–Villavicencio highway took 200 lives and blocked the only paved road from the
interior to the plains. Panic spread throughout the Llanos as scarcities grew in
gasoline and other imported necessities. Agricultural produce ready to ship to
Bogotá spoiled for lack of an alternative route. The resumption of traffic on
the road by August did little to alleviate the frustrations of producers or their
fears for the systematic growth of the region. They pointed out that a government that designates one-third of its territory as "the future of Colombia" and

yet constructs to that area only one paved road, which is subject to frequent landslides, can hardly be said to have committed itself to a realistic plan of development *(El Tiempo,* June 21 and 29, 1974). A study of the historical sources tends to confirm Brunnschweiler's observation that as long as the Llanos are not truly vital to the welfare of the Colombian interior, they will continue to function as a "permanent" frontier. The tragedy at Quebradablanca is a recent and dramatic manifestation of the chronic abandon in which the Llanos have been traditionally maintained.

REFERENCES

ARCHIVAL MATERIAL
1837, 1847.   Archivo Nacional: Gobernación de Casanare, 1837, tomo 16, folio 513; 1847, tomo 19, folios 436-446.
1892.   Anales del Senado, Número 21, p. 167, Sept. 29.
BRUNNSCHWEILER, DIETER
1973.   The Llanos frontier of Colombia: Environment and changing land use in Meta.   Latin American Studies Center, East Lansing, Michigan, Monogr. no. 9, pp. 1-3, 62.
CODAZZI, AGUSTÍN
1856.   Informe sobre la provincia de Casanare, 376 pp.   Comisión Corográfica, Bogotá. (Reprinted 1959, Banco de la República, Bogotá.)
CRIST, RAYMOND E., and GUHL, ERNESTO
1957.   Pioneer settlement in eastern Colombia.   Ann. Rpt. Smithsonian Inst. for 1956, pp. 391-414, illus.
GROOT, JOSÉ MANUEL
1870.   Historia eclesiástica y civil de Nueva Granada, vol. 3, pp. 496-499.   Bogotá. (1953 ed., publ. by Editorial ABC.)
HERNÁNDEZ C., TOBIAS
1904.   Informe del Intendente Nacional de Casanare, March 9, p. 27.   Bogotá.
LOY, JANE M.
1976.   The Llanos in Colombian history—some implications of a static frontier.   Univ. Mass. Progr. in Latin Amer. Stud., Occ. Pap. Ser., no. 2, 23 pp. (Originally delivered as a paper at the University of Connecticut History Colloquium, Storrs, Conn., Oct. 16, 1974.)
1977.   Elegance, ecology, and egrets.   Américas, vol. 28 (October 1977), pp. 19-24. (Reprinted as "Elegancia, ecologia, y garzas," in Trocha (Villavicencio), vol. 4, no. 29, pp. 12, 17-18; and no. 30, pp. 16-17.)
1978.   Rebellion in the Colombian Llanos: The Arauca affair of 1917.   The Americas, vol. 34, April, pp. 502-531.
MARTIN, F. O.
1929.   Explorations in Colombia.   Geogr. Rev., vol. 19, pp. 621-637, illus.
MORENO, JUAN NEPOMUCENO
1832.   Gaceta de la Nueva Granada, no. 9, enero 29.

ORTEGA RICAURTE, ENRIQUE
  1943.   Villavicencio (1842-1942), monografía historica, 110 pp.   Prensa de la
           Biblioteca Nacional, Bogotá.
PLAZAS OLARTE, HUMBERTO
  1944.   Los territorios nacionales, pp. 139-159.   Facultad de Ciencias Econo-
           micas y Jurídicas, Universidad Tavernana, Bogotá.
TAYLOR, GEORGE ROGERS, ed.
  1972.   The Turner thesis concerning the role of the frontier in American histo-
           ry, ed. 3.   Heath-Raytheon, Boston.
WEST, ROBERT O.
  1962.   The geography of Colombia.   Pp. 3-21 *in* "The Caribbean: Contempo-
           rary Colombia," A. Curtis Wilgus, ed.   Gainesville, Florida.

JANE M. LOY

Remote-sensing Analysis of Prehistoric Human Occupations in the Chaco Canyon Region, New Mexico

Principal Investigator: Thomas R. Lyons, National Park Service, Albuquerque, New Mexico.

Grant No. 1177:   For a remote-sensing analysis of prehistoric human occupations at Chaco Canyon, New Mexico.

The Remote Sensing Project of the Chaco Center, a joint operation of the National Park Service and the University of New Mexico, has for several years been investigating various remote-sensing techniques. The purpose of these studies was the application of remote-sensing methods to problems of archeology and cultural-resource management. The principal target of study was Chaco Canyon National Monument in northwest New Mexico. Much of this research was supported by a grant from the National Geographic Society, and results are embodied in the reports listed here in the References.

Research was conducted in a number of areas of remote sensing, including theory of data use, aerial image interpretation in archeological survey, aerial imagery use in archeological excavation, photogrammetric mapping and map interpretation, and analysis of thermal infrared imagery.

Thomas R. Lyons, Remote Sensing Division, Southwest Cultural Resources Center, National Park Service, Albuquerque, was the scientific leader of the project. James I. Ebert, Charles Randall Morrison, and Robert K. Hitchcock were research assistants. In addition, the following authors of reports contributed to the project: Dwight L. Drager, Richard W. Loose, and Basil G. Pouls.

Theory

For archeology as well as for other disciplines some remote-sensing procedures provide for the simultaneous collection of several categories of data, e.g., cultural, floral, pedological, geological. Aerial black-and-white prints and color transparencies were found in our investigations to be excellent tools for site location and prediction and for associated environmental studies.

Inference plays an essential part in the interpretation of aerial imagery. Recognition patterns are developed and, with some knowledge of the significance of shapes and tonal variations in an image, inferences can be drawn concerning the identification of phenomena and the presence of associated features.

Perhaps the most rigid and controlled application of remote-sensing procedures is in photogrammetric mapping. This requires the establishment of surveyed ground control of the target area and aerial stereoscopic photography of a specified type and scale. Accurate site maps have been constructed with the aid of a stereo plotter and the controlled stereo imagery. The technique is particularly useful for large sites and excavations.

Two papers have been published as a result of this project which address themselves to the questions of the general principles of remote sensing and to the applications of remote sensing to archeology (Ebert, 1977; Ebert and Lyons, 1976).

Image Interpretation in Archeological Survey

A number of remote-sensing techniques were found to be useful as tools for site exploration and discovery. The simplest approach is the first scan examination of aerial imagery in an effort to identify sites and culturally disturbed areas. Though many sites are too small to be seen even on large-scale imagery, other cultural activity areas can often be recognized. In and around Chaco Canyon National Monument, the primary area of study, an extensive network of prehistoric roadways was identified and mapped from aerial photography. In this case the roadway network could not have been mapped without the use of aerial photography. Perhaps the most efficient use of aerial photography in archeology is not in finding unknown sites, but rather in accurately plotting sites that are located through aerial or ground search techniques.

The current method of mapping sites during archeological survey is to mark their locations on a United States Geological Survey topographic quadrangle of the area being surveyed. Since the minimum contour interval on USGS topo sheets is 20 feet, it is often extremely difficult to identify the exact location of the site with any degree of confidence. Aerial photographs, however, contain much more information than does a topographic representation of the surface of the earth. Natural and cultural features are clearly represented, and the position of an archeological site can be easily identified by its relationships to the obvious physical features near it. Further, the site can readily be relocated at a later date if necessary. Loose and Lyons (1976b) point out several ways in which aerial photography can increase the efficiency of archeological survey.

The interpretation of imagery other than photographic can sometimes be of use as an exploratory technique. Loose (1976) discusses the use of an airborne videotape system to identify linear features. Videotape is very effective for this purpose because of the inherent properties of television systems which tend to emphasize linearities.

Excavation and Analysis

Remote-sensing techniques were found to be useful when employed in conjunction with archeological excavations. The documentation of test trenches can be accomplished with great precision when recorded on aerial photographs. Also, the comparison of aerial photos taken at varying times of the year, or of those taken before and after erosion or natural succession has occurred, often shows patterns on the land which cannot be discerned by looking at a single photo. Both of these methods were used in the study discussed by Loose and Lyons (1976a).

Remote sensing also contributes to the interpretation or analysis of archeological phenomena. The extensive roadway network discussed above connected many of the large Bonito Phase pueblos in Chaco Canyon with each other and with other far-flung communities. Through the use of remote-sensing techniques the extent of the roadway network became apparent, and a possible explanation for the existence of the roads was suggested. Lyons and Hitchcock (1977) discuss the work that was carried out in this connection.

Mapping and Map Interpretation

One of the most important projects carried out was the development of highly accurate mapping procedures for use in archeology. Most archeological mapping is done by plane table and alidade field procedures. The mapping discussed by Pouls, Lyons, and Ebert (1976) was shown to be more economical than field mapping when applied to large sites such as those in Chaco Canyon. The accuracy of photogrammetric mapping greatly exceeds that of more traditional procedures. The knowledge gained has already been applied to current excavations being carried out by the National Park Service. A program of phase mapping, that is, photogrammetric mapping of the site at the end of each field season, has been instituted in conjunction with the long-term excavation of Pueblo Alto, a major Bonito Phase site in Chaco Canyon National Monument. To date, photogrammetric maps have been completed (see

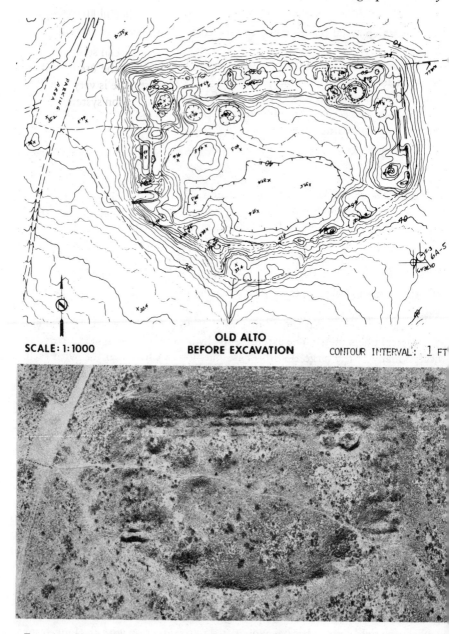

OLD ALTO
BEFORE EXCAVATION

CONTOUR INTERVAL: 1 FT

Fig. 1.   *Upper:* Photogrammetric map of Pueblo Alto Ruin, Chaco Canyon National Monument, prior to excavation (contour interval, 1 ft.). *Lower:* Aerial photograph, 22 December 1972, of Pueblo Alto Ruin prior to excavation.

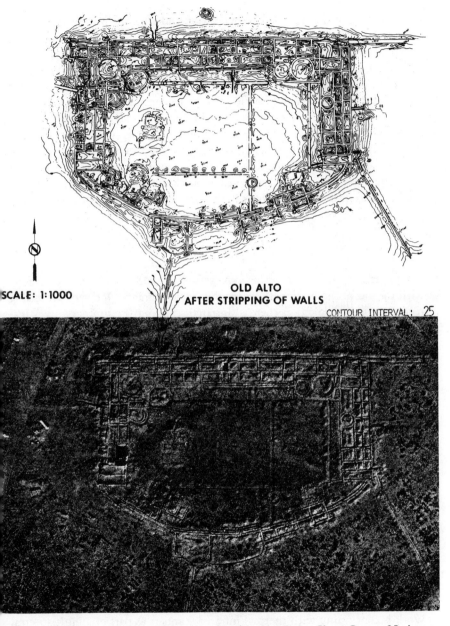

SCALE: 1:1000

OLD ALTO
AFTER STRIPPING OF WALLS

CONTOUR INTERVAL: 25

Fig. 2. *Upper:* Photogrammetric map of Pueblo Alto Ruin, Chaco Canyon National Monument, after stripping of masonry walls (contour interval, 25 cm.). *Lower:* Aerial photograph, 12 September 1976, of Pueblo Lato Ruin after stripping of masonry walls.

figs. 1 and 2) of the site prior to excavation and after the initial stripping of walls.

Because photogrammetric maps are extremely accurate, they can be used for the development of data difficult to obtain in any other way. Drager (1976) shows how photogrammetric data can be evaluated in a manner which may shed some light on prehistoric behavior patterns, as do Lyons, Ebert, and Hitchcock (1976). The use of satellite imagery provides a broad perspective and allows a truly regional viewpoint from which to begin to analyze interactions not only between various human groups but also between man and his environment. The discovery that the Anasazi roadway network served to tie the settlements in Chaco Canyon with resource areas lying around the fringe of the San Juan Basin could not have been documented without the use of a map based on aerial photography and satellite imagery.

Experimentation

Experimentation with other remote-sensing techniques was also begun with the aid of the National Geographic Society grant. One very promising technique in archeology is thermal infrared scanning. Preliminary investigations in the Chaco Canyon area show that, at least in an arid environment, thermal IR can be a very useful technique for discovering certain types of archeological phenomena.

In the desert, thermal IR can be used to isolate water retentive features. Archeologically, this generally means masonry structures which tend to trap water, subterranean structures such as pithouses which contain fill materials with different water retentive properties than the surrounding soil, old roads or trails with concave cross-sections, water control features (on natural drainages) used to slow or divert runoff for agricultural purposes, and any other cultural disturbance of the natural environment which would tend to change the water retentive characteristics of the area of disturbance.

Initial investigations of the first thermal IR mission conducted in the area of Kin Bineola, a major Chaco outlying ruin situated in a large alluvial basin, identified an Anasazi dam built to capture runoff from a mesa top as it exited from the mouth of an arroyo and thus irrigate a large cultivable area (fig. 3). Also identified on the thermal IR imagery was a possible spring about 150 meters from Kin Bineola which may have served as a water source for the pueblo's prehistoric inhabitants. Prehistoric use of the spring is unverified. Work is continuing with thermal infrared scanners as part of a multispectral scanning experiment. No final report has been prepared to date, since the project has not yet been completed.

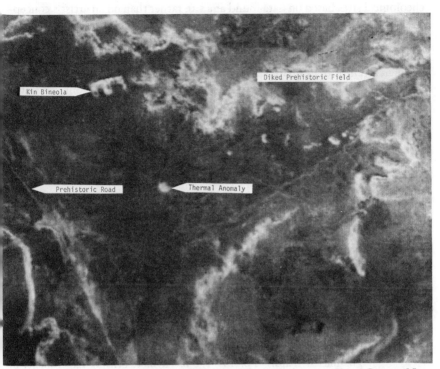

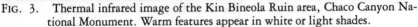

FIG. 3.   Thermal infrared image of the Kin Bineola Ruin area, Chaco Canyon National Monument. Warm features appear in white or light shades.

Summary

Many of the procedures examined in this project have proved to be extremely useful to archeologists and will no doubt continue to grow in use.

The major uses of remote-sensing techniques at this time are for exploration and image interpretation. Experimental testing of new types of remote-sensing instruments is also being carried out to determine the applicability of these new devices to archeology.

Many of the projects supported by the present grant are continuing. Photogrammetric mapping is being carried beyond the simple production of topographic maps of archeological sites (Borcher, 1980; Ireland, 1980). Through the use of computer analysis, digitized versions of the maps are being prepared for the determination of volumetric data which can be most useful to archeologists who are in the planning stages of excavation. Also, computer procedures are anticipated which will allow the graphic reconstruction of archeological sites based on data found at a site rather than on an artist's conception of what the site should have looked like. (McCharen, 1979).

Experimentation with thermal scanning (Williams, 1981) and false-color infrared imagery (Ehrenhard, 1980; Ehrenhard and Wills, 1980) will continue in an attempt to evaluate various remote sensing instruments for their use in archeology. New types of platforms—bipods, balloons, airfoils, and others—have been and will continue to be tested as ways to elevate cameras for site recording (Klausner, 1980; Boyer, 1980).

REFERENCES

BORCHER, PERRY E.
  1980.   Terrestrial photogrammetry of cliff dwellings in the canyons of Arizona. Pp. 347-370 *in* "Cultural Resources Remote Sensing," Thomas R. Lyons and Frances Joan Mathien, eds.   Cultural Resources Management Division, National Park Service, Washington, D. C.
BOYER, W. KENT
  1980.   Bipod photogrammetry.   Pp. 327-346 *in* "Cultural Resources Remote Sensing," Thomas R. Lyons and Frances Joan Mathien, eds.   Cultural Resources Management Division, National Park Service, Washington, D. C.
DRAGER, DWIGHT L.
  1976.   Anasazi population estimates with the aid of data derived from photogrammetric maps.   Pp. 157-176 *in* "Remote Sensing Experiments in Cultural Resource Studies: Non-destructive Methods of Archeological Exploration, Survey and Analysis," Thomas R. Lyons, ed.   Reports of the Chaco Center no. 1.   Chaco Center, National Park Service, Albuquerque, New Mexico.
EBERT, JAMES I.
  1977.   Remote sensing within an archeological research framework: Methods, economics, and theory.   Pp. 169-201 *in* "Aerial Remote Sensing Techniques in Archeology," Thomas R. Lyons and Robert K. Hitchcock, eds.   Reports of the Chaco Center no. 2.   Chaco Center, National Park Service, Albuquerque, New Mexico.
EBERT, JAMES I., and LYONS, THOMAS R.
  1976.   The role of remote sensing in a regional archeological research design: A case study.   Pp. 5-9 *in* "Remote Sensing Experiments in Cultural Resource Studies: Non-destructive Methods of Archeological Exploration, Survey, and Analysis," Thomas R. Lyons, ed.   Reports of the Chaco Center, no. 1.   Chaco Center, National Park Service, Albuquerque, New Mexico.
EHRENHARD, JOHN E.
  1980.   Cultural resource inventory of the Big Cypress Swamp: An experiment in remote sensing.   Pp. 105-118 *in* "Cultural Resources Remote Sens-

ing," Thomas R. Lyons and Frances Joan Mathien, eds. Cultural Resources Management Division, National Park Service, Washington, D. C.

EHRENHARD, ELLEN B., and WILLS, W. H.
1980.   Ninety Six national historic site South Carolina.   Pp. 229-292 *in* "Cultural Resources Remote Sensing," Thomas R. Lyons and Frances Joan Mathien, eds.   Cultural Resources Management Division, National Park Service, Washington, D. C.

IRELAND, ARTHUR K.
1980.   Cost effective mapping.   Pp. 371-388 *in* "Cultural Resources Remote Sensing," Thomas R. Lyons and Frances Joan Mathien, eds.   Cultural Resources Management Division, National Park Service, Washington D. C.

KLAUSNER, STEPHANIE
1980.   Bipod photography: Procedures for photographic mapping of archeological site.   Pp. 293-326 *in* "Cultural Resources Remote Sensing," Thomas R. Lyons and Frances Joan Mathien, eds.   Cultural Resources Management Division, National Park Service, Washington D. C.

LOOSE, RICHARD W.
1976.   Air-borne TV as an archeological remote sensing tool.   Pp. 77-80 *in* "Remote Sensing Experiments in Cultural Resource Studies: Non-destructive Methods of Archeological Exploration, Survey, and Analysis," Thomas R. Lyons, ed.   Reports of the Chaco Center no. 1.   Chaco Center, National Park Service, Albuquerque, New Mexico.

LOOSE, RICHARD W., and LYONS, THOMAS R.
1976a.   The Chetro Ketl field: A planned water control system in Chaco Canyon.   Pp. 133-156 *in* "Remote Sensing Experiments in Cultural Resource Studies: Non-destructive Methods of Archeological Exploration, Survey, and Analysis," Thomas R. Lyons, ed.   Reports of the Chaco Center no. 1.   Chaco Center, National Park Service, Albuquerque, New Mexico.

1976b.   Use of aerial photos in archeological survey along the Lower Chaco River drainage.   Idem, pp. 69-71.

LYONS, THOMAS R.; EBERT, JAMES I.; and HITCHCOCK, ROBERT K.
1976.   Archaeological analysis and imagery of Chaco Canyon region, New Mexico.   Pp. 304-306 *in* "ERST-1: A New Window on our Planet," Richard S. Williams and William D. Carter, eds.   U. S. Geol. Surv. Prof. Paper 929.

LYONS, THOMAS R., and HITCHCOCK, ROBERT K.
1977.   Remote sensing interpretation of an Anasazi land route system.   Pp. 111-134 *in* "Aerial Remote Sensing Techniques in Archeology," Thomas R. Lyons and Robert K. Hitchcock, eds.   Report of the Chaco Center no. 2.   Chaco Center, National Park Service, Albuquerque, New Mexico.

MCCHAREN, JOE, W.
1979.   Users manual for CHACO MESH.   New Mexico Engineering Research Institute, University of New Mexico, Albuquerque, New Mexico.

POULS, BASIL G.; LYONS, THOMAS R.; and EBERT, JAMES I.
   1976.   Photogrammetric mapping and digitization of prehistoric architecture: Techniques and applications in Chaco Canyon National Monument. Pp. 103-114 *in* "Remote Sensing Experiments in Cultural Resource Studies: Non-destructive Methods of Archeological Exploration, Survey, and Analysis," Thomas R. Lyons, ed.   Reports of the Chaco Center no. 1.   Chaco Center, National Park Service, Albuquerque, New Mexico.
WILLIAMS, DAVID H.
   1981.   Computer recognition of prehistoric roads.   Final Report, Schellenger Research Laboratories, Electrical Engineering Department, University of Texas at El Paso, Texas.

THOMAS R. LYONS
DWIGHT L. DRAGER

Vocalization in Wild Red Wolves and Coyotes

Principal Investigator: Howard McCarley, Austin College, Sherman, Texas.

Grant No. 1163: For a comparative study of vocalization in red wolves, coyotes, and hybrids.[1]

This study was designed to find out whether vocalization patterns of wild coyotes *(Canis latrans)* and wild red wolves (*C. rufus*) were sufficiently species-specific for field identification. Implicit in the study was the development of techniques useful for assessing present red wolf-coyote interrelationships.

Vocal responses from wild canids were evoked by a variety of methods, but mostly by human vocal imitations. Spontaneous sounds were obtained when and where possible. Wild canid vocalizations were recorded in Arkansas (Stone County); Louisiana (Calcasieu[2] and Cameron[2] Parishes); Oklahoma (Bryan, Leflore, Marshall, and McCurtain Counties); and Texas (Archer, Brazoria, Chambers,[2] Duval, Fannin, Grayson, Jefferson,[2] Lamar, Matagorda, Nacogdoches, Red River, San Patricio, Titus, and Webb Counties). The majority of recordings were obtained between January 1973 and September 1974.

Analysis of tape recordings was made with a Kay Electric Co. Sound Analyzer (Sonagraph). Evaluation of resulting sonagrams provided data on (1) pattern or configuration of vocalization, (2) Hz of fundamental frequency at beginning, middle, and end of sound, and (3) duration of sound.

A baseline for the range of variation of coyote vocalization was established using coyote populations in three south Texas counties (Duval, San Patricio, and Webb). These populations were selected because there was no suggestion of hybridization with other canid groups (Paradiso and Nowak, 1971).

---

[1] This study was made possible by grants from the National Geographic Society, the World Wildlife Fund, and a sabbatical leave by Austin College. Gracious help and cooperation were received from many ranchers and individuals. I am particularly indebted to Glynn Riley and Aaron Long, DVM, for without their advice, help, and hospitality the work would have been much more difficult. Rodney Nicely, Ray Thomas, and Larry Reaves were my research assistants, and I am grateful for their help, voices, and companionship.

[2] Counties included in currently recognized red-wolf range and the only areas where presumed red wolves were heard and/or recorded.

Determination of the range of variation for red-wolf vocalization was considerably more difficult than for coyotes. Russell and Shaw (1971) published a sonagram of the first 2.4 seconds of a presumed red-wolf howl. The quality of reproduction was too poor to be of much value, and their discussion of harmonics, pitch, and duration was difficult to reconcile with my data from the same area. A recording of a captive red wolf, made by Mrs. R. T. Odum of Vinton, Louisiana, in December 1971 was lent to me. Considerable harmonic distortion and wind noise were present in her recording, but I was able to produce some sonagrams of the howls of this captive animal ("Lobo"). Recordings were secured also of a red wolf in the Oklahoma City Zoo. Whether these animals were good red wolves is, however, open to interpretation. Pimlott and Joslin (1968) and others reported the howl of a red wolf to be similar to that of the timber wolf (*C. lupus*), and with the help of L. David Mech and Fred Harrington recordings of wild *lupus* were secured in Superior National Forest. Within the red-wolf range, vocalization responses ranged from those very similar to timber wolves and captive red wolves to those clearly from coyotes. Consequently, to arrive at any sort of standard for red-wolf vocalization, I was forced into the circular reasoning that in the red-wolf range those animals vocalizing most like captive red wolves and wild *lupus* and least like coyotes were presumed red wolves.[3]

Comparison of Red-wolf and Coyote Vocalization

On the basis of available data the evoked vocal repertoire of coyotes and red wolves included sounds of about the same type, with the exception of two coyote sounds I have named the *laugh* and the *gargle*. The infrequent occurrence, however, of these two sounds in evoked coyote responses reduced their usefulness as a distinguishing characteristic.

Evaluation of the sonagrams of chorus responses of all canid groups from the south-central United States showed an almost complete continuum from the very chopped-up response of coyotes to the very smooth and harmonious response of presumed red wolves. The choppiness and irregularity of coyote responses were due to the short duration of long sounds, the sharp rise and fall in pitch of the long sounds, and the presence of many short sounds. In red wolves the smoothness was the result of much longer duration of long sounds.

---

[3] On December 4-6, 1974, recordings of the vocalization of 11 known red wolves were obtained in the Point Defiance and Woodland Park Zoos in Tacoma and Seattle, Washington. Preliminary review of these recordings substantiates the discussion on comparison of red-wolf and coyote vocalization.

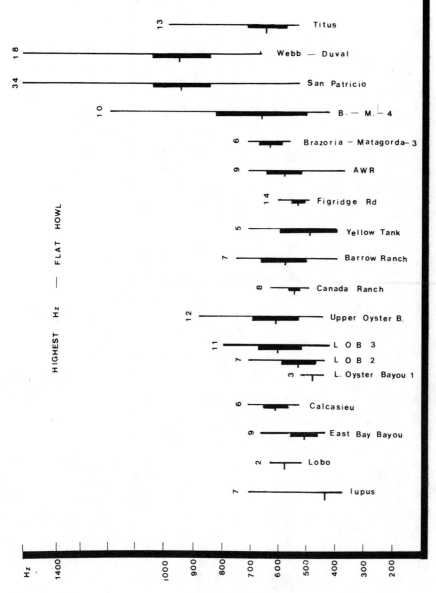

FIG. 1.   The mean, extremes, and 2x the SE of the mean on each side of the mean for the highest fundamental Hz of flat howls of 16 canid groups from Texas and Louisiana, one captive red wolf (lobo), and one *C. lupus* group from Minnesota. Sample size is shown at top of each plotting.

TABLE 1.   Variation in Fundamental Frequencies of Flat Howls of Selected Canid Groups

The mean, standard error of mean and extremes are shown for beginning, middle (highest), and ending frequencies. The same data are given for duration.

Locality	N	Beginning Hz	Middle Hz	Ending Hz	Duration
San Patrico Co.[1]	34	680±25(475-1260)	946±53(528-1500)	688±26(366-1126)	2.0±.12(1.0-3.8)
Webb-Duval Cos.[1]	18	639±19(495- 792)	943±54(660-1500)	697±23(563- 880)	2.4±.18(1.4-4.2)
Brazoria-Matagorda[2]	23	682±28(594- 935)	736±43(420-1188)	667±42(396-1126)	2.4±.20(1.2-4.4)
Titus Co.[3]	13	605±33(440- 880)	638±37(528- 990)	592±40(420- 935)	3.0±.18(1.6-3.9)
AWR[4]	9	511±60(375- 630)	579±32(375- 704)	566±44(475- 660)	2.1±.78(1.0-3.2)
Upper Oyster Bayou[4]	12	429±13(375- 528)	501±19(440- 660)	435±19(375- 594)	3.5±.42(1.0-5.3)
Lower Oyster Bayou[4]	11	555±15(420- 594)	603±43(420- 792)	412±26(295- 563)	3.0±.24(1.9-3.9)
Barrow Ranch[4]	7	482±56(375- 660)	581±42(396- 750)	482±33(396- 563)	4.2±.34(2.6-4.8)
Calcasieu Parish[4]	6	573±44(475- 660)	608±23(528- 704)	562±54(440- 704)	5.5±.41(3.8-5.8)
Canada Ranch[4]	8	545±35(495- 594)	545±13(495- 630)	486±34(475- 563)	4.9±.03(4.8-4.9)
Yellow Tank[4]	5	467±41(375- 630)	491±50(396- 704)	502±49(396- 704)	3.8±.71(1.2-5.7)
East Bay Bayou[4]	9	438±13(396- 528)	507±24(440- 660)	420±16(375- 495)	3.6±.57(1.0-5.3)

[1] Baseline reference for coyotes.
[2] Presumed hybrid population.
[3] Typical east Texas canids.
[4] Packs within currently recognized red-wolf range. The Yellow Tank and East Bay Bayou packs are probably the best examples of red wolves.

The most common vocalization of both red wolves and coyotes was a sound designated the flat howl. It was easily identified and was the most useful single sound type by which to distinguish the two forms. Paul Joslin (in an undated report to the IUCN on the status of the red wolf) said, "The only reasonably reliable way to differentiate red wolves from coyotes in the field was on the basis of voice characteristics. The coyote has a peculiarly sharp rise in pitch to its call which the wolf call lacks. Moreover, its call is much higher in pitch generally and each call is usually of much shorter duration."

Data presented in table 1 and figure 1, however, show that there was no sharp statistical distinction in frequencies (pitch) and duration of known coyote howls (San Patricio, Webb, and Duval Counties) from the howls of all animals in the red-wolf range. The data in table 1 for the East Bay Bayou and Yellow Tank animals describe the variation and pitch of red-wolf flat howls. Figure 1 shows a treatment of the highest fundamental frequencies in graphic form. In this case a nonoverlap of two standard errors of the mean indicates a significant difference at the 0.05 percent level. On this basis only the San Patricio, Webb, and Duval County samples differed significantly from all other samples. Similar treatment of beginning and ending frequencies and duration showed similar results. Thus there was a wide overlap of lower Hz of coyote howls with upper Hz of presumed red-wolf howls. These data do support Joslin's statement, but they show also that in the south-central United States in 1973 and 1974 a simple evaluation and comparison of fundamental Hz and duration was inadequate to distinguish all animals as either coyote or red wolf, simply because one does not know where to draw the dividing line.

An additional and very helpful diagnostic clue to the identity of the vocalizing animal was the manner in which the flat howl began. In coyotes the highest fundamental frequency of the howl was usually achieved within 0.2 second from beginning and nearly always prior to the midpoint. Presumed red-wolf howls did not achieve peak frequency until at least 0.6 second after beginning and often not until after the midpoint of the howl had passed. I think Joslin was referring to this in his comment on the "peculiarly sharp rise in pitch of coyotes." Further, the last 0.2-0.4 second of a coyote flat howl was generally of the same amplitude as preceding sound and in the last 0.1-0.2 second there was usually a sharp drop in pitch. In red wolves the howl (as in *lupus*) ordinarily lost amplitude gradually in the last portion of the howl, and while the pitch sometimes dropped, it was gradual rather than sharp.

In summary, this study revealed that there were, on the average, distinguishable differences in the vocalization of coyotes and red wolves, but these differences were more qualitative than quantitative. Diagnosis depended largely on a subjective judgment based on type of vocalization, dominant frequency, duration, and vocalization configuration. Identification of animals within the red-wolf range was fairly clear for coyotes and red wolves, which represented opposite extremes of a spectrum of variation. The presence of hybrid type animals with intermediate vocalizations greatly complicated the identification and those animals vocalizing in an intermediate manner cannot always be positively identified as to species.

This study is continuing under a contract effective November 1, 1974, with the Regional Office, U. S. Fish and Wildlife Service, Albuquerque, New Mexico, using my evaluation of recordings made by U. S. Fish and Wildlife Service personnel. The objective of this ongoing research is to use the techniques developed with support from National Geographic Society and World Wildlife Fund to help evaluate and assess the distribution and social relationships of the kinds of canids now present in the red-wolf range.

REFERENCES

McCARLEY, HOWARD
   1978.   Vocalizations of red wolves *(Canis rufus)*.   Journ. Mamm., vol. 59,
            no. 1 (February), pp. 27-35.
PARADISO, JOHN L., and NOWAK, R. M.
   1971.   A report on the taxonomic status and distribution of the red wolf.
            Spec. Sci. Rpt. Wildl. no. 145, U. S. Fish and Wildl. Serv., 36 pp.
PIMLOTT, DOUGLAS H., and JOSLIN, PAUL W.
   1968.   The status and distribution of the red wolf.   Trans. 33d Amer. Wildl.
            and Nat. Res. Conf., Washington, D. C., pp. 373-389.
RUSSELL, DENNIS N., and SHAW, JAMES H.
   1971.   Distribution and relative density of the red wolf in Texas.   Proc. 25th
            S.E. Assoc. Game and Fish Comm., pp. 131-137.

HOWARD McCARLEY

Vegetation Investigation in the North Cascade Range of Washington, 1973

Principal Investigator: Richard N. Mack, Department of Botany, Washington State University, Pullman.

Grant No. 1208:   In support of a study of forest types of the Washington North Cascade Range.

The field season from mid-June to late August, 1973, was spent in the study area, the North Cascade Range of Washington. Fieldwork consisted of locating all potentially undisturbed stands which would be sampled in detail for climax status. All the stands within 100 meters of roads and trails in the Okanogan National Forest were reconnoitered. Lack of past disturbance was based on three criteria: (1) No obvious logging or extensive grazing activity in the stand; (2) the lack of any charcoal layers in the O soil horizon within the first decimeter of mineral soil depth; and (3) presence of large-boled tree individuals.

Stands were then reconnoitered using a standard semiquantitative assessment of the coverage (dominance) classes of each species in the stand (Daubenmire, 1959; Daubenmire and Daubenmire, 1968). In addition, the elevation aspect percent slope and depth to bedrock of the site was recorded. Owing to the extensive logging and burn history in the National Forest, many stands proved unsuitable for further sampling. In all, 40 stands were found in which there had been little or no disturbance (including fire). The majority of these were higher elevation forest types (reflecting the greater disturbance at lower elevations nearer Winthrop and Mazama, Washington). These high elevation forest types fit well within the habitat types described by Daubenmire and Daubenmire (1968) for eastern Washington and northern Idaho, and types recognized by McLean (1970) in the Similkameen Valley of southern British Columbia.

Habitat types recognized on the east slope of the North Cascade in Washington during this study are:

Pseudotsuga menziesii-Physocarpus malvaceus
Pseudotsuga menziesii-Calamagrostis rubescens
Tsuga heterophylla-Pachistima myrsinites
Abies lasiocarpa-Pachistima myrsinites
Abies lasiocarpa-Vaccinium scoparium
Pinus albicaulis-Abies lasiocarpa

Initially, this study was to be expanded into a comprehensive classification of the plant communities in this region. It was my hope that the initial reconnaissance conducted with the funds provided by the National Geographic Society would form the basis for this larger study. However, the U. S. Forest Service was unable to provide this support and the study was terminated after June 1974. Information derived from the fieldwork in 1973 did provide the basis for a survey of the pollen spectra in these forests, published in 1978 (Mack et al.).

The support of the National Geographic Society was gratefully acknowledged in this publication.

REFERENCES

DAUBENMIRE, R.
    1959.   A canopy-coverage method of vegetation analysis.   Northwest Sci.,
             vol. 33, pp. 43-66.
DAUBENMIRE, R., and DAUBENMIRE, JEAN B.
    1968.   Forest vegetation of eastern Washington and Northern Idaho.   Wash.
             Agric. Expt. Sta. Tech. Bull. 60.
MACK, RICHARD N.; BRYANT, VAUGHN N., JR.; and PELL, WILLIAM
    1978.   Modern forest pollen spectra from eastern Washington and northern
             Idaho.   Bot. Gaz., vol. 139, no. 2, pp. 249-255.
MCLEAN, A.
    1970.   Plant communities of the Similkameen Valley, British Columbia and
             their relationships to soil.   Ecol Monogr., vol. 40, pp. 403-424.

RICHARD N. MACK

Biology of the Australian Desert Charadrii, *Peltohyas* and *Stiltia*

Principal Investigator: Gordon L. Maclean, University of Natal, Pietermaritzburg, South Africa.

Grant No. 1253:   To study the biology of the Australian desert shorebirds *Peltohyas* and *Stiltia*.

This résumé covers the work done by me in Australia during the period July 1974 to February 1975. The purpose of the expedition was to study the breeding biology of the Australian dotterel *(Peltohyas australis)* and the Australian pratincole *(Stiltia isabella)*. My wife accompanied me and acted as field assistant throughout the study. We succeeded in answering most of the questions about *Stiltia* that we had set out to answer, but *Peltohyas* proved to be a more difficult subject to study than we had anticipated. *Peltohyas* did not breed anywhere in Australia during our stay, and so we got no information on breeding biology, but we did accumulate a lot of information about its ecology, behavior, and systematic position.

Itinerary

During July and August 1974 we took a car trip from Canberra westward as far as the Flinders Ranges in South Australia. On the way we stopped over in Kerang, Victoria, to visit Vic Lowe and his son Tom, who have had both study species nesting in their area; however, it was too early for the arrival of *Stiltia,* and *Peltohyas* was absent. Everywhere it was raining and had been doing so for the past 18 months, so that the movements of the birds were greatly affected. Furthermore, vegetation was tall, even in the arid zones, and birds were hard to find.

On our return journey to Canberra we spent much time in the region between the Flinders Ranges and Broken Hill, New South Wales, but again we found neither species. After the 16th International Ornithological Congress in Canberra, we went to Fowlers Gap Arid Zone Research Station and remained there from September 1974 to the end of January 1975. Both species were present at least part of the time. We also made two trips north to the vicinity of Tibooburra, where both species were common and where *Stiltia* was breeding in large numbers.

During February we traveled north to Alice Springs and Mount Isa. *Stiltia* was present at Mount Isa, but we did not see any *Peltohyas* on this trip. We returned to South Africa on February 13, 1975.

Results

Peltohyas australis was common on Fowlers Gap and northward throughout the study period. It occurred in flocks of 2 to 100 birds, most of which were initially in breeding plumage, but later on most of the birds were in eclipse plumage. This was the first surprise of this study, because eclipse plumage has never been reported in this bird. The breeding plumage has a strong black pattern on the head, neck, and chest; this pattern is lost in nearly all nonbreeding adults. Specimens were collected and checked to confirm that they were adults in nonbreeding condition and not just immatures.

The second discovery was that *Peltohyas* is almost exclusively nocturnal, especially in hot weather. On cloudy days it is quite active. On hot sunny days it is inactive, spending its time under bushes or simply out in the open sunshine dozing. As soon as the sun goes down, the flocks become suddenly active and begin to feed.

The food of *Peltohyas* is said to consist mainly, if not entirely, of insects, but in fact we found that this species feeds mainly, and sometimes almost exclusively, on plant material, ranging from succulent leaves of a variety of indigenous plants, common to the claypans on which these birds usually live, to seeds and inflorescences. They do, however, take some insect food, notably small beetles and ants. They appear never to drink and are quite independent of water.

Peltohyas possesses a large salt gland supraorbitally, with which it no doubt processes excess electrolytes in the body fluids, obtained from its food. The histology of these glands will be looked at when time permits; they are at present in tubes of fixative in my laboratory. I also collected gonads for histological study. Toward the end of the study period it seemed as if some of the adults were coming into breeding plumage, but there was no sign of breeding behavior at all.

General behavior patterns were studied in detail. They all resemble those of the plovers and not at all those of glareolids. My observations therefore confirm those of Bock who studied the osteology and morphology of *Peltohyas* and concluded that it was a plover and not a courser.

Peltohyas was highly nomadic, even during the study period, coming and going in what seemed to be an unpredictable way. These movements were not apparently associated with rain. It was interesting that nearly all the arid-zone bird species bred during the spring and early summer at Fowlers Gap, but *Peltohyas* did not. The reasons for this are not clear, but my impressions are that *Peltohyas* is a winter breeder throughout its range, although a few pairs may nest as late as December or as early as February. This needs confirmation. "Out-of-season" nesting may in some way be affected by rainfall.

The first flock of *Stiltia isabella* was seen over Fowlers Gap on October 1, 1974, but it did not stay. Small flocks were seen for short periods at local dams during October, but none stayed for more than a day. At the beginning of November *Stiltia* was well into its breeding season north of Tibooburra, New South Wales. The birds were nesting on gibber plains within about 2 kilometers of a small water-filled pan. The first chicks were about 4 days old, one other set of eggs was hatching, but most of the eggs were fresh or half incubated. At the end of the second week of November several more clutches had been laid, and there were several broods of young about.

Adult pratincoles were nesting in small colonies (a fact never mentioned in the literature), just like the Old World pratincole species. At no time did we find breeding pratincoles more than 2 kilometers from water, either in the form of natural pans or man-made tanks. The adults fed mostly around the waters, catching some of their food on the wing but most on the ground. Both sexes incubated the clutch of two eggs, nest-relief occurring about every 2 hours.

Ambient and incubation temperatures were taken under a great variety of conditions; the nesting adults are capable of withstanding very high ambient temperatures. On hatching, the chicks are led by the parents to a nearby bush or grass tuft where the chicks stay in the shade. The parents bring food from nearby, or from the waterside, carrying it in the bill. The parent lands, runs to the chicks' refuge, and calls them out for feeding. The chicks then return to the refuge.

Data on food and feeding of adults were also obtained. The adults also drink freely. Behavior of adults shows that they are very closely related to the pratincoles of the Old World, although they show strong affinities with the coursers too; they are, however, true pratincoles.

By late November *Stiltia* had begun to nest on the shorelines of natural and artificial waters on and around Fowlers Gap, so that studies could continue in this region. By the end of December all pratincoles had left the area on their northward migration, and they were encountered again on the airfield at Mount Isa in mid-February.

REFERENCES

Jesson, R. A., and Maclean, Gordon L.
  1976.   Salt glands in the neonatal Australian pratincole.   Emu, vol. 76,
           p. 227.
Maclean, Gordon L.
  1976a.   Rainfall and avian breeding seasons in north-western New South Wales
           in spring and summer 1974-75.   Emu, vol. 76, pp. 139-142.
  1976b.   A field study of the Australian pratincole.   Emu, vol. 76, pp. 171-182.
  1976c.   A field study of the Australian dotterel.   Emu, vol. 76, pp. 207-215.
  1977.   Comparative notes on black-fronted and red-kneed dotterels.   Emu,
           vol. 77, pp. 199-207.

                                                              Gordon L. Maclean

Archeological Research in the Ariari River Basin, Western Meta, Colombia

Principal Investigator: John P. Marwitt, University of Akron, Akron, Ohio.

Grant Nos. 1199, 1338.   For fieldwork leading to a construction of an archeological chronology for the Ariari River Basin, Colombia.[1]

There is very little archeological information available on the plains *(llanos)* of eastern Colombia, since archeological research there is still in its infancy. The limited data on hand are the result of surveys and test excavations that have been conducted only since about 1972. Moreover, information is restricted to a single locality in the vast expanse of the lowlands. Neither museums nor private collections contain specimens of prehistoric artifacts from the llanos, and the colonists of the region, some of whom were active treasure-hunters in their previous highland homes, have shown little interest in the local sites with their unspectacular pottery and lack of valuable gold objects.

Probably because of the general lack of knowledge, the cultures of the llanos, both historic and prehistoric, are usually presumed to have been small and mobile, constrained by scarce resources and passively recipient of influences from other "more advanced" regions such as the Amazon Basin or the Andean Highlands. However, ethnohistorical evidence (Morey, 1975) suggests that this traditional picture is in error, at least in regard to groups inhabiting the flood plains of the major rivers at the time of European contact. Limited archeological data suggest that the size and complexity of at least some of the prehistoric societies may have been underestimated as well.

Environment

The llanos give the viewer an impression of a uniform lowland plain, but this plain is by no means uniform in regard to such important environmental

---

[1] Fieldwork in the Río Ariari Basin was made possible, in addition to the grants from the National Geographic Society, by funds from the University of Akron Faculty Research Committee. Grateful acknowledgment is made also to Robert V. Morey, Salomón Rivera, James Zeidler, and Alicia Gallo Marwitt for assistance in the field, and to the Instituto Colombiano de Antropolgía for its valuable cooperation.

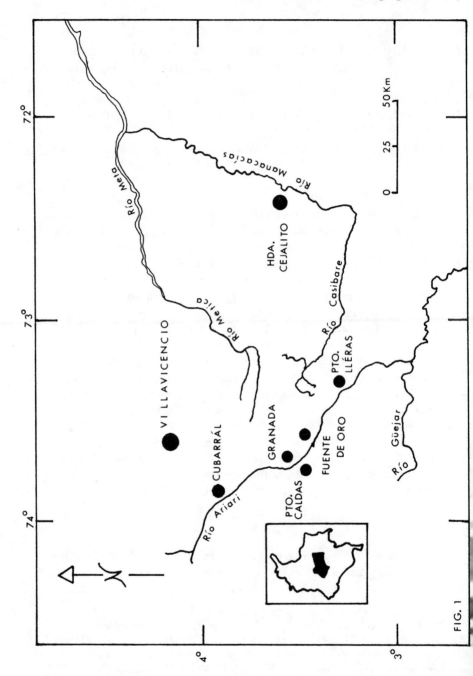

FIG. 1

factors as the availability of arable soil, the danger of seasonal flooding, and the distribution of wild plant and animal life. Soils suitable for sustained cultivation are restricted almost entirely to the flood plains of the major rivers and a few of the smaller streams. Typically the flood plains are rather narrow and are covered by dense gallery forest. Most are annually inundated or are subject to periodic flooding during the long rainy season. Interfluvial savanna soils are lateritic, and even the soils of the flood plain are relatively poor, since the aluvium on which they are based is low in nutrient bases (Brunnschweiler, 1972). But even though they have limited agricultural potential according to modern standards, the river flood plains support the majority of the useful plant and animal resources of the llanos, and with very few exceptions evidence for prehistoric occupation of the region is confined to these comparatively rich bottomlands.

Research in the Ariari Basin

The single area of the llanos where a planned program of archeological research has been undertaken is the upper Ariari River drainage, located in the western third of the Departamento del Meta (Marwitt, Morey, and Zeidler, 1973; Marwitt, 1978). Approximately 235 kilometers in length, the Río Ariari rises in the Páramo of Sumapaz, southeast of Bogotá, and forms a principal affluent of the Río Guaviare, itself a major tributary of the Orinoco. The Ariari transects a number of environmental zones including Andean piedmont, savanna, and hill land (serranía). With its tributaries it drains a significant portion of the best agricultural land in eastern Colombia. In addition to the agricultural potential of the Ariari Basin, the river is strategically located, in that it could have served as a corridor to channel cultural exchanges between the Orinoco and Amazon River Basins and the Andean Highlands.

Archeological surveys have located a total of 24 archeological sites in the Ariari drainage, roughly between Cubarrál in the northwest and Puerto Lléras in the southeast (see fig. 1). With the exception of three sites that were reported by informants to have been occupied during the historic period, archeological remains are confined to the Ariari flood plain and to terraces within a kilometer or so of the river. The absence of sites in the interfluvial savanna presumably indicates that the grasslands were exploited only lightly by the prehistoric peoples who situated their villages near the river because their subsistence economies emphasized the exploitation of riverine and/or gallery forest resources. However, it is possible also that modern patterns of land use could account for an apparent absence of archeological sites in the savanna. Today, these grasslands are used primarily as pasture for cattle, and the heavy grass mat, which is rarely plowed by ranchers, may conceal the remains of earlier human use and occupation.

Many of the Ariari sites are quite large in areal extent, covering as much as 12 acres, and are marked by dense but apparently random accumulations of cultural debris. There are no artificial earthworks or structural remains. Only one site had localized concentrations of refuse which could represent middens associated with the use of particular structures.

Of the 24 surveyed sites, 8 have been tested. All are rather shallow, with cultural material limited to the 30 centimeters or so of dark-gray alluvium that overlies sterile reddish-yellow clay. Local farmers have reported finding pottery more than 100 centimeters below the modern surface, but such reports probably refer to graves excavated for burial urns. These urns are occasionaly found (and unfortunately discarded) by the farmers. No stratification can be seen in the zone of cultural deposition and none of the sites tested to date has produced any evidence of sequent occupations. All appear to reflect unbroken, probably year-round use, judged from the amount of refuse and the lack of any stratigraphic evidence which would indicate abandonment and subsequent reoccupation.

Artifacts

Cultural materials recovered from the test excavations and from surveys include abundant pottery sherds, large manos, cylindrical stone chisels, and polished petalloid stone celts. A single flat cruciform pottery stamp has also been found. It has an incised design on the stamping surface and a conical zoomorphic nubbin or adorno on the top surface to serve as a handle.

Ariari ceramics have provisionally been classified into three wares on the basis of temper. The most common ware, comprising over 50 percent of the total ceramic sample from every site but one, is tempered with crushed sherds. A preliminary analysis of rim fragments indicates that the dominant vessel form is a large deep plain jar with a flat base and slightly rounded walls which are very thick at the base and thin toward the rim. Crushed sherds were also used as tempering material for circular manioc (?) griddles with slightly raised edges, polished top surfaces and rough unfinished bottoms. Other vessel types include small ollas with flared rims and circular bowls with rim lugs and zoomorphic adornos representing fish, turtle or bird heads. Less common are bowls with square outlines, nearly vertical walls, slightly peaked rims and rounded bases.

Only 6 percent of the sherd-tempered sample shows evidence of decoration. Incision is the most common decorative technique, and it occurs along with rim modeling in a band below the rims of bowls and ollas. A few sherds have poorly preserved evidence of a red slip and crude designs of dots, wavy lines, and chevrons applied with white pigment to the slip or to unslipped vessel exteriors.

Second to crushed sherds as a tempering material is coarse sand and grit, which comprises between 20 and 40 percent of the samples from most sites and 62 percent from one site. In a minority of sand-tempered sherds, the sand is combined with small pellets of light-gray clay. Vessel forms for this ware appear to be roughly similar to those in the sherd-tempered category, except that square bowls are absent and a few composite rim vessels are represented. An anthropomorphic burial urn discovered by a farmer near Puerto Limón also has sand temper. The body of the urn is roughly trapezoidal and divided into two parts by a deep groove. On the upper part are incised and modeled facial features. The lower body has two composite U-shaped arms made by incision, and attached to the carinated base of the urn body are modeled legs and feet, which serve as a pedestal. At the time of discovery, the urn mouth was covered with an inverted bowl and the body contained the badly decomposed bones of a child.

Decorated sherds make up less than 5 percent of the sand-tempered sample. Painted designs are the most common and are similar to those found on sherds in the first category, above. Only eight sand-tempered sherds show evidence of surface manipulation by incising and/or modeling.

Seven sherds and an additional partially restorable vessel are tempered with burned tree bark *(cariapé)*. None are decorated. The partially restorable vessel is a jar with a slightly hipped profile, about 80 centimeters high and 50 centimeters in maximum width.

In general, all the ceramics from the Río Ariari show a family resemblance and all are presumed to have been made locally, with the possible exception of the *cariapé*-tempered specimens. Vessels tend to be poorly made, with coarse unsmoothed exteriors and thick walls. Decoration is rare and the designs are poorly executed. Since all the tested sites were shallow, no statement can be made about ceramic change over time within any of the sites. Both sand- and sherd-tempered wares were found at all surveyed and tested sites, and so the geographic distributions of the two wares appear to be same. However, sand tempering is a more common attribute of sherds from sites in the Puerto Caldas area than elsewhere. Three tested sites in the vicinity of Puerto Caldas have from 80 to 50 percent frequencies of sand tempering, compared to an average of 31 percent for four tested sites near Puerto Santander, about 25 kilometers to the southeast. There is no north-to-south gradient in the frequency of the two temper types, however, as shown by the fact that two sites near

Fuente de Oro (approximately midway between Puerto Caldas and Puerto Santander) have a 26 percent frequency of sand temper. Decorated sherds, both painted and surface manipulated, have a high frequency in the southeastern part of the research area. This is partly due to the over all higher frequency of sherd tempering there, but even sand-tempered sherds are more often decorated in collections from near Puerto Santander than in collections from other areas.

Cultural Sequence and Dating

Owing to the shallowness of the sites and the likelihood of postoccupational disturbance, charcoal found in the cultural deposits is not judged suitable for C^{14} age determination. At present, only two absolute dates are available, based on radio-carbon assay of *cariapé*-tempering material from two partially restorable vessels excavated in the vicinity of Puerto Caldas. On the basis of the two dates and associated ceramics, two phases have provisionally been defined (Marwitt, 1978).

The Puerto Caldas phase, which has a single C^{14} date of 760 ± 110 B.C. (RL-545), is characterized by a heavy preponderance of sand over sherd-tempered ceramics. About 20 percent of the pottery sherds have brushed exteriors, and about 10 percent show evidence of an exterior red slip. There is little plastic decoration, and apart from slipped sherds there is no evidence of painting.

The Granada phase is dated to A.D. 810 ± 100 (RL-544) and shows an 18-percent reduction in the frequency of sand tempering. No brushed or slipped sherds are present. Decorative techniques include modeled rim adornos and designs painted in white pigment.

Since each of the phases has only one C^{14} age determination, dating is very tentative, especially since there is not a great deal of ceramic change in the 1,600 years that presumably separate the two C^{14} dates. Further, the traits that define the phases are excessively general owing to the paucity of decorated ceramics and/or other diagnostic artifacts. Therefore the phases should not be extended beyond the local area of Puerto Caldas at this time.

External Relations

In the absence of firm dating and good comparative material from other areas of eastern Colombia, statements about the chronological position and external relationships of the Ariari material can be made only with caution. There are, however, a number of ceramic traits that suggest that the main affinities of the Ariari pottery are with assemblages from Amazonia, rather than with collections from the environmentally similar savannas of northeastern Colombia and southwestern Venezuela. For instance, sherd tempering is rarely found in the Orinoco Basin but comprises a majority temper type in a number of collections from the Amazon Basin (Evans and Meggers, 1968). In addition, sherds with clay pellets included in the temper have been reported from several sites in the upper Río Caquetá region (Broulliard, personal communication, 1973), and Meggers (personal communication, 1972) also reports a few such sherds from sites in the upper Río Napo drainage of eastern Ecuador. Other specific, though probably not diagnostic, trait correspondences between the Ariari drainage and Amazonia are bowls with square outlines, and anthropomorphic burial urns with L- or U-shaped arms. According to Lathrap (personal communication, 1973), a number of painted sherds and modeled adornos from the Ariari sites can probably be assigned to the widespread Amazonian Polychrome horizon (A.D. 600-1300), although a few of the zoomorphic rim lugs in the Ariari collection also have rather close counterparts in the Arauquinoid subtradition of the middle Orinoco region in Venezuela. The cruciform pottery stamp mentioned above is most reminiscent of stamps from the Corobál phase of the Ventuari-Manipiáre drainage in the upper Orinoco region (Evans, Meggers, and Cruxent, 1959).

As yet there is no evidence for a long period of cultural development in the Ariari drainage, and the high degree of ceramic uniformity argues that all the sites can probably be assigned to a single local tradition with roots in the Amazon Basin between the 7th and 14th centuries, A.D. Evidence of Andean influence or contact is lacking, and it seems unlikely that the entire Ariari complex represents the diffusion of a highland ceramic tradition to the llanos on an early time level. Accordingly, it is a plausible speculation that the Ariari complex reflects the diffusion of a tropical forest culture pattern out of the Amazon Basin, possibly by way of the Río Guaviare, or overland to the Guaviare and lower Ariari from the headwaters of the Río Uaupés.

Conclusions

Even the scanty data available indicate that the prehistory of the llanos is very complex. It is doubtful that there is a single cultural tradition to which the known archeological materials from the llanos can be assigned. Just as the llanos are geographically transitional between the highlands and the Amazon Basin, the prehistoric cultures of the region seem to be culturally transitional in the sense that they were subject to a variety of influences from other areas. The Ariari drainage, for instance, appears to be closely affiliated with the tropical forests of the Amazon Basin, while the northern and eastern borders of the Colombian llanos have cultural connections to central and southwestern Venezuela. Oddly, neither trade artifacts nor other indications of Andean contact have been found in the Ariari region, even though it is close to the Andes and has easy access to the highlands.

The prehistoric economic pattern of riverine-based llanos groups seems to have included the cultivation of bitter manioc, as is shown by the presence of pottery griddles. Maize also may have been grown, if the large stone manos found in a few of the Ariari sites are correctly interpreted as corn-grinding implements. It is a certainty that the flood-plain gallery forests were also exploited for a variety of wild food and other resources. Savannas on the other hand seem to have been cultivated only as an adjunct to circumscribed riverine flood plains (Reichel-Dolmatoff and Reichel-Dolmatoff, 1975) and appear not to have been occupied on a regular basis by horticultural groups, though they were undoubtedly used to provide some wild food resources. Although the interfluvial savannas were occupied in historic times by the Guahibo and related foragers, the archeological data will not permit a conclusion as to whether the parallel adaptations of flood-plain cultivation and interfluvial foraging are ancient in the llanos, or whether the foragers were originally riverine groups who were displaced by larger and better organized groups of intrusive farmers.

Information from archeology does lend support to the abundant ethnohistorical evidence (Morey, 1975), which shows that the resources of the Colombian llanos were adequate to support fairly large and well-organized societies, perhaps on the order of a chiefdom. In the Ariari region, at least, the large and closely spaced archeological sites argue for a considerable population in the gallery forest. Artificial earthworks at Hacienda Cejalito in the Manacacías region (Reichel-Dolmatoff and Reichel-Dolmatoff, 1975) also suggest a large sedentary society with a stable economic base and a system of cooperative labor that may have been centrally directed.

Much more archeological research is needed in eastern Colombia, but even the few available data reinforce the importance of the region as a potentially crucial zone of culture contact and diffusion between the highlands of Colombia and several lowland regions with different cultural histories.

REFERENCES

BRUNNSCHWEILER, DIETER
1972.   The llanos frontier of Colombia: Environment and changing land use in Meta.   Michigan State Univ. Latin Amer. Studies Center, Monogr. 9, 71 pp. East Lansing.

EVANS, CLIFFORD, and MEGGERS, BETTY J.
1968.   Archeological investigations on the Río Napo, eastern Ecuador. Smithsonian Contr. Anthrop., vol. 6, xvi+ 127 pp., illus.
EVANS, CLIFFORD; MEGGERS, BETTY J.; and CRUXENT, JOSÉ M.
1959.   Preliminary results of archaeological investigations along the Orinoco and Ventuari Rivers, Venezuela.   Actas 33d Congr. Int. Americanistas, vol. 2, pp. 359-369. San José, Costa Rica.
MARWITT, JOHN P.
1978.   Investigaciónes arqueológicas en los Llanos Orientales de Colómbia. El Dorado (Greeley, Colorado), vol. 3, no. 1, pp. 42-61.
MARWITT, JOHN P.; MOREY, ROBERT V.; and ZEIDLER, JAMES A.
1973.   Reconnaissance of the upper Ariari River region, Department of the Meta, eastern Colombia.   El Dorado (Greeley, Colorado), vol. 1, pp. 1-4.
MOREY, NANCY C.
1975.   Ethnohistory of the Venezuelan and Colombian llanos.   Doctoral dissertation, University of Utah. (Unpublished.)
REICHEL-DOLMATOFF, GERARDO, and REICHEL-DOLMATOFF, ALICIA
1975.   Ancient field systems in the Orinoco plains of Colombia. (Unpublished MS.)

JOHN P. MARWITT

Pleistocene Vertebrates from Deposits of Lake Bonneville, Utah

Principal Investigator: Wade E. Miller, Brigham Young University, Provo, Utah.

Grant No. 1268: In support of the investigation of vertebrate fossils from deposits of Lake Bonneville, Utah.

Pleistocene Lake Bonneville covered most of the western half of Utah and extended into parts of eastern Nevada and southern Idaho (fig. 1). Its size was roughly comparable to present-day Lake Michigan. Lake Bonneville deposits offer some of the most likely sediments in the state of Utah to contain a good record of Late Pleistocene vertebrate life. Information derived from this life is important to an understanding of faunal distributions and climatic conditions during the Late Pleistocene in western North America. The geographic position of Utah is significant in that it is intermediate between the West Coast and Great Plains, regions that have yielded the most extensive Pleistocene faunas from North America. Utah is additionally of importance in that three major physiographic provinces, the Basin and Range, Rocky Mountains, and Colorado Plateau, meet there. To date only a modest number of Pleistocene faunas have been reported from areas between the West Coast states and Great Plains; and as a result desired data are lacking.

Lake Bonneville evidently began as a series of independent lakes that occupied the deeper parts of the numerous basins in the western half of Utah. As the water regimen shifted to one of greater moisture these separate lakes coalesced to form one body. According to Bissell (1968) this probably occurred about 100,000 years ago; however, no precise datings have yet been made that would yield an accurate determination. Both before and after a single lake was formed, numerous streams emptied into the many basins containing standing water. It is at these sites that the greatest accumulations of terrestrial vertebrates can be expected. Marshy areas that evidently were associated with parts of the lake also must have allowed for preservation of some vertebrates.

Surprisingly few vertebrate fossils have been previously reported from Bonneville deposits and, enigmatically, most of these have come from the base of the very steep Wasatch Front along the eastern shoreline rather than from the relatively more gentle slopes elsewhere. One of the first reports on fossil vertebrates from Bonneville sediments was made by King (1878). He identified the skull of a bison and bones of a cervid (erroneously designated a

473

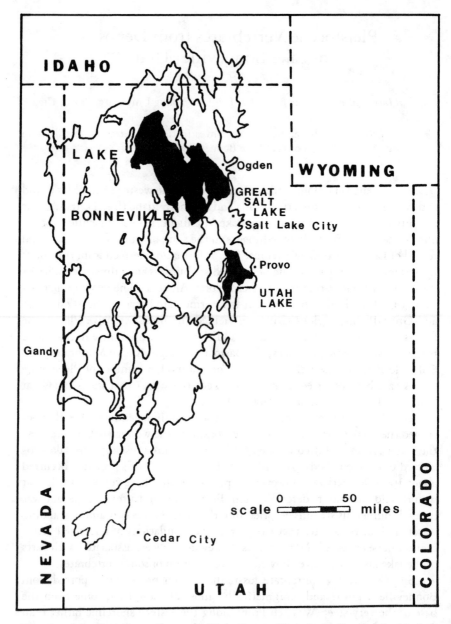

FIG. 1.   Map showing areal extent of Lake Bonneville at its highest level with dark
areas indicating its present-day remnants, the Great Salt Lake and Utah Lake.

reindeer). Since King's report, only a few articles have been published on vertebrates from Lake Bonneville deposits. Identified fossils in these articles include mammoth *(Mammuthus)*, horse *(Equus)*, mountain sheep *(Ovis)*, "musk-oxen" *(Symbos* and *Bootherium)*, bison *(Bison)*, and five genera of fishes. Authors who contributed to this knowledge are: Eardley (1955), Gilbert (1890), Hansen (1928), Madsen et al. (1976), Smith et al. (1968), Stokes and Condie (1961), Stokes and Hansen (1937), and Stokes et al. (1966).

The limited numbers of fossils previously reported from Bonneville deposits were not the result of deliberate searching but rather came about as accidental finds incident to various excavations. To my knowledge the present project has been the first attempt to make a relatively extensive field search for them. Unfortunately most theoretically promising localities proved disappointing by their lack of specimens. Numerous sand and gravel pits, which in southern Idaho have yielded abundant fossils, were not productive. However, one of these pits was forced to close temporarily several years ago because of an archeological dig; and as a result few of the gravel-pit owners or managers were cooperative.

My assistants in the present project were Kurt Camp, Sharen Campbell, and James Barton.

Scope of the Survey

Since Lake Bonneville deposits cover such an extensive area, it was considered feasible to survey only the most promising parts from widely separated locales that might contain fossil vertebrates. Collections were to have been made from as many different fossil-bearing horizons as possible. The fossils thus obtained would have been identified and information extracted as it bore on climate, distributions, and environments. Comparisons to West Coast and Great Plains faunas would also have been made. The paucity of fossils found after extensive searching was both surprising and disappointing. It is still my opinion, however, that significant fossiliferous deposits are contained in Bonneville sediments. Although relatively few fossils were uncovered as a result of this study, the information they have provided is of significant value. I will continue my search for Bonneville fossils.

Survey Method

All available literature was first consulted in order to determine what vertebrate fossils had been recovered previously from Lake Bonneville deposits, their exact locations, and types of sediment in which they were found. A

search was next made for persons who might have knowledge of fossils collected but not reported. This involved contacting institutions of higher learning
in Utah as well as companies who did excavating in the Bonneville basin. The
third method used consisted of plotting Bonneville lake levels on a relatively
large-scale map (1:500,000) of Utah. This was done in order to delineate the
exact areal extent of probable deposits and topographic conditions near the
shorelines of the different lake levels.

Where information in the literature was sufficiently specific, a reconnaissance of reported field sites was made in an attempt to recover additional fossils. The greatest number of existing Bonneville fossils, a few dozen
specimens, is located at the University of Utah. Their locality data were utilized in an attempt to recover more fossils. The plottings of lake levels on the
map were used to identify sites of deposition where vertebrate fossils were
most likely to occur. These sites were then systematically investigated.

Results of Survey

Only a few of the published articles reporting vertebrate fossils from Lake
Bonneville deposits gave specific enough information to enable us to relocate
the sites involved. And just one of these, Eardley (1955), resulted in finding
additional specimens. Unfortunately these specimens, mostly of horse
(Equus), were so well cemented in calcareous rock that their recovery was im-
practical. This site is located on an army base (Camp Williams) about 20
miles south of Salt Lake City.

The localities that looked promising when plotted on the map proved disappointing when actually surveyed. Only one unquestioned fossil, a partial
horn core of a musk-ox-like animal *(? Symbos)*, was found by this method. It
came from the mouth of Spanish Fork Canyon in central Utah. Additionally,
only a few bone fragments of questionable antiquity were found. Since, however, many of the plotted locations have not yet been checked, the possibility
of productive sites still remains.

The understandable, but regrettable, position taken by many sand- and
gravel-pit owners of withholding valuable information, or not allowing an inspection to be made on their property for fossils, probably prevented discovery
of additional sites. One cooperative owner did report finding a fossil while
processing gravel. Upon inspection we recovered two cervical vertebrae of another musk-ox-like bovid. This find was in Springville (central Utah).

Although the above find was not spectacular, the local newspapers picked
up the story and included a brief discussion of the work we were doing on this
National Geographic Society grant. A few weeks later a bone was struck in a

shallow excavation in the town of Sandy (about 10 miles south of Salt Lake City). The discoverer, who had read the account of our research, mistakenly contacted the University of Utah rather than Brigham Young University. This resulted in the University of Utah's recovery of the fossil material, approximately one-third of an adult mammoth skeleton. National television coverage was given to the actual recovery. We were called upon by the University of Utah to lend assistance, and I made the specific identification (Madsen et al., 1976).

In part as a result of my work on the present project, personnel from the Bureau of Land Management in Utah learned of my research interests and experience in Pleistocene fossils. They informed me of a cave in westernmost Utah that contained bones. This cave (Crystal Ball Cave) is located in Gandy Mountain, an outlier of the Snake Range of eastern Nevada. At its highest level, the Lake Bonneville shoreline reached the base of Gandy Mountain as attested to by nearby lake terraces. The cave entrance is above the highest lake level but wind-blown silts, which line the cave floor, were probably, at least in part, derived from Bonneville sediments. Some of the fossils found in the cave represent animals that must have frequented the ancient lake shore. Several fish vertebrae from the cave may represent a meal brought up from the lake by some carnivore. Eolian deposits in the cave are mostly concentrated in shallow crevices. It is from these sediments that most of the bones were recovered through screening operations. The density of bones is extremely high in parts of the cave where hundreds of specimens were obtained from a single screen. Although some screening was done in the cave, most specimens were recovered by taking the sediment out in bags and screening it in the fossil laboratory at Brigham Young University. Most fossils are from relatively small animals, but a few represent large ones such as horse and camel. Identified genera are given below:

Class Osteichthyes
    Infraclass Teleosti

Class Reptilia
    Order Squamata
        Family Iquanidae

Class Aves
    Order Falconiformes
        Genus ? *Aquila*

Class Mammalia
    Order Chiroptera
        Genus cf. *Myotis*

Class Mammalia—*continued*
    Order Carnivora
        Genus *Felis*
        Genus cf. *Smilodon*
        Genus cf. *Spilogale*
        Genus cf. *Vulpes*
    Order Rodentia:
        Genus *Marmota*
        Genus *Spermophilus*
        Genus *Dipodomys*
        Genus *Perognathus*
        Genus *Microtus*
        Genus *Neotoma*
        Genus *Peromyscus*

Class Mammalia—continued

Order Lagomorpha
Genus *Lepus*
Genus *Sylvilagus*

Order Perissodactyla
Genus *Equus*

Order Artiodactyla
Genus *Camelops*
Genus *Hemiauchenia*
Genus *Antilocapra*

The Crystal Ball Cave fauna represents the most numerous and diverse assemblage which can be considered as part of the present project. Additional work will soon be done and a scientific paper describing it in detail will be made. Continued searching will go on as financing permits to locate vertebrate fossils from deposits of Lake Bonneville.

REFERENCES

Bissell, Harold J.
1968. Bonneville, an Ice-Age lake. Brigham Young Univ. Geol. Studies, vol. 15, no. 4, 66 pp., illus.
Eardley, Armin J., ed.
1955. Tertiary and Quaternary geology of the eastern Bonneville Basin. Utah Geol. Soc. Guidebook, no. 10, 132 pp. illus.
Gilbert, Grove K.
1890. Lake Bonneville. U. S. Geol. Surv. Monogr. 1, 438 pp., illus.
Hansen, George H.
1928. Hairy mammoth skeleton in Utah. Proc. Utah Acad. Sci., Arts and Letters, vol. 6, pp. 7-8.
King, Clarence
1878. Report of the geological exploration of the fortieth parallel. U. S. Army Dept. Engr. Prof. Papers, vol. 1, no. 18, pp. 1-803, illus.
Madsen, David B.; Currey, Donald R.; and Madsen, James H.
1976. Man, mammoth and lake fluctuations in Utah. Utah Div. State Hist., Antiq. Sec. Select. Papers, vol. 2, no. 5, pp. 45-58, illus.
Smith, Gerald R.; Stokes, William L.; and Horn, Keith F.
1968. Some Late Pleistocene fishes of Lake Bonneville. Copeia, 1968, no. 4, pp. 807-816, illus.
Stokes, William L., and Condie, Kent C.
1961. Pleistocene bighorn sheep from the Great Basin. Journ. Pal., vol. 35, no. 3, pp. 598-609, illus.
Stokes, William L., and Hansen, George H.
1937. Two Pleistocene musk-oxen from Utah. Proc. Utah Acad. Sci., Arts and Lett., vol. 14, pp. 63-65.
Stokes, William L.; Anderson, Megan; and Madsen, James H.
1966. Fossil and subfossil bison of Utah and southern Idaho. Proc. Utah Acad. Sci., Arts and Lett., vol. 43, pp. 37-39.

Wade E. Miller

Bioturbation of Carbonate Reef Sands

Principal Investigator: Jack Morelock, University of Puerto Rico, Mayagüez, Puerto Rico.

Grant No. 1229:   For a study of bioturbation of marine sediments.

Time-lapse photography and sediment analyses were used to compute the rate of sediment reworking by *Balanoglossus, Holothuria,* and *Callianassa* in a carbonate sand backreef environment. Burrowing organisms disrupt the stratigraphy of sediment deposits and may mix relatively young and old sediment, making interpretation of the geological history of sedimentation difficult. The extent of mixing and the resulting changes are important factors in geological interpretation. The patterns left by different animals are unique and may themselves be useful in interpretation of ancient environments.

Balanoglossus and *Holothuria* ingest the sediment to obtain nourishment. *Callianassa* displaces the sediment both in feeding and in burrow construction and builds an elaborate burrow system that may be more than a meter in diameter and a meter deep.

The study site, Enrique reef, is approximately 800 meters long and is aligned approximately east-west (fig. 1). It is on a shallow carbonate shelf that averages 18 to 20 meters deep except for reef areas. The diurnal tides of the southwest coast of Puerto Rico are less than 0.25-meter amplitude (Glynn, 1973), allowing a distinct zonation of coral species and definite stable zonation of the environment. Sessile organisms in the shallow reef apron benefit because they do not have the stress of exposure at low tide. Waves approach Enrique reef from the southeast and wash over it, assuring mixing on the reef apron that prevents marked temperature or salinity differences. There is a low velocity current system over the reef.

Saunders and Schneidermann (1973) divided the area from the shore to Enrique Reef into six environments on the basis of physiographic position, gross sediment type, and characteristic bottom communities. The bioturbation was done in the environment that they describe as *reef apron,* which is a shoal area of sand deposition lying leeward of the living coral-reef structure. The maximum width of this zone is 200 meters and the water depth varies from 0.3 to 3 meters. The reef apron is bordered on the south by the *Porites* reef flat and the reef structure and on the north by a barren lagoon and slope. The lagoonal bottom is dominantly silt and clay. The slope of approximately

479

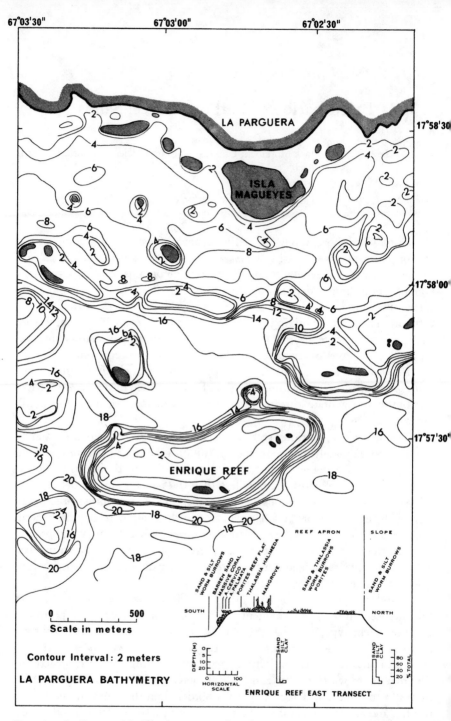

FIG. 1. La Parguera shelf bathymetry and geological environment of study area.

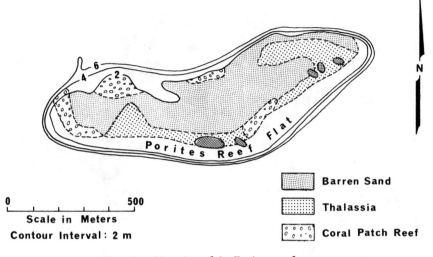

0 _____ 500
Scale in Meters
Contour Interval : 2 m

☐ **Barren Sand**

☐ **Thalassia**

☐ **Coral Patch Reef**

FIG. 2.   Zonation of the Enrique reef apron.

25° between the lagoon and apron is medium- to coarse-grained sand. There is extensive burrowing activity on this slope.

The sand apron is thoroughly reworked by burrowing organisms. The topographic lows between burrows are filled with coral rubble, whole shells, and some silts. The reef apron can be divided into three zones: barren sand, coral patch reef, and *Thalassia* meadows (fig. 2).

The *Porites* flat is discontinuous across the length of the reef. It consists of dense colonies of *Porites porites* with adjacent areas of coral rubble and clumps of *Halimeda* (Morelock et al., 1977).

Time-lapse underwater photography, underwater observations, sediment collection, and aquarium studies were used to compute the rate of sediment reworking and to observe its effects. The time-lapse sequences were taken with a 16-millimeter Bolex camera in a Sea Research and Development Underwater Housing (fig. 3). Night sequences were shot with movie lights powered by two 12-volt car batteries modified for submersion. These were pulsed by the time-lapse system. Periods of sediment reworking and frequency were computed from frame by frame examination. These data were combined with collection and weighing of sediment deposited by *Callianassa* during a 24-hour period and by removal and weighing of sediment in the digestive tracts of *Holothuria* to obtain accurate values.

A population survey of *Balanoglossus*, *Callianassa*, and *Holothuria* was

FIG. 3.   Underwater time-lapse movie camera set up in an area of *Holothuria* burrows.

made, and as the following tabulation shows, *Callianassa* is the dominant burrowing organism:

Organism	Individuals per square meter	Grams of sediment reworked per day
Callianassa	1.9	120
Holothuria	0.23	34
Balanoglossus	<0.1	280

An individual *Callianassa* reworks an average of 120 grams of sediment per day, and *Holothuria* and *Balanoglossus* rework 34 and 280 grams per day, respectively. Based on the population density and rates of reworking, the reef-apron sediments could be completely reworked in 17 years to a depth of at least 1 meter.

   Callianassa is present in all parts of the reef apron but has a higher concentration in the sand and coral areas (fig. 4). *Holothuria* are almost exclusively in areas with a *Thalassia* bottom. There were very few *Balanoglossus* burrows present, and all were in sand areas. In the *Thalassia* meadows, the densities of *Holothuria* and *Callianassa* populations were the same, 0.76 individual per

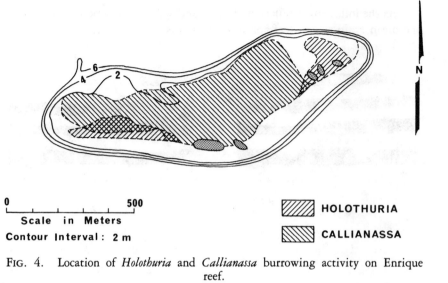

0 _____ 500
Scale in Meters
Contour Interval: 2 m

⊘ HOLOTHURIA

⊠ CALLIANASSA

FIG. 4.   Location of *Holothuria* and *Callianassa* burrowing activity on Enrique reef.

square meter, but because of the difference in rate of sediment reworking, *Callianassa* is responsible for 78 percent of the reworked sediment.

The extrusion of sand from the excurrent opening of the *Callianassa* burrow is frequent, but the mounds reach a limiting maximum size owing to wave forces. The size of the mounds varies across the reef apron in direct relationship to measured wave forces. The development of *Callianassa* mounds and rate of mound building were studied by leveling a 4-meter-square area, which was observed, photographed, and measured over a 3-week period following the leveling. The leveled area was largely rebuilt after only 4 days, but was still distinguishable from the surrounding mounds. By the end of 19 days no difference could be distinguished between the leveled area and the surrounding undisturbed mounds. The mounds that appeared after leveling were the result of normal daily activity of the animals that were already occupying the underlying burrow system. This demonstrates that the mounds are continuously replenished with sediment and are not just the product of construction of the original burrow.

Disruption of strata by burrowing *Holothuria* was studied in partitioned aquaria that were floored with an alternation of light and dark sediment layers. The maximum depth of sediment disruption was 15 centimeters. The disruption varied from bending of the sediment layers to complete mixing of particles (fig. 5).

As the following tabulation of grain and sediment characteristics shows, the mean grain size of reef-apron sediments is relatively uniform except for

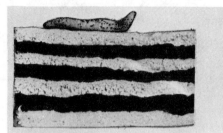

0-Days

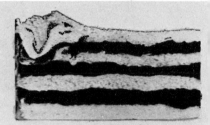

16-Days

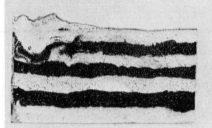

9-Days

32-Days

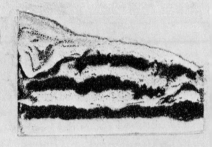

46-Days

Fig. 5. Disruption of sediment stratification by *Holothuria* burrowing activity.

material from *Holothuria* mounds, which are composed of significantly finer sediment:

Sample type	Mean grain size (mm)	Sorting	% fines	% Organic carbon
Balanoglossus	0.42	1.30	3.38	0.15
Callianassa	0.43	1.20	2.10	0.36
Holothuria	0.34	1.34	4.53	0.24
Intermound areas	0.44	1.32	4.29	0.29

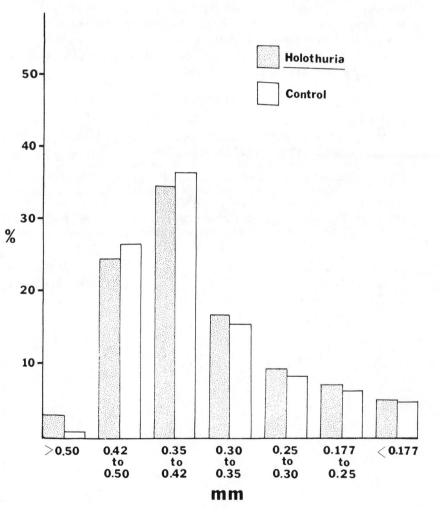

FIG. 6.   Alteration of grain size by *Holothuria*.

The *Holothuria* are either selectively choosing smaller grains to ingest or reducing the size of grains that pass through the digestive tract. Since these are carbonate sediments, the pH of the tract may be sufficiently acid to cause grain-size reduction. To test this possibility sediments were collected and screened through a 0.50-millimeter and a 0.35-millimeter pair of sieves to obtain a uniform sand with a range of 0.35- to 0.5-millimeter diameter. This sand was used to floor an aquaria occupied by *Holothuria*.

Comparison of the amount of sediment by weight in each of the sieve classes for reworked and control samples of this sediment shows that *Holothuria* reworked material contains comparatively less sediment in the larger-sized classes and more sediment in the classes smaller sized than the control sample (fig. 6). This strongly suggests that size reduction has taken place during a relatively short period of sediment reworking.

REFERENCES

GLYNN, PETER W.
    1973.   Ecology of a Caribbean coral reef. The *Porites* reef-flat biotope, pt. 1: Meteorology and hydrography.   Marine Biol., vol. 20, pp. 297-318.
MORELOCK, JACK; SCHNEIDERMANN, NAHUM; and BRYANT, WILLIAM R.
    1977.   Shelf reefs, southwestern Puerto Rico. Pp. 17-25 *in* "Reefs and Related Carbonates."   Amer. Assoc. Petrol. Geol. Studies in Geology, no. 4.
SAUNDERS, C. E., and SCHNEIDERMANN, NAHUM
    1973.   Carbonate sedimentation on the inner shelf Isla Magueyes, Puerto Rico, 77 pp.   Water Resources Research Institute, University of Puerto Rico, Mayaguez.

JACK MORELOCK
SCOTT MATHEWS

Terrestrial Avian Fossils from Mesozoic Strata, Baja California, 1973

Principal Investigator: William J. Morris, Museum of Natural History, Los Angeles County; Occidental College, Los Angeles, California.

Grant No. 1215:   In support of a survey for terrestrial avian fossils from Mesozoic strata in Baja California.

The occurrence of Late Cretaceous mammals, dinosaurs, and small reptiles from the "El Gallo" Formation, El Rosario, Baja California, is well documented (Morris, 1973, 1976). Collection of this significant West Coast vertebrate fauna has continued for the past decade with the support of the National Geographic Society and sponsored by the Natural History Museum of Los Angeles County.

The subject of this report is the discovery of fragments of a small bird and an expedition undertaken to find additional specimens. The significance of these fragmentary specimens is that they are from the only Mesozoic terrestrial bird reported since the discovery of *Archeopteryx*. The specimens have been designated by Brodkorb (1976) a new genus and species, *Alexornis antecedens,* and a new order (Alexornithiformes) and family (Alexornithidae)[1] have been erected.

The first specimens were found while cataloguing a collection of small reptile bones from Baja California. Two fragmentary bones suspected of being avian were brought to my attention by curatorial assistant Michael Greenwald. Dr. Hildegarde Howard confirmed their avian status and the specimens were sent to Dr. Pierce Brodkorb of the University of Florida for study. Dr. Brodkorb informed us of the significance of these fossils, and a field party was organized in hopes of finding additional specimens. Twelve more fragments were discovered (locality, LACM 7256), representing the pectoral girdle, wings, and legs. All specimens, including the holotype and paratype humeri (LACM 33213), are considered to be the property of the Mexican Government

---

[1]The taxonomic categories were named in honor of Dr. Alexander Wetmore, on the occasion of his 90th birthday, "who, in addition to his many other accomplishments, has done more to foster paleornithology and has described more species of fossil birds than any other author" (Brodkorb, 1976).

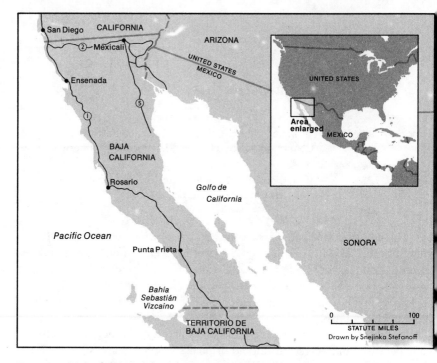

FIG. 1.   Map of Baja California showing localities where Mesozoic and Tertiary vertebrates have been collected. The bird locality where *Alexornis antecedens* Brodkorb
was discovered is about 0.5 kilometer west of El Rosario.

and have been released to the Instituto de Geología, Universidad Nacional
Autónoma de México.

The following details from Brodkorb's description of *Alexornis antecedens*
are considered significant to this report:

Paleontologic evidence from overing units and K/Ar dates of underlying
tuff (73 ± 2 million years) indicate that the specimens of *Alexornis antecedens* are
Late Campanian.

Three species of land birds have been described from the Late Cretaceous,
Caenagnathus collinsi, C. sternbergi, and *Gobipteryz minuta. Caenagnathus* is now
considered a theropod dinosaur, and *Gobipteryx* is not convincingly avian and
is considered taxa incertae sedis. Consequently there are, aside from *Alexornis,*
no land birds known from the Cretaceous Period, and, indeed, the only other
Mesozoic land bird is the Jurassic genus *Archaeopteryx*.

Brodkorb reasons that since many groups of land birds occur in Early Tertiary deposits, they must have been present and undergoing adaptive radiation during the Cretaceous. *Alexornis,* a small bird about the size of a sparrow, was among these.

On the basis of morphology and temporal occurrence Brodkorb suggests that *Alexornis* is the presumptive ancestor of the avian order Coraciiformes (kingfishers, hoopoes, hornbills, motmots, and allies) and Piciformes (woodpeckers, hornbills, honeyguides, toucans, and allies).

REFERENCES

BRODKORB, PIERCE
   1976.   Discovery of a Cretaceous bird, apparently ancestral to the orders Coraciiformes and Piciformes (Aves: Carinatae).   Pp. 67-73 *in* "Collected Papers in Avian Paleontology Honoring the 90th Birthday of Alexander Wetmore," Smithsonian Contr. Paleobiology, no. 27, 211 pp., illus., Storrs L. Olson, ed.
MORRIS, WILLIAM J.
   1973.   Mesozoic and Tertiary vertebrates in Baja California.   Nat. Geogr. Soc. Res. Rpts., 1966 Projects, pp. 197-209, illus.
   1976.   Mesozoic and Tertiary vertebrates of Baja California, 1968-1971.   Nat. Geogr. Soc. Res. Rpts., 1968 Projects, pp. 305-316, illus.

WILLIAM J. MORRIS

Adaptations for Tropical Survival in Wintering North American Birds

Principal Investigator: Eugene S. Morton, National Zoological Park, Washington, D. C.

Grant No. 1266:   To study the adaptations for tropical survival of North American birds.

Climatic changes on the Isthmus of Panama during the northern winter offer a natural experiment to provide information on the behavioral ecology of migrant birds. During the September-to-January portion of the wintering period wet-season conditions prevail across the isthmus. Then the dry season begins in January and continues until May, after most migrants have left for the north. In addition, the Pacific side of the isthmus is generally drier than the Atlantic side. These divergent climatic conditions occurring over short distances provided an experimental background against which I asked several questions:

1. Do population shifts occur and in what direction?
2. Are there changes in diet that reflect food availability changes during the two seasons?
3. Does foraging behavior change?
4. Does social tolerance change? Do species show any shifts in social behavior that may reflect competition for food?

Data on these questions provided insight on questions of more general interest: What effects will habitat changes, especially forest destruction, have on the survival of North American migrants? Can we learn something about evolutionary processes by comparing the tropical- and temperate-zone adaptations of species that exist in both places?

Data were collected primarily through direct field observation, with foraging behavior dictated directly into a cassette recorder. Specimens for stomach content analysis were collected by shooting. Figure 1 illustrates the major study areas. Numbers 1 through 8 refer to Pacific side sites and 9 through 12 to Atlantic slope locations. Complete data were published in Keast and Morton (1980).

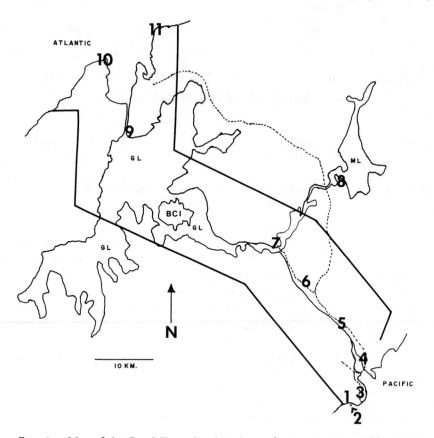

Fɪɢ. 1.   Map of the Canal Zone showing the study sites: 1, Fort Kobbe; 2, Fort
Kobbe mangrove island; 3, Far Fan; 4, Balboa; 5, Morgan's Gardens; 6, Summit
Gardens-Madden Forest; 7, Gamboa-Pipeline Road; 8, Madden Lake; 9, Gatun;
10, Fort Sherman; 11, Galeta mangroves. BCI = Barro Colorado Island.

Population Shifts from Dry to Wet Season

Species having territorial social systems showed no shifts in numbers,
whereas species that are not strictly territorial did shift. The yellow warbler
(*Dendroica petechia*) remained common in late scrub habitats and mangroves.
Northern waterthrush (*Seiurus noveboracensis*), Kentucky warbler (*Oporornis for-
mosus*), and Acadian flycatcher (*Empidonax virescens*) remained equally common

throughout the wintering period in all study areas. These last three species occupy forest habitats near the ground where relatively moist conditions prevail even during dry season. However, there was a difference in density, with higher numbers recorded from the Atlantic slope. Thus, they remain where they initially settle in the fall but prefer the habitats found in wet areas.

Another set of species, comprising those that join mixed species flocks, showed decided population shifts. Tennessee warbler *(Vermivora peregrina)*, bay-breasted warbler *(Dendroica castanea)*, chestnut-sided warbler *(Dendroica pensylvanica)*, black-and-white warbler *(Mniotilta varia)*, yellow-throated vireo *(Vireo flavifrons)*, and summer tanager *(Piranga rubra)* decreased greatly in the drier habitats during the early dry season.

For some of these species (discussed under food habits, below) the shift occurred in two dimensions; they left the drier side but also they tended to be found most frequently in mature forest habitat, whereas before the dry season they were found in second growth and late scrub habitats most frequently.

Changes in Diet

These data are based on stomach contents and observations of foraging birds. The stomach-content analysis was performed in a "double blind" manner to avoid any bias. Stomachs were removed from the birds and given a number, and a second person measured the contents without knowledge of the species. Again, the territorial species showed no change in diet composition from one season to the other, nor did these species' diets differ from temperate to tropical zones. They remained insectivorous.

This was decidedly not the case for others that are also insectivorous in the temperate zone. Tennessee warblers became nectar feeders, showing a decided preference for *Combretum* flowers during its flowering season from December to January. Not all Tennessee warblers were permitted access to the flowers, owing to strong intraspecific competition for them. So, while some birds maintained territorial rights to *Combretum* flowers, others existed in small social flocks foraging for insects, primarily larvae gleaned from leaves.

Several species began eating fruit when it became available during the mid dry season (March). Bay-breasted warblers began eating *Miconia argentea, Didymopanax morototoni,* and several other species at this time. Although none became strictly frugivorous, in baybreasts the sizes of insects eaten during the dry season were significantly smaller than those of insects taken in the wet season. Chestnut-sided warblers, which fed near baybreasts, did not show an insect-food size change between seasons.

Foraging Behavior Changes between Wet and Dry Seasons

Foraging behavior was recorded directly into a cassette tape recorder in the field. I classified the foraging movements into the following categories: hops, flights, peers, pecks, hover-gleans, fly-catches, and chase-downs. Thus, the rate of foraging could be calculated, as well as the use of various methods in finding prey. These observations were restricted to foliage-gleaning species of parulids. The territorial yellow warbler showed no change in rate or methods used between the two seasons. It remained strictly insecti-vorous. The bay-breasted warbler foraged much more slowly during the dry season, when it was eating some fruit, than during the wet season (0.260 vs. 0.384 move per second). However, the chestnut-sided warbler foraged equal-ly fast in both seasons and was a faster forager over all than the bay-breasted warbler (0.485 move per second). Tennessee warblers were slow foragers but tended to inspect leaves closely. This is probably related to their diet of larvae, which often match closely the color of their substrate and must be searched for slowly and intensively. Another intensive forager was the golden-winged war-bler *(Vermivora chrysoptera)*. All the 14 individuals observed were with mixed species flocks (only one goldenwing per flock), and all foraged by peering into dead leaves caught in vines and tree crowns. This is a specialization not report-ed for this species from its temperate-zone range.

One generality can be mentioned here. Warbler species that carry their tails cocked up when foraging (American redstart, *Setophaga ruticilla;* chest-nut-sided warbler; magnolia warbler, *Dendroica magnolia)* forage more rapidly than other species, and they do not change foraging rates between wet and dry seasons. They also use the chase-down type of foraging move more often than the rest, and they take relatively larger insects. This indicates a foraging mode that involves the dislodging of insects, by shaking leaves as they bounce rapid-ly among them and/or by frightening them through the constant motion of the cocked tail and wing movements. With this energetically costly foraging mode, the birds do not "waste" energy pursuing small insects but optimize their energy balance by pursuing only larger ones. Chase-downs take place on the average once every 45 seconds of foraging time.

Does Social Tolerance Change?

I am using the term "social tolerance" rather than "territoriality" here be-cause I mean more than defense of territory. Some species occur as single indi-viduals when encountered even though they may be interspecifically social in mixed species flocks (black-and-white warbler, American redstart, golden-winged and blue-winged [*Vermivora pinus*] warblers). Other species are tolerant of conspecifics being nearby at some times and in some habitats but not at other times or places. Tennessee warblers were found to exhibit these divergent tendencies in relation to the food type being utilized. When feeding on abundant nectar supplies, these warblers vigorously defended their territories. However, when they were away from nectar, or excluded from it by conspecifics, they were among the most social of the wintering species. Groups of 3 to 10, rarely single birds, would be found foraging for larvae in foliage. These intraspecific flocks exhibit a communication system that is more complex than that of any other parulid; flock movement is coordinated by an increasing call note rate just before takeoff. Food-source richness therefore seems to dictate the social tolerance levels in Tennessee warblers, just as it has been shown to do in many species of nectar-feeding birds. It is easy to explain the adaptiveness of high energy expenditure involved in the defense of nectar, for it constitutes a concentrated source of energy. But why be social apart from nectar sources when the flocking birds are still competing for larvae? I believe it is the intensive searching needed to find larvae, plus the relatively large size of larvae, that favor sociality here. Species that forage "intently" would be vulnerable to predators unless they occur in groups (Willis, 1972). The social tolerance of the Tennessee warbler is thus "fine tuned" to its sources of energy.

The Tennessee warbler's congener, the golden-winged warbler, is never social intraspecifically. Its foraging method of looking into dead leaves caught in vines is an "intense" foraging mode, but the dead leaf substrate is also rather uncommon. Selection has favored low social tolerance here perhaps because the high energy cost in exploring dead leaves would not be favorably compensated for if other competing golden-winged warblers were tolerated.

Bay-breasted warblers and, to a lesser extent, chestnut-sided warblers illustrated an adjustment to the seasonal changes in their social tolerance. During the wet season bay-breasted warblers were found in mixed species flocks containing several to many conspecifics, but they were also found defending territories. I did not collect sufficient numbers of this species to determine if territorial individuals constituted a single sex or age class, but it was my impression that they were adults of both sexes. All territorial individuals were found in the same habitat structure: second-growth forest having a low canopy that was beginning to shade out some of the lower bushes. It seems most probable that bay-breasted warblers become socially intolerant for basically the same energetic reasons mentioned for Tennessee warblers. This type of forest structure presents them with optimum foraging volume such that it is energetically advantageous for individuals to exclude conspecifics. In this case the defended resources are less obvious to the human observer than the nectar source is with Tennessee warbler territoriality. In mature forests the habitat structure is such that bay-breasted warblers must move farther to find optimum foraging substrate, since the lower canopy is widely separated in this situation. Thus, defense of the large area required in mature forests is not feasible.

Territorial bay-breasted warblers were often accompanied by single chestnut-sided warblers. Chestnut-sided warblers occupied mature and second-growth habitats but were more abundant in the former.

As mentioned above, many warbler species seemed to "disappear" with the beginning of the dry season but return with the ripening of certain fruits in March. Bay-breasted warblers showed high intraspecific social tolerance at this time, in decided contrast with their wet-season behavior described above.

Prothonotary warblers occurred at all seasons in intraspecific flocks of up to 25 individuals as well as singles both in interspecific flocks and alone. Single birds were always males; females were either with a single male or with a larger flock. This species was also peculiar in that flocks roosted at night together in much the same way that blackbirds do. They had staging areas where birds congregated before the entire flock took off together to roost in dense foliage or possibly hollows. No other parulids showed this behavior, even those that formed mixed species flocks during the day. They roosted as isolated individuals.

Yellow warblers, although primarily territorial throughout the wintering period, illustrate the importance of winter behavior to our understanding of adaptations. It has long been known that the northernmost populations of yellow warblers are quite dull greenish in juvenal plumage. I was able to show that this dullness is due to selection for winter survival. The southern populations breed and migrate before the northern ones and take up the good habitats long before the northern juveniles migrate. Thus, selection has favored dull plumage such that they will not evoke aggressive behavior from the bright-yellow birds. The northern birds remain nonterritorial and quite socially tolerant. They join mixed flocks and even feed on nectar with Tennessee warblers, something never seen in yellow forms (Morton, 1976a).

Synopsis

Although I have data on more species than I have reported here, the family Parulidae illustrates the diversity in wintering strategies found among "northern" birds when they are in the tropics. If anything, this diversity shows that they do not just "fit in" in the tropics but are in fact tropical birds themselves. Their only distinction is that they do not breed there—they briefly return to take advantage of the flush of insects in the temperate zone during its spring and early summer. That many migrants feed on items such as fruit and nectar or in specialized niches such as dead leaves, things that they do not do in the temperate zone, only points out why they leave the tropics—to take advantage of the insect flush for breeding (Morton, 1973). Many neotropical migrant species, particularly those that are foliage gleaners for insects in the temperate zone, become dependent on plant products (nectar and fruit) while in the tropics. Neotropical migrants that occupy ground in forests and bushy habitats in the temperate zone tend to occupy similar habitats in the tropics and change very little in food habits or social tolerance.

The diversity in the behavioral ecology of tropical migrants during their wintering season points to some unsuspected complications for their conservation. Except for stationary, territorial species habitat requirements are not easily assessed because these vary during a single season. Thus, for example, bay-breasted warblers are utilizing late-scrub or second-growth forest for most of the season but require more mature habitats for a still quite critical short time between wet and dry seasons. Furthermore, and this needs further research, food-rich habitats paradoxically may not be the only critical requirements. If social tolerance decreases when food richness favors territoriality, certain sexes and age classes may be forced into mature forest habitats. The destruction of mature forests may inadvertently cause a skewed sex ratio, reducing breeding pairs in the temperate zone and resulting in a wildly oscillating population. In general, what seems most suitable for winter habitat is a mosaic of mature and second-growth forest (Morton, 1976b; and pers. comm. in Karr, 1976). The general lesson is that we cannot be satisfied with general statements about habitat requirements. We need much more information about the changes in food and social tolerance that may occur within a single wintering season before we can either assess the impact of habitat changes in Latin America or extract scientific generalizations about tropical adaptations from that which the actions of migrants have to tell us.

The data resulting from their study are to be found in chapter 30 of Keast and Morton (1980).

REFERENCES

KARR, JAMES R.
   1976.   On the relative abundance of migrants from the North Temperate Zone in tropical habitats.   Wilson Bull., vol. 88, pp. 433-548.
KEAST, A., and MORTON, E. S., EDS.
   1980.   Migrant birds in the neotropics: Ecology, behavior, distribution, and conservation.   Smithsonian Institution Press, Washington, D. C.

MORTON, EUGENE S.
1973.   On the evolutionary advantages and disadvantages of fruit eating in tropical birds.   Amer. Nat., vol. 107, pp. 8-23.
1976a.   The adaptive significance of dull coloration in yellow warblers. Condor, vol. 78, no. 3, p. 423.
1976b.   Behavioral ecology of some tropical migrants.   Paper presented at annual meeting of American Ornithologists' Union.
1979.   Effective pollination of *Erythrina fusca* by the orchard oriole (*Icterus spurius*): Coevolved behavioral manipulation?   Ann. Missouri Bot. Gard., vol. 66, pp. 482-489.
WILLIS, EDWIN O.
1972.   The behavior of spotted antbirds.   Amer. Orn. Union. Orn. Monogr. no. 10, 162 pp.

EUGENE S. MORTON

Natural History of the Yosemite Toad

Principal Investigator: Martin L. Morton, Occidental College, Los Angeles, California.

Grant No. 1277:   For a study of the energetics and natural history of the Yosemite toad *(Bufo canorus)*.

The Yosemite toad *(Bufo canorus)* was discovered by C. L. Camp in 1916 during a survey of the fauna of the central Sierra Nevada conducted by the University of California. Since that time interest in this species has focused primarily on its taxonomic relationship to a presumed ancestral group, *B. boreas*.

Several characteristics of *B. canorus* make it an interesting and important animal to study. It is found only at high altitude and in areas of greatest snowfall in the Sierra Nevada. It is active above ground for only about four months of the year (June through September). Breeding occurs in June in shallow pools formed from melting snow. It is diurnally active and, among mature individuals, sexually dimorphic in coloration. The last two characteristics are rare among North American toads and may be related to conditions imposed by life at high altitude.

A question of great interest is how this animal is adapted in terms of energetic strategies employed during breeding and hibernation. This has been a focal point in our study of *B. canorus* begun in 1971 at Tioga Pass as an adjunct to work being conducted on other vertebrates at high altitude. In the summer of 1974 the study of these toads was escalated upon receipt of support from the National Geographic Society. A sabbatical leave for work on impact of coal-fired powerplants on vertebrate populations in eastern Montana intervened in 1975.

Our progress in this study is summarized below.

Natural History

In order to obtain accurate long-term information on life-table functions such as mortality and longevity we began toe-clipping toads in 1971. Counting a small batch of 46 clipped in September 1975, we have now marked a total of 824 individuals, as follows:

Year	Adult males	Adult females	Immatures
1971	76	12	0
1972	34	11	42
1973	186	53	42
1974	277	38	7
1975	36	10	0
Total	609	124	91

From survivors among this pool of marked individuals we are obtaining valuable information on population dynamics and life history. For example, both sexes breed for the first time as three-year-olds. Both sexes are philopatric, but adult females return to the pools in alternate years whereas males return every year. We censused one major set of breeding pools every year beginning in 1972. A large number of males survived and returned, a fact most noticeable in 1974 because we were working full time on toads. The annual recapture of toe-clipped adult male *Bufo canorus* at the same breeding pool was as follows:

		Subsequent recapture					
Year clipped	N	1972		1973		1974	
		N	(%)	N	(%)	N	(%)
1971	99	40	(40.4)	36	(36.4)	24	(24.2)
1972	90	--	--	28	(31.1)	23	(25.6)
1973	188	--	--	--	--	109	(62.3)

From these known individuals we are learning a great many things such as rates and length of movements to and from breeding areas and about growth rates of animals beyond 3 years of age (toe-clipping of immature animals younger than 2 has not been successful because of continued toe growth). For example, the mean snout-vent lengths of adult male *Bufo canorus* of known age were found to be as follows:

Age (years)	Snout-vent length (cm)		
	(N)	Mean	SD
3	(17)	4.99	0.16
4	(18)	5.41	0.16
5	(17)	5.75	0.19
6	(8)	5.94	0.17
7+	(2)	6.13	----

Obviously, we will be able eventually to determine maximum life span in this species.

In addition these marked animals enhance and stimulate additional work. For example, a Ph.D. candidate at the University of Michigan, Cindy Kagarise, cooperated in this study beginning in summer of 1976. Her work on the mating system of *B. canorus* will be of great value because she is observing individuals of known age and history.

Energetics

Collected specimens were used to measure seasonal changes in stored energy with respect to age and reproductive status. Key data include those on fat body, gonad, and liver weight, percent body lipid, liver carbohydrate, and blood glucose.

There was about a fivefold seasonal change in total body lipid in adult males and an eightfold change in fat body weight (table 1).

The same trends were seen in females, but the relationship of energy reserves to reproductive cycle is more complex because about half of the adult females in a given year are nonreproductive and are in the process of growing ova for the next year's breeding season (table 2).

Blood glucose and liver glycogen decreased after emergence, then increased steadily thereafter at least until August (table 3). Livers decreased in

TABLE 1.   Seasonal Changes in Testes Weight, Fat Body Weight, and Total Body Lipid in Adult Male *Bufo canorus*

	Mean testes wt. (mg)	N	Mean fat body wt. (% body wt.)	N	Mean total lipid (% body wt.)	N
1-10 June	57.2	17	0.29	17	1.48	8
11-20 June	51.3	17	0.27	17	1.16	10
21-30 June	53.5	16	0.20	16	1.24	10
1-10 July	33.1	12	0.34	12	2.82	12
11-20 July	42.6	9	0.74	9	3.17	4
21-31 July	45.1	15	1.15	15	3.82	10
1-10 August	46.1	7	0.87	7	2.74	7
11-20 August	34.2	9	1.15	9	3.15	7
21-31 August	42.0	14	1.24	14	3.52	12
1-10 Sept.	45.0	3	0.80	4	3.10	4
11-20 Sept.	68.7	10	1.27	13	4.28	11
21-30 Sept.	55.0	2	1.68	2	5.10	2

size soon after emergence and breeding, then more than doubled in size before hibernation.

These data show that energy is stored for the 8-month hibernation period both as fat and as carbohydrate. Energy stores are not totally depleted upon emergence. This is undoubtedly of great adaptive value in that migration to breeding pools often occurs over great expanses of snow without benefit of food. Also, preliminary examination of stomachs indicates that male toads do not eat while in the lek. They may be living on stored reserves the entire two to three week period.

TABLE 2.   Seasonal Changes in Ovarian Weight, Fat Body Weight, and Total Body Lipid in Female *Bufo canorus*

	Mean ovarian wt. (mg)	N	Mean fat body wt. (% body wt.)	N	Mean total lipid (% body wt.)	N
1-15 June						
Reproductive	4098	12	0.42	12	3.73	8
Nonreproductive	1240	1	0.33	1	--	--
Immature	68	1	0.98	1	--	--
16-30 June						
Reproductive	550	7	0.87	7	2.76	7
Nonreproductive	930	1	2.46	1	--	--
Immature	--	--	--	--	--	--
1-15 July						
Reproductive	457	3	0.94	3	2.75	7
Nonreproductive	2577	3	0.98	4	--	--
Immature	173	3	3.85	3	--	--
16-31 July						
Reproductive	1115	2	1.18	2	2.90	6
Nonreproductive	3200	1	0.40	1	--	--
Immature	274	3	1.66	3	--	--
1-15 August						
Reproductive	1280	1	1.05	1	3.78	5
Nonreproductive	1990	4	1.45	4	--	--
Immature	--	--	--	--	--	--
16-31 August						
Reproductive	1645	3	1.79	3	4.47	4
Nonreproductive	4390	1	0.49	1	--	--
Immature	--	--	--	--	--	--
1-15 September						
Reproductive	1950	1	0.54	1	3.03	3
Nonreproductive	3600	1	0.81	1	--	--
Immature	200	1	0.97	1	--	--

TABLE 3. Seasonal changes in blood glucose and liver carbohydrate (primarily glycogen) in adult *Bufo canorus*

	Mean blood glucose (mg %)	*N*	*Mean liver wt. (mg)*	*Mean liver glycogen (mg/g)*	*Total liver glycogen (mg)*	*N*
5-6 June	37.7	5	520	40	20.8	5
14 June	34.8	4	323	38	12.3	9
22 June	34.6	6	395	33	13.0	8
30 June	25.4	4	312	48	15.0	5
15 July	62.0	4	546	87	47.5	7
1 August	92.9	5	660	97	64.0	5

It is clear that our data need shoring up and amplification in many areas. Difficulties in obtaining a power source for analytical instruments has been a factor. We have also exercised considerable restraint in collecting because we were not sure until recently that *B. canorus* existed in substantial numbers.

MARTIN L. MORTON

Mineralogy and Distribution of Clay-size Material, Turnagain Arm, Alaska

Principal Investigator: Neal R. O'Brien, State University of New York, Potsdam, New York.

Grant No. 1209[1]: To study mineralogy and distribution of clay sediments, Turnagain Arm region, Alaska.

Turnagain Arm is located in the vicinity of Anchorage, Alaska (approximately lat. 61°N., long. 150°W.), and is a tidal estuary at the head of Cook Inlet (fig. 1). During low tide the tidal flat sediment is exposed to the air and hence weathering processes. The original intent of this project was to sample clay sediment systematically from the source (i.e., at glacial terminii and rivers flowing into the Arm) and along the axis of the Arm into Cook Inlet. The main emphasis was to determine if diagenetic changes in sediment actually do take place in a typical subarctic intertidal environment. The significance of this study was to shed more light upon the role of chemical weathering in a subarctic environment. Clay sediment was selected for investigation because it should reflect weathering influences better than other sediment sizes.

I initially sampled clays at the main sources of sediment being delivered to the Arm (e.g., Portage Glacier and Portage Creek, Spencer Glacier, and Placer River) and made an attempt to collect suspended sediment in other tributary streams to the Turnagain Arm (e.g., Twenty-mile River, Glacier Creek, Granite Creek, Sixmile Creek, Bird Creek, and others). Early in the fieldwork it became apparent that these creeks were only an insignificant supplier of sediment owing to the low sediment load in them. Portage Creek and Placer River appeared to be the more important sediment contributors even though their load was very low.

Upon X-ray analysis of the mineralogy of the clay-size sediment it became apparent that there was no lateral variation in mineral composition from the source along Turnagain Arm toward its mouth. In fact, both X-ray and electron microscope analysis (figs. 2, 3) indicated the original clay material was not subjected to intense chemical weathering at its source or during diurnal

---

[1] This research was financially supported also by the Arctic Institute of North America.

505

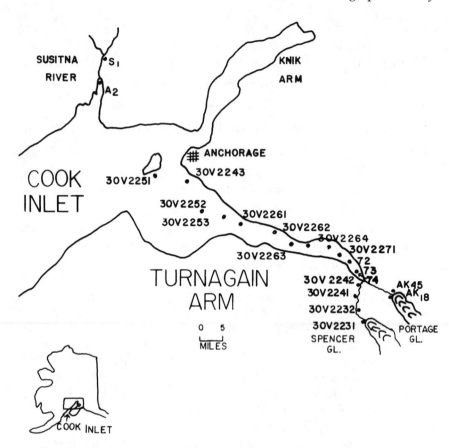

Fig. 1.   Sample locations of clay-size sediments, Turnagain Arm, Alaska.

exposure on the tidal flat. Thus, because of the well-crystalline nature of the original minerals deposited in the tidal estuary, diagenetic effects appeared minimal. Field observations also suggested to me that the vast majority of sediment was actually not coming from the Spencer and Portage Glacier source but was actually being brought into the Arm by incoming tides from the open water of the Cook Inlet and subsequently trapped in the Arm. To test this hypothesis I expanded the scope of the project by doing more detailed sampling at the mouth of Turnagain Arm and the Susitna River.

In the remainder of this paper I offer evidence to support the statement that the Susitna River is a major sediment contributor and that this sediment is brought by incoming tides into the Turnagain Arm, where it is trapped and deposited as far into the Arm as the mouth of the Portage Creek. The Susitna clays are distinctive and have a mineralogy different from the clays in the Portage and Placer rivers. Results show that Susitna clay is found in the sediment of the Turnagain Arm.

Methods

The field sampling program was conducted during the period August 8-22, 1973. Bottom sediment and suspended load sediment samples were obtained at various locations in the Turnagain Arm region. Over 60 sediment samples were collected. Key sample locations are shown in figure 1. Samples labeled AK, A2, S1 were taken at the edge of the tidal flat or from tributary streams. Samples labeled 30V were collected mainly in the center of the tidal flat during low tide and thus are the most useful in determining mineral distribution.

The oriented aggregate technique was used to prepare some of the more highly concentrated clay suspensions for X-ray analysis. This technique consists of drying a dispersed clay suspension on a glass slide. The more dilute dispersed suspensions were filtered through 0.45μ millipore filters. Upon drying, each filter coated with an oriented clay aggregate was carefully taped onto a glass slide and inserted into a General Electric XRD-6 diffraction unit (Cu K∝ radiation, Ni filter, 45 KV, 30 MA). A scan was made at $2°2\theta$ per minute from $3°-30°2\theta$ on the less than 2μ fraction. Some samples were glycolated overnight and X-rayed; however, owing to the absence of expandable clays this technique did not yield additional mineralogical information. All samples were slow scanned in the $24°-26°2\theta$ range to differentiate kaolinite from chlorite. The total size fraction was also analyzed to determine nonclay minerals present. Selected samples were also replicated and observed in the electron microscope.

Figure 2 shows a typical X-ray trace of the clay-size mineralogy in the Turnagain Arm region. Clay-size minerals (rather than "clay minerals") would best describe the mineral assemblage, which appears to be a product of glacial abrasion. An electron micrograph also indicates a lack of wide-scale alteration, owing to chemical weathering at the source or after deposition (fig. 3). Mica and chlorite dominate in the less than 2μ size as well as in the total size fraction, which contains lesser amounts of feldspar, quartz, hornblende, and diopside. Mica was identified on the basis of a strong 10 Å peak but weak 5 Å peak. Chlorite was identified on the basis of an intense peak at 14 Å. All other orders of chlorite are present in every sample up to and including the (004) reflection. Slow X-ray scanning from $24-26°2\theta$ revealed a strong peak

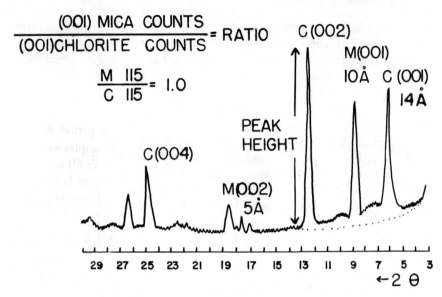

FIG. 2.   Typical X-ray diffraction pattern of less than 2μ clay-size material, Turnagain Arm, Alaska.

in the vicinity of $25.2°2\theta$ for all samples and was identified as the (004) reflection of chlorite. No evidence of kaolinite or expandable clays was found in any sample.

Data representing the relative abundance of clay size material are presented in the form of a mica to chlorite ratio (table 1). Since the peak height on an X-ray trace may be proportional to the amount of clay-size mineral present, I measured the peak heights in millimeters of the 001 mica and 001 chlorite and determined the ratio of the heights (fig. 2). The resulting figure (the mica/chlorite ratio) thus is used as a semiquantitative method of representing relative clay-size mineral abundance. A ratio of 1.0 indicates equal parts mica and chlorite, while a ratio of 2.5, for example, signifies the presence of much more mica than chlorite.

Results

Only the X-ray data from the most significant samples are here reported (fig. 1). These data, however, adequately represent the total mineralogy of all samples collected. Mica and chlorite dominate in the less than and greater than 2μ size fractions. X-ray and electron-microscope results indicate the well-crystalline nature of the clay-size minerals, suggesting minimal chemical weathering and diagenetic activity (figs. 1-3). Mica is more abundant at the

FIG. 3. Electron micrograph of clay-size material being deposited in Turnagain Arm (sample material 30V2232-Placer River). X 16,000.

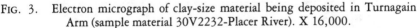

mouth of Turnagain Arm and decreases slightly in abundance toward its head. Suspended sediment from the Susitna River (which flows into Cook Inlet) also possesses abundant mica relative to chlorite. Susitna River mineralogy is almost identical to the mineralogy of sediment at the mouth of Turnagain Arm. Both areas have sediment with an approximate 2 to 1 mica to chlorite ratio (table 1). This ratio is in marked contrast to the 1.0 ratio of clay sediment being deposited at the head of the Arm by the glacial meltwater of Placer and Portage rivers (e.g., see fig. 4, and table 1, samples AK 18, 30V2231). Thus, throughout Turnagain Arm, the sediment has a higher mica content than the sediment being brought into the Arm by tributary streams. This observation led me to conclude that the Portage, Placer, and other tributary rivers are not the main contributors to the sediment presently being deposited in the Arm. Circulation patterns and tidal movements in the upper part of the Cook Inlet

TABLE 1.—Mineralogy of Sediment
P = Predominant   M = Minor
A = Abundant   T = Trace

| Sample | Clay-size fraction | | Mica to chlorite ratio | Total Sample | | | | | |
	Mica	Chlorite		Mica	Chlorite	Feldspar	Quartz	Hornblende	Diopside
30V2251	P	A	2.3	P	A	M	M	M	M
30V2243	P	A	1.8						
30V2252	A	A	1.1	T	T	M	M		
30V2253	A	A	1.3						
30V2261	P	A	1.6						
30V2263	P	A	1.6						
30V2264	P	A	1.4						
30V2262	No clay		---						
30V2271	P	A	1.7						
30V2272	P	A	1.4						
30V2273	P	A	1.7						
30V2274	P	A	1.9	P	A	M	M	M	M
30V2242	A	A	0.9	A	A	M	M	-	-
30V2241	A	A	1.0	A	A	M	M	-	-
30V2232	A	A	1.1						
30V2231	A	A	1.1						
Si	P	A	2.3						
Az	P	A	2.5						
Ak18	A	A	1.0						
Ak45	A	A	1.0						

near Anchorage suggest that the higher micaceous clay-size sediment could be carried into the Arm by incoming tides from another source. The evidence suggests this source is in the Susitna River drainage basin. A surface current pattern based upon ERTS satellite imagery shows Susitna River clays could be carried into Turnagain Arm (Anderson et al., 1973, fig. 35, p. 43). The higher micaceous clay-size sediment from the Susitna River is apparently carried out into Cook Inlet where some of it is caught up in the circulation pattern and subsequently carried during high tide into Turnagain Arm, where it becomes trapped and buried.

Conclusion

Results indicate that diagenetic changes are not apparent in the recently deposited clay sediment in Turnagain Arm. It is suggested that this is due to

FIG. 4. Portage Glacier and Portage Glacier Lake. Portage Lake is the source of Portage Creek. Photo taken at sample location AK 18.

the minimal effect of chemical weathering in altering the sediment at its source in this subarctic environment.

The most important result of the study is the suggestion that the clay-size sediment in Turnagain Arm is derived mainly from a source in the Susitna River drainage basin. The bulk of the clay-size sediment in the Arm is higher in mica content than is being supplied by the two tributary rivers at its head. Susitna River sediment has a high mica content and apparently is flushed into Turnagain Arm where it accumulates. This study, then, supports the value of using clay-sediment mineralogy in determining sediment source and the distribution patterns in the Turnagain Arm area.

As an outgrowth of this study, I collected additional clay sediment in the Knik Arm and from the Matanuska River and Knik River in order to understand the source and mineralogy of sediment in the Knik Arm. Results of this study will be forthcoming.

REFERENCES

ANDERSON, D. M.; CROWDER, W. K.; GATTO, L. W.; HAUGEN, R. K.; MARLAR, T. L; McKIM, H. L.; and PETRONE, A.
1973.   An ERTS view of Alaska. Cold Region Res. and Eng. Lab. Techn. Rpt. 241, 50 pp.

NEAL R. O'BRIEN

Systematics and Zoogeography of the Neotropic Genus *Epirhyssa* (Hymenoptera, Ichneumonidae)

Principal Investigator: Charles C. Porter, Fordham University, Bronx, New York.

Grant No. 1170:   To study the systematics and zoogeography of the wasps of the ichneumonid genus *Epirhyssa*.[1]

For the past 10 years I have been studying the taxonomy, zoogeography, and biology of South American parasitic wasps belonging to the subfamilies Ephialtinae and Gelinae (Porter, 1974) of the family Ichneumonidae. Current work, supported by the National Geographic Society, involves particularly the genus *Epirhyssa* Cresson. As part of this undertaking I spent 10 weeks in Bolivia and Argentina during June, July, and August 1973, devoting most of the time to field observations and to intensive collecting. I revisited several proven localities and explored a number of previously unstudied areas. Throughout most of the trip I was aided by a graduate student assistant, Edward Demarest of Fordham University, and in Bolivia I was accompanied also by Dr. Lionel Stange, a specialist in Neuroptera and aculeate Hymenoptera presently employed by the Argentine Universidad Nacional de Tucumán.

Through these efforts 4,200 Hymenoptera were collected and prepared, including many ephialtines of *Epirhyssa* and related genera. Much of this material represents new and previously uncollected species, contributes new locality records that enlarge our understanding of ichneumonid distribution in South America (fig. 4), or adds to our knowledge of the biology of certain ich-

---

[1] The National Geographic Society grant supported fieldwork on the project during 1973. A Fordham University faculty research grant allowed me to have the services of a graduate assistant during most of my stay in Argentina and Bolivia. Drs. José A. Haedo, Abraham Willink, and Raymond Laurent of the Instituto Miguel Lillo at Tucumán, Argentina, made available the collections and vehicles of their institute. Dr. Domingo Jakúlica of the Universidad Nacional de Salta facilitated access to virgin forest on his property near Aguas Blancas on the Argentine-Bolivian border. In Bolivia, we were greatly helped by Ingeniero Oscar Terán of the Comisión Nacional para el Estudio de la Caña y del Azucar at Santa Cruz. Ing. Terán put us in contact with a most reliable driver, Sr. Lionel Arredondo, and arranged for us to leave two Malaise traps (fig. 3) on the grounds of the Agricultural Experiment Station at Gral. Saavedra near Santa Cruz.

neumonids. For example, we now know that *Epirhyssa,* unrecorded from Argentina before 1969, actually has six species in that country (Porter, 1975). Critical analysis of this and other material—involving the preparation of taxonomic monographs with keys, descriptions, and illustrations—has been published (Porter, 1978). Here I present a synthesis of field observations with regard to mimetic complexes, zoogeography, and other topics of general interest.

Mimetic Complexes

One result of these studies has been to show that many species of *Epirhyssa* belong to mimetic complexes, whose models are furnished by stinging social vespids and odoriferous ichneumonids of the genera *Ephialtes* and *Coccygomimus* (Porter, 1970).

Epirhyssa oranensis (Porter, 1975), for example, is a bright black and yellow wasp 15-20 millimeters in length and easily spotted as it flies slowly about 1 meter off the ground in broken sunlight above the dark-green understory vegetation of northwest Argentine subtropical wet forests. Obviously, it is an insect of aposematic rather than cryptic coloration. Since the female cannot sting and since neither sex gives off an offensive odor, it appears to be a palatable and defenseless species that gains protection by resembling some dangerous or distasteful model. In this case the model certainly is *Stelopolybia pallipes anceps* (Willink, 1952), an aggressive ground-nesting social vespid of much the same size, color pattern, and flight habits as *E. oranensis. Stelopolybia* probably is the commonest hymenopteron of the area and, like most vespids, will sting painfully if restrained or if its nest is molested. Indeed, the utility of *Stelopolybia* as a model is shown by the fact that *E. oranensis* is but one of the northwest Argentine insects that mimic it. Other *Stelopolybia* mimics found in habitats studied during 1973 include the ichneumonids *Dolichomitus zonatus, Ephialtes bazani, Coccygomimus sumichrasti, C. tomyris, Theronia lineata, Labena* sp., *Exetastes* sp., *Coelorhacis* sp., *Dusona* sp., *Metopius* sp., *Colpotrochia* (2 spp.), *Cubus* sp., *Carinodes* sp., and *Tricholabus* sp. (male only); a gigantic chalcidid of the genus *Spilochalcis;* a eumenid of the genus *Eumenes;* the unaggressive social vespid *Mischocyttarus alfkenii zikanii;* the pompilids *Chirodamus argentinicus* (male only) and *Poecilopompilus polistoides;* sphecids of the genus *Cerceris* and of an unidentified gorytine genus; and even a few insects of other orders, such as certain day-flying moths, a common tipulid dipteron, and some cicadellid Homoptera. Undoubtedly, this mimetic complex is so large and pervasive not only because of the abundance of the chief model but also because some of its other members likewise are protected from natural enemies by aggressive or repulsive mechanisms. For example, the eumenids, pompilids, and sphecids involved are all capable of stinging, although much less severely than *Stelopolybia*. (Curiously, most species of the social wasp genus *Mischocyttarus* seem reluctant to sting when seized in the hand or even when their nests are picked up with the fingers for examination. Consequently, this genus must be reckoned a mimic rather than a model.) Moreover, the common ephialtine ichneumonids *Ephialtes bazani, Coccygomimus sumichrasti,* and *C. tomyris* (Porter, 1970) give off when disturbed a potent formaldehyde-like secretion, which probably makes them distasteful to predators and which is so volatile that a collector may realize from the odor alone that one of these ephialtines has entered his sweeping net as he passes it at random through the undergrowth. Thus there are multiple natural selective pressures that would determine a black-and-yellow-striped and -banded pattern among Hymenoptera and similar insects of the north Argentine subtropical forests, and for this reason the mimetic complex centered around *Stelopolybia pallipes anceps* is an especially large one. Protection of this type would seem particularly advantageous for *Epirhyssa* because its females, which parasitize wood-boring insect larvae, spend a large part of their lives ovipositing in dead and dying tree trunks, and while the ovipositor is buried 25 or even 50 millimeters deep in the wood they are fixed to the spot, conspicuous and vulnerable.

We should note also that *Stelopolybia pallipes anceps* is not the only social vespid in northern Argentina that forms the center of a mimetic complex. *Polybia ruficeps, P. ignobilis, P. sericea,* and *Brachygastra lecheguana* also have a number of mimics. *P. ruficeps* is a slender black wasp with fine yellow markings on the thorax and gaster and with most of the head pale rufous. A new species of the eumenid genus *Zethus* discovered during this year's fieldwork, as well as a chalcidoid of the genus *Leucospis,* a sapygid of the genus *Huarpea,* several unaggressive social wasps of the genus *Mischocyttarus,* such eumenids as *Stenodynerus* spp. and *Ancistrocerus clarizianus,* and some sphecids of the genus *Ceceris* all resemble *P. ruficeps. Polybia ignobilis* is an opaque, black species copied by eumenids of *Eumenes, Pachymenes,* and other genera as well as by a few ichneumonids, such as certain *Colpotrochia* and *Setanta. Polybia sericea,* a big reddish-brown species with golden thoracic pubescence, is paralleled by some eumenids and by the sphecid *Isodontia costipennis.* Indeed, *costipennis* shows geographic variation with regard to this mimicry: specimens from Tucumán Province, where *P. sericea* does not occur, display less golden pubescence than do those from the north of Salta, where *sericea* abounds. *Brachygastra lecheguana,* a short, stout black wasp with dull yellow markings has numerous eumenid mimics—principally *Pachyodynerus*—and is mimicked as well by some anthidiine bees and Diptera.

Another mimetic association involving certain species of *Epirhyssa* centers around aposematically colored braconid wasps of the subfamily Braconinae. These are characterized by their dark wings—often marked with pale crossbands—frequently bright yellow pterostigma, and shining black or black and red body. When restrained they produce an unpleasant odor and thus would appear to be distasteful to predators. A variety of nonodoriferous ichneumonids has the same color pattern, including in Argentina species of *Calliephialtes, Clydonium, Acrotaphus, Zaglyptomorpha,* and *Epirhyssa phoenix* (Porter, 1975) from the northeastern provinces of Corrientes and Misiones.

Finally, observations in Amazonian rain forest at Buena Vista, Bolivia (fig. 1), revealed that local populations of *Epirhyssa peruana* belong to a mimetic complex, one of whose models is the big vespid *Polistes testaceicolor* (Porter 1978, pp. 353-355). This *Polistes* has the head, mesosoma, and two basal gastric segments pale red-brown with yellow markings, while the apical part of its gaster is black; it stands out dramatically in its swift flight among the undergrowth plants of the forest. In the same habitat occur several other Hymenoptera of similar size and color pattern, including a vespid of the genus *Mischocyttarus* and, in addition to the *Epirhyssa* already mentioned, another ichneumonid of the genus *Dolichomitus.* Future collecting probably will reveal other members of this complex, since we would expect it to be small at Buena Vista on the extreme southern edge of Amazonian forest.

It will be noted that the above provides the second case of an *Epirhyssa* and a *Dolichomitus* pertaining to the same mimetic series. We have already mentioned that the northwest Argentine *E. oranensis* bears great resemblance to the local geographic race of *D. zonatus.* Furthermore, in northeast Argentina *Epirhyssa celaena* (Porter, 1975a, 1978) frequents the same forests as a superficially almost identical black *Dolichomitus.* In fact, this similarity between *Epirhyssa* and *Dolichomitus* exceeds a general correspondence in color and shape. These two belong to the same subfamily (although different tribes) and share many gross morphological features. Both, moreover, parasitize larvae of wood-boring insects and have the long ovipositor and slender, cylindrical body associated with that type of life history. It is practically impossible for the collector to distinguish similarly colored *Epirhyssa* and *Dolichomitus* in the field, as the characters separating them require at least a hand lens to be seen clearly. Neither *Epirhyssa* nor *Dolichomitus* seems to have any intrinsic mechanism for discouraging predators and both are especially vulnerable while stuck in the wood for oviposition. The presence of similarly colored *Dolichomitus* and *Epirhyssa* at many Neotropical localities, therefore, would seem to be the result of independent mimicry by both genera of protected vespids and ichneumonids flying in the same habitat.

Fig. 1.　Amazonian rain forest at its southernmost limit just west of Buena Vista near Santa Cruz de la Sierra, Bolivia. Note the profusion of epiphytes and understory vegetation. Especially characteristic of this biotic province are the prop-root-supported palms, *Iriartea exorrhiza,* of which two specimens appear toward the left margin of the picture. This locality is inhabited by three species of *Epirhyssa,* one of these a mimic of the large and brightly colored stinging vespid *Polistes testaceicolor.* (Photo by Edward Demarest, July 1973).

Phaenology

Epirhyssa and most other ichneumonids of the north Argentine subtropical forests do not occur with uniform abundance throughout the year but show pronounced and fairly regular seasonal peaks and minima. *E. oranensis,* for example, has been collected only during the cooler winter and spring months of June, July, August, and October. Indeed, repeated collecting over a period of six years has given us a good picture of the annual variation in abundance of Ichneumonidae inhabiting the northwest Argentine Selva Chaqueña. This is a subtropical deciduous forest. It has about 700-1,200 millimeters of rain per year and most of this falls between November and April. After April, a gradual drying trend, which may not be completed until July or August, leads up to the almost rainless winter months of August and September. Temperatures in the Selva Chaqueña regularly attain 45° or even 50°C. during the warmer half of the year and in winter highs of 25°-30°C. are the rule. A few frosts occur each winter, but these rarely are severe enough to reduce insect populations

FIG. 2.   Chaco Seco near Las Cejas in Tucumán Province, Argentina. This is dry Subtropical Thorn Scrub with only 500 to 800 millimeters of rain per year, most of which falls in summer. Characteristic flora include *Opuntia quimilo*, the large cactus in the foreground, and spiny shrubs of such genera as *Acacia, Prosopis, Cercidium,* and *Celtis*. At the latitude of northern Argentina this inhospitable community constitutes a barrier between the Andean and southeast Brazilian wet forest ichneumonid faunas. (Photo by C. C. Porter, April 1966).

drastically. The best season for ichneumonids in the Selva Chaqueña is April to June (as observed at Río Pescado and Tartagal in Salta Province). July and August also provide good collecting, with a slow falloff toward the middle of August, as the worst part of the dry season approaches. Late August and September, when most of the trees are leafless, are extremely poor for ichneumonids, but with the first foliage and rains of October there is a dramatic upsurge, reaching almost the levels attained during the fall peak. By the third week in November ichneumonids have become relatively scarce again, and they remain uncommon throughout the summer. Consequently, the hymenopterous fauna of the Selva Chaqueña is very different at different times of year. In the spring, fall, and most of the winter ichneumonids predominate, although aculeates are moderately conspicuous. In summer, ichneumonids and many other parasitica diminish but aculeates, such as vespids, eumenids, and pompilids become extremely common. During the driest part of late winter, parasitica again are rare but one finds a great variety of Eumenidae and Apoidea.

Similar annual cycles prevail for the Ichneumonidae of most other Argentine Biotic Provinces, including the wetter Selva Tucumano-Boliviana and

FIG. 3. Malaise trap set up in Amazonian rain forest 17 kilometers east of Villa Tunari, Bolivia. These traps afford a useful supplement to hand techniques in the collecting of aerial insects. The tentlike structure, made of dacron marquisette or similar material, is placed across a forest path or other insect flightway. When flying insects strike the middle partition, their instinctive reaction is to attempt escape by flying upward. This brings them to the anterior peak of the trap, where a large opening leads into an inverted plastic jar beneath which is attached a similar jar partially filled with alcohol. Most specimens entering the upper jar eventually fall into the alcohol and are preserved. Malaise traps usually will obtain 10 to 50 ichneumonids per day, plus hundreds of other insects. (Photo by Edward Demarest, July 1973).

the drier Chaco (fig. 2). Indeed, only the high, arid Subandean and Andean deserts show a different pattern, in which maximum abundance coincides with the summer months of December to March (Porter, 1975b). Furthermore, although it has not yet been possible to observe the tropical forests of Bolivia at all seasons of the year, there is evidence that the ichneumonids of these regions likewise reach spring and fall maxima and summer minima. As pointed out by Townes (1972), ichneumonids are fragile insects much subject to desiccation and depend principally upon dew as a source of water to drink. Rain alone, even in wet forests such as those of northwest Argentina, may not suffice them because it rarely falls often enough to insure the daily supply of moisture they need. Furthermore, in the summer wet season nightly cooling may not be sufficient to provide a consistent source of dew. On the other hand, the Argentine forests studied have much dew every morning during spring, fall, and early winter, when the day-night temperature differential may be as much as 30°C. The lower temperatures of this season also may cause less evaporation through the rather weakly sclerotized cuticle of many ichneumonids. At least in Argentina, however, it is not true as Townes asserts (1972, p. 241) that "Ichneumonids are common *throughout the growing season . . .* at higher altitudes where night cooling is greater and in moist climates where the atmosphere is habitually closer to the dew point." Even the higher levels of the Argentine wet forests between 1,500 and 2,000 meters and with an annual rainfall of 2,500 millimeters show an overwhelming summer decline in abundance of parasitic Hymenoptera, although their foliage remains dripping wet throughout the season. Thus, availability of water to drink is only one of the factors that determine subtropical and tropical ichneumonid phaenology. Another important factor may be the life cycles of the hosts of these parasitic insects. Ichneumonids attack primarily the immature stages (larvae and pupae) of Lepidoptera and Coleoptera, orders whose adults are especially numerous during summer and whose earlier instars predominate at other times.

Another aspect of phaenology observed for *Epirhyssa* and the majority of north Argentine ichneumonid genera is that their daily activity period changes radically from the hotter to the cooler part of the year. During comparatively hot months, such as October and November, ichneumonids fly mostly from 9:00 to 12:00 and again from 16:00 to sunset, avoiding water loss by hiding in shady places during the hours of maximum temperature. From June to August, however, they barely commence activity by 12:00, peak between 13:00 and 15:00, and disappear rapidly after 16:00. In winter, of course, nightly lows may approach freezing, and, although the daily maximum usually is between 25° and 30°C., these mild temperatures conducive to insect activity are not attained much before noon.

Zoogeography

Epirhyssa is a Neotropic element, having its center of abundance and diversity in tropical and subtropical America and reaching the Nearctic with

---

FIG. 4.   Map of South America showing localities where species of the genus *Epirhyssa* have been collected. Note that most records either are from the Andean cloud forests of Perú, Bolivia, and northwest Argentina or from the equally wet tropical and subtropical forests of southeast Brazil and adjoining Corrientes and Misiones provinces of Argentina. There are no records from the dry Chaco of north-central Argentina, western Paraguay, and southeastern Bolivia. The Amazon Basin has a few *Epirhyssa,* but, as is true of most insects, the genus does not seem especially common or diverse there.

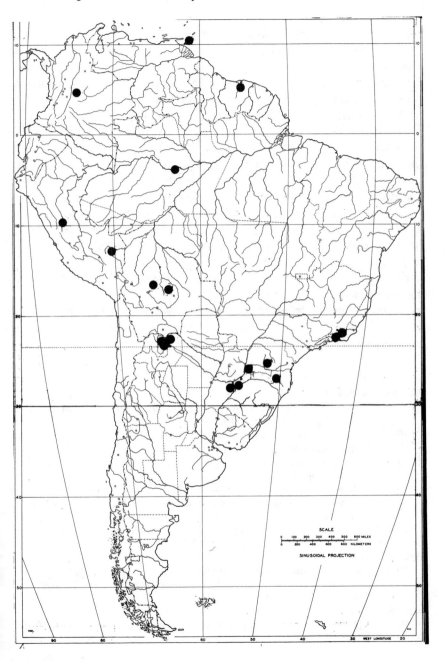

but a single species that has attained southern Arizona.

Like most ichneumonids, *Epirhyssa* is restricted to humid forests and in South America it has had two major centers of speciation: (1) The Andean Cloud Forests and (2) the wet forests of the southeast Brazilian coastal mountains (fig. 4). For example, in Argentina one *Epirhyssa* inhabits the northwestern Selva Tucumano-Boliviana and Selva Chaqueña and five more are in the northeastern Selva Misionera, which forms part of the southeast Brazilian biotic province. At present, direct interchange between Andean and Brazilian ichneumonid faunas is blocked at the latitude of northern Argentina by the Chaco Seco (fig. 2)—a 1,000 kilometer stretch of dry thorn scrub in which few forest insects can survive; but doubtless these elements merged during Pleistocene glacial maxima when the world's climate was wetter and arid zones were smaller and less rigorous. Indeed, the history of much of the South American entomofauna is one of radiation in southeast Brazilian and Andean centers, exchange between these centers during wetter epochs, and partial or complete isolation of eastern and western populations during arid glacial minima. Much speciation in *Epirhyssa* seems to have occurred through this mechanism. The single northwest Argentine species, for instance, has two close relatives in Misiones, which probably represent invasions of the southeast by Andean stocks during two different glacial maxima.

REFERENCES

PORTER, CHARLES C.
  1970.   A revision of the South American species of *Coccygomimus*.   Studia Entomologica, vol. 13, pp. 1-192.
  1974.   New species and records for the genus *Mesostenus* in South America.   Acta Zool. Lilloana, vol. 31, pp. 27-46.
  1975a. A revision of the Argentine species of *Epirhyssa*.   Acta Zool. Lilloana, vol. 31, pp. 125-158.
  1975b. Relaciones zoogeográficas y origen de la fauna de Ichneumonidae en la provincía biogeográfica del monte del noroeste Argentino.   Acta Zool. Lilloana, vol. 31, pp. 175-252.
  1978.   A revision of the genus Epirhyssa.   Studia Entomologica, vol. 20, pp. 297-412.
TOWNES, HENRY K.
  1972.   Ichneumonidae as biological control agents.   Proceedings of the Tall Timbers Conference on Ecological Control by Habitat Management, vol. 3, pp. 235-248.
WILLINK, ABRAHAM
  1952.   Los véspidos sociales argentinos . . .   Acta Zool. Lilloana, vol. 10, pp. 105-151.

CHARLES C. PORTER

The Caballo Muerto Complex: An Investigation of Cupisnique Culture

Principal Investigator: Thomas G. Pozorski, Carnegie Museum of Natural History, Pittsburgh, Pennsylvania (formerly at University of Texas, Austin, Texas).

Grant No. 1167:   For an investigation of Cupisnique culture: The Caballo Muerto complex, north coast of Peru.

The Caballo Muerto complex was discovered and named in 1969 by members of the Chan Chan-Moche Valley project under the direction of Dr. Michael E. Moseley and Dr. Carol J. Mackey. Prior to this time its existence was unknown, probably because of the amount of attention paid to other important sites in the Moche Valley, such as Chan Chan. Once the complex had been dated to Cupisnique or Chavín times, preliminary excavations under the auspices of the Chan Chan-Moche Valley project were undertaken by Luis Watanabe of the University of San Marcos early in 1972. His excavations revealed, among other things, that at least one mound, Huaca de los Reyes, contains a number of impressive mud friezes. My own excavations at Caballo Muerto were carried out between October 1973 and April 1974 for a total of five months. Six weeks of this time were spent at Huaca de los Reyes. Support for my work was generously supplied by the National Geographic Society and the Institute of Latin American Studies of the University of Texas at Austin. I surveyed and excavated under Supreme Resolution no. 2947, given to the Chan Chan-Moche Valley project by the Instituto Nacional de Cultura of Peru.

Caballo Muerto Complex

The Caballo Muerto complex is located at the mouth and partially within the Río Seco Quebrada between the Cooperativa Laredo and its old annex of Galindo on the north side of the Moche Valley, Peru. The complex consists principally of eight platform mounds, made of cobbles and boulders wet-laid in a mud matrix, which are distributed over an area of about 2 kilometers north-south by 1 kilometer east-west. Individual mounds vary in size from 24 by 25 by 2 meters high to 100 by 120 by 18 meters high, though in terms of over-all area and components Huaca de los Reyes is the largest. Each mound is large enough to be a corporate labor structure, that is, a structure built by an organized group of people at least partially supported by a separate group who are food-producers. All but one of the mounds are clustered on the south side of the complex; the exception, however, seems to be connected with the other mounds via a wide road. The mounds show some temporal differentiation among themselves and probably had multiple and possibly different functions. The exact mound sequence, however, rests on ceramic and architectural data which has been published elsewhere (Pozorski and Pozorski, 1979; Pozorski, 1975, 1976, 1980, n.d.). Most of the mounds are interconnected by megalithic walls, but the majority of these walls were found to date to later pre-Columbian times because they were built over abandoned mounds.

Huaca de los Reyes

This mound is the best-preserved and most elaborate, in terms of decoration and layout, of all the mounds within the Caballo Muerto complex. My excavations here were guided by information gathered during the previous excavations and mapping. My focus was primarily on entrance and access patterns within the site and on the clarification of several places that were architecturally unclear. A secondary focus was the partial clearing of certain rooms in an attempt to ascertain functional aspects of the site. Finally, as more of a surprise than a plan, the discovery of several new and different friezes added considerably to the total amount of data obtained.

Huaca de los Reyes is located with its back face along the east side of the latest cut of the Río Seco Quebrada. This location was presumably intentional, probably to restrict access to the mound area. The layout of the site consists of two main bilaterally symmetrical platform mounds. Each mound has a pair of lateral wings extending eastward, forming two overlapping U-shaped configurations, each opening N.85°E. The upper or west platform mound stands about 6 meters high with its pair of lateral wings (designated upper), which border a central plaza (designated upper), resting on top of the lower or east platform mound. The lateral wings (designated lower) of the lower mound extend to the east from its face and also border a plaza (designated lower), somewhat larger than the upper plaza. The height of the lower mound is about 5.5 meters, but since it is built on a much lower level than the upper mound, the perceived difference between the heights of the mounds is greater. Also included in the layout are two sets of side platform mounds, one set (designated eastern) flanking the east face of the lower mound and the second (designated western) flanking the upper wings. Additional features include various walls and benches south of the upper mound, walls and a small eastward-facing platform with at least two plazas north of the upper mound, a small two-room structure just west of the upper mound, and a large plaza east of the lower wings. Friezes are present on the east faces of both principal mounds as well as the entire sides of their corresponding lateral wings that face inward toward the centers of their respective plazas. Also, friezes exist on the east faces of all the lateral wings of the west-side platforms and on top of the upper main mound.

Excavations in several places revealed at least two, and possibly three, construction phases. This evidence remains scanty, however, since extensive excavations would have called for the destruction of the ultimate construction layer. Unless otherwise indicated, the following description is of the last construction phase.

Adobe Friezes

Each frieze is made of adobe mud laid over a matrix of cobbles, boulders, and mud mortar. The excavation of each adobe frieze involved a preliminary clearing of the wall-fall of cobbles, adobe nodules, and earth in front of the frieze. This was followed by a fine cleaning of the frieze surface with an awl and small paintbrush. An intact frieze surface could be distinguished by a yellowish finishing clay and, occasionally, faint white paint, which probably acted as a base for other colors. Once cleaned, each frieze was photographed and drawn and then covered with the same excavated earth and cobbles. All friezes were cleared by my workmen except the northern ones on the east face of the lower mound, one column in the south lower wing, and two side panels and parts of two niches on the east face of the upper mound.

In the lower plaza there are two basic types of friezes: (1) large adobe heads and (2) standing bipedal figures, usually associated with smaller design elements. The first, and more impressive, type of frieze is the large adobe head, bearing human as well as feline characteristics. There are six of these set in niches along the east face of the lower mound, three to the north and three to the south of the central colonnade area. The condition of the excavated heads varies, but the one uncovered by my workmen is fortunately the best-preserved. Each head varies slightly in details, but basically each faces east and has a frowning mouth with interlocking canines, a broad, flat nose, and rectanguloid eyes apparently looking straight ahead. Each head measures about

180 centimeters across and 60 centimeters deep and probably once stood at least 2 meters high. The only large-scale representation even vaguely similar to these heads known on the north coast of Peru were Idolos V and VI at Moxeke in the Casma Valley, the feline figure set in the central staircase at Punkuri in the Nepeña Valley, and those on Limoncarro Temple in Jequetepeque uncovered by Dr. Zevallos Quiñones in 1968.

The second, and more numerous, type of frieze is the bipedal, presumably human, figure. Along each lateral wing of the lower mound there is a bipedal figure adorning the plaza-side face of each of the columns in the front row. Each of these figures stands on the floor of the colonnade with its feet parallel and slightly apart, with the toes pointing toward the plaza. The feet extend out from the face of the column an average of 30 centimeters. Often, but not always, there is a fanged, outward-looking profile head to the left and right of the feet. Preservation varied, but usually about 30 centimeters of the height of each frieze has been conserved. Exceptions to this are the end columns, which, preserved up to 1 meter high, reveal the rest of the figure's legs, possibly part of a vestment, and a pendant snake head.

Each six-room structure at the ends of the lower wings has two wide niches that also contain bipedal figures. To each side of the upper portions of the legs are a snake head, apparently emanating from the body of the figure, and some other, as yet unclear, representations.

Bipedal figures are also present along the colonnade area of the east face of the lower mound on all four plaza-side faces of the front row of columns. They form the two entrance panel friezes off the extreme ends of this front row. These figures differ in that the feet are less three-dimensional than the ones on the lateral wings and are situated on top of elements of each of the outward-looking fanged profile heads to the left and right.

The plaza-side faces of the front columns of the east-side platform mounds may have once contained friezes, but none of them is preserved well enough to be certain.

For the west-side platform mounds, each of the lateral wings contains a niche with a mud frieze. Each is of a standing feline with clawed feet and a tail that has been elaborated into a serpent head. The friezes are arranged in a bilaterally symmetrical manner with respect to the east-west axes of each mound. This means that for each mound the south wing has the head to the north and the tail to the south while the north wing is just the opposite.

For the upper plaza there is somewhat more variety. On each of the lateral wings there are two central columns with friezes; two entrance friezes adjacent to the columns; and two niches with friezes, one on each side of the colonnade area. Along the east face of the upper mound there are two central columns with friezes, two entrance panel friezes adjacent to the columns, and four niches with friezes, two niches on each side of the colonnade area. On the plaza-side column faces of both the upper wings of the plaza side and along the east face of the upper mound are standing bipedal figures situated on a decorated border formed by a pair of profile heads. The same is true for all the entrance panel friezes of the upper wings and of the upper mound, though quite often the profile heads differ markedly.

Each niche of the upper wings contains a frieze pattern consisting of two side elements of either downward-looking or inward-looking agnathic heads, plus a center element of two upward-looking heads joined at the top of their heads. The center element is a semirectangular projection from the plane of the two side elements, in which all the projection is decorated by friezes. The total width of each niche is about 1.7 meters, with each element, the two sides and center, occupying roughly one-third of the total width. The best-preserved stands about 40 centimeters high, but undoubtedly they were much higher.

The niches along the east face of the upper mound are of about the same dimensions and form as those of the lateral wings. The frieze designs, however, all differ from one another. Center elements basically appear to be different forms of feet, while side elements vary from upward-looking heads to inward-looking heads to downward-looking heads. These are descriptions for the upper set of friezes only, however, for below the floor level of each niche lies another stratigraphically earlier frieze. The basic earlier design is a bipedal figure standing on two pedestal bases flanked by outward-looking profile heads. Three of these follow this pattern closely, but one frieze has a bipedal figure standing on two sculptured heads accompanied by much different, more curvilinear, profile heads to each side. These offer substantial proof of at least two construction stages for the upper main mound.

With respect to the summit of the upper main mound, one full-round adobe head was found in situ on the northwest corner of a rectangular column located on the south lateral platform. Its condition was far from perfect, but it seems to have faced the interior of the mound, possibly over a sunken room.

Style

Style, defined as the representation of certain forms and motifs in a prescribed manner, varies considerably at Huaca de los Reyes. While certain figures are common and repetitive, their manner of execution differs markedly. The best example of this is the bipedal figure, which is generally depicted in a three-dimensional, almost full-round manner, but also is portrayed in both bas-relief and engraving. If depth of execution is used as a criterion for style definition, then there are at least three styles, or three variations of the same style, represented at Huaca de los Reyes.

Most figures are repetitive at the site, and differences among them can probably be attributed to individual artistic variation. However, in certain places there is more variation than artistic license allows. This is especially true for the upper plaza. Of the four entrance panel friezes on the upper wings, three depict a bipedal figure standing on inverted agnathic heads while a fourth figure stands on an upright head. Along the east face of the upper mound, of four friezed early niches, three have regular, somewhat rectangular fanged profile heads. The fourth also depicts fanged profile heads but is done in a much more curvilinear, high-relief style. Lastly, in addition to a distinctive incisionlike technique, the entrance friezes and columns of the upper main mound depict profile heads containing nonfanged mouths and circular eyes. Hence, if style is defined by spatial correspondences, then here, too, are depicted either at least three styles or an extremely wide variation of one general style.

Dating

Relative intrasite dating makes the stylistic interpretations of the friezes even more interesting. The majority of the friezes are all contemporaneous. This conclusion is based on architectural connections of floors and walls plus symmetrical architectural layout. This dating is supported by ceramic evidence. Though certain areas have concentrations of vessels apparently purposely broken, all architectural units contain the same types of ceramics. The stratigraphically earlier friezes of the niches on the upper mound are probably not much earlier than the upper friezes because (1) the architectural construction techniques and layout are the same and (2) the ceramics are the same for both sets of friezes. The stylistic ties between the common profile fanged heads of the older upper mound niches and the later ones of the lower plaza are closer than the ties among the contemporary older niches themselves. Hence, the situation at Huaca de los Reyes is this: A large number of friezes, largely contemporaneous, have been found in situ. If found as isolated examples and then compared, several friezes would probably be classified stylistically and chronologically distinct. However, since they are known to be contemporaneous, they must represent either (1) an extreme variation of one style, a stand which, if taken, calls into question the very definition of style, or (2) two, three, or more styles being used at one point in time. In either case, great chronological change is not indicated.

Radiocarbon dates are available for three mounds. All samples were submitted to the laboratory of the University of Texas. Dates from the same level within one mound on the south side of the Caballo Muerto complex, Huaca Herederos Chica, were 1090 B.C. ± 60 (Tx-1937) and 1500 B.C. ± 70 (Tx-1938). Samples from postholes associated with the earlier construction phase of the upper mound of Huaca de los Reyes yielded dates of 1190 B.C. ± 60 (Tx-1973), 1360 B.C. ± 80 (Tx-1972), and 1730 B.C. ± 80 (Tx-1974). A single date from a sealed floor of Huaca Gravalito on the east side of the Caballo Muerto complex is 440 B.C. ± 70 (Tx-1939). The dates for the former two sites are surprisingly early for a supposed Cupisnique or Chavin site. All these dates could be still earlier since cane, the material used, reputedly yields dates 250 to 300 years too young.

The relative dating based on ceramics, however, supports the radiocarbon dates. The ceramics from Huaca de los Reyes and Huaca Herederos Chica are very similar. A majority of the ceramics are crude utilitarian wares with a relatively small percentage of finer wares. Fine ware decoration is limited to incised lines, often delimiting punctated areas, graphite or manganese paint bands, and occasional applique bands with large indentations. No definite feline motifs or circular decoration was found. Burnishing varies from high and even to low and streaky. Major forms are neckless ollas, open bowls, and stirrup-spout bottles. The wares, decoration, and forms correspond to those found at the coastal Initial Period site of Gramalote on the north side of the Moche Valley and possibly to other pre-Chavin sites on the coast as well.

The ceramics of Huaca Guavalito and another mound, Huaca la Cruz, are somewhat different. Certain wares, decoration, and forms continue, but others are absent and new ones appear. Most significant is the presence of Chavin incised circles with central dot designs at Guavalito.

Function of Huaca de los Reyes

A question still to be resolved is: What kind of site was Huaca de los Reyes? Obviously it was an important center, probably with religious functions, but the amount of utilitarian pottery at the site, and at other mounds within Caballo Muerto, argues for something more than a "ceremonial center." The amount of alluvium burying the foundations of several of the Caballo Muerto mounds indicates that the ground surface in Early Horizon times was at least 6 meters below the present surface. Hence, there could have been numerous dwellings among the mounds. Also, surface evidence on nearby hills indicates equally early domestic occupation. Still, the mounds would have stood in marked contrast to any domestic house and would have been associated with different activities. Undoubtedly, at Huaca de los Reyes there were specific functions connected with different parts of the site, but as yet these have not been differentiated.

The site was designed for maximum effect once one was inside. Virtually all of the friezes face plaza areas where vision is best. Interior architecture is all finely plastered as opposed to the unplastered exterior sides of mounds. Thus, from afar, Huaca de los Reyes looked like an ordinary stone huaca, but once one was within the "U" and approaching the lower main mound, the combination of finely plastered architecture and colored friezes over 2 meters high must have been overwhelming.

Furthermore, the architectural relationships between the lower plaza, the upper plaza, and the summit show a gradual narrowing of available space for groups of people. It appears that once within the site, the various areas became less public, with more restricted access as one went west and finally up into the innermost rooms of the summit of the upper main mound.

Comparisons with Other Early Peruvian Mounds

During my stay in Peru I had the opportunity to visit several other Chavin or reputedly Chavin sites both on the coast and in the sierra. On the coast I saw Limoncarro and several cemeteries in the Jequetepeque Valley, Huaca de la Pampa de Jaguay in the Chicama Valley, and Huaca de Los Chinos and Menocucho in the upper Moche Valley. South of the Moche, I visited, or at least saw, two mounds in the Viru Valley, a 14-mound complex in Chao; Punkuri and Cerro Blanco in Nepeña; Cerro Sechin, Taukachi, Konkan, Sechin Alto, Pampa de las Llamas, Moxeke, and La Cantina in Casma, and Las Haldas south of Casma; several unnamed mounds in Huarmey; Cocharcas, Cerro los Taros, Chupa Cigarro Chico, Chupa Cigarro Grande, Pampa de Chupa Cigarro Grande, Li-31, and the Lighthouse site in the Supe Valley; and the Garagay and San Humberto mounds of the Chillon Valley near Lima.

In the sierra, where travel is more difficult, I managed to see Kumbemayo near Cajamarca, Pumakayan in Huaraz, and the type site of Chavin de Huantar in Chavin.

My general impression is that the majority of mounds of the Early Horizon, or at least the very early ceramic period, are clustered between the Casma and Supe Valleys. This may be a bias of sampling on my part, but the frequency of mounds within the relatively small areas of these valleys is undeniable. Other valleys to the north and south do contain early sites, but they are harder to find and consequently make one wonder if this is a pattern reflected by present-day roads and nearby environs or a true reflection of the number of early sites that exist. The same can be said of the sierra, selva, and montaña regions, only more so.

With respect to the dating of early mounds and sites, lack of excavation leaves little that one can say besides a more or less intuitive feeling of earliness based on observations of architectural layout. Little or no precise chronological, let alone functional, studies can be made without excavation. The sheer number of mounds within the Casma-Supe region bespeaks of great importance either diachronically as a long mound-building tradition, synchronically as a rapid florescence and relatively short expanse of time of a very high culture, or some combination of both. Like most things, the final analysis will probably lie in between the two extremes. The present pattern suggests that while Caballo Muerto (and in particular Huaca de los Reyes) is impressive, it lies near the northern limits of Early Horizon site distribution and is not large in relation to several sites farther south. Therefore, I would think that Caballo Muerto is more of a regional outlying post or center of a larger cultural phenomenon centered in the Casma-Supe region.

As for origins, the present site distribution also suggests that the beginnings of what is recognized as the Chavin art and architectural style could very well have originated, for a large part, in the Casma-Supe region. The corresponding high number of large preceramic sites in the same region supports the hypothesis, thus providing for a smooth cultural continuity without major outside influences. Whatever the true story was, however, remains for future investigations.

REFERENCES

POZORSKI, THOMAS G.
1975.   El complejo Caballo Muerto y los frisos de barro de la Huaca de los Reyes.   Rev. Mus. Nac., Lima, Peru, vol. 41, pp. 211-251.
1976.   Caballo Muerto: A complex of early ceramic sites in the Moche Valley, Peru.   Ph.D. thesis, University of Texas at Austin.   University Films, Ann Arbor, Michigan.
1980.   The Early Horizon site of Huaca de los Reyes: Societal implications. Amer. Antiquity, vol. 45, pp. 100-110.
1981.   Early stratification and subsistence systems: The Caballo Muerto complex.   Pp. 225-255 *in* "Chan Chan: The Andean Desert City," Kent C. Day and Michael E. Moseley, eds.   School of American Research, Advanced Seminar Series, University of New Mexico Press, Albuquerque, New Mexico.

POZORSKI, SHELIA, and POZORSKI, THOMAS G.
  1979.   An early subsistence exchange system in the Moche Valley, Peru.
           Journ. of Field Archaeol., vol. 6, no. 4, pp. 413-432.

                                                        THOMAS G. POZORSKI

The Coral Reef Fishes of the Solomon Islands

Principal Investigator: John E. Randall, Bernice P. Bishop Museum, Honolulu.

Grant No. 1220:   In support of a study of the coral reef fishes of the Solomon Islands and New Guinea.

A. W. Herre (1931) prepared a checklist of the fishes of the Solomon Islands after making a collection of 189 species of fishes at Ysabel Island in 1929. His list contains only 344 species. Since this checklist appeared, there has been only one collection of significance from these islands—that of W. Chapman during World War II. This collection, largely unreported, is housed principally at the U. S. National Museum of Natural History.

By virtue of their proximity to New Guinea and Indonesia, which have the richest marine biota in the world, the Solomons could be expected to have a fish fauna at least four or five times as great as the number of Herre's checklist. To collect and photograph the fishes of the Solomon Islands, with emphasis on coral reef fishes, was the objective of the month-long expedition that began on July 4, 1973. The other participating ichthyologists were Dr. Walter A. Starck II, whose superbly equipped 64-foot research vessel *El Torito* (fig. 1) was our principal base of operations (see July 1973 issue of *Seacraft*); Dr. Gerald R. Allen, then working for the Australian Museum but now curator of fishes of the Western Australian Museum; Dr. Barry Goldman, who with his wife, Lois, sailed their 32-foot sloop *Bundoon* to the Solomons; and Wade Doak of New Zealand, an eminent underwater photographer.

The first 12 days of fieldwork we spent at Guadalcanal, followed by 3 days at Savo, 4 at Florida Island, 8 at Alite Reef (off Malaita), and 4 final days back at Guadalcanal.

Randall and Allen then proceeded for 5 days of fish collecting and photography to New Britain, where they were joined by undersea photographer Roger Steene of Cairns, Australia. After New Britain, 13 days were spent in New Guinea (9 at Madang and 4 at Port Moresby).

Many different collecting methods were employed, but most fishes were taken with the ichthyocide rotenone, the anesthetic quinaldine, spears, and dynamite. Dr. Goldman made quantitative assays of reef-fish populations from dynamite stations. A few of the larger bony fishes and sharks were collected with powerheads (explosive-tipped devices).

Fig. 1.   *El Torito* at Sandfly Passage, Florida Island, Solomon Islands.

Starck and Randall (fig. 2) often wore striped wet suits while diving in the hope that this pattern would discourage sharks from closely approaching them. Starck developed this concept in the Coral Sea after noting that sea snakes, often ringed with black, seemed to enjoy immunity from predation. He also performed a field experiment there to test this pattern by offering food to sharks and other large predaceous fishes on solid-colored and banded rods. The food at the end of the solid-colored rod was taken first, and considerable time generally passed before bait on the banded rod was seized. Starck's striped suit certainly had a repelling effect on a group of small sharks at Lord Howe Island (Doak, 1974), which may have been Galápagos sharks *(Carcharhinus galapagensis)*. In the Solomon Islands the effect of the striped suits was far less conclusive, and Randall was closely approached on several occasions by gray reef sharks *(C. amblyrhynchos)* and once by a bull shark *(C. leucus)*. Later field tests sponsored by the U. S. Navy at Enewetak, Marshall Islands, and off southern California, revealed no positive effect of the striped suit on sharks, though Galápagos sharks were not among the species observed (Rhett McNair, personal communication).

Particular emphasis in the fish collecting was placed on the deeper diving depths, not infrequently to 150-200 feet. It was in these greater depths, generally, that we obtained our most exciting fishes.

The collections of fishes were divided between the Bishop Museum in Honolulu and the Australian Museum in Sydney, with the first series going to the former institution.

The expedition was very successful, yielding many new records of fishes (not fully studied, hence not yet enumerated). Approximately 35 new species of fishes were discovered, as well as a new wrasse genus. Some papers have already appeared describing these fishes, others are in press, and a number are "on the drawing board."

Allen concentrated on the damselfishes (Pomacentridae). He collected 54 new records of damselfishes from the Solomon Islands, thus bringing the known species of this family to 98, among them a new *Abudefduf* (fig. 3, top) (Hensley and Allen, 1977), and a new *Chromis,* which will be described by Randall in a revision of the Indo-Pacific species of this large genus. Solomon Islands material was important in another of Allen's pomacentrid papers (Allen, 1975a), as it was in studies of the wrasse genus *Paracheilinus* (Allen, 1974; Randall and Harmelin-Vivien, 1977). Allen and Randall (1977) revised the Indo-Pacific sharpnose puffers *(Canthigaster);* among their new species was one collected in a deep rotenone station off Florida Island.

In the same deep station two new cardinalfishes *(Apogon)* were collected (Fraser and Randall, 1976) as well as a new seabass of the genus *Liopropoma,*

Fig. 2.   John E. Randall at Alite Reef, Solomon Islands. (Photo by Gerald R.
Allen.)

which will be described by Randall and Taylor in a revision of the Indo-Pacific
species of this genus.

Collections of other serranid fishes during the expedition were of particular importance. Allen and Starck (1975) named a new grouper *(Cephalopholis
xanthopterus)* and many lovely anthiine fishes were taken, some of which have
been described (Randall and Lubbock, in press).

Solomons specimens and photographs of angelfishes of the genus *Genicanthus* permitted the completion of a revision of this group (Randall, 1975).

A paper on Indo-Pacific pipefishes (Dawson and Randall, 1975) incorporated Solomon Islands material.

A new garden eel of the genus *Taenioconger,* which was collected with rotenone in 120 feet off the wreck of a Japanese troopship 7 miles west of Honiara,
is described, along with another new *Taenioconger* from French Polynesia, in a
paper by Böhlke and Randall (in press).

A special effort was made to collect gobiid fishes of the genus *Cryptocentrus*
and allied genera that live symbiotically in burrows with alpheid shrimps, and
several new species were obtained. Revisions of the large genera *Cryptocentrus*
and *Amblyeleotris* are in progress by Douglass F. Hoese and Randall.

FIG. 3. Specimens of the (top) damselfish *Abudefduf lorenzi* Hensley and Allen, from Florida Island, and the seabass *Anthias pleurotaenia* (Bleeker), male color phase, from Savo Island, Solomon Islands. (Photos by Gerald R. Allen.)

FIG. 4.   A scorpaenid fish (*Amblyapistus* sp.) from Guadalcanal. (Photo by Gerald R. Allen.)

A new goby of the genus *Valenciennea*, collected in the harbor of Honiara, will be described by Hoese and Helen Larson of the Australian Museum in their revision of this genus.

Underwater observations and collections of parrotfishes were useful in linking sexually dichromatic pairs of parrotfishes (Randall and Choat, 1980). The same was true for the Labridae, particularly the genus *Halichoeres; H. argus* and *H. leparensis* were shown to be color forms of the same species, as were *H. gymnocephalus* and *H. chloropterus* (Randall, in press). Valuable specimens were procured of the labrid genera *Stethojulis, Pseudocheilinus, Cirrhilabrus, Leptojulis,* and *Pseudojuloides.* A revision of *Pseudojuloides* has been completed (Randall and Randall, in press), as has one on *Leptojulis* (Randall and Ferraris, MS.). Studies of the other genera are continuing.

A total of 468 fishes were photographed after removal from the sea by Randall during the expedition. Allen took 1,000 underwater photos of fishes. A number of these have appeared in his excellent book, "Damselfishes of the South Seas," published in 1975. Starck and Doak also took many underwater photographs. Doak (1975) has written an interesting book, "Sharks and Other Ancestors," which includes an account of the ichthyological expedition to the Solomon Islands.

REFERENCES

ALLEN, GERALD R.
1974.   A review of the labrid genus *Paracheilinus* with the description of a new species from New Guinea.   Pacific Sci., vol. 28, no. 4, pp. 449-455, illus.
1975a. Four new damselfishes (Pomacentridae) from the southwest Pacific. Proc. Linn. Soc. New South Wales, vol. 99, no. 2, pp. 87-99.
1975b. Damselfishes of the South Seas, 240 pp.   T. F. H. Publications, Inc., Neptune City, New Jersey.
ALLEN, GERALD R., and RANDALL, JOHN E.
1977.   Review of the sharpnose pufferfishes (subfamily Canthigasterinae) of the Indo-Pacific.   Rec. Australian Mus., vol. 30, no. 17, pp. 475-515.
ALLEN, GERALD R., and STARCK, WALTER, A., II
1975.   *Cephalopholis xanthopterus,* a new species of serranid fish from the Great Barrier Reef and Melanesia.   Rec. Western Australian Mus., vol. 3, no. 3, pp. 245-249.
BÖHLKE, JAMES E., and RANDALL, JOHN E.
1981.   Four new garden eels (Congridae: Heterocongrinae) from the Pacific and Indian oceans.   Bull. Mar. Sci., vol. 31, no. 2, pp. 366 ff.
DAWSON, CHARLES E., and RANDALL, JOHN E.
1975.   Notes on Indo-Pacific pipefishes (Pisces: Syngnathidae) with description of two new species.   Proc. Biol. Soc. Washington, vol. 88, no. 25, pp. 263-280, illus.
DOAK, WADE
1974.   Revolutionary weapon anti-shark wet suit.   Skin Diver, June 1974, pp. 87-88.
1975.   Sharks and other ancestors, 333 pp.   Hodder & Stoughton, Auckland, New Zealand.
FRASER, THOMAS F., and RANDALL, JOHN E.
1976.   Two new Indo-West Pacific cardinalfishes of the genus *Apogon.*   Proc. Biol. Soc. Washington, vol. 88, no. 47, pp. 503-508, illus.
HENSLEY, DANIEL A., and ALLEN, GERALD R.
1977.   A new species of *Abudefduf* (Pisces: Pomacentridae) from the Indo-Australian Archipelago.   Rec. Western Australian Mus., vol. 6, no. 1, pp. 107-118.
HERRE, ALBERT W.
1931.   A check list of fishes from the Solomon Islands.   Journ. Pan-Pacific Res. Inst., vol. 6, no. 4, pp. 4-8.
RANDALL, JOHN E.
1975.   A revision of the Indo-Pacific angelfish genus *Genicanthus,* with descriptions of three new species.   Bull. Mar. Sci., vol. 25, no. 3, pp. 393-421, illus.
1980.   Two new Pacific labrid fishes of the genus *Halichoeres,* with notes on other species of the genus.   Pacific Sci., vol. 34, no. 4, pp. 415-432.
RANDALL, JOHN E., and CHOAT, J. HOWARD
1980.   Two new parrotfishes of the genus *(Scarus)* from the Central and South Pacific, with further examples of sexual dichromatism.   Zool. Journ. Linn. Soc. vol. 70, pp. 303-419.

RANDALL, JOHN E., and HARMELIN-VIVIEN, MIREILLE L.
   1977.   A review of the labrid fishes of the genus *Paracheilinus* with description of
            two new species from the western Indian Ocean.   Bull. Mus. Nat.
            Hist. Nat. (Paris), ser. 3, no. 436, pp. 329-342.
RANDALL, JOHN E., and LUBBOCK, ROGER
   1981.   A review of the serranid fishes of the subgenus *Mirolabrichthys* (Anthi-
            inae: *Anthias*), with descriptions of six new species.   Sci. Contr. Nat.
            Hist. Mus. Los Angeles County, no. 333, pp. 1-27.
RANDALL, JOHN E., and RANDALL, HELEN A.
   1981.   A revision of the labrid fish genus *Pseudojuloides,* with descriptions of five
            new species.   Pac. Sci., vol. 35, no. 1, pp. 51-74.

                                                                JOHN E. RANDALL

Marine Mollusks of Some Island Groups of Polynesia

Principal Investigator: Harald A. Rehder, National Museum of Natural History, Smithsonian Institution, Washington, D. C.

Grant Nos. 1145, To carry on fieldwork in the faunally unknown westernmost
1250, and 1650. islands and atolls of French Polynesia (Maupiti to Bellingshausen) and on Tubuai Island in the Austral Group, 1973;
and to study the marine mollusks of the Tokelau Islands,
1976.

Investigations on Some Outer Islands of Polynesia, 1973

In continuation of the support already given by the National Geographic Society to my study of the marine mollusks of Polynesia (Rehder, 1971; Rehder, 1974; Randall, 1978), I was given the opportunity to visit some islands and atolls in French Polynesia to complement my previous fieldwork in the area.

In the introductory paragraphs of my (1971) account of the 1967 National Geographic Society-Smithsonian-Bishop Museum Expedition to the Marquesas and Pitcairn, I summarized my research project on the marine mollusks of Polynesia, mentioning that there still were areas within the Polynesian province of whose marine life little was known. To study the littoral fauna of some of these areas and make representative collections of mollusks, was the object of the trip supported by the National Geographic Society's 1973 grant.

It was my plan to spend two months in French Polynesia, assisted by my wife, Lois; and, using Tahiti as a base, to visit those islands about which either nothing or very little was known regarding their molluscan fauna.

Of the six islands and atolls chosen, the most important ones in my view were the three atolls and one island at the westernmost end of French Polynesia—Maupiti, Mopelia, Scilly, and Bellingshausen. They lie between the larger Society Islands and the Cook Islands, from both of which groups I had already at hand adequate material; I had nothing, however, from the intervening 400 miles.

Maupiti, Mopelia, Scilly, and Bellingshausen are rarely visited and their marine fauna at the time of my visit was unknown. Maupiti now has a small

541

airstrip and is served by small planes flying twice a week from Bora Bora and Raiatea. The other three are copra-producing atolls, leased by a company owned by M. Robert Hervé of Papeete, Tahiti. They are served every month or two by a ship bringing in supplies and taking back to Papeete full sacks of copra.

Because of the unscheduled and irregular nature of the boat service to the three atolls of Mopelia, Scilly, and Bellingshausen, our program of work in the area had to be arranged around the sailing date of this vessel.

For this reason I called on M. Hervé the morning after my wife and I arrived in Tahiti on March 26, 1973. From him and from the captain-owner of the *Auura Nui,* the boat that would be taking us to the atolls, I learned that the vessel would be leaving sometime during the following week.

A few days before our scheduled departure for the outer islands I was informed that the *Auura Nui* would leave on April 9, three days later than planned. In the following three weeks the departure date was put off exactly seven times, largely because a needed part to repair the engine had to be flown in to Papeete. To put our waiting period to some use, my wife and I collected some specimens on the fringing reef near the hotel where we were staying.

Finally, on Wednesday, April 25, at 2:45 p.m., the *Auura Nui,* a small, steel-hulled freighter, about 25 meters in length, with a crew of about six, left the dock at Papeete and headed for the pass. In order to time our arrival at Mopelia in the early daylight hours, the captain decided to spend the night in Pao Pao Bay, Moorea, and leave from there very early in the morning.

Mopelia, reached on Friday, April 27, early in the morning, has a government meteorological station on it and we were carrying on board a considerable quantity of supplies and equipment for the station. After entering the lagoon and anchoring off the village, the whaleboat of the village came out and took in one load of supplies, returning with a load of sacks of copra. The boat then took Lois and me to the island, and for five or six hours we collected both on the oceanside reef and in the lagoon before returning to the ship.

It was after six o'clock when the *Auura Nui* left Mopelia, having taken on about 30 tons of copra, and early the next morning we arrived at Bellingshausen, where my wife and I were able to spend almost all day collecting while the crew and plantation workers unloaded supplies and took the copra on board.

Early the next morning we arrived at Scilly and here again we went ashore in the second boat. On landing we were immediately welcomed to a large "fare tamaa" or eating place, open on all sides and covered with a palm-thatched roof. A long table was in the center of one half, and in the other half an open fire was burning. Here we were greeted by a large, portly woman, obviously the matriarch of the clan. She and most of her fourteen children, her grandchildren, and their spouses and friends, made up the labor force of the island. Most of them were at breakfast, either at the table or sitting at the sides of the hut, or were busy with the preparations. Breakfast consisted of large bowls of coffee, cabin biscuits, fish, pork, taro, and other native foods. Dogs, cats, pigs, and fowl ran free everywhere in the little settlement.

After breakfast Lois and I left with our equipment and collected first on the ocean reef and then in the afternoon in the lagoon, making good collections in both places. Since we were scheduled to spend the night on shore, we joined the villagers and crew at supper, after which I joined some of the young girls at the bowling game of petanque until it got too dark to see the jack. One of them was from the island of Rapa and had been there when I was on the *Westward* visiting there in 1971. She very kindly moved out of her house and let us spend the night there—it was not, however, particularly restful because of the noise of pigs quartered below the house, the men playing petanque outside by the light of Coleman lanterns, and the happy sounds of guitars and singing voices.

The morning noises of the village awakened us early, and by 8:00 a.m. we, together with crew, some pigs, baby turtles, and miscellaneous other goods, left in two whaleboats and crossed the lagoon to a safer pass, where the *Auura Nui* awaited us. At 2:00 p.m. we left Scilly and headed back to Papeete, where we arrived at 4:00 a.m. on Wednesday, May 2, and by 5:30 were back at our hotel.

We now began preparation for our trips to Tubuai and to Tetiaroa Atoll. After purchasing our tickets and some needed supplies, we left at noon Saturday, May 5, for Tubuai, in the Austral Islands.

We spent six days on this hilly island, which lies 460 kilometers due south of Tahiti and is 10 kilometers long and 5 kilometers wide. Our visit began auspiciously with a cordial welcome by the late M. Charles Doom, a leading citizen there, who put us up in a nearby house that he owned.

Every day we made trips from our house to collect at localities on the north, south, and east coasts. Twice we were taken by boat to motus, or islets, on the eastern part of the barrier reef, where a fine series of mollusks was gathered.

On Friday, May 11, we left Tubuai, arriving back at the Faaa airport in Tahiti at 3:30 p.m., and during the next week we prepared for shipment the collections we had made in Tubuai and arranged for our visits to Tetiaroa Atoll, 26 miles north of Tahiti, and to Maupiti in the western Society Islands.

On Thursday, May 17, Lois and I made the 20-minute flight to Tetiaroa Atoll, which is roughly square in outline, measures about 6 by 7 miles and has no pass into the lagoon. It had been bought some years earlier by Marlon

Brando, who at the time of our visit was trying to develop the atoll into a restricted tourist resort with full attention to possible deleterious impact on the environment. The atoll may eventually become a national marine park. In this connection Mr. Brando was interested in having a survey made of the atoll's flora and fauna, and the purpose of our visit was to make a representative collection of the mollusks.

We were quartered in the main building of the construction camp and in the four days that we were on the atoll we made comprehensive collections on motus on the north, west, and south sides of the atoll.

On Monday, May 21, we returned to Tahiti and two days later flew to Bora Bora, where we changed to a smaller plane that in 25 minutes took us to Maupiti, a small volcanic island that rises to about 700 feet, is about $1\frac{1}{2}$ miles long, and is surrounded by a barrier reef, the northern half of which consists of two large motus. It lies 30 miles west of Bora Bora and is the westernmost inhabited island in the Society group. To the west of it lie the three small atolls that we had visited four weeks earlier.

We were fortunate to find comfortable quarters in a private home, and for a week we collected on the main island and on the motus on the barrier reef, obtaining a good representative series of the molluscan fauna. Three times we went with natives in their motorboat or pirogue to different motus, and while they worked in their watermelon patches we collected on the outer reef, the shore, and in the lagoon. In our collecting efforts we were aided by a young American couple, staying in the same home, who gathered shells for us on several of their outings to the outer reef by canoe.

On May 30, Wednesday, we left Maupiti to return to Tahiti with stopovers in Bora Bora and Raiatea. On June 2 we arrived at Faaa airport near Papeete and a week later we left for meetings in Queensland, Australia.

Results

Our collecting efforts in the various islands we visited were most successful. All the material has been sorted and catalogued and although some has been identified and recorded, much still remains to be critically studied.

While waiting for the *Auura Nui* to take us to the western atolls we managed to collect 55 lots and 836 specimens on Tahiti. On Mopelia, Bellingshausen, and Scilly we gathered a total of 249 lots and about 2,200 specimens. On Tubuai we collected 264 lots and 1,550 specimens, and on the atoll of Tetiaroa 389 specimens and about 2,280 specimens. Finally on Maupiti our collection of mollusks amounted to 567 lots and 2,250 specimens.

Collecting Mollusks on the Tokelau Islands, 1976

Situated almost equidistant from the Samoan Islands to the south, the Phoenix Islands to the north, the Ellice Islands (now called Tuvalu) to the west, and the Northern Cook Islands to the east, lie the Tokelau Islands. They consist of three atolls, to which group I add Swains Island, since it is related to them geographically and ethnologically, though not politically.

In 1976 the marine mollusks of the Tokelau Islands were completely unknown, and since they lie close to the junction of the Polynesian, the Micronesian, and the eastern Melanesian biogeographical provinces, it was therefore important to determine to which of these biogeographical provinces the Tokelaus should be assigned, or whether the fauna showed any commingling of the faunas of these three provinces. To find an answer to these questions was the purpose of this project, supported by the National Geographic Society's grant in 1976.

In April 1976 my wife and I were invited to join a cruise that would be visiting the Tokelau Islands. A year before, I had been visited by Sandy A. Mactaggart of Edmonton, Alberta, Canada, who was contemplating taking his family on a lengthy cruise through the Pacific, and who wished to undertake during this cruise some worthwhile scientific project. On that first visit and in the course of subsequent correspondence we discussed island groups to visit, possible projects, and the proper procedures and equipment needed to carry them out. In the year between our first meeting and the invitation to join the Mactaggart family, their yacht *Zolana* had been undergoing extensive alterations and testing. In June 1976 the *Zolana* left Florida to head through the Caribbean for the Panama Canal and the Pacific. My wife and I agreed to meet them in Pago Pago, American Samoa, where we arrived on November 2 and where, on Sunday, November 7, the *Zolana* came in. Three days later, we sailed out of Pago Pago Harbor bound first for Apia on Upolu in Western Samoa.

The *Zolana* is a twin-screw auxiliary ketch, 33 meters (108 feet) long, with a steel hull, teak deck, and with a downwind squaresail rig added by the Mactaggarts to her original fore- and aft-rigging. Besides her crew of seven she can accommodate about ten persons.

The Mactaggart family, consisting of Sandy and Cécile Mactaggart and two of their children, was accompanied by Alane Fuldner, a friend who helped with the children's schooling, and Isao Morikawa, houseman. Cécile Mactaggart was keenly interested in and knowledgeable about mollusks and had acquired a select number of reference books on shells. On the islands visited in the course of the earlier part of the cruise she had acquired a collection of shells and we spent most of the afternoon after leaving Apia discussing the shells and identifying some of her collection.

Rather early in the morning following our departure we arrived in Apia to pick up some supplies not obtainable in American Samoa. We spent one night in the harbor and at about noon on November 12 we left again, heading for Swains Island, which we reached the following morning, and after an early lunch on board, went ashore.

Swains Island has long been in the possession of the Jennings family and many of its present inhabitants, now numbering only about 30, are descendants of Eli Jennings, who settled here in 1856 with his Samoan wife Malia. When our parties landed we were welcomed by Wally Jennings, greatgrandson of Eli, and Mrs. Jennings.

The island was once an atoll but the lagoon has been cut off from the sea for some time so that it is now somewhat reduced in size, with the water almost fresh. On a visit here three years earlier I had collected along the lagoon shore and found only dead shells of common lagoon-dwelling bivalves, and living specimens of a freshwater gastropod species, found throughout the Pacific area, that was undoubtedly carried here as eggs or as young specimens on the feet or feathers of waterfowl.

We spent all afternoon on the island. Lois and I and Cécile Mactaggart, Isao, and the children went off in two groups to collect on the reef and beach. It was nearly dark when the last boat returned to the *Zolana,* but since the shelling had not been very successful on Swains (particularly since the lagoon had become a lake), it was decided to push on to the Tokelaus. On the following morning I went over the shells collected on Swains and labeled the collection, placing in alcohol those collected alive.

At about noon we came up on Fakaofu, the southernmost of the Tokelau Islands, an atoll about $7\frac{1}{4}$ miles long and $5\frac{1}{2}$ miles wide. A boat came out to the *Zolana* and we went ashore to the main island of Fenuafala where we collected mainly on the lagoon side before returning to the boat. That night the *Zolana* hove to off Fakaofu.

The following day, after a meeting in the morning with the elders in the meetinghouse, during which we were formally welcomed, we went in boats to an islet on another side of the atoll where in the afternoon we collected in the lagoon as well as on the ocean reef.

We were at Fakaofu all the following day, and in the afternoon the villagers put on a dance show for our benefit. Sandy recorded it in sound on a portable television camera, and later in the evening he played it back for the villagers who came on board the *Zolana* to see and hear themselves on TV.

On the morning of November 17 we arrived at Nukunono, but only

Sandy and some others went ashore in the morning, Sandy bringing me back some shells he had collected.

The following day we all went ashore at the village, crossing the lagoon in small island boats to an islet on the further side, where we collected and had lunch. Back on board in the late afternoon, I labeled and prepared the shells that we had gathered and entered the data in my field book.

The *Zolana* remained off Nukunono during the night and the next day visits were made to the island but I stayed on board, as I had somehow acquired a strained back muscle. In the afternoon the people of Nukunono put on a feast and dance program for the *Zolana* visitors and again in the late afternoon people from the village came to see themselves on the screen.

Sometime during the night the *Zolana* left Nukunono and early the next morning arrived at Atafu, the last and smallest of the Tokelaus. We were at Atafu for three days but I did not go ashore at all because of my back. On the first day most of the party went to the village where they again had a ceremony of welcome; collecting activities, however, were hampered by heavy rains. On the second day, November 21, a Sunday, the whole Mactaggart family and Isao went ashore in two trips in an outrigger canoe, landing on the reef well to the south of the village, as the elders of the village did not want any activity by us near the village for fear it would be a distracting influence on the Sunday afternoon service. They returned at about 4 o'clock with a good collection of shells which I prepared and labeled.

The following day most of the group went ashore again with the television equipment to attend a feast that the people were preparing for us. Again I stayed on board, but the others had a fine feast complete with speeches and gift exchanging, followed later by the purchase of native handcraft. Again, as on the other islands, several boatloads of people from the village came aboard to see the sound film that Sandy had taken in the morning. That evening we left the Tokelaus and set sail for Funafuti in the Ellice Islands now known as Tuvalu.

During the next day, as we headed almost due west, Lois and I packed the preserved material in plastic bags. On the 24th, we had our Thanksgiving dinner in the evening out on deck under the stars, as we were to cross the date line that night and so would lose Thursday the 25th, Thanksgiving Day.

The next day, the 26th, we arrived at Funafuti, Tuvalu, where we were able to anchor in the quiet of the lagoon. The *Zolana* remained here four days while Lois and I tried to arrange for our passage out of Funafuti. The plane reservations we had made in Pago Pago for a flight to Fiji turned out to be nonexistent, but a cargo-passenger vessel, the *Cenpac Rounder,* belonging to the Nauru Line was expected in a few days and would go on to Apia in Samoa. She actually arrived in the lagoon on November 29, and during the intervening time that we spent ashore we did some collecting on the lagoon shore especially near the hotel.

On November 30 we left the *Zolana* and, with our luggage plus two drums of shells and collecting equipment, moved to the *Cenpac Rounder,* where we enjoyed the luxury of a large stateroom.

On December 1, at midafternoon the *Cenpac Rounder* left Funafuti for Savaii, which we reached early on the morning of December 3, docking at Asau, on the north coast near the western end. During the two days we were there we managed to collect a few mollusks.

On December 5 we left Asau, arriving at Apia that afternoon, and disembarked on the next day in the pouring rain. When we arrived in American Samoa that same afternoon after the short flight from Upolu, our trip was virtually over. On the following day we flew on to Honolulu and then home.

Results

Our three weeks with the Mactaggarts on the *Zolana* were a wonderful and unforgetable experience and we are grateful to Sandy and Cécile for giving us the opportunity to join them, for being such delightful hosts, and for helping us in so many ways to make our collecting efforts in the Tokelau Islands a success. Although we were in the Tokelaus only ten days, our collections numbered 677 lots, comprising about 1,600 specimens, a good representative collection from a malacological "terra incognita."

REFERENCES

RANDALL, JOHN E.
  1978.   Marine biological and archeological expedition to Southeast Oceania. Nat. Geogr. Soc. Res. Rpts., 1969 Projects, pp. 473-495.
REHDER, HARALD A.
  1971.   Malacological expedition to the tropical South Pacific.   Nat. Geogr. Soc. Res. Rpts., 1965 Projects, pp. 213-218.
  1974.   Marine biological research in southeastern Polynesia.   Nat. Geogr. Soc. Res. Rpts., 1967 Projects, pp. 243-254.

HARALD A. REHDER

The Extinct Mammalian Order Desmostylia

Principal Investigator: Roy H. Reinhart, Miami University, Oxford, Ohio.

Grant No. 1172: In support of a study of the extinct mammalian order Desmostylia.[1]

Seldom has a group of mammalian vertebrate fossils evoked as many variant taxonomic designations as has the Desmostylia. Since the teeth were first described by Marsh in 1888, these animals have been assigned to the orders Sirenia, Proboscidea, Multituberculata, and Monotremata and referred to Pantodonta, Amblypoda, and Condylarthra. The unsettled taxonomic position has been further emphasized by assigning the desmostylids to the superorder Paenungulata, a broad hypothetical group designed to demonstrate a relationship of the orders Pantodonta, Dinocerata, Pyrotheria, Proboscidea, Embrithopoda, Hyracoidea, and Sirenia. Recent work by Japanese scholars has suggested a connection with pigs (Artiodactyla) or tapirs (Perissodactyla). With no duplication among the above, this represents an assignment to 12 different mammalian orders. One reason for the paradox of multiple taxonomic assignments has been the paucity of cranial and skeletal remains until very recently. The present study classifies a number of problems of taxonomic synonymy and establishes a better diagnosis for each species as well as for higher taxons.

Scope of Project

The project was divided into two parts—preparation and restoration of fossil specimens, and fieldwork. Before formal study could begin it was necessary to prepare many rare well-preserved fossil desmostylids collected chiefly along the southern half of the Oregon coast as well as from a singular site near

---

[1] Study and preparation of specimens were supported by the Smithsonian Institution in 1972 and from 1974 to 1977. Fieldwork and fossil preparation in 1973 were sponsored by the National Geographic Society. Varied support was provided by Miami University, Oxford, Ohio, throughout the study. In addition, my thanks are extended to Dr. Clayton E. Ray of the United States National Museum of Natural History, Washington, D. C.; Dr. Frank C. Whitmore, Jr., of the U. S. Geological Survey, Washington, D. C.; and Charles A. Repenning of the U. S. Geological Survey, Menlo Park, California.

Avenal, California. Funded preparation was carried out by students under my direction beginning in the summer of 1972.

Preparation has been an arduous task; hence a time factor is involved that necessitates a critical evaluation of one or two specimens as completed. Emphasis has been given to restoration of the crania although some postcranial elements have also been prepared. While awaiting the restoration of key specimens, field studies were undertaken in Oregon and California in the summer of 1973 to determine the stratigraphic sequence in which the specimens were collected, as well as to study mineralogical, paleontological, and geological evidence to aid in reconstructing environmental conditions in which these animals lived. As the specimens were collected previous to the initiation of the project, investigation consisted primarily of a clarification of geological conditions at the collected sites. The study in Oregon was a joint undertaking in conjunction with representatives from the U. S. Geological Survey, Division of Stratigraphy, Menlo Park, California, the Oregon Geological Survey, and the Smithsonian Institution. Fieldwork was followed by a study of vertebrate collections at the U. S. Geological Survey, Division of Stratigraphy, Menlo Park, at the University of California, Berkeley, and at Stanford University, all of which house desmostylid specimens in varied stages of preparation.

A similar study was made in the summer of 1975 under the auspices of the Society of Systematic Zoology. This included a field conference and a symposium entitled "Advances in Systematics of Marine Mammals." Speakers for the symposium included many important workers on fossil marine mammals in the United States together with a number of representatives from other countries.

Specimens Studied

Specimens used in this study were collected by the well-known collector of fossil marine mammals, the late Douglas Emlong of Lincoln City, Oregon. The Emlong collection was purchased in 1967 by the Smithsonian Institution and Mr. Emlong continued his fieldwork under Smithsonian auspices. For a complete account of this significant collection of marine mammals see Ray, 1976. A generalized description of the major new, undescribed specimens from Oregon and California prepared and used in this study to date follows:

    a. *Cornwallius* crania of a young, perhaps newly born individual, a juvenile, and a mature adult. To these are added 4 partial mandibles and isolated postcranial elements presumed to belong to this genus on the basis of geographic location, the proximity of identifiable specimens

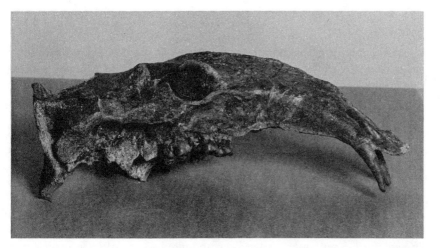

FIG. 1. Lateral view of *Cornwallius sookensis,* from Yaquina Formation, Upper Oligocene, Oregon. Cranial length, 528 millimeters.

of *Cornwallius,* and the age of the strata in which they were found. These specimens are from the Yaquina Formation, Upper Oligocene of Oregon.

b. Crania of a juvenile and an adult of a new species of *Desmostylus* from the Nye Formation, Lower Miocene of Oregon. To this is added two mandibles, of which the younger of the two individuals resembles *Desmostylus* = *(Kronokotherium) brevimaxillare.*

c. Three crania of *Desmostylus cymatias* representing two immature individuals and one adult from the Astoria Formation, Middle Miocene of Oregon.

d. Two mandibles considered referable to *Desmostylus cymatias?* from the Astoria Formation, Oregon.

e. Two partial crania of adults of *Desmostylus hesperus* from an upper member of the Temblor sandstone, late Middle Miocene of California. More than half of each cranium is present.

f. Varied numbers of postcranial elements that belong chiefly with the crania listed above.

Many other specimens have been collected but, because of the necessary lengthy preparation, only the more significant specimens are being studied for this project.

Results Obtained

Although formal description of specimens is progressing, a final report has not been compiled. The following results represent preliminary conclusions, some of which are in the process of being finalized.

1. The affinities of the order Desmostylia to other mammals remain uncertain, although with present information most students of the subject now favor some relationship to primitive Perissodactyla (particularly tapirs), to primitive Artiodactyla (particularly Suina), and to Proboscidea and Sirenia (see Ijiri and Kamei, 1961; Shikama, 1967).

2. Presence of fossil remains in near-shore shallow-water marine facies indicates that the preferred environment of desmostylids was in shallow marine water in lagoons, inland seas, or similar areas protected from the open ocean. The type of terrestrial locomotion remains uncertain. Skeletons, unknown until recent years, have been mounted as plantigrade quadrupeds standing upright on land (Shikama, 1967, 1968). Terrestrial movement suggested by Repenning and illustrated in an article by Zuidema (1970, p. 23) differs markedly from that proposed by Japanese students. Repenning suggested that the specific form *Paleoparadoxia* rested and humped about on land as do sea lions with the forefeet extended backward as flippers. I have not had the opportunity to make a detailed evaluation of the postcranium but can state that movement of any of the desmostylids on land was slow and awkward. Conversely all of the desmostylids appear to have been well adapted to water and were undoubtedly skillful swimmers. Illustrations by Shikama (1967), portray *Paleoparadoxia* in various swimming positions.

3. Probable food habits of desmostylids remain a subject of debate. Cheek teeth of this animal group are structurally designed to resist crushing stress better than those of any other known mammal since component parts of each tooth are essentially solid enamel cylinders. The general opinion is that their feeding habits ranged from herbivorous to omnivorous in that they may have eaten bottom-dwelling animals such as mollusks and crustaceans in addition to plants.

4. A study of desmostylid cranial specimens from California and Oregon indicates that five definitive desmostylids existed along these coastal areas in a time period ranging from the Upper Oligocene to the Upper Miocene. These include *Cornwallius sookensis, Desmostylus hesperus, Desmostylus cymatias*, a new species of *Desmostylus*, and *Paleoparadoxia tabatai*.

5. Recent discovery of columns of *Desmostylus* cheek teeth (Reinhart, 1976) from the phosphate pits of the "Bone Valley Formation," Florida, extended the upper stratigraphic range of the genus and the order Desmostylia

from late Miocene to Mio-Pliocene or to Middle Pliocene (Hemphillian) according to the age designation given to the Bone Valley Formation. This is the first desmostylid authenticated not from the Pacific region. Previously desmostylid remains had been found from the circum-North Pacific region down to Baja, California, but reports on fragmentary teeth, incorrectly identified, have been attributed to *Desmostylus* from various localities. Two such misidentified specimens are *Cryptomastodon* from Java and *Desmostylus* from Texas.

6. A point of major importance in this project is the establishment of a more substantive diagnosis for the genus *Cornwallius* and the differentiation of that genus from *Paleoparadoxia*. Previous to this study *Cornwallius* has been known only from a small number of cheek teeth of which about half were fragmented and, recently, from a small femur referred to this genus. Because of the paucity of specimens much doubt had been cast upon its validity as a genus differing from *Paleoparadoxia*.

7. The newly prepared postcranial elements of *Desmostylus* are relatively abundant as compared with the small number presumed to belong to *Cornwallius*. One of the few bones available for comparison between the genera is the pelvis, which reveals noticeable differences in the two forms. An evaluation of this information will be made when the postcranium is studied.

8. It has not been resolved whether the California *Desmostylus hesperus* and the Japanese *Desmostylus hesperus japonicus* should be in synonymy or be differentiated. In the past few fossil remains attributed to these two forms were from comparable portions of the animal, therefore comparison was difficult. Present studies of the cranium suggest some differences exist. A cranium, widely illustrated for many years as belonging to *D. hesperus,* is now referable to *D. cymatias.* New cranial specimens belonging to *D. hesperus* have been found and this is the first time that the cranium of this species from California has been known.

9. The study to date indicates that the trivial name of *Desmostylus cymatias* for the Oregon Astoria Formation desmostylids will be retained and accepted after a proper diagnosis is determined.

10. A portion of a mandible from Kamchatka, *Kronokotherium brevimaxillare,* is regarded as *Desmostylus* but whether referable to *D. hesperus, D. hesperus japonicus,* or *D. brevimaxillare* is not known at this stage of the study. A comparable mandible which is much more complete has been collected from the Nye Formation, Lower Miocene of Oregon, but conclusions beyond those stated will be deferred pending a more thorough study. The mandible from Kamchatka is believed to belong to a juvenile referable to *D. hesperus japonicus.*

11. The rostrum and mandible of all desmostylids are elongate but differ

in width as well as number, shape, and development of canines and incisors. The cranium of *Cornwallius* has the narrowest rostrum of the desmostylids, and bears large powerfully developed canines and three pairs of small rounded, weakly developed incisors of which I^3 is vestigial. The anterior end of the mandible, only partially known, held one pair of canine tusks, circular in cross-section, similar to those of all members of *Desmostylus* and one smaller pair of incisors I_3.

Paleoparadoxia, with the broadest rostrum of the desmostylids, has moderately developed canines in both the maxillaries and mandible and three pairs of spatulate, procumbent incisors in either jaw. I^3 approaches caniniform structure.

Desmostylus hesperus japonicus has one pair of well-developed maxillary canines; an equal-sized individual of *D. hesperus* from the Temblor Formation of California has one pair of small or rudimentary canines. The small canine size in the California specimen may be an example of dimorphism, the California form being a female, or the condition may signify a gradual loss of maxillary canines in both sexes. The Japanese specimen is of Lower Miocene age, the California specimen from the upper Middle Miocene. Upper incisors had disappeared in *D. hesperus* and *D. hesperus japonicus.* In the mandibles of both forms there is one pair of well-developed procumbent canines and one smaller, moderately developed pair of procumbent incisors.

Desmostylus cymatias has a moderately broad rostrum with no evidence of canines or incisors. The adult is essentially edentulous but rudimentary cheek teeth were present. If younger crania are correctly assigned to this species, well-developed cheek teeth are present in young individuals. The question then arises, "Can an individual desmostylid lose its cheek teeth as it grows older and are the cheek teeth replaced by a horny pad?" Mandibles from the same stratigraphic unit and geographic area may be assignable to this species or to *D. hesperus.* These bear one pair of canines and one pair of incisors as in known mandibles of *D. hesperus.*

12. A study of recently prepared specimens from the Temblor Formation, Garzas Creek, near Coalinga, California, suggests *Vanderhoofius coalingensis* should be placed in synonymy with *Desmostylus hesperus.* Further evaluation is necessary to determine if this suggestion is correct.

REFERENCES

IJIRI, S., and KAMEI, T.
    1961.   On the skulls of *Desmostylus mirabilis* Nagao from South Sakhalin and of *Paleoparadoxia tabatai* (Tokunaga) from Gifu Prefecture, Japan. Earth Science, no. 53, pp. 1-27.

RAY, CLAYTON E.
  1976.   Fossil marine mammals of Oregon.   Syst. Zool., vol. 25, no. 4, pp.
          420-436.
REINHART, ROY H.
  1959.   A review of the Sirenia and Desmostylia.   Univ. California Publ. Geol.
          Sci., vol. 36, pp. 1-146.
  1976.   Fossil sirenians and desmostylids from Florida and elsewhere.   Bull.
          Florida St. Mus., vol. 20, no. 4, pp. 187-300.
SHIKAMA, T.
  1967.   Postcranial skeletons of Japanese Desmostylia. Limb bones and sternum
          of *Desmostylus* and *Paleoparadoxia* with considerations on their evolution.
          Spec. Pap. Pal. Soc. Japan, vol. 12, pp. 1-202, illus.
  1968.   Additional notes on the postcranial skeletons of Japanese Desmostylia.
          Sci. Rpt. Yokohama Nat. Univ. (sect. 2), no. 14, pp. 21-26.
ZUIDEMA, HENRY P.
  1970.   Fossil sea mammal.   Sea Frontiers, vol. 16, no. 1, pp. 20-24, illus.

ROY H. REINHART

Search for Fossils in New Zealand and Australia

Principal Investigators: Thomas H. V. Rich, National Museum of Victoria, Melbourne, Australia; and Patricia V. Rich, National Museum of Victoria and Department of Earth Sciences, Monash University, Clayton, Victoria, Australia.

Grant Nos. 1276, 1562. For a reconnaissance survey of potential pre-Pleistocene fossil tetrapod sites in New Zealand; and for excavation of Miocene tetrapods in the Tarkarooloo sub-Basin, South Australia.

Mesozoic and Tertiary Tetrapods in New Zealand

Geophysical evidence gathered primarily during the past decade and a half indicates that New Zealand separated from the remainder of the former southern supercontinent Gondwanaland by late Cretaceous time, about 85 million years ago. This long separation from other land masses well explains the highly unique or endemic character of the terrestrial vertebrates that inhabited these islands immediately prior to the arrival of man during the past few thousand years. Another aspect of this tetrapod fauna is that it is not as diverse as might be expected for a land area of its size. A possible explanation for such low diversity is that during Oligocene time, about 30 million years ago, the encroaching sea may have covered as much as two-thirds of what is today New Zealand and probably reduced it to an archipelago of smaller islands rather than primarily two large ones as now. The work of MacArthur and Wilson (1967) predicts a decrease in diversity of a fauna with such a reduction in land area. It may be that at least part of the low diversity of the present day tetrapod fauna is owing to this Oligocene reduction in land area rather than solely the much more recent cooling and glaciation of the last 1.8 million years, the Pleistocene epoch.

One way of substantiating or denying these ideas would be the recovery of an adequate fossil record of the tetrapods in New Zealand from the late Cretaceous to the Pleistocene. Fortunately, extensive nonmarine deposits formed during this time interval exist in New Zealand and have the potential of yielding such a record. As yet, tetrapod fossils have been recovered there only from sediments younger than 2.4 million years. Our project was an attempt to find older tetrapods in New Zealand in order to throw light on these problems.

After an extensive review of the geological literature, a number of sites were chosen for firsthand examination as potential sources of fossils based on

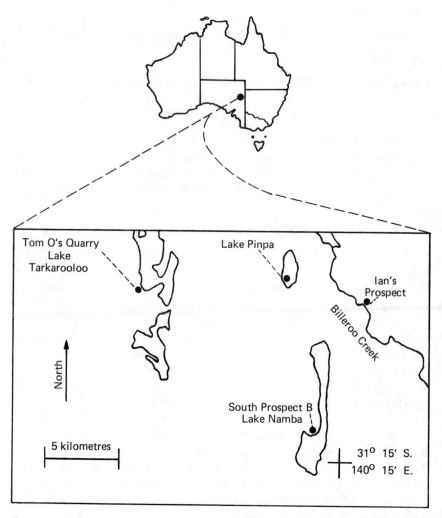

FIG. 1.   Locality map showing sites visited in the Tarkarooloo sub-Basin, South
Australia, during the 1976 field trip. (Drawing by S. Brown.)

similarity with localities elsewhere in the world where fossil bones had been
previously discovered. On arriving in New Zealand, we first visited the offices
of the Geological Survey in Lower Hutt to supplement this information with
firsthand knowledge of geologists currently active in the areas to be visited.

We spent a short time at Greymouth inspecting a number of Cretaceous
units interbedded with coal deposits. Because no indication of fossils was encountered, the investigation there was not prolonged. We then spent three

weeks meticulously examining two open-cut coal mines in the vicinity of Ohai, a small town near the southern end of South Island. More than 60 distinctive rock types were encountered interbedded with the Cretaceous and Eocene coal deposits, indicating that a wide variety of depositional environments was represented. Specimens of the freshwater mollusk *Hyridella* occurred frequently in the Eocene Beaumont Coal Measures, but unfortunately not a single scrap of fossil bone was found.

Another area examined was a large lake deposit formed during Miocene times in south-central South Island, named the St. Bathans Beds. Both freshwater mollusks and fishes had been reported from this widely exposed unit. During a period of three days spent in this area, we attempted without success to find deposits of this ancient lake that might have been laid down close to shore where remains of land-dwelling tetrapods might be expected.

The final area of investigation was in the lower gorge of the Waipara River about 50 kilometers north of Christchurch. In that area was located a small, lenticular-shaped body of sediment that contained about 300 isolated whole bones and fragments of tetrapods quite similar to ones living today in New Zealand. The lens was surrounded by and initially thought to be contemporaneous with other sediments regarded without question as medial Miocene in age, approximately 12 million years old. Because no tetrapods of comparable age are known elsewhere in New Zealand, the fact that the fossil bones were referable to modern genera did not necessarily imply that the assemblage was much younger than medial Miocene. It is quite conceivable that New Zealand's tetrapods have evolved very slowly since that time, and thus collections from the medial Miocene and Recent might resemble one another quite closely. Eventually, however, a chemical analysis of bone from this site revealed that the collagen content was so great that the fossil tetrapod remains could be no older than a few thousand years. More details concerning this collection can be found in Rich, Rich, et al. (1979).

In an attempt to encourage others to continue the search for pre-Pleistocene tetrapods in New Zealand, a short paper describing the criteria used for selecting potential fossil sites by scrutiny of the geological literature was written (Rich, 1975). By way of example, 21 promising potential sites were briefly described.

As so often happens in scientific research, fortuitous events lead to results quite unexpected at the outset of an investigation. In the midst of the work on this project, casual inspection of a fossil owlet-nightjar specimen at the Canterbury Museum, Christchurch, revealed that it was flightless or nearly so. This observation resulted in a detailed functional re-analysis of the specimen (Rich and Scarlett, 1977) as well as a similar analysis of the interrelationships of the flightless New Zealand goose *Cnemiornis* and the Australian *Cereopsis,* now in progress by P. V. Rich and R. J. Scarlett.

Miocene Tetrapods in South Australia

In 1971 and again in 1973, Dr. Richard H. Tedford of the American Museum of Natural History, New York, led field parties exploring for fossil vertebrate remains in the Tarkarooloo sub-Basin east of Lake Frome, South Australia. Here specimens were found at a number of sites in the medial Miocene Namba Formation (Callen and Tedford, 1976), two of them being Lake Pinpa and South Prospect B on Lake Namba (see fig. 1).

In 1974, at the invitation of the Australian Army, a field party from the National Museum of Victoria spent ten days in this same region, revisiting previously discovered sites and exploring for new ones. Among the new fossil localities found were one that was in the Namba Formation (Tom O's Quarry) and a second (Ian's Prospect), which may be of mixed provenance. The Pleistocene Eurinilla Formation (Callen and Tedford, 1976) is definitely present at Ian's Prospect and quite fossiliferous there. Beneath the unquestioned Eurinilla is a green clay, which may be part of the Namba Formation and could be fossiliferous. The reason for doubt as to whether the green clay is in fact fossiliferous is that on every visit to the site, this unit has been submerged beneath standing water in the bottom of Billeroo Creek. At the time of the initial discovery in 1974, a dasyurid jaw belonging to a previously unknown genus and species, *Wakamatha tasselli* Archer and Rich 1979, was recovered in unconsolidated sediment at the bottom of the creek under about 50 centimeters of water. Consequently, the source of the specimen is uncertain but *W. tasselli* appears to be quite primitive and suggests that at least in part, the fossils from Ian's Prospect may be Miocene in age.

Because Ian's Prospect yielded a new taxon during the single day spent there in 1974, it was decided to make it the primary objective for a return visit sponsored by the Society in 1976. Upon revisiting the site, it was found that not only was it underwater as before but in addition, a thick, malodorous sludge had accumulated on the bottom of Billeroo Creek, which hampered operations severely. After some attempts were made to overcome the problems presented by the site, it was decided to abandon it for that season and work elsewhere.

Most of the previously discovered sites in the Namba Formation which had yielded some vertebrate fossils were then visited and material of importance collected at three of them. One of these was Lake Pinpa where the type specimen of a new genus and species of diprotodontid marsupial, *Raemeother-*

ium yatkolai Rich, Archer, and Tedford, 1978, was collected. This species is part of the Ericmas fauna (Tedford et al., 1977) and is the smallest as well as oldest and most primitive member of its family. The second site, also part of the Ericmas fauna, was South Prospect B on Lake Namba where a new genus and species of extremely primitive phalangerid was found.

The final site to be visited was Tom O's Quarry on Lake Tarkarooloo. When discovered in 1974, this site had then yielded the first remains from the Tarkarooloo sub-Basin of *Ngapakaldia tedfordi*. This palorchestid had been previously found in the Ngapakaldi fauna east of Lake Eyre and was regarded as medial Miocene in age. On the return trip, the site was given a low priority because from a two-ton sample collected in 1974, very little other fossil material had been recovered and, hence, the locality seemed to lack promise. However, a careful excavation in 1976 soon began to yield a consistent return of material and so work was continued.

The process of excavation was carried out in two phases. First the fossiliferous deposit was dug with hand tools and every effort was made to locate specimens in situ. Specimens thus encountered were carefully removed from the ground and preserved. Once the fossiliferous matrix had been dug up, it was taken to an artificial lake a few kilometers away and placed in a sieve. The sieve was shaken in water and this caused much of the matrix to pass through the wire mesh, leaving behind gypsum crystals, pebbles, and pieces of fossil bone and teeth. This residue was dried and then carefully sorted to recover the desired fossils. In this manner the record of the smaller animals was greatly increased. Approximately eight tons of matrix was treated in this fashion.

Tom O's Quarry was worked for six weeks until exhausted at the end of the 1976 trip. Because many of the different animals represented in the collection were poorly known, another three weeks were spent there in 1977 under the sponsorship of the Australian Research Grants Committee attempting to locate a new concentration of fossils. In carrying out this work, an effort was made to understand what the local topography had been during the Miocene, when the bones were deposited, in order to predict where additional accumulations might be found. Figure 2 shows the positions of the various excavations and auger holes at the fossil site. The contours are drawn on top of a massive uniform clay which immediately underlies the fossil-bearing unit. These contours suggest the presence of an ancient stream channel, the axis of which is indicated by the dashed line extending downstream from B to A. Figure 3 is a diagramatic reconstruction of the sequence of events that resulted in the cross-section now seen along BA.

During Stage 1, the massive, uniform clay beneath the bone-bearing unit was deposited to an unknown height above its present level. Erosion followed

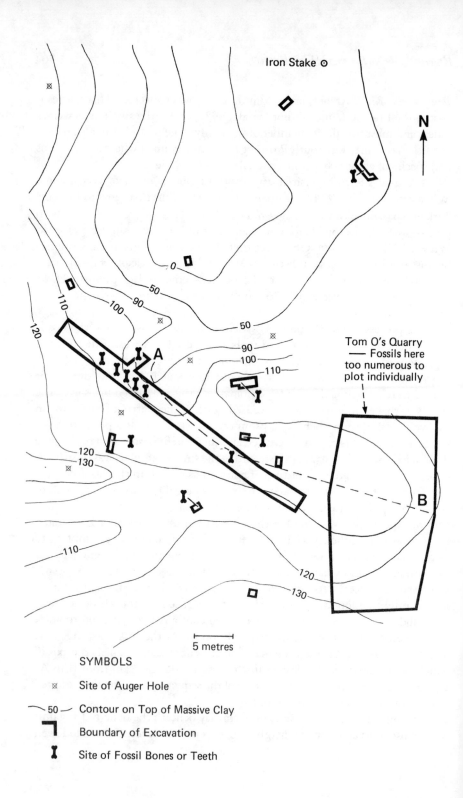

Iron Stake ⊙

N

Tom O's Quarry
— Fossils here
too numerous to
plot individually

A

B

5 metres

SYMBOLS

⊠ Site of Auger Hole

⌒50⌒ Contour on Top of Massive Clay

⌐ Boundary of Excavation

𝕀 Site of Fossil Bones or Teeth

FIG. 2. Map of Tom O's Quarry and immediate surroundings. Contours are elevations in centimeters drawn on top of uniform, massive clay that immediately underlies the fossil bone-bearing unit. The 'O' contour is 350 centimeters below top of iron stake shown in the upper righthand corner of the map. A former stream channel is suggested by the contours; section BA (see fig. 3) is drawn down the axis of this paleochannel. (Drawing by D. Stephens.)

in Stage 2 and a channel was cut into it. Filling of this channel by a relatively pure, quartzose sand took place during Stage 3. During Stage 4, much of the quartzose sand was removed during a second cycle of downcutting when a new channel was formed. However, remnants of this relatively clay-free sand remained, giving undulatory character to the bottom of the palaeochannel. At the beginning of Stage 5, bones and teeth were deposited along the clay galls and sand when the third cycle of deposition started. Many of the fossils show signs of extensive abrasion, suggesting that they had been transported for a long distance before finally being deposited where they were found. Deposition continued in Stage 5 until an alternating sequence of sands and clays was built up. Apparently, the surrounding area had been swept nearly clean of bones and teeth in the initial deposition of this cycle for they are encountered only rarely above the basal 10 centimeters of the palaeochannel. Stage 6 continues, for this is the present cycle of erosion that is forming the modern landscape.

Tom O's Quarry was one depression in the bottom of the palaeochannel. Downstream from Tom O's Quarry 30 meters to the west is another such area where some bones were found during the 1977 work. Apparently, only the outside of a sharp bend in the palaeochannel was excavated there and this may explain why fossil remains were much less abundant in that region than at Tom O's Quarry. Clearly an area to sample in the future is the concave side of the bend in the palaeochannel at this second site where more fossils may have been deposited in the slower moving waters of the former stream.[1] Unfortunately, it is not possible to work eastward, upstream from Tom O's Quarry, because that site is at the edge of modern Lake Tarkarooloo and the sediments which might have contained fossil bones there have been removed by the present cycle of erosion.

Fossils collected at Tom O's Quarry and within 30 meters of it from the same stratigraphic unit are collectively referred to as the Tarkarooloo local fauna. The mammals in it are listed below. The letters in parentheses give the nature of representation of each taxon in the collection: P, premolar; M, molar;

---

[1] Such an excavation was made in 1979 and about 30 additional specimens were recovered.

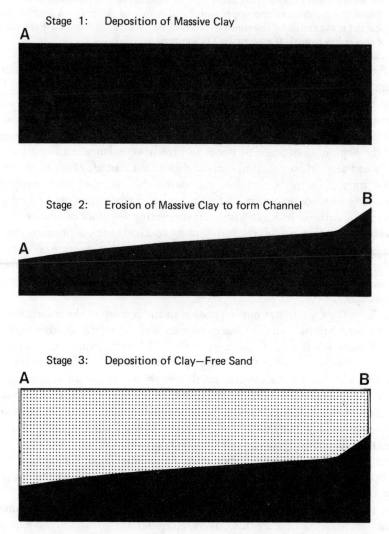

FIG. 3.   Longitudinal sections along the axis of the paleochannel passing through Tom O's Quarry showing the sequence of events that resulted in the fossil accumulation. Horizontal scale 1:500, vertical scale 1:25. (Drawing by S. Brown.)

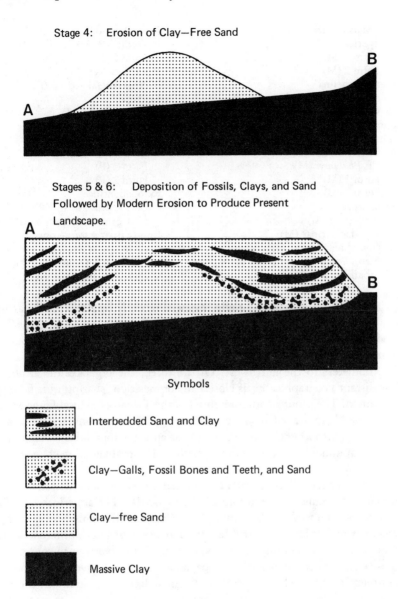

Stage 4: Erosion of Clay—Free Sand

Stages 5 & 6: Deposition of Fossils, Clays, and Sand Followed by Modern Erosion to Produce Present Landscape.

Symbols

Interbedded Sand and Clay

Clay—Galls, Fossil Bones and Teeth, and Sand

Clay—free Sand

Massive Clay

J, jaw (may be edentulous); and S, partial skull. 'Form' is used when more than a single genus of a given family is present in the fauna and the material cannot be assigned to a known genus and may be insufficient as a basis for the formal proposal of a new taxon.

Order Marsupicarnivora
  Dasyuridae
    Form 1 (M, J)
    Form 2 (M)
Order Peramelina
  Peramelidae
    Cf. *Perameles* (P, M, J)
Order Diprotodonta
  Phalangeridae
    Cf. *Trichosurus* (P, M)
    Cf. *Phalanger* (M)
    Form 1 (M)
    Form 2 (M)
  Petauridae
    Petaurinae (M)
    Pseudocheirinae (M)
  Wynyardiidae
    Namilamadeta snideri (S, P, M)
  Vombatidae (M)

Phascolarctidae
  Form 1 (P, M)
  Form 2 (M)
Palorchestidae
  Ngapakaldia tedfordi (P, M, J, S)
Macropodidae
  Cf. *Setonix* (P, M)
  Form 1 (M)
Potoroidae (M)
  Cf. *Bettongia* (P)
  Form 1 (P)
  Form 2 (P)
Ektopodontidae
  Cf. *Ektopodon* n. sp. (P, M, J)
  New genus and species (M)
Family *incertae sedis*—one? form
  about size of *Propleopus oscillans*,
  closest to potoroids in the few
  characters ascertainable

Three Australian faunas briefly reviewed recently by Archer and Bartholomai (1978), are considered to be of approximately the same age as the Tarkarooloo local fauna: the Ericmas and Pinpa faunas collected only about 10 kilometers to the east and the Ngapakaldi fauna collected east of Lake Eyre, 300 kilometers to the northwest. Of the three, the Ngapakaldi, although most distant geographically, is closest in composition, sharing nine families in common. The groups not represented in the Tarkarooloo local fauna are all rare in the Ngapakaldi fauna: i.e., Chiroptera, Thylacoleonidae, Burramyidae, and Ornithorhynchidae. Peramelidae and Macropodidae, which have their oldest undoubted records in the Tarkarooloo local fauna, may be present in the Ngapakaldi fauna.

The Pinpa fauna lacks several groups that are well represented in the Tarkarooloo local fauna; i.e. Potoroidae, Macropodidae, Phalangeridae, and Palorchestidae. However, the Pinpa fauna has the Burramyidae as a rare element, which is lacking in the Tarkarooloo local fauna. The differences may be owing either to a slightly greater age for the Pinpa fauna or to contrasting depositional environments, the Pinpa fauna being preserved in dolomitic claystones and green clays probably reflecting a lacustrine situation, the Tarkarooloo assemblage being collected from a channel sand. Not as readily understood are the differences between the Ericmas fauna and the Tarkarooloo local fauna, for both are known from channel deposits at approximately the same stratigraphic level in the Namba Formation. With only five families, the known Ericmas fauna is much less diverse, but of these, three, the Ornithorhynchidae, Diprotodontidae, and Platanistidae,[2] are not known in the Tarkarooloo local fauna, suggesting that significant environmental differences existed between the two.

Compared with all three of these other approximately contemporaneous faunas, the Tarkarooloo local fauna is distinguished by a diversity of macropodids, potoroids, and phalangerids, groups which, if present in the others, are restricted to fewer taxa.

REFERENCES

ARCHER, MICHAEL, and BARTHOLOMAI, A.
    1978.   Tertiary mammals of Australia: synoptic review. Alcheringa, vol. 2, pp. 1-19.

ARCHER, MICHAEL, and RICH, THOMAS H. V.
    1979.   *Wakamatha tasselli* gen. et sp. nov., a fossil dasyurid (Marsupialia) from South Australia convergent on modern *Sminthopsis*. Mem. Queensland Mus., vol. 19, no. 3, pp. 309-317.

CALLEN, R. A., and TEDFORD, RICHARD H.
    1976.   New late Cainozoic rock units and depositional environments, Lake Frome area, South Australia. Trans. Roy. Soc. South Australia, vol. 100, pp. 125-168.

MACARTHUR, R. H., and WILSON, EDWARD O.
    1967.   The theory of island biogeography, 198 pp., illus. Princeton University Press.

RICH, PATRICIA V., and SCARLETT, R. J.
    1977.   Another look at *Megaegotheles*, a large owlet-nightjar from New Zealand. Emu, vol. 77, pp. 1-8.

RICH, THOMAS H. V.
    1975.   Potential pre-Pleistocene fossil tetrapod sites in New Zealand. Mauri Ora, vol. 3, pp. 45-54.

RICH, T.H.V., and ARCHER, MICHAEL
    1979.   *Namilamadeta snideri*, a new diprotodontan (Marsupialia, Vombatoidea) from the medial Miocene of South Australia. Alcheringa, vol. 3, pp. 197-208.

RICH, T.H.V.; ARCHER, M.; and TEDFORD, R. H.
    1978.   *Raemeotherium yatkolai*, gen. et sp. nov., a primitive diprotodontid from the medial Miocene of South Australia. Mem. Nat. Mus. Victoria, vol. 39, pp. 85-91.

---

[2] R. Ewan Fordyce (pers. comm.) has recently examined the cetacean material from the Ericmas fauna and has concluded that it should be allocated to the Rhabdosteidae.

RICH, T.H.V.; RICH, P. V.; FORDYCE, R. E.; GATEHOUSE, P.; and SCARLETT, R. J.
   1979.   A deceptive terrestrial vertebrate fossil site on the Waipara River, North Canterbury, New Zealand.   Pp. 25-57 *in* "Birds of a Feather, Osteological and Archaeological Papers from the South Pacific in Honour of R. J. Scarlett," A. J. Anderson, ed.   Archeological Association Monograph II, British Archaeological Reports International Series 61.
TEDFORD, R. H.; ARCHER, M.; BARTHOLOMAI, A.; PLANE, M.; PLEDGE, N. S.; RICH, T.H.V.; RICH, P. V.; and WELLS, R. T.
   1977.   The discovery of Miocene vertebrates, Lake Frome area, South Australia. Bur. Mineral Resour., Journ. Australian Geol. Geophys., vol. 2, pp. 53-57.

THOMAS H. V. RICH
PATRICIA V. RICH

The Ethnohistory of the Caroline Islands

Principal Investigator: Saul H. Riesenberg, National Museum of Natural History, Smithsonian Institution, Washington, D. C.

Grant No. 1143: For study of the ethnohistory of the Caroline Islands.

Dr. Saul H. Riesenberg, Senior Ethnologist at the Smithsonian Institution, and his wife, Mrs. Mildred R. Riesenberg, spent the summer of 1973 in England under a grant from the National Geographic Society carrying on ethnohistorical research on Micronesia at various libraries, archives, and museums in London, Taunton, and Cambridge. Most of the research was done at the British Museum, particularly in the Department of Manuscripts. In addition, varying amounts of time were spent in research at the following institutions: In London, the India Office Library and Records, Orbit House; the Public Record Office, Admiralty section and Foreign Office Correspondence and Treaties; the Ministry of Defence, Naval Historical Branch; the National Maritime Museum, Greenwich; the Royal Anthropological Institute of Great Britain and Ireland; the Royal Geographic Society; and the School of Oriental and African Studies. In Taunton, the Ministry of Defence, Hydrographic Department. In Cambridge, the Jardine, Matheson and Company Archive, in the Cambridge University Library.

The purpose of this research was an attempt to fill a gap in American scholarship in regard to the ethnohistory of the islands of Micronesia, which are presently a Trust Territory of the United States. Other areas of the Pacific have been more or less intensively covered by specialists in this field of research from various parts of the world, but the Caroline Islands have been neglected to a surprising degree, and interest by American ethnohistorians has been almost nil. Dr. Riesenberg had in previous years explored the documentary repositories of the United States, Australia, and New Zealand for the kinds of materials germane to this research, and has now extended his investigations to England. He and Mrs. Riesenberg have now compiled a large body of information of historical and ethnographic nature from ships' logs, diaries, letters, journals and various other kinds of unpublished documentary materials.

From the work done in England have developed, in whole or in part, the publications listed below.

REFERENCES

RIESENBERG, SAUL H.
1974. Six Pacific island discoveries. The American Neptune, vol. 34, no. 4, pp. 249-257.
1975. The ghost islands of the Carolines. Micronesica, vol. 11, no. 1, pp. 7-33.
1979. Six Pacific discoveries. Guam Recorder, vol. 9 (second series), pp. 10-15.
FISCHER, JOHN L.; RIESENBERG, SAUL H.; and WHITING, MARJORIE G.
1977a. Luelen Bernart. The Book of Luelen, xxx + 193 pp. Pacific History Series No. 8, Australian National University Press.
1977b. Annotations to the Book of Luelen, 200 pp. Pacific History Series No. 9, Australian National University Press.

SAUL H. RIESENBERG

Ecology and Social Organization of the Banded and Dwarf Mongoose

Principal Investigator: Jon P. Rood, Serengeti Research Institute, Seronera, Tanzania.

Grant No. 1282: For a study of the ecology and social organization of the banded and dwarf mongoose, Serengeti National Park, Tanzania.

Among small carnivores, relatively large, multi-male groups occur only in the social mongooses. It is of considerable interest to observe the dynamics of such societies and draw comparisons with other group-living mammals such as the large social carnivores and primates. The objectives of the present study were to describe and compare ecology and social organization in two diurnal social mongooses, the banded mongoose *(Mungos mungo)* and dwarf mongoose *(Helogale parvula)*, and assess the adaptive significance of their societies. Fieldwork in the Serengeti National Park, Tanzania, commenced in February 1974, under the support of the National Geographic Society. The banded mongoose had been previously studied for two years in Rwenzori National Park, Uganda (Rood, 1974, 1975), and the present project provided an opportunity to extend these observations and investigate the ecology and behavior of this species in a variety of habitats. Although dwarf-mongoose behavior had been studied in the laboratory (Rasa, 1972, 1973a, 1973b, 1973c) it had not been previously investigated in the field.

Cooperative hunting is an important function of group life in the large social carnivores, but my studies in Uganda showed that banded mongooses find their food individually, displaying little obvious cooperation. It appeared that group defense and cooperative care of the young were the most important benefits of group life in this species. Banded mongooses display a cooperative guarding or "babysitting" system in which one or two individuals, often males, remain at the den to guard the young while the main pack is out foraging (Rood, 1974). One objective of the present study was to determine if dwarf mongooses displayed a similar cooperative system for guarding the young and, if so, what social roles were present.

Methods

Study methods used included fecal analysis for determination of food habits, live-trapping and individual marking, age determination from tooth replacement and wear, regular pack counts to assess population dynamics, and all-day watches—both at breeding dens and by following packs—to obtain quantitative data on social interactions, range occupancy distribution, activity budgets, predator reactions, and the social roles involved in vigilance behavior and care of the young. Mongooses were initially marked individually with Nyanzol dye, but as this wore off in about three months considerable time was spent in experimenting with more permanent marking methods. Eventually I adopted a freeze-marking technique by clipping the hair of a mongoose in a distinctive pattern of spots and lines and spraying Freon 12 from an aerosol can onto the bare skin for 8 seconds. The Freon killed the melanocytes in the hair follicles, producing permanent white marks on the animal when the hair grew back in. This method was found suitable for dwarf mongooses but did not work well with banded mongooses, and I eventually reverted to dye-marking this species.

Three study areas were established, one on the eastern short-grass plains for banded mongooses, one in the central woodlands for dwarf mongooses, and one in the western corridor where observations of both species living sympatrically could be conducted. Aerial photographs were taken of these study areas and all mongoose sightings and den sites were plotted on maps made from these.

Results

BANDED MONGOOSE.   This study has demonstrated that ranging patterns in the banded mongoose vary widely with habitat. For example, on the Serengeti short-grass plains, mongoose packs use overlapping home ranges of approximately 40 square kilometers and in the dry season travel up to 10 kilometers per day in search of food. On Mweya Peninsula, in Rwenzori Park, Uganda, where food and cover are more abundant, packs use ranges that average less than 1 square kilometer and travel slightly over 2 kilometers per day (Rood, 1975).

On the short-grass plains each mongoose pack uses about 15 dens consisting of spring-hare holes and rock crevices in kopjes. Banded mongooses are dependent upon the over 1 million wildebeest that migrate to the plains during the rainy season. The dung they deposit supports an abundance of dung beetles, which form the mongooses' main food resource. A mongoose pack spends approximately 60 percent of its day in foraging for food.

The open-plains habitat supports a variety of raptors and large carnivores, which are potential mongoose predators. A mongoose pack appears to have a mental map of its home range, and the pack typically flees to the nearest set of holes at the approach of a large predator. Packs of over 10 mongooses respond aggressively to ground predators up to the size of a jackal by bunching together and chasing them. Raptors on the ground are also chased off, and on one occasion I observed a mongoose climb a tree to a height of over 4 meters to attack a martial eagle that had just captured a juvenile from its pack.

In January 1975 I was lucky enough to observe a split in a pack of 24 mongooses. The groups of 13 and 11 both continued to use the original range for several weeks after the initial split and both broke up temporarily into groups of 8 and 5, and 8 and 3, respectively. In addition, one mongoose from the 11 temporarily joined the 13. During the period of instability following the split frequent aggressive interactions occurred between the groups—often when two groups attempted to use the same den—and several individuals had most of the hair pulled from their tails. The situation was resolved in late February when the larger of the two groups emigrated. The remaining pack was later live-trapped and found to consist of old individuals.

DWARF MONGOOSE. Although confined to the woodlands, the dwarf mongoose is the most abundant mammalian carnivore in the Serengeti ecosystem. In 1974, 8 packs used the 2.2-square-kilometer woodland study area, and the density was approximately 35 dwarf mongooses per square kilometer. Pack size averaged 10 individuals, considerably smaller than that of the banded mongoose, which lives in packs averaging about 15 individuals. Dwarf-mongoose packs occupy overlapping home ranges of about 40 hectares each. Within its range each pack uses about 15 dens, which are typically in *Macrotermes* mounds but also in hollow logs and rock crevices. Beetles and termites are the most important elements in the diet, and each individual finds its own food.

A dwarf-mongoose pack contains an alpha male (the male that has priority in mating with estrous females) and an alpha female (the female that regularly breeds). The alpha individuals are typically the oldest male and female in the pack. In the Serengeti *Helogale* is a seasonal breeder with peak birth periods correlating with months when rainfall is usually highest. In 1974, the last litters were born in May, and none were recorded until the following November.

As in the banded mongoose, cooperation is evident in both care of the young and antipredator behavior, indicating that these two aspects are important functions of group life in the social mongooses. Young dwarf mongooses are guarded at the den by one or more pack members while the rest of the pack forages. These babysitters change frequently throughout the day so that all pack members have an opportunity to obtain food. In marked packs it was possible to determine which individuals stayed with the young, and it was found that the most active babysitters were the young of the previous breeding season and the subordinate adult females. The alpha female and the adult males rarely stayed with the young, and the alpha female was usually the first to leave the den in the morning, returning only for short periods throughout the day to nurse her young. Among mammals, this babysitting system, with its frequent changeovers throughout the day, appears unique to the social mongooses.

Another altruistic act in the care of the young, which was observed in both banded and dwarf mongooses, was feeding, usually by the younger pack members. Most feeding I observed occurred during the approximately 3-week period between the time the young first emerged from the den at 3 to 4 weeks old and the time when they began to leave with the pack on morning foraging trips at about 6 to 7 weeks. An individual would collect an insect and run to the den with it; one or more juveniles would rush to the feeder and either take the food from its mouth or eat it after it dropped to the ground.

The *Helogale* antipredator system seems adaptive for a small carnivore foraging in widely dispersed groups where cover is abundant. Dwarf mongooses average only about 300 grams in weight and are therefore subject to predation from a wider variety of predators than is the larger banded mongoose. Also, because of their smaller size, aggregation of the pack is unlikely to intimidate a predator, and bunching and chasing of potential predators do not occur. The dwarf-mongoose antipredator system is based on vigilance. Individuals spend up to 50 percent of their time atop termite mounds scanning for predators. The alpha male is particularly vigilant and makes approximately twice as many head turns as other pack members while on termite mounds. If a mongoose detects a predator it responds with loud alarm calls, which warn other pack members. Largely because of this efficient antipredator system, adult mortality is similar to that in the banded mongoose (approximately 10 percent per year).

While juveniles are recruited into their natal packs, emigration of some yearling and young adult dwarf mongooses was found to occur in both sexes. Emigrating groups sometimes attempt to join other packs, thus promoting gene flow within the population. On one occasion I was fortunate enough to observe the integration of two immigrant males into the L pack. I first observed the two intruding males on the study area watching the L pack about 100 meters away. In the ensuing month they trailed the pack, attempting to approach the females but often being chased by the two adult resident males. Of these two males the younger (M4) was considerably more aggressive than the alpha male (M11) in chasing off the intruders. Of 26 observed chases, 21 were by M4, 3 by M11, and in two M4 initiated the chase and M11 joined him. When the intruding males were able to make contact with the females the encounters were friendly, often consisting of the male grooming and marking the female. Throughout the month the intruders appeared extremely nervous, frequently giving alarm calls while trailing the pack, and submissive paw lifts in contacts with females. They denned near the L pack at night and sometimes attempted to approach it at dusk but were chased off by M4. After a month of trailing the pack, however, they finally were able to enter the L pack den after dark and the following morning emerged apparently as integrated pack members. Their initial behavior was marked by frequent rapid grooming of the females and one another and submissive paw lifts to pack members. Both males appeared to have lost considerable weight during the month it took them to join the pack.

Concluding Remarks

While this report covers the period of National Geographic Society support, i.e., from February 1974 to April 1975, it should be pointed out that the project is still continuing under the auspices of the Max Planck Institut für Verhaltensphysiologie. The initial period of Society support provided important baseline data, and the marking technique worked out then has allowed a great deal of information on individual life histories, immigration and emigration from the packs, and genetic relationships within the packs to be accumulated. Recent work in sociobiology (e.g., Wilson, 1975; West Eberhard, 1975) has provided a theoretical framework for the analysis of the altruistic behavior so common in banded and dwarf mongoose society and its probable evolution through kin selection. During the study two new packs have formed on the *Helogale* study area, and knowledge of the genetic relationships occurring in these will allow kin selection theory to be tested in the field. A large number of mongooses have now been individually marked, and it is hoped that the mongoose monitoring program at the Serengeti Research Institute can be continued on a long-term basis.

REFERENCES

Rasa, O.A.E.
  1972. Aspects of social organization in captive dwarf mongooses. Journ. Mamm., vol. 53, pp. 181-185.
  1973a. Intra-familial sexual repression in the dwarf mongoose *Helogale parvula*. Die Naturwiss., vol. 6, pp. 303-304.

RASA, O.A.E.—continued

1973b. Prey capture, feeding techniques, and their ontogeny in the African dwarf mongoose, *Helogale undulata rufula*. Zeitschr. für Tierpsychol., vol. 32, pp. 449-488.

1973c. Marking behaviour and its social significance in the African dwarf mongoose, *Helogale undulata rufula*. Zeitschr. für Tierpsychol., vol. 32, pp. 293-318.

ROOD, JON P.

1974. Banded mongoose males guard young. Nature, vol. 248, p. 176.

1975. Population dynamics and food habits of the banded mongoose. East Afr. Wildl. Journ., vol. 13, pp. 89-111.

1978. Dwarf mongoose helpers at the den. Zeitschr. für Tierpsychol., vol. 48, pp. 277-287.

1980. Mating relationships and breeding suppression in the dwarf mongoose. Anim. Behav., vol. 28, pp. 143-150.

———. Intergroup transfer by male and female dwarf mongooses. Behav. Ecol. and Sociobiol. (In press.)

ROOD, JON P., and NELLIS, D.

1980. Freeze marking mongooses. Journ. Wildl. Man., vol. 44, pp. 500-502.

WEST EBERHARD, M. J.

1975. The evolution of social behavior by kin selection. Quart. Rev. Biol., vol. 50, pp. 1-33.

WILSON, EDWARD O.

1975. Sociobiology, the new synthesis, 697 pp. Harvard University Press.

JON P. ROOD

The Breeding Season of Talapoin Monkeys

Principal Investigator: Thelma E. Rowell, University of California, Berkeley, California.

Grant No. 1245:   For a study of talapoin monkeys *(Miopithecus talapoin)* during the breeding season.

The work under this grant was carried out in association with Dr. A. F. Dixson, now at the Wellcome Institute for Research, Regent's Park, London. This research was a continuation of my work carried out two years previously at the same site, in the Mbalmayo Forest Reserve, Cameroon. At that time the social organization of talapoin monkeys in the interval between the birth season and the mating season was described. A troop was found to consist of about 70 animals, within which subgroups of three main types could be identified: "all-male" subgroups included adult and large juvenile males; "female-infant subgroups" including females of all ages and small juveniles of both sexes; and "juvenile subgroups" of medium-sized juveniles with a single adult male. Most interactions occurred within these subgroups, so that no overt interactions between adult males and adult females were recorded in a 3-month study (Rowell, 1973). Clearly this organization could not remain the same throughout the year—it must change at least during the breeding season. The present study, then, was timed to cover the brief annual mating season of talapoins in that area, which I knew must occur in January and February at Mbalmayo, Cameroon. The objectives were to observe the onset of the mating period, to find out how the social organization seen earlier changed to accommodate male/female interaction, and to see how the original organization reformed at the end of the mating season.

Dr. Dixson and I worked independently, following adjacent troops of talapoins. We left the house well before dawn each day to walk down through the plantations and the forest to be at the river by first light. Talapoins always sleep at the river's edge in curtains of creepers overhanging the water. We could find the dormitory in a canoe—my tracking assistant, Joseph Djampene, was also a skilled canoeist. The talapoins left their dormitory about dawn, and we followed them on foot, using our knowledge of their habitual routes to go ahead and meet them in those few places where visibility was good, otherwise recording brief glimpses of behavior and all their noises as we followed them through dense vegetation. In the secondary growth in aban-

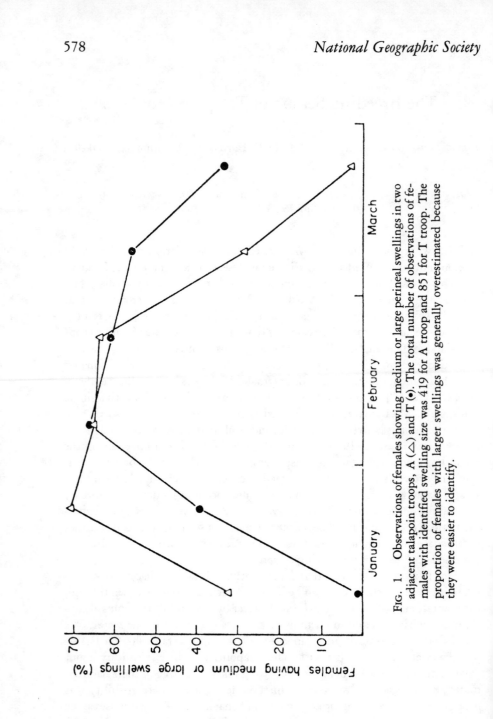

Fɪɢ. 1.   Observations of females showing medium or large perineal swellings in two adjacent talapoin troops, A (△) and T (●). The total number of observations of females with identified swelling size was 419 for A troop and 851 for T troop. The proportion of females with larger swellings was generally overestimated because they were easier to identify.

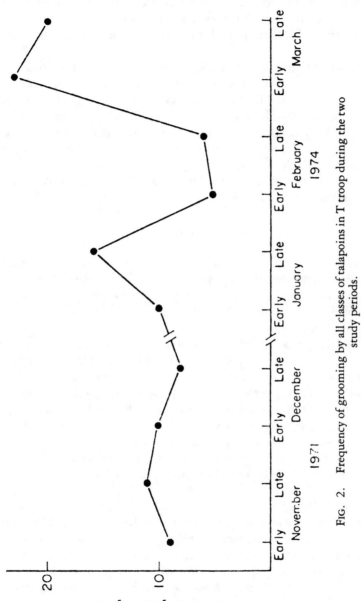

FIG. 2.   Frequency of grooming by all classes of talapoins in T troop during the two study periods.

doned plantations they could be within 20 feet and still be invisible, but thanks to my experience with the species in captivity I could usually identify the social activity that accompanied any noise even when the animals were out of sight.

The main objective of observations (made with 10 x 40 Leitz binoculars) was to record associations by age/sex categories and to identify and count members of subgroups. All social interactions were recorded. The progress of the mating season could be followed by noting whenever possible the state of the perineal skin of adult females. During the breeding season the perineum swells in the follicular phase of menstrual cycles, and the female is receptive only when it is enlarged, pink, and shiny.

Observations were made for 6 or 7 hours each day, or until we lost the animals, from February 5 to March 26, 1974, 6 days a week.

Results

Findings of this study have been published in full elsewhere (Rowell and Dixson, 1975), and the following is a summary of that report.

Time Course of the Mating Season. Figure 1 shows the proportion of the adult females that were seen to have swellings in each 2-week segment of the study. Their presence can be used to define the mating period. The season was so short and sharply defined that it was possible to detect a difference in timing in the adjacent troops of about 2 weeks: mating probably started at the very end of December in A troop, but not until toward the end of January in T troop; A troop's mating period was over by the last week of March, but a low level of sexual activity was still seen in T troop in that week. The difference in timing is large given the brevity of the season as a whole, and we take it to indicate that whereas the over-all timing of the mating season is related to the long dry season (which runs from December to March) the onset of mating in each troop is determined by social facilitatory effects which vary from troop to troop.

Start of the Mating Season. The first change in behavior associated with the mating season was actually seen at the end of the first study: in December, groups of adult and juvenile males begin to mob and chase each other conspicuously through the trees. The next change was that adult males were occasionally seen traveling with adult female-infant subgroups. This began at least 10 days before any sexual behavior was seen, when all the females' perinea were still in the resting state.

End of the Mating Season. The mating season was not completely over by the time we had to leave, but changes had begun which allowed us to see how the return to "normal" social organization would occur. There was an increase in noises associated with fighting as the season progressed. As most fights were heard rather than seen, we could not identify the aggressors. Of the identified aggressors in both studies, adult males were twice as frequent as adult females. More than half of the aggression by females was seen in March as the breeding season ended (table 1).

TABLE 1. Incidence of Aggression by Adult Male and Female Talapoins in T Troop

	1971		1974		
	Nov.	*Dec.*	*Jan.*	*Feb.*	*March*
No. of aggressive males	9	6	17	12	16
No. of aggressive females	2	1	6	2	14

Both males and females mainly attacked adult and large juvenile males. Although not conclusive, there therefore seems to be circumstantial evidence that attacks on males by females that are no longer receptive are the main mechanism by which the separate-sexed subgroups are reformed at the end of the mating season.

Grooming and Mating Behavior. For many species there is a strong association between heterosexual grooming and mating. In the talapoin groups grooming was seen less frequently as the mating season got underway, and grooming increased greatly as the mating period came to an end. Most grooming seen involved juveniles and females; males groomed one another; heterosexual grooming was observed only during the mating period but comprised only 7 of 120 grooming episodes where both partners were identified. Grooming is not a prominent part of sexual interaction in this species (fig. 2).

Most of the 24 observed copulations occurred in February in both troops. Except for two females at the very end of the mating season, all copulations were with females with maximally swollen shiny pink perineal swellings. Most if not all the adult males were copulating. There was no sign of consort behavior; a male would approach a female from 20 or 30 meters and after mating each would leave in a different direction. The male was sometimes seen to join an all-male group after copulating (in captivity ejaculation is followed by a refractory period of about an hour). It seems certain that females were mated to a succession of males in a short space of time while maximally swollen.

Social Organization during the Breeding Season. Throughout the study, the subgroup types seen in the earlier study could be observed. As soon as the

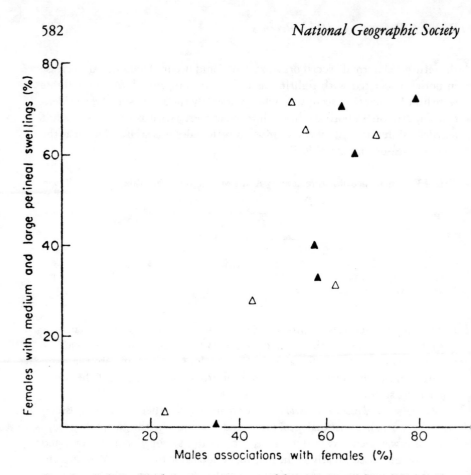

FIG. 3.   Relationship between percentage of females that had medium or large swellings and the percentage of male associations that included females in A (△) and T (▲) troop talapoins. Each point represents data from one 2-week period.

mating season began, however, associations containing both adult males and females became the most frequent. The higher proportion of females that were swollen, the higher the proportion of males that was seen in association with females (fig. 3). This suggests the possibility that males were attracted to the female groups by the sight of large swellings although as we have seen the first male/female associations occurring before any swellings had developed.

Male/female subgroups seemed to fall into two types. The first type observed, in which an adult male joined a group of females and juveniles, was seen throughout the mating season. At the height of the season there was typically more than one male, but females always outnumbered males by a large margin, and juveniles outnumbered the females. At the height of the season a second type of male/female subgroup appeared in which males outnumbered females and there were no juveniles accompanying the females. As this second type of subgroup became more frequent the proportion of juveniles in the first type increased. Thus receptive females seemed to be leaving their infants with the other small juveniles in the mainly female subgroups and joining groups of males. The routes taken by the mainly male heterosexual groups were like those of all-male subgroups, while the mainly female subgroups tended to stay lower in the thicker cover, as was typical of female-infant subgroups. Females with large swellings were more frequent in the mainly male subgroups and females with small swellings were more frequently associated with juveniles; but copulations occurred in both types of subgroup.

Significance

The social organization we found is unlike anything that has been described for other Old World primates in either the mating season or the non-mating season form, and the rapid shift from one to the other for the duration of the brief breeding season is also unique. There is an interesting parallel with the social organization of the squirrel monkey in the New World, which may be particularly important because the habitat occupied by the two species, the flood plains of forest rivers, is also very similar. An adaptive influence of ecology on social behavior is frequently postulated but evidence in support of such an effect is difficult to obtain.

The mechanism of change from one pattern of organization to the other involved movement of males at both the beginning and the end of the mating period, although their withdrawal from female groups at the end may have been in response to female threats. The preliminary change in male behavior may provide the cue by which the breeding of the troop is tightly synchronized.

REFERENCES

ROWELL, THELMA E.
1973.   Social organization of wild talapoin monkeys.   Amer. Journ. Phys. Anthrop., vol. 38, pp. 359-397.
ROWELL, THELMA E., and DIXSON, A. F.
1975.   Changes in social organization during the breeding season of wild talapoin monkeys.   Journ. Reprod. Fert., vol. 43, pp. 419-434.

THELMA E. ROWELL

The Mandinko of Pakao: The History, Social Structure, and Ethnobotany of a Manding People

Principal Investigator: Matt (David Matthew) Schaffer, St. Simons Island, Georgia.

Grant Nos. 1269, 1504.   For a study of the Mandinko of Pakao, southern Senegal.

From January 1, 1974, until February 1, 1975, my wife and I carried out research in anthropology in the West African country of Senegal. Ten months of fieldwork in Pakao villages (see fig. 1) were complemented by 3 months in Dakar, where necessary archives and libraries were consulted. The 13 months of work constituted an expansion of 5 months spent in the Pakao village of Dar Silamé (see fig. 2) during the latter half of 1972.

Pakao lies in the middle of Senegal's Casamance *Région.* It is considered by its devoutly Islamic residents to be a holy land and regularly receives pilgrims from the north of Senegal, The Gambia and Guinea Bissau. The people speak Mandinko and for the most part call themselves Mandinko, although the two leading families of Dramé and Sylla are descended from Saraholle and Diak-hanke stock.

Myths collected in 1974 about the founding of villages reveal the pattern of the Manding connection. Villages in the Pakao center trace their origin directly to *Manding,* the Mali Empire whose greatest expansion occurred in the 13th and 14th centuries. Neighboring villages emphasize their link to Mandinko kingdoms of the Gambia River, to Kabu in Guinea Bissau, or to the Islamic center in Karantaba, where *marabouts* (from Dramanet in Mali) first established themselves in Pakao itself. The founding of Karantaba and villages derived from it such as Dar Silamé signals the rise of an Islamic system adjacent to the old *soninke* (infidel) center.

In the heart of Pakao lie three villages, Mankono Ba, Soumboundou, and Dar Silamé, known in oral history as "the triangle," "the three stones of the cooking fire," and "the boundary of the entrance into heaven." It was here and across the river in Karantaba that the 1974 field trip concentrated.

The legend of the triangle was important in the decision on where to conduct research, for it implies an indigenous structural concept in which the social principles of Islam and old Mandinko have been synthesized. Traditions

585

record that Mankono was founded by a Keita of the royal ruling clan of *Manding*, and today this village is composed of *sula*, caste nobles. Soumboundou is in contrast a village composed of *nyamalo* caste smiths, leather-workers, and praise-singers. Its legendary founder was a *fino* (praise-singer) named Camera who also traveled from *Manding*. Dar Silamé was the base from which a Diakhanke *marabout* named Sylla led the Islamic revolution of 1843 and 1844 against local *soninke* kings.

The legend of Sylla Ba's revolution is probably the key myth recounted in Pakao today. A substantial number of documents in the Senegalese National Archives deal with this period, offering an unusual opportunity to compare mythical and eye-witness accounts of the same events. It is particularly important to study the revolutionary period in order to understand changes enacted because of it. The impact of the Sylla struggle must become a prime focus in the study of modern Pakao society. Historical research makes it possible to document social changes begun in 1843 whose effects are evident in the ethnographic and demographic studies recently brought to completion.

Four versions of the Sylla Ba legend as recounted in Dar Silamé can be compared initially to isolate some principles of village-level social organization. When read alongside archival material, the same legends demonstrate a high degree of historical cover-up. The supposedly accurate eye-witness version correspondingly fails to appreciate what the mythical elaborations single out—namely, the concentration of revolutionary actions against a *soninke* king's village.

A rather detailed description of pre-1843 Pakao can be elicited from two 1849 articles by Bertrand-Bocandé (including the earliest known map of Pakao villages)[1] and from reports dated 1837-1841 dealing with French efforts to establish a commercial center in Sédhiou and a system of trading posts in village areas where fierce warfare erupted. Manduari, the capital that Sylla Ba destroyed, did exist. It is distinctly listed as one of four rotating capitals of a Pakao kingdom where it was the king's residence just before 1843. About 1840 Pakao was one of seven adjacent kingdoms, all of which today bear its name. The principal family of the kingdom was not Dramé or Sylla, but Manjan, except for Manduari where it was Sounkouiab.

The political system after Sylla is quite different and might be described as one of nonkingship, favoring village autonomy and rejecting any higher structure except, debatably, in war. The innovating effect brought about by

---

[1] Bertrand-Bocandé, "Notes sur la Guinée Portugaise ou Sénégambie Méridionale," *Bulletin de la Société de Géographie*, Mai et Juin 1849, no. 65-66, p. 323, and Juillet et Août, no. 67-68, pp. 60-61.

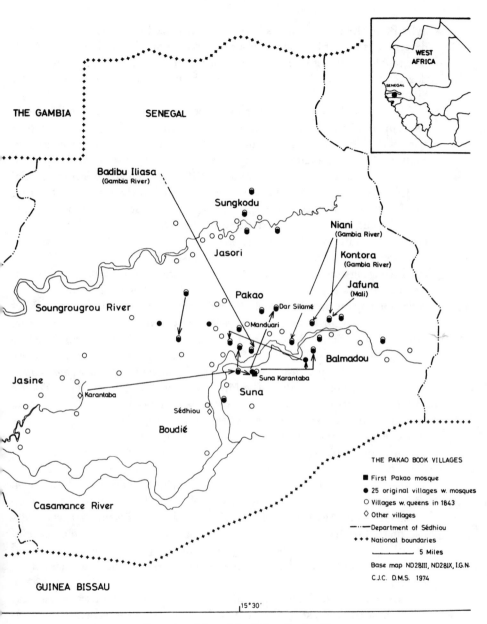

FIG. 1.   Map of the Pakao Book village.

Sylla Ba in the political arena becomes internalized in the social order as his descendants in Dar Silamé and elsewhere rise in number and prestige. A demographic study begun in 1972 provides several human indices showing the degree to which Sylla hamlet differs from the four other major hamlets in Dar Silamé.

In 1973 Sylla's last surviving grandson led a small group of followers in founding the first Mandinko village in more than a hundred years. Our return trip in 1974 permitted documentation of this event as well as the continued analysis of polarity and alliance in Dar Silamé and other villages.

Yet it became increasingly obvious in 1974 that an appreciation of social transformation is incomplete unless its impact upon the structures favoring continuity is examined. A disequilibrium model must be developed capable of explaining the changes brought about since the Islamic revolution in the context of traditional social institutions.

One such structure is dual organization, which is formalized in the political distinction chief-imam and in the verbal categories for village space, *santosu* and *dumasu* (upper village and lower village). Research in this area has been aided by the drawing of detailed maps of the triangle villages and of Karantaba. Duality in Pakao is nevertheless deceptive. The additional spatial categories *temasu* and *bantosu* (center village and outer village) are employed for a larger village such as Mankono Ba where they imply a more complex structure. The triadic political system of Mankono, chief-imam-*kanda* (*kanda* means lineage noble), reflects the importance of third parties. The evidence suggests that triadic and doubled structures have been built on to the more original dual system implied by *santosu-dumasu*.

The matrilateral preference in Pakao marriage can be linked to dual organization. In the triangle villages and in Karantaba pairs of hamlets are associated in a *sanao* (literally cross-cousin) marriage relation across the *santosu-dumasu* boundary. Legends note that the patrilineal ancestors of two such hamlets are the village founder and his sister's son. Their descendants build up a *sanao* relation. Against a background of this and other formal aspects to Pakao marital exchange, statistical studies suggest that the high incidence of matrilateral cross-cousin choice follows alliance lines even when they are created inside a *santosu* division, as happened between Cissé and Sylla hamlets in Dar Silamé.

Systems of caste, class, and the political organization of women appear also to have been adjusting themselves. In these systems considerations of status are paramount and a method of evaluation had to be devised. A careful statistical examination of attitudes was conducted in *sula* caste Mankono Ba and in *nyamalo* caste Soumboundou.

All the living men and women ever married in the two villages were asked to rank *sula* and *nyamalo* against each other. They were also asked to rank a third, *jungo* (slave), caste among three types of *nyamalo* praise-singers (*cora*, *fino*, and *joka*).

For the ranking of class attitudes, the system used in *Social Mobility in Britain* was modified.[2] A seeding arrangement was developed in which 18 occupational categories were broken down into 6 groups of 3. Each of the 6 triads could be ranked easily, producing 6 categories considered most important. These intermediate 6 could again be ranked in 2 groups of 3. The final 2 most important categories could then be ranked against each other. In a literal point evaluation system with a maximum index of 3 plus 3 plus 2, all 18 categories have an average number between 1 and 8.

Finally, the persons interviewed were asked to list the three most important women in the village. The result is a quantification of a hierarchical organization whose differentiation is not parallel to the male model, and whose leader or queen (*muso mansa*) is politically unique.

Ranking systems can thus be determined for the two villages in terms of caste, sex, age, and other referents.

It is in the area of male and female age-sets that one best observes in Pakao how continuity is institutionalized in a structure capable of altering itself without losing its principles of organization. A demographic study of Dar Silamé permits one to appreciate that age-sets are by no means static structures, but begin as sections (*sapada*) that merge into single sets (*kuro*) of varying age-spans and overlapping membership. The sets in the Dar Silamé case study continuously adjust themselves within certain limits and cut across *sula*, *nyamalo*, and *jungo* caste distinctions.

Throughout the field study in Pakao great attention was given to the use of plants and plant classification. The most striking physical aspect of a Pakao village is the network of sacred trees in and around it. Villagers routinely gather medicinal and food plants from the forest. Legends frequently cite the plant world.

The ethnobotanical research thus early on assumed a parallel importance with studies of history and social structure. This area of the Pakao project was directed by my wife, Christine Cooper, working in the field as well as in the Forest Herbarium of Oxford University.

---

[2] Glass, D., ed., *Social Mobility in Britain* (first published in 1954, reprinted by Redwood Press Limited, Trowbridge and London, 1971). See in particular chapter 2, "The Social Grading of Occupations" by C. A. Moser and J. R. Hall, pp. 29-50.

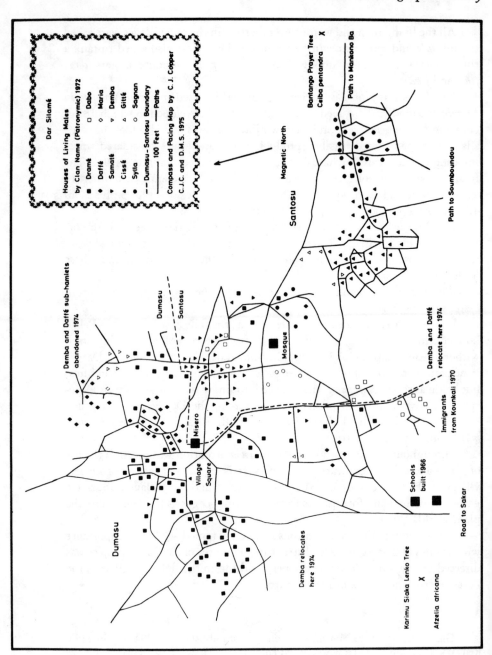

Dar Silamé

Houses of Living Males
by Clan Name (Patronymic) 1972

■ Dramé   □ Dabo
♦ Daffé   ◇ Maria
■ Samaté   ▽ Demba
▲ Cissé   △ Gitté
● Sylla   ○ Sagnan

– – Dumasu – Santosu Boundary
——— 100 Feet ——— Paths

Compass and Pacing Map by C. J. Caper
C.J.C. and D.M.S. 1975

Magnetic North

Santosu

Dumasu
Santosu

Demba and Daffé sub-hamlets
abandoned 1974

Misero

Village
Square

Dumasu

Demba relocates
here 1974

Karimu Siaka Lenko Tree
X
Afzelia africana

Road to Sakar

Schools
built 1966

Immigrants
from Kounkali 1970

Demba and Daffé
relocate here 1974

Mosque

Path to Soumboundou

Path to Mankono Ba

Bantango Prayer Tree
Ceiba pentandra   X

About 1,000 plant items were collected during all seasons of the year. They were initially identified by Kaoussou Sambou, a botanist at I.F.A.N. of Dakar University, and then shipped to England. These dried leaf, root, and bark specimens have been catalogued by Christine. Photographs of both living and dried specimens have also been placed at the museum along with relevant taped interviews.

Once an initial plant list was established, it was read to three famous specialists in Karantaba, Mankono, and Dar Silamé. They were asked to list the use of a plant and the meaning of its name. They also gave the indigenous classification of the plant and the Mandinko color for its leaves, bark, immature seeds, and fruit, as well as mature seeds and fruit. Finally, informants were asked to name colors on a standard chart.

All the colors of the Mandinko plant world were thus classified into *koita,* *wuleta,* and *finta* (roughly white, red, and black), even though additional words could be given for colors on the standard chart. All the plants could be typed into seven classifications, *iro* (tree), *tengo* (palm), *fito* (bush), *numbo* (vine), *jambo* (grass), *nyamo* (weed), and *fifengo* (planted thing). Several of the plants are linked in pairs distinguished by *muso-ke* (female-male) or *koyo-fingo* (white-black) suffixes to the same root word. These and other less used plant classifications will be the subject of much analysis.

The botanical research provided a basis for the gathering of extensive information on Pakao Mandinko concepts of body, medicine, and disease. Owing to intense local interest in *boro* (roughly medicine), it would have been oversight not to investigate pointedly. Medicines employ both chemical and magical ingredients and are administered in a variety of ways including, most notably, the wash. A number of case studies were maintained from 1972 until 1975 concerning problems such as elephantiasis, leprosy, and mental illness. Attention was given to the nature of societal relations with a terminally or seriously ill person.

Women's medicine and child-care practices comprise a central portion of the data recorded. For this secretive subject one often had to wait for the observable fact around which an interview could be conducted. Initially, women were evasive when questioned about ingesting earth, a practice relating to pregnancy reported in literature from The Gambia. Several months later a pregnant woman was observed casually leaving a ricefield trail to pick soft, gray rock (*kabakoyo*) from an anthill before eating a handful. She explained that the medicine would give her a boy (which it did) and would also safeguard her pregnancy. Other women added later that such treatment should occur only from the fifth through the ninth or tenth month of pregnancy and that sand (*kinyo*) might be eaten in order to have a girl.

Concern over the mortality of children produced not only a vast array of medicine but also an important social institution, the *dembajasa*. This is a woman who because of high infant mortality changes her name and occasionally acts out ritual transvestism to insure the survival of future children. The names chosen are non-Mandinko and usually *soninke;* so it is not inconceivable to detect a resistance element in the *dembajasa* that dates from the abduction of many girls into slavery during the Islamic revolution era.

Selections from pre-20th century books on Afro-Arabic charms known as grigris (*safo*) permit study of yet another class of *boro*. *Safo* are believed capable of healing, protecting, and causing great harm, including death, divorce, impotency, destitution, and even the destruction of an entire village. One of the great tests of a *safo's* power is *fangsabo* (the machete test) in which men are protected from self-inflicted knife wounds on the day of circumcision of their sons.

A formidable medicine is *búnyu furó,* which is composed of chicken feathers, millet stalks, and cracked pots and is placed in an area one wishes to protect. Without the maker's special blessing, a trespasser would become ill and eventually die.

Analysis of this medical data is still at a tentative stage, but it should afford an understanding of a pre-Islamic belief system that continues to flourish. Significantly, the Pakao word *boro,* also pronounced *bori,* has been listed by Delafosse and others as the Manding word for fetish.[3]

Recent studies such as *La Pharmacopée Sénégalaise Traditionnelle* will also make it possible to study Pakao medicinal plants from both a pharmacological and a cross-cultural point of view.[4]

Some information collected during months of fieldwork was quite unexpected. Perhaps the most intriguing of the many oral traditions recorded are stories recounted by one elder that bear a resemblance to the Uncle Remus tales. It was also not anticipated that permission would be granted to witness two of the more secretive rituals, *jundifanokuola* (the washing of the clothes of the dead), and certain events related to *ke kwiyung* (boys' circumcision).

My fluency in Mandinko improved steadily during the fieldwork, so that I was able to understand informants speaking to each other. When Assane Seck, the Senegalese Foreign Minister, happened to visit a village where I was working, I was able to converse with him in Mandinko.

---

[3] Delafosse, M., *La Langue Mandingue et ses Dialectes (Malinké, Bambara, Dioula),* tome 1 (Librairie Orientaliste Paul Geuthner, Paris, 1929), p. 471.

[4] Adam, J. G., and Kerharo, J., *La Pharmacopée Sénégalaise Traditionnelle, Plantes Médicinales et Toxiques* (Editions Vigot Frères, Paris, 1974), 1,011 pp.

FIG. 3. The *kangkurao* is a mask in which the wearer covers his entire body with the blood-red bark of the *fara* tree. The mask is brought out to place prohibitions, to supervise work, and to frighten off cannibal-witches (*bwa*).

A second National Geographic grant was received for the year 1975 to facilitate the processing of materials collected in the field. Detailed maps of four villages and of the Pakao area were prepared by Christine Cooper. She also completed the placing of botanical specimens in the Oxford Herbarium. Some 5,000 photographs were edited so that enlargements of the best ones could be made for eventual publication. My D.Phil. thesis was completed, and the degree was awarded in Oxford on February 28, 1976. The thesis was entitled "PAKAO A Study of Social Process among a Mandinko People of the Senegambia."

In 1975 the analysis of the Pakao field materials concentrated primarily on social organization. The principle of complementary opposition was found to be significant. The elected positions of chief and imam (mosque leader) are opposite in their secular and ecclesiastical authority. A pervasive opposition exists in the Mandinko distinction between *santo* (upper) and *duma* (lower). For example, the division of all Pakao villages into a minimum of *santosu* (upper village) and *dumasu* (lower village) is a very striking feature of social organization. Age-sets are related within either the men's or the women's sequence by a system of paired rankings that distinguish adjacent sets as "upper" (*santanko*) and "lower" (*dumanko*). The *sula* and *nyamalo* castes are contrasted locally as opposites, although they are not distinguished as upper or lower.

The large number of historical sources makes it possible to study Pakao as a society in duration, whose changes are sometimes dramatic. The jihad of 1843 not only destroyed the monarchy but also made it possible for *marabouts* (religious specialists) to become the dominant occupational class in the society of today. Before the jihad they lived in segregated villages, separate from non-Muslims. In modern times they are found in all villages and in all three castes.

Yet the process of Islamization in Pakao, completed by about 1850, does not imply the destruction or radical alteration of all pre-Islamic institutions. The best example of this is found in the persistence of the *kangkurao,* a mask (fig. 3) in which the wearer completely covers his body with the blood-red bark of the *fara* tree (*Piliostigma thonningii*). The *kangkurao* seems inconsistent with Islam because it is a graven image and an omnipotent force of social control, which is alternative to Allah. The *kangkurao* nevertheless flourishes in Pakao, where it is brought out to supervise work, to enforce prohibitions, or to frighten off cannibal-witches (*bwa*).

Islam has become a relatively conservative force in Pakao, tolerating institutions of caste, cross-cousin marriage, and the *kangkurao,* while perpetuating itself in village mosques and Koranic schools. Because of Islam, most Mandinko men in Pakao can read and write their language in Arabic script. A document about local religious history and geography, called "The Pakao Book" (see map, fig. 1), has been circulated widely among villages.[5] It is, in conclusion, an irony that this Islam which is so devoutly practiced in Pakao has ceased to be a consciously innovative force in society.

REFERENCE

SCHAFFER, MATT (DAVID MATTHEW), and COOPER, CHRISTINE
    1980.   Mandinko: The ethnography of a West African Holy Land.   In "Case Studies in Cultural Anthropology," ed.   George and Louise Spindler, 116 pp. illus.

MATT (DAVID MATTHEW) SCHAFFER

---

[5] Schaffer, Matt, "Pakao Book," *African Languages/Langues Africaines,* 1975, vol. 1, pp. 96-123.

Ecology of the Jackass Penguin (*Spheniscus demersus*), with Special Reference to Conservation of the Species

Principal Investigator: W. Roy Siegfried, Percy FitzPatrick Institute, University of Cape Town, Rondebosch, South Africa.

Grant Nos. 1267,   To study the behavioral adaptations of the jackass penguin to
1599.   a hot, arid environment.

A predominantly aquatic habitat has been the major factor shaping the evolution of penguins. Penguins possess a variety of anatomical and physiological adaptations, facilitating the maintenance of thermal homeostasis in an environment of thermal conductivity 30 times greater than that of air. These adaptations include dense waterproof plumage, extensive arteriovenous heat-exchange systems, and thick subdermal fat deposits. Polar-ranging penguins are only slightly better insulated than temperate species such as the jackass penguin (*Spheniscus demersus*).

Penguins, especially those species that breed in relatively hot temperate environments, tend to be overinsulated for life on land. The jackass penguin breeds on low-lying islands around the southern and southwestern coasts of Africa. These islands lie close to land, and their climate is dominated by proximity to the cool Benguela Current. Insulation is high, though ambient temperatures are modified by frequent cool sea breezes. Consequently the islands are arid and sparsely vegetated. One major part of the research program concerns a study of the behavior, physiology, and anatomy of the jackass penguin in relation to adaptation for avoiding conditions of heat stress in hot terrestrial environments.

This research bears on efforts to conserve the presently declining jackass penguin population. The decline has been taking place over, at least, the last half-century. The rate and extent of this decline, both past and present, are not fully known. While the exact causes of the decline are a matter for speculation, there is little doubt that alteration of the nesting habitat of the jackass penguin has played a role. Most of the islands used as breeding stations by the bird have been exploited for guano. Removal of topsoil has exposed unstable substrata. Furthermore, on certain islands areas have been paved in an attempt to facilitate the collection of guano. These practices probably helped to depress the species' nesting success, though other factors as well contribute to a decline in reproductive output. The research program includes a number of projects designed to allow identification and evaluation of the various factors influencing the breeding success of this penguin.

Thousands of jackass penguins have been oiled as a result of ships foundering or discharging oil at sea. Much money and effort go into cleaning survivors and attempting to rehabilitate them for normal life in the wild. The research program is attempting to evaluate the success of the rehabilitation procedures, through computer-based analyses of data derived from recoveries and "controls" of banded birds. Populations of thousands of individually flipper-banded rehabilitated and "normal" penguins are being monitored for differential mortality. This project also provides information on the movements of jackass penguins.

Results

Jackass penguins tend to be nocturnal at their breeding stations, most activity occurring during the relatively cool hours of dawn and dusk (Frost, Siegfried, and Burger, 1976). Consequently, the species' communication system places emphasis on vocalizations (Eggleton and Siegfried, 1979). Birds nesting in burrows are protected from intense solar radiation during daytime and experience a relatively equable microclimate. Birds nesting in burrows tend to raise more young than birds nesting in the open (Frost, Siegfried, and Cooper, 1976). Birds nesting in the open, and individuals that are molting, employ behavioral and physiological strategies facilitating radiation and convective heat loss (Frost, Siegfried, and Burger, 1976). Extensive arteriovenous associations occur in the head, axillae, and legs of the jackass penguin (Frost, Siegfried, and Greenwood, 1975). It appears that a shunt mechanism, which bypasses arteriovenous associations in the humeral plexus, facilitates heat loss when required. In general, however, the species' arteriovenous associations are adaptations for heat retention in a cool aquatic environment, and, in this connection, jackass penguins have been observed sun-bathing while at sea (Cooper, 1977a).

Birds at sea tend to flock, forming communal feeding and loafing groups (Siegfried, Frost, Kinahan, and Cooper, 1975). Groups and single birds show well-developed antipredator responses to killer whale vocalizations (Frost, Shaughnessy, et al., 1975). Other predators of the jackass penguin include Cape fur seals and sharks (Cooper, 1974 and unpubl.). Young birds disperse away from their natal areas, spending relatively long periods at sea while undertaking long-distance movements (Cooper and Randall, 1981). Adult birds show a strong fidelity to breeding and molting sites used in previous seasons. Jackass penguins accumulate extensive fat reserves in preparation for the annual molt-fast (Cooper, 1978). Young birds also need to store large deposits of fat prior to fledging, and this requirement often cannot be met by the parent birds whose foraging success appears to be influenced by the commercial fishing activities of man (Cooper, 1977b). However, virtually nothing is known about the effect of the modern fishing industry on the relative abundance and availability of pelagic, shoaling fishes to the jackass penguin (Jackson, Siegfried, and Cooper, 1975). Being flightless, and consequently having a relatively restricted foraging range, penguins must be reliant upon a highly predictable rate of encounter with their mobile prey. Indeed, it is difficult to see how flightlessness could have evolved in the absence of a predictable temporal and spatial pattern of prey distribution (Frost, Siegfried, and Cooper, 1976).

The numerical status of the jackass penguin has declined steadily over the past 100 years, from more than one million to a currently estimated total of 172,000 birds (Frost, Siegfried, and Cooper, 1976). This apparently persistent trend suggests that ecological and demographic factors are contributing to the species' decline (Jackson, Siegfried, and Cooper, 1975). Frost, Siegfried, and Cooper (1976) and Cooper (1980) have identified and evaluated some of the factors influencing the species' population dynamics, and it emerges that oiling probably is not of major significance in contributing to the decline of the population. A study is currently under way to evaluate the success of procedures aimed at rehabilitating oiled jackass penguins (Morant, Cooper, and Randall, 1981).

REFERENCES

ANONYMOUS
1977.   The great egg robbery . . . and what came after.   Afr. Wildl. Mag., vol. 31, p. 29.
COOPER, JOHN
1974.   The predators of the jackass penguin *Spheniscus demersus*.   Bull. Brit. Orn. Club, vol. 94, pp. 21-24.
1977a.   Jackass penguins sunning at sea.   Auk, vol. 94, no. 3 (July), pp. 586-587.
1977b.   Energetic requirements for growth in the jackass penguin.   Zool. Africana, vol. 12, no. 10, pp. 201-213.
1978.   Moult of the black-footed penguin.   Intern. Zoo Yearbook, vol. 18, pp. 22-27.
1980.   Breeding biology of the jackass penguin with special reference to its conservation.   Proc. IV Pan-African Ornithological Congress, pp. 227-231.

COOPER, JOHN; and RANDALL, ROD. M.
 1981.   Range and movements of the Jackass Penguin *Spheniscus demersus*. *In* "Proceedings of the Symposium on Birds of the Sea and Shore, 1979," John Cooper, ed.   African Seabird Group, Cape Town.
EGGLETON, PATRICIA; and SIEGFRIED, W. ROY
 1979.   Displays of the jackass penguin.   Ostrich, vol. 50, no. 3, pp. 139-167.
FROST, PETER G. H.; SHAUGHNESSY, P. D.; SEMMELINK, A.; SKETCH, M.; and SIEGFRIED, W. ROY
 1975.   The response of the jackass penguin to killer whale vocalisations. South Afr. Journ. Sci., vol. 71, pp. 157-158.
FROST, PETER G. H.; SIEGFRIED, W. ROY; and BURGER, ALAN
 1976.   Behavioural adaptations of the jackass penguin, *Spheniscus demersus*, to a hot, arid environment.   Journ. Zool. (London), vol. 179, pp. 165-187.
FROST, PETER G. R.; SIEGFRIED, W. ROY; and COOPER, JOHN
 1976.   Conservation of the jackass penguin (*Spheniscus demersus* (L.)).   Biol. Cons., vol. 9, pp. 79-99.
FROST, PETER G. H.; SIEGFRIED, W. ROY; and GREENWOOD, PETER J.
 1975.   Arterio-venous heat exchange systems in the jackass penguin *Spheniscus demersus*.   Journ. Zool. (London), vol. 175, pp. 231-241.
HOLMES, M.
 1976.   Cry of the jackass, 128 pp.   Hugh Keartland, Cape Town.
JACKSON, FRANK; SIEGFRIED, W. ROY; and COOPER, JOHN
 1975.   A simulation model for the population dynamics of the jackass penguin. Trans. Roy. Soc. South Africa, vol. 42, pp. 11-21.
JOHNSON, P. G.
 1976.   As free as a bird, 209 pp.   Struik, Cape Town.
MORANT, PATRICK D.; COOPER, JOHN; and RANDALL, ROD. M.
 1981.   The rehabilitation of oiled jackass penguins, 1970-1980.   *In:* "Proceedings of the Symposium on Birds of the Sea and Shore, 1979, John Cooper, ed.   African Seabird Group, Cape Town.
SIEGFRIED, W. ROY
 1977.   Packing of jackass penguin nests.   South Afr. Journ. Sci., vol. 73, pp. 186-187.
SIEGFRIED, W. ROY; FROST, PETER G. H.; KINAHAN, J. B.; and COOPER, JOHN
 1975.   Social behaviour of jackass penguins at sea.   Zool. Africana, vol. 10, no. 1, pp. 87-100.

W. ROY SIEGFRIED

Colonial Impact on the Kamba System of Survival: A Regional Perspective on an Economic System in Change in Kenya

Principal Investigators: Marilyn Silberfein and John Pawling, Department of Geography, Temple University, Philadelphia, Pennsylvania.

Grant Nos. 1278, 1279. For an investigation of the relation of rural migration to expansion of commerical agriculture in Tanzania, and for study of a semi-arid drainage basin in central Tanzania for potential agricultural development.[1]

The area in which this study was carried out is a composite of highlands and lowlands (fig. 1). Granitic hill massifs reach an elevation of over 7,000 feet while the general height of the floodplains varies between 3,000 and 4,000 feet. The hill slopes were covered primarily by forests in the nineteenth century, but by the beginning of the colonial period much of the agriculturally desirable land had been stripped of tree growth. The low-lying areas are covered with a mixture of thornbush, herbaceous plants, and scattered trees in varying proportions.

The region is characterized by erratic precipitation. Rainfall is received during a primary maximum (October-November) and a secondary maximum in March-April. There is substantial variation in rainfall, however, from one year to the next as well as from the hills to the plains (table 1). Even more important than the total amount of precipitation is the distribution of rainfall through the growing season. When rainfall is received in infrequent heavy bursts, as is often the case, there is excessive runoff and erosion. An inadequate soil moisture supply which causes stunting or wilting of plants is a further consequence of the interplay of short, intensive moist periods followed by longer dry phases.

---

[1] As will be noted, the location of the research is different from the one for which the grants were originally awarded. When we originally applied for research clearance from the government of Tanzania, we both experienced long waiting periods, and still had not received clearance as of two months before the proposed starting date for the project. Rather than chance a last-minute rejection, we decided to change locations and carry out our research in the Thwake River basin region of Machakos District, Kenya.

TABLE 1.   Average Annual Inches of Precipitation in Selected Areas of Machakos
District, 1943-1960 (Source: Annual Agricultural Reports)

	Elevation		
	High[a]	Medium[b]	Low[c]
1943	23	23	21
1944	35	28	21
1945	26	27	24
1946	38	30	26
1947	48	36	35
1948	42	30	28
1949	20	21	16
1950	25	20	19
1951	62	70	53
1952	31	28	17
1953	31	27	26
1954	36	29	26
1955	34	31	28
1956	32	30	26
1957	44	40	35
1958	37	32	27
1959	28	25	18
1960	27	20	16
Average:	34	30	25

[a]Includes Machakos, Mbooni, Kilungu, Iveti, and Matungulu Divisions.
[b]Includes Mukaa and Okia Divisions.
[c]Includes Makueni, Wamunyu, Kisau, and Kibauni Divisions.

As of the nineteenth century Machakos District was an area of scattered
settlement and a widely dispersed population which was gradually expanding
into northern and southern frontier areas. Most of the inhabitants were involved in the subsistence production of such basic crops as maize and beans,
combined with cattle keeping. A limited amount of exchange also existed;
one type involved the trading of goods derived both locally and further inland
with the coastal Swahili-speaking settlements, while the other took place between the highlands over 5,000 feet (primarily fruits, vegetables, surplus
maize or other crops) and the lowlands (cattle products).

In order to endure in a difficult environment, the Kamba people of Machakos District devised an elaborate system of survival based in part on agricultural techniques that had evolved through trial and error, symbiotic
relationships between the occupants of different ecological zones, and a high

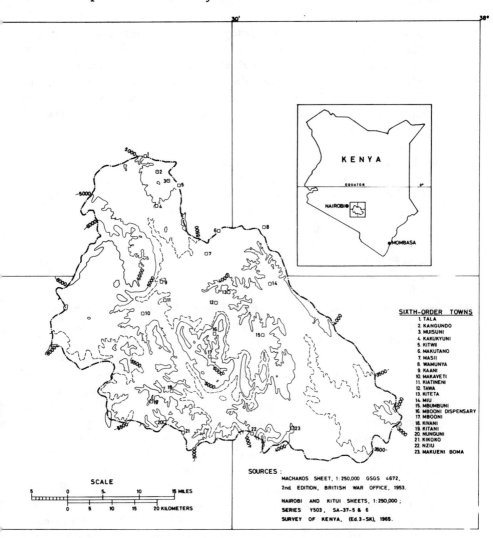

FIG. 1.   Thwake River Basin, Machakos District, Kenya.

degree of mobility. This system was disrupted by the advent of the colonial period in the late 1900's.

This study represents an attempt to evaluate the colonial impact on the Kamba system of food production. The hypotheses examined were: (1) That the Kamba had developed complex strategies for ensuring their livelihood, based on a high degree of flexibility; (2) that the colonial government undermined this system without substituting alternative strategies (the role played by the British administration reflected an insensitivity to Kamba perceptions of reality and the basic structure of their established mode of earning a livelihood); and (3) that the colonial administration, in the process of creating subregional disparities in level of economic development, broke down the complementarity that had previously existed between highland and lowland in Machakos District.

This examination of some of the deleterious effects of colonialism in a particular setting fits well with current reinterpretations of the colonial period. Numerous scholars, working primarily on a national or multinational scale, have described an actual decline in the quality of life experienced by subject peoples as a result of colonial economic policies designed to serve the needs of metropolitan powers (Brett, 1973; Leys, 1974). In some cases the negative attributes of colonial programs were not intentional, but rather resulted from a lack of knowledge on the part of administrators as to the intricate and sensitive relationship of subsistence cultivators and environmental constraints (Kjekshus, 1977). Methods of agriculture appropriate for commercialized midlatitude situations were arbitrarily incorporated into established tropical systems that had evolved gradually in keeping with local conditions. The colonial administrators neglected to investigate the possible consequences of their actions for these integrated systems; rather they perceived each intervention as an isolated phenomenon (Datoo, 1977).

In order to assess the colonial impact in rural Machakos District, numerous source materials were utilized. Most important were the colonial archives, including the records of the agricultural department and of the political arm of the government. Published books and articles and unpublished memos and reports were obtained as well. Interviews were conducted with past and current agricultural department personnel and other individuals (missionaries, administrators) who were involved with either the imposed or the indigenous agricultural system. Finally, extensive interviews were conducted with a sample of farmers from selected regions of Machakos District. They were asked to discuss their agricultural activities with special reference to system constraints and to identify elements of change and continuity in their approach to cultivation problems. The discussion that follows summarizes the information derived from all of these sources.

Discussion

In order to survive periods of erratic rainfall, the pre-colonial Kamba developed adjustments which can be viewed as a continuum, since they varied

FIG. 2.   Unfenced water pools in sand river, Machakos District. Intermittent discharge channel as it appears at the end of five-month dry season. Note granitoid gneiss outcrops, on right-hand bankside, which also serve as buried aquaclude to preserve downslope water-flow through the sandy aquifer.

according to the severity of the water shortfall. These adjustments readily divide into five spheres of activity: (1) the agricultural system proper, (2) the carrying out of rituals, (3) the establishment of interdependencies, (4) participation in supplemental (nonagricultural) pursuits, and (5) the use of staggered mobility. Each of these areas will be briefly described in turn.

1. *Agricultural System.*   At the beginning of virtually every growing season farmers would utilize such practices as planting drought-resistant crops, producing a small surplus, planting in moist depressions. In this way it is possible to salvage some harvest in the event of unpredictable, irregular precipitation. Greater emphasis was placed on each of these techniques whenever rainfall totals fell below the average for several years in succession. At the same time additional activities were initiated, such as an increase in the total area planted or more complete weeding to cut down evapotransportation. Efforts to obtain and control scarce water supplies were expanded, including well-digging in dry river beds (fig. 2). Cattle would be increasingly relied on as a direct source of emergency foodstuffs.

2. *Ritual Continuum.*   A complex sequence of rituals dealing with the supernatural evolved in Ukambani. The natural landscape was seen to be filled

with symbols and signs, and animal sacrifices were made at planting and harvest time to ensure satisfactory production. These ceremonies became much
more substantial when precipitation decreased, since the failure of the rains
was associated with the displeasure of the supernatural.

3. *Interdependence Continuum.* This refers to the exchanges between ecologically varied zones described elsewhere.

4. *Supplemental Activities.* Although many Kamba engaged in nonagricultural activities during years of average or normal rainfall, viz., hunting and
trading, the involvement of individual farmers in these kinds of pursuits increased markedly during times of environmental stress. Economic adjustments included the increased application of labor to the production of bricks
and charcoal, and the selling of cattle. Also important was the collecting of
natural products to replace missing food items in the daily diet; fish, fruit,
berries and roots, not usually taken under normal conditions, became important dietary substitutes.

5. *Mobility Continuum.* The Kamba were known for their capacity to
move over long distances for the purpose of colonization and trade, but their
mobility also provided a mechanism for survival. The most basic form of this
strategy was the practice of field-dispersals. By maintaining plots at several
elevations, the cultivator ensured that below-normal yields might be balanced
by greater productivity on the higher slopes. It was also common to keep cattle on the lower elevation farms while hillside plots were utilized for crops.

When environmental conditions deteriorated, the Kamba were ready to
implement additional components of their dispersion strategy. Initially, more
males might become involved in hunting or gathering activities in order to
generate income for deflecting crop losses. In a more difficult situation, children might be sent away while parents attempted to salvage a meager harvest.
Under the most extreme conditions, whole families were forced to relocate,
sometimes over long distances. As a rule such movements were temporary,
but they became permanent if subsequent obstacles made it difficult to return
to Machakos District.

The set of adjustments described above were first subject to colonial influence after the establishment of the British protectorate in Kenya in 1895. Following a period of resistance to British rule, colonial policies were devised and
implemented among the reluctant Kamba that were to create long-range
problems for the district. Taxes were introduced in 1901 and shortly thereafter the district was divided into areas called locations, most of which corresponded to a distinct physical region such as a hill massif or floodplain
compartment and included an average of six distinct communities (fig. 3).

FIG. 3.   Machakos District, Kenya, showing location boundaries.

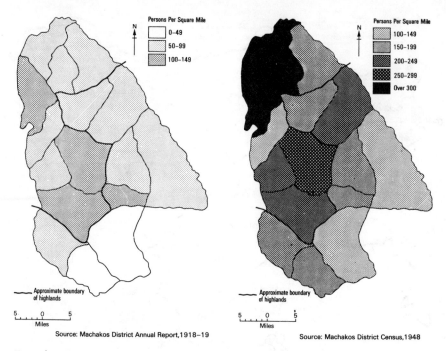

FIG. 4.   Population Density, Machakos District, 1919 (left), and 1948 (Sources: Machakos District Annual Report, 1918-1919 and Census, 1948).

At the same time, land was being taken from African inhabitants and opened to European settlement. The excuse given for land alienation was the sparse population of the district. Reports of missionaries and travelers during the late 1800's allude to a paucity of occupants in selected areas. According to one commentary "areas cultivated were small and much of the wood cut down was replaced naturally" (J. A. Stuart Watt, Private Papers, Rhodes House, Oxford).

These observations reflected the limited perspective of the outsider as much as the reality of conditions in Ukambani. To those unfamiliar with an agricultural system that required a temporary fallow, the territory available to the Kamba may have seemed adequate. This impression was artificially rein-forced by population losses during the 1899 famine and a tendency for assess-ment of the population land balance to be made in the sparsely settled lowlands of the district. Certainly, the more discerning observers mentioned either (1) that it was difficult to estimate population densities since fields were scattered and dwellings often hidden or (2) that some of the hill massifs were fairly thickly populated (Watts, 1900, p. 270). In effect, land alienation was based on an inaccurate view of the contemporary situation and on slight con-

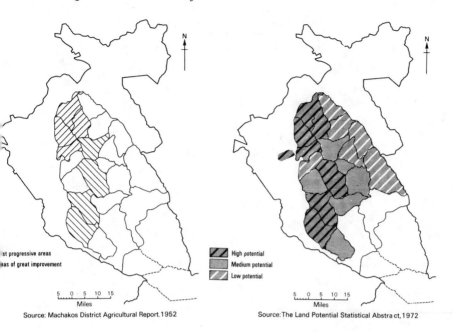

High potential
Medium potential
Low potential

5 0 5 10 15
Miles

5 0 5 10 15
Miles

Source: Machakos District Agricultural Report, 1952

Source: The Land Potential Statistical Abstract, 1972

FIG. 5. Progressive area indicators (left), as shown in Machakos District Agricultural Report, 1952; and land quality, as shown in the Land Potential Statistical Abstract, 1972 survey.

cern with the impact of either population growth or precipitation shortfalls on the future agricultural needs of the Kamba. Actual population growth in Machakos District can be observed on Figure 4.

Kenya government policy, as it emerged after 1910, focused on encouraging Africans both to produce enough for subsistence needs and to make themselves available as laborers, goals that were frequently contradictory. No coherent approach was developed to prevent famine; instead, a limited program was devised that included the endorsement of drought-resistant crops, the sale of cattle from "overstocked" reserves, and an inadequate famine relief program. Meanwhile, European immigrants controlled marketing boards, monopolized much of the best land, and dominated access to agricultural inputs and the extension service.

Under these circumstances, the Kamba continued to pursue their established techniques for coping with drought, even though some of these techniques were being challenged. Ritual activities were being undermined as missionaries spread an alternative belief system, and the mobility strategy had been limited by land alienation.

610   *National Geographic Society*

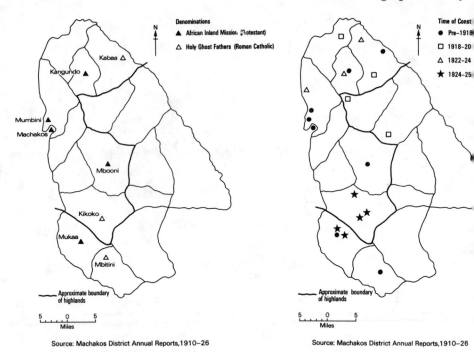

Source: Machakos District Annual Reports,1910–26   Source: Machakos District Annual Reports,1910–26

FIG. 6.   Distribution of missions (left) and schools (Source: Machakos District
Annual Reports, 1910-1926).

It was not until the 1930's that government officials began to take an active interest in African smallholders. In the midst of the worldwide depression
increased productivity on African holdings came to be viewed as a potential
source of much-needed revenue. It was during this phase of increased government involvement in African agriculture that the policy of subregional favor-
itism emerged. Attention was focused on the high-potential land in the
highlands, which had exhibited a relatively positive reaction to cash cropping, while the lowlands were neglected (fig. 1, 5). The government in effect,
initiated a self-fulfilling policy: the highlands produced the most impressive
results in terms of registered farmers, acres in cash crops, new crops cultivated, and highest yields; but the accomplishments of the highland farmers were
to a great extent due to better roads, better marketing facilities, and an unequal share of the agricultural inputs available to the district.

Meanwhile, the lowlands, viewed a problem area by the government, fell
further behind. The dryer areas were administered through somewhat of a
holding action in which the negative effects of droughts were minimized, but
almost no activist policy was pursued that would have improved the commer-

cial status of both livestock keeping and agrarian-based activities. A statement made in the [Kenya] Agricultural Report of 1938 (p. 9) sums up this attitude: "Yields are improving in the higher areas which are more fertile but in other areas it is difficult to see much improvement and the soil is becoming even more impoverished."

The emergence of the important highland-lowland dichotomy was further reflected in the locations of missions and schools. The first permanent missions were established in the vicinity of Machakos town (fig. 6). Once these sites were occupied, the next locations to be chosen were in the highlands, where an equitable temperature regime and a presumption of high agricultural potential were combined with a relatively large number of potential converts to Christianity. A few missions were founded just beyond the hill massifs of the edge of the lowlands (Mukaa, for example) but for a long time much of the southern and eastern parts of the district was uninfluenced by either the direct or indirect ramifications of Christian proselytizing (Forbes-Munro, 1975, p. 121).

The government followed the missions' lead by encouraging primary education in bush schools. Almost all of these schools were within or close to the highlands in spite of attempts to achieve district-wide coverage (fig. 6, right). According to government commentaries, schools were to be built in specific lowland communities but there was no real effort to produce any financial assistance needed for this particular plan (Agricultural Report, 1919). As late as 1927, when 21 additional bush schools were designated, the new sites were once again located predominantly in the highlands.

Another factor which contributed to the highland/lowland dichotomy was an economic focus on agrarian rather than pastoral activities, a situation best suited to the better-watered highlands, where fruits, vegetables, and wattle could be grown. The price of maize nearly doubled during the 1920's while the price of hides actually fell (Van Zwanenberg, 1974, p. 44). Cattle prices in the early 1920's to late 1930's fluctuated considerably but a downward trend was definitely established.

The differences between lowland and upland continued to be intensified by the prejudices of the agricultural administration. In 1932, the following statement was made concerning the introduction of new seed as well as improved maize varieties: "work in the district has concentrated on the more advanced areas but it is hoped to get to the arid areas shortly." During the 1930's the district agricultural officer took the position that only selected areas would be worth the investment of introducing new crops and ox-carts.

As for the dryer areas, there was little expectation of success because of "lower rainfall, unresponsiveness, and the relatively larger holdings that were

FIG. 7.   Natural stream pool and "leaking" weir-dam bridging one of the few rocky
constriction sites of arly tributary to the Thwake River. A dry sand stream is located
to the right of the weir (not shown) and is separated from the standing pool by a
restraining fence that is shown in disrepair.

deemed necessary for each farm unit" (Agricultural Report, 1936, p. 12).
Only one major effort was made to introduce a new crop, an experiment with
cotton planting in the 1930's. Although almost 3,000 acres were eventually
planted, yields remained low, undermining the initial enthusiasm for a crop
that "provides a useful contract between the government and the more remote
parts of the district and without which many farmers will have no cash" (Agricultural Report, 1940, p. 3). The effort was eroded by administrative coer-
cion, low market prices, pest problems, and drought, and was finally
abandoned without a sufficiently long trial period. The combined effect of all
these factors was to create two very different sets of social and economic conditions. While the highlands prospered, the south and east fell into an increasingly backward role.

   The 1930's and 1940's can be considered a period of mounting stress in
Machakos District, characterized by population growth and increasing erosion, along with a general land deterioration. Throughout this period Kamba
survival strategies continued to operate, although at a reduced scale. The mobility strategy was modified to emphasize squatting, the exchange of labor on
European farms for a small wage or the right to cultivate a subsistence plot and

FIG. 8.   Subterranean weir under construction at approximately 100 feet beneath the wooded crest of Mbooni Hill. A natural cleft (upper right) in the bedrock serves to concentrate percolating ground water to move downslope along discharge channels delineated on the bedrock topography. Once the concrete weir and discharge pipe were in place, and after the excavation was filled, a perennial water supply was available with a flow of up to 25 gallons per hour.

graze a few cattle. Other attempts to use the mobility strategy to deal with drought and population growth were frequently met with frustration, primarily because of increasing population density.

Other aspects of the traditional Kamba strategy became less significant with the expansion of commerical agriculture. Some practices changed in form but not necessarily in substance. Just as additional sources of income during periods of stress had once been sought from hunting and trade, so the Kamba of the inter-war period looked to the production and sale of bricks and charcoal for the same purpose. The Kamba came to seek supplemental income from the sale of labor, and many young men attempted to earn wages in the cities and commercial farming enterprises of Kenya. The impact on village life of this type of migrant labor was much greater than during the earlier period of hunting and long-distance trade, however, since more than 50 percent of the male inhabitants of a community might be absent at any one time.

The colonial government's reaction to environmental deterioration was based on a sequence of technical solutions that included reconditioning of the reserve (grass planting, terracing, the closure of selected pastures to cattle) and forced destocking. By the 1950's such programs had expanded to include extensive dam-building and the creation of settlement schemes (figs. 7, 8, 9). At no time were indigenous Kamba approaches to dealing with problems of waste shortfalls or other aspects of the environment examined, nor was cognizance taken of the negative impact on the Kamba of earlier land alienations. According to the colonial administration the Kamba were ruining their land with "primitive techniques, overstocking, and timber cutting," and the only antidote was a combination of conservation measures and planting of drought-resistant crops (Agricultural Report, 1925-26). The Kamba were predictably dissatisfied with the government programs and frequently refused to cooperate. In the case of forced destocking, the Kamba reaction was sufficiently negative to cause an indefinite postponement of the project.

Attempts were also made in the 1950's to expand African cash-crop cultivation, a process which contributed to the further differentiation of highland and lowland Machakos. Both the prejudices of the agricultural staff on this issue, and the result of the unequal distribution of resources during earlier decades, continued to show up clearly in the agricultural reports. In 1951, the position of areas over 5,000 feet was further improved by the introduction of coffee, which, along with the already established crops—cattle, vegetables, fruits and wheat—provided a range of options to local farmers.

The lowlands during the postwar period were still considered barely suitable for the expansion of commercial agriculture. Some limited progress was also made in improving lowland agriculture, but this was definitely a secondary priority. The 1951 Agricultural Report, discussing the reintroduction of cotton to the district, describes the lowlands as still primarily subsistence oriented, with a population that is apathetic and backward because "no future is seen in the industrious working of the land which seems unable to give them a living." Few crops other than cotton received more than cursory attention for possible commercialization efforts. Tobacco was grown briefly until local fuel supplies proved to be inadequate, and sisal was experimented with until the market was judged to be too unpredictable.

The dissemination of improved farming techniques was also less successful than expected. Farmer response was limited because the infrastructure was inadequate or because extension agents, poorly versed in the details of the local farming system, could not integrate this established system with unfamiliar methods and crops. Furthermore, the extension staff was often unable to communicate with the mass of the Kamba peasantry, devising messages best suited to the few farmers who were completely integrated into the commercial sector.

FIG. 9. Water-conserving agricultural terraces in the Mbooni Hills. Subsurface bedrock, mantled with relatively thin soils, keeps downslope movement of soil moisture within the reach of rooted crops. Terrace-risers, in this case, are constructed of field stone because of the steeply pitching slopes.

It was not until the early 1970's that the highland/lowland dichotomy was fully acknowledged. The "marginal areas syndrome" in the lowlands was recognized, and was attributed as much to neglect as to local physical conditions or a fatalistic attitude among the inhabitants. It was also acknowledged that research and extension efforts had been focused on highland crops and problems, and that a more balanced program was required. This turnabout reflects in part the very practical need to make the lowlands more suitable to supporting a rapidly growing resident population as well as the spillover from the crowded uplands. There are now several programs that have been designed for the specific crop and technology needs of semi-arid areas which should make a substantial contribution in the near future.

The returns from the questionnaires indicated that most farmers in Machakos District now utilize wells, boreholes, or water catchment areas created by dams. They use plow and oxen and build either ridges or terraces. They grow cash crops and may hire laborers to assist in the process. A minority have begun to use manure and insecticide. Such farmers, although they still have recourse to part of their system of survival, have integrated established practices with selected imported technologies, a process that augurs well for the future of the district.

REFERENCES

BRETT, E. H.
1973.   Colonialism and underdevelopment in East Africa.   Nok Publishers, New York.

DATOO, BASHIR A.
1977.   Peasant agricultural production in East Africa: The nature and consequences of dependence.   Antipode, vol. 9, no. 1, pp. 70-77.

FORBES MUNRO, J.
1975.   Colonial rule and the Kamba.   Clarendon Press, Oxford.

GOVERNMENT OF KENYA
1931-1956.   Agricultural Reports, Machakos District.

GREGORY, J. W.
1896.   The Great Rift Valley.   John Murray, London.

HEYER, J.; IRERI, D.; and MORRIS, J.
1971.   Rural development in Kenya.   East African Publishing House, Nairobi.

KJEKSHUS, HELGE
1977.   Ecology control and economic development in East African history.   University of California Press, Berkeley.

LEYS, COLIN.
1974.   Underdevelopment in Kenya.   University of California Press, Berkeley.

OWAKO, F. N.
1969.   The Machakos problem: A study of some of the aspects of the agrarian problems of Machakos District, Kenya.   Unpublished Ph.D. thesis, University of London.

RUTHENBERG, HANS
1966.   Agricultural policy in Kenya, 1945-1965.   Springer-Verlag, Berlin.

VAN ZWANENBERG, R.
1974.   The development of peasant commodity production in Kenya.   The Economic History Review, ser. 2, vol. 27, no. 3.

WATTS, RACHAEL S.
1900.   In the heart of savagedom.   Marshall Bros., Ltd., London.

SILBERFEIN, MARILYN
——.   Differential development in Machakos District, Kenya.   *In* "Pastoral and Agricultural Economics in The Harsh Lands of Africa," Earl Scott, ed.   (In press.)

MARILYN SILBERFEIN

Recovery and Study of Middle Cretaceous Vertebrate Fossils in North-central Texas

Principal Investigator: Bob H. Slaughter, Director, Shuler Museum of Paleontology, Southern Methodist University, Dallas, Texas.

Grant No. 1200: For recovery of the only known Cretaceous mammal locality in North America—Greenwood Canyon, Montague County, Texas.

During the summer of 1973 the Shuler Museum of Paleontology re-initiated the search for rare lower (or middle) Cretaceous vertebrate fossils in north-central Texas. Efforts were concentrated in Greenwood Canyon (Montague County) as that locality was in danger due to erosion-retarding dams then under construction. Other localities were also located and studied to produce faunas of different deposition with which to compare.

The technique used was to quarry large quantities of sands and clays where fossil bone was weathering out. It was then trucked to the outdoor laboratories at Southern Methodist University, Dallas, Texas, where it was dried and washed through 0.7-millimeter sieves. The concentrates were then sorted under binocular microscopes for the recovery of the smallest vertebrate remains.

Portions of a camptosaur and a sauropod were recovered and are under study by Dr. Wann Langston, director of the Vertebrate Paleontology Laboratories at the Balcones Research Center, Austin, Texas. The small reptiles, frogs, and salamanders are on loan to Dr. Richard Estes, San Diego State University, for study. The fish study has been completed by Dr. John T. Thurmond of Birmingham-Southern College. The multiberculate mammals are the subject of a paper in preparation by myself and William D. Turnbull of the Field Museum of Natural History (Chicago).

Thus far these interesting deposits have produced three new species of elasmobranch fishes, two new genera and five new species of actinopterygian fishes, a new family of urodels, and five new genera of therian mammals and one of a triconodontid. The mammalian taxa include the earliest known placental mammals, the earliest known marsupial mammals, the latest known occurrence of symmetridonts, and the latest abundant occurrence of triconodonts. This represents an increase of the known American Lower Cretaceous fauna since 1970 by some 1,000 percent.

Not only have new forms come to light as a result of this work, but also considerable information concerning the probable preferred habitat of a number of small vertebrates has accumulated. For example, it is found that *Hybodus butleri* and *Lonchidion anitae* occur only in fresh water, as demonstrated by their consistent association with frogs and salamanders and not with rayfishes and pycnodonts. *Hybodus parvidens*, on the other hand, occurs only with rays and pycnodonts.

It has been possible to map full marine deposits as well as those of bay and brackish-water deposits and fresh-water sediments. From these maps we can establish the direction of the beachline in Albian times.

The faunas have demonstrated also that there is a faunal break 15 feet above the bottom of the Paluxy Formation and that the fauna below this point is more like that of the basal Travis Peak and Glen Rose Formations. Above this point the fauna becomes a part of a faunal province with the overlaying Walnut Formation. Thus the stratigraphy precision is vastly increased.

New taxa will continue to be recognized for some time to come from the collections now under study.

Papers resulting directly from this work since 1973 are listed below:

REFERENCES

THURMOND, JOHN T.
    1974.   Lower vertebrate faunas of the Trinity Division in north-central Texas.
            Geoscience and Man, vol. 8, pp. 103-129, illus.
SLAUGHTER, BOB H.
    1977.   A search for the ancestors of the ancestors.   Texas Parks and Wildl.
            Mag., vol. 35, pp. 6-7.
SLAUGHTER, BOB H., and TURNBULL, WILLIAM D.
    ———.   Multituberculate mammals of the Paluxy Formation. (In preparation.)

BOB H. SLAUGHTER

Ecology and Behavior of Rhesus Monkeys (*Macaca mulatta*) in Nepal

Principal Investigator: Charles H. Southwick, University of Colorado, Boulder, Colorado (formerly at The Johns Hopkins University, Baltimore, Maryland).

Grant Nos. 1239 and 1521.   To study the ecology and behavior of rhesus monkeys in Nepal.

A field study of rhesus monkeys in Nepal was undertaken from June 1974 to August 1976. Rhesus populations were investigated in three areas (fig. 1): (1) Temple and parkland habitats on the edge of Kathmandu at an altitude of 4,400 feet, (2) lowland terai jungle in the Karnali-Bardia wildlife reserve in southwestern Nepal at an altitude of 600 feet, and (3) pine-oak forests around Rara Lake in the mountains of northwestern Nepal at altitudes of 10,000 feet. These areas sampled the three basic habitats in which rhesus monkeys live in Nepal: Temple grounds and parklands surrounded by intensive agricultural cultivation in an intermontane valley, lowland deciduous monsoon forest at the edge of the Gangetic basin and the Himalayan foothills, and montane deciduous-evergreen forest in the Central Himalayan range.

The Kathmandu rhesus populations live on the grounds of ancient temples, and interact closely with the human community in and around the temples. One population of approximately 300 monkeys in 5 social groups lives in Swayambhu, a Buddhist temple site at least 2,000 years old on the western side of Kathmandu city. The other population of about 320 monkeys ranges over a complex of parks, residences, and temples at Pashupati, a Hindu temple site also more than 2,000 years old located on the eastern side of Kathmandu city (fig. 2).

Both temples include open and wooded parklands, and Pashupati contains small forested tracts. The rhesus monkeys in these locations provide ideal opportunities for studies of primate population dynamics, home range patterns, and the utilization of time, space, and habitat by rhesus monkeys. They are also ideal for the analysis of social behavior in different environments, and interactions between monkeys and people.

In contrast, the Karnali-Bardia and Rara Lake areas offer opportunities to study rhesus in forest habitats with less frequent human contact. Even in these

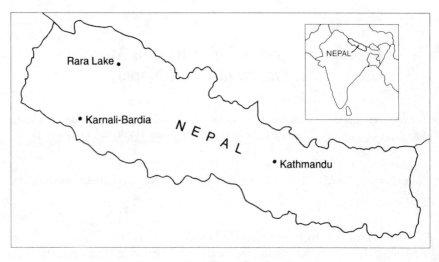

FIG. 1.   Locations of study areas.

areas, however, rhesus monkeys interacted with people and agricultural activities at times.

The terai forests of Karnali-Bardia represent the typical "jungle" and wildlife areas of Nepal and northern India. They are ecotonal zones between the Gangetic plain and the first range of Himalayan foothills, characterized by deciduous forest, primarily sal (*Shorea robusta*), terminalia (*Terminalia tomentosa*), sheesham (*Dalbergia sissoo*), acacia (*Acacia catechu*), banyan (*Ficus bengalensis*), pipal (*F. religiosa*), and more than one hundred other species of trees, shrubs, and vines. Rainfall is 50 to 80 inches during the monsoon season of June to September, with the remainder of the year quite dry. The climate is similar to that of the Gangetic plain, and the area is subject to increasing agricultural invasion.

The montane forests of the Rara Lake area in northwestern Nepal at altitudes around 10,000 feet are dominated by blue pine (*Pinus excelsa* or *Pinus wallichiana*), western Himalayan spruce (*Picea smithiana*), fir (*Abies spectabilis*), birch (*Betula utilis*), and several species of oaks (*Quercus* spp.). Small cultivated fields also occur around the lake, with crops of barley, wheat, corn, millet, potatoes, apples, pulses, and spinach. The climate is cool and moist with winter snows.

These diverse habitats illustrate the wide range of ecological and behavioral adaptability of the rhesus monkey, probably the greatest of any species of nonhuman primate.

FIG. 2. Adult male and female rhesus monkeys, Abraham and Deborah, at Pashupati, Kathmandu. (Photo by Jane Teas.)

Scientific Background

Rhesus monkeys occur naturally from Afghanistan in the west to Hong Kong in the east, but the heart of their geographic range and region of greatest natural abundance is north-central India and southern Nepal. Rhesus have been used extensively in biomedical research and laboratory studies of behavior for more than fifty years, but the first field studies of their ecology and behavior on the Asian subcontinent were not begun until 1959. Most field studies have been undertaken in India, where the monkeys, however, have been subjected to intensive trapping pressure with the result that both their population ecology and behavior has been affected (Southwick, Beg, and Siddiqi, 1961a, 1961b, 1965; Southwick and Siddiqi, 1977). In Nepal, rhesus monkeys have not been trapped, nor have they been studied prior to our own investigations. They afford substantial advantages for both behavioral and ecological studies of macaques in natural settings.

Results

POPULATION ECOLOGY

In the terai forests of Karnali-Bardia, 10.6 square miles of forest were surveyed in February and March, 1976, by foot transects, with the sighting of 8 groups of rhesus monkeys and 21 groups of langurs (*Presbytis entellus*). This provided a population estimate of 0.75 rhesus groups per square mile (0.29 groups per square kilometer), and 1.98 langur groups per square mile (0.76 per square kilometer).

Rhesus groups varied from 20 to 51 individuals, averaging 32 per group. Langur groups varied from 12 to 40 and averaged 26.2 individuals per group.

The rhesus group density of Karnali-Bardia was very similar to that observed in Corbett National Park, India, in similar forest habitat (Southwick, Beg, and Siddiqi, 1961a and 1961b), where 0.27 groups per square kilometer were found. Group size in Corbett was higher, however, averaging 50 individuals per group, so over-all population density in Corbett was 13.5 individual rhesus per square kilometer compared to only 9.3 rhesus per square kilometer in Karnali-Bardia.

The Karnali-Bardia rhesus population had a low ratio of immature individuals to total population (0.44), whereas that in Corbett had a higher ratio (0.50) indicating better reproduction and survival of young. In previous primate population studies, an immature to adult ratio of 0.50 has been considered necessary for long-term population maintenance (Southwick and Siddiqi, 1977), suggesting that the Karnali-Bardia population was not in a strong position in 1975.

In the pine-spruce-oak forests of northwestern Nepal in the vicinity of Rara Lake rhesus monkeys were found in October 1975 at an altitude of 10,000 feet, and they were reliably reported to ascend a ridge at 12,000 feet. This probably represents a high altitude record for rhesus monkeys (Richie et al., 1978). Only one group was found, consisting of 39 individuals, including 3 adult males, 17 adult females, 8 infants, and 11 juveniles. The immature ratio was 0.49, indicating that this group was near the edge of long-term maintenance. Obviously the survival or mortality of each immature individual is of rather critical importance to this small isolated population.

Several features of the Rara Lake environment aided the survival of rhesus monkeys during harsh winters at this altitude: (1) The southern exposure of the forest forming their primary home range; (2) the climate-moderating influence of the lake, which does not freeze; (3) the presence of two villages with agricultural crops; and (4) the easy access to lower altitudes in the Mugu Karnali Valley near the forest.

More detailed population studies have been conducted on the Kathmandu populations at Swayambhu and Pashupati over a period of four years from 1974 to 1978. The last two years of 1977 and 1978 have been supported by an Earthwatch program under the Center for Field Research in Belmont, Massachusetts.

The total populations of Swayambhu and Pashupati have been relatively stable, varying from 266 to 327 monkeys for Swayambhu and from 300 to 335 monkeys for Pashupati. The numbers of groups have remained constant, 5 for Swayambhu and 7 for Pashupati.

Both of the Kathmandu populations have had a very favorable age ratio, with an average of 57.5 percent of the total population immature. Normally, this demographic pattern should produce population growth in the order of 10 to 15 percent per year, yet these populations have been intrinsically regulated without trapping or external removal.

The mechanisms for intrinsic population regulation seem to be low natality (an average of 63% of adult females produced one young per year from 1974 through 1977, compared to 78% to 90% in comparable Indian populations), and high adult mortality (25.8% per year in Kathmandu, compared to 12.5 to 17.5% per year in comparable Indian populations).

Infant mortality in Kathmandu (21.5% per year) was slightly higher than in India (15.5% to 17.7%), but juvenile loss rate was much lower (17.0% in Kathmandu compared to 31.5% to 53.9% in India). The high juvenile loss rate in India reflects trapping loss, since this age class was extensively trapped prior to April 1978, when India issued an export ban on all rhesus monkeys.

All of the above data indicate that the primary mechanisms of population regulation in the Kathmandu rhesus are reduced birth rates and high adult mortality. The real causes for these demographic characteristics are unknown; we do not know, for example, the relative roles of disease, nutrition, or behavior in determining these patterns. These unknowns represent challenges for future research.

HOME RANGES AND THE UTILIZATION OF SPACE

The rhesus groups of Swayambhu had overlapping home ranges varying in size from 6 to 15 hectares. Overlap occurred primarily around the temples, garbage dumps, water holes, and major access paths. Each group also had a core area of utilization which was fairly exclusively occupied; these tended to be places for resting, grooming, and play, and were located away from major food resources.

Similar patterns of home range occurred at Pashupati, except that the spatial dimensions varied more, from 2.5 to 24 hectares. In general the largest groups had the largest home ranges with the most favorable habitat, though many specific exceptions occurred. At Swayambhu, the two largest groups, Rex's (138 monkeys) and Omshalla's (64 monkeys), had the largest home ranges, whereas Falstaff's (29) and Cyan's (30) had the smallest. The home ranges of Rex's group and Omshalla's were similar in size, but Rex's group had the most favored habitat in terms of access to the temple, and an eastern exposure which gave them early morning sunshine (advantageous after cold nights), and afternoon shade (advantageous during very hot days).

At Pashupati, the two largest groups, Burger's (71 monkeys) and Gandalf's (65 monkeys) also had the largest home ranges and best access to the main temple. Home ranges were not entirely stable from year to year, but often changed dramatically as the size, leadership, or dominance relationships of the groups changed.

THE UTILIZATION OF TIME

In the study of behavior, emphasis was placed on the quantitative analysis of behavioral profiles (that is, the relative amounts of time spent in various activities), and on the influences of various ecological factors (habitat, season, and time of day) on behavioral profiles.

Behavioral profile data were obtained by counting the numbers of observed monkeys engaged in each behavior every 10 minutes during each hour and a half observation period. The data were then converted to the mean numbers and percentages of monkeys engaging in each of 10 basic types of behavior throughout the observation period. Normally 6 to 9 hours of observation were made per day, and the basic behavioral profile data involved a total of 1,506 hours of observation over a 12-month period. Typically 15 to 20 individual monkeys were under surveillance at any given time. Special behavioral data were obtained on aggressive behaviors, grooming, feeding, and maternal-infant relationships, since these represent social interactions of particular interest in understanding group dynamics and behavioral ecology.

For all individuals throughout the entire year, feeding and locomotion were the most important behavioral activities, accounting for 52 percent of the monkeys' time. If looking behavior and grooming (fig. 3) are added, fully 87 percent of their total behavior is accounted for (fig. 4). Play activities, mostly by juveniles, occupied only 3 percent of the total activity budget; agonistic behavior, 2 percent; and sexual behavior, 1 percent.

Behavioral profiles varied according to age class, season, habitat, and time of day, and the data yielded a great many details on these variations. In general, adults spent considerably more time grooming, resting, looking, and engaged in sexual and agonistic behaviors than juveniles. Juveniles spent

FIG. 3.   Juvenile grooming adult female, Anita. (Photo by Thomas Richie.)

more time in feeding on natural vegetation and play. Both age classes spent comparable amounts of time in feeding from human sources, and in locomotion.

Seasonal changes in behavior were most conspicuous during the fall, when mating occurred, and the spring and early summer when births occurred. The fall mating season was accompanied by a significant increase in grooming, sexual behavior, and feeding from human sources. Agonistic behavior also showed an increase in the fall, but the increase was not statistically significant. The spring birth season showed remarkably few significant changes in behavioral profile: There was some tendency toward an increase in resting, a decrease in locomotion, looking, human feeding, and agonistic behavior. None of these changes was statistically significant, however, by Duncan's multiple-range test.

Habitat had a number of significant influences on behavior. In the Swayambhu temple grounds, the monkeys were most actively engaged in feeding from human sources, looking, and locomotion. The parklands were characterized by significantly higher percentages of resting, play, and grooming, all quiet activities. The forest habitat was characterized by moderation in all behaviors; that is, no behavior was significantly the most or the least compared to other habitats. We had anticipated that the forest environment would result in significantly less agonistic behavior, as was shown in studies of forest-dwelling rhesus in India in comparison with temple, village, and urban monkeys (Southwick, 1972), but this was not the case. The rhesus in Pashupati forest showed only slightly less aggression than those in Swayambhu temple and they actually showed more than those in Pashupati and Swayambhu parklands. None of these differences was significant, however. Our only explanation is that the Kathmandu rhesus are basically temple monkeys, even though they venture into parklands and forest patches. Apparently their brief sojourns in the forest do not modify their aggressive behavior significantly.

The time of day modified behavior by producing a higher frequency of resting, grooming, and feeding from human sources during the morning, and more feeding from natural vegetation in the afternoon. There was not significant variation between morning and afternoon behaviors in other categories.

The variables of season, habitat, and time of day did not interact in any significant way on the monkeys' behavior; that is, the same general seasonal changes occurred independently in each habitat and in both morning and afternoon time periods. Complete data and more detailed analyses of all of these topics are presented in other papers and publications (Taylor, 1976; Teas, 1975, 1978, 1980).

GROOMING

More detailed data on grooming showed that adult females were twice as active in grooming as juveniles and three times more active than males. The most frequent groomers were also the most frequent recipients. Females groomed females the most; males groomed other males most frequently, and juveniles divided their grooming equally between females and other juveniles. Female and juvenile grooming peaked in the winter, whereas male grooming showed its highest frequency in late winter and spring. Habitat influenced grooming significantly, with lowest grooming frequencies in the temple, moderate levels in the forest, and highest frequencies in the parklands.

AGONISTIC BEHAVIOR

The Kathmandu rhesus had high levels of aggression (averaging 1.71 aggressive encounters per monkey per hour), four to eight times higher than comparable groups in India (averaging 0.24 to 0.40 aggressive encounters per monkey per hour) (Southwick, Siddiqi, Farooqui, and Pal, 1974). Despite the high level of aggression, 94 percent of all aggressive conflicts in Kathmandu were threat-and-chase interactions only, and did not involve physical contact.

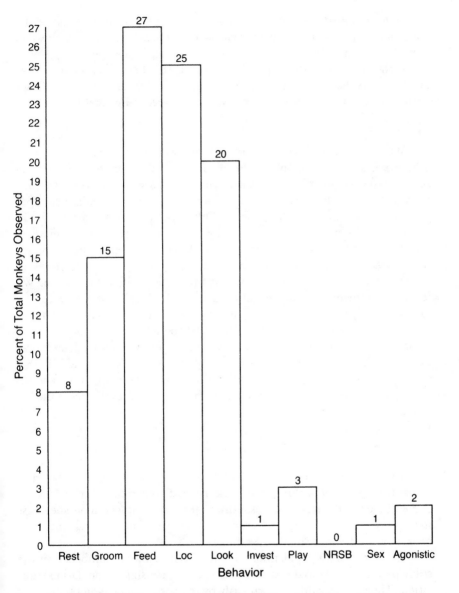

FIG. 4.   Behavior profiles (resting, grooming, feeding, locomotion, looking, inves-tigating, playing, nonreproductive sexual behavior, sex, and agonistic) for 12 months, a.m. and p.m., adults and juveniles, all seasons and all habitats averaged, totaling 1,506 hours of observation, 1974-1975.

Males initiated more than twice as many aggressive interactions as females and four times more than juveniles. The seasonal increase in aggression in the fall was mainly due to an increase in male aggression.

Although we lack direct proof, we feel that the high levels of aggressive behavior may have population significance by acting as a general stressor agent and thereby increasing adult mortality and reducing natality.

PARENTAL CARE

Maternal care in the Kathmandu rhesus was typical of that described in other studies of rhesus monkeys elsewhere, with the exception that mothers showed reduced grooming of infants. Female rhesus with infants showed appropriate protective and restrictive behavior but only 0.13 grooming bout per hour was directed toward their infants. Other studies of rhesus maternal care do not quantify grooming, but they imply that substantially more mother-infant grooming is typical. If there is indeed less maternal grooming of infants in the Kathmandu rhesus, this may contribute to the relatively high levels of infant mortality, though we cannot assess the role of infectious disease. We feel the Kathmandu rhesus were also subject to high levels of infectious disease, especially respiratory and enteric infections such as tuberculosis and dysentery, and these would impact most seriously on infants.

Several cases of the care of infants by adult males were observed, and these have been described in detail in a separate publication (Taylor et al., 1978). One dominant male adopted an orphaned infant two years in a row, and attempted in each case to care for the infant, but in both cases the infant died of starvation.

Summary

A field study of rhesus monkey ecology and behavior was undertaken in Nepal from June 1974 through August 1978. Population counts were conducted in lowland terai forest in southwestern Nepal, upland montane forest in northwestern Nepal, and in Kathmandu Valley in central Nepal. Intensive behavioral studies were done in Kathmandu.

The Kathmandu populations were relatively stable in numbers over the study period, and showed intrinsic biosocial mechanisms of population regulation. These were manifested primarily by reduced birth rates and high adult mortality rates. To a lesser extent, they also showed high infant mortality rates. Population trends of the forest groups are unknown, but age structure data indicated that these populations may be declining or are barely holding their own.

Behavioral studies focused on home ranges, behavioral profiles, and environmental influences on behavior. Home ranges of different groups overlapped, but virtually all groups had core areas of exclusive use. In behavioral profiles, the monkeys spent 87 percent of their daytime in feeding, locomotion, looking behavior, and grooming. Specific time budgets varied between sex and age groups, season of the year, time of day, and habitat.

Grooming was the most prevalent direct social interaction and was dominated by adult females. The Kathmandu rhesus were highly aggressive, although 94 percent of their aggressive behavior was noncontact.

The entire study emphasizes the role of the environment in shaping behavior, and the importance of behavior in the ecological adaptations of rhesus monkeys.

Acknowledgments

This research was supported by the National Geographic Society; we are indebted to Barry Bishop, Edwin Snyder, Paul Oehser, Mary G. Smith, and Joanne Hess of the Society for their guidance and encouragement at important phases of the study. In Nepal, we would like to thank Professors D. R. Uprety, and D. D. Bhatt, Dr. K. R. Pandey, and Mrs. Bina Pradhan of Tribhuvan University; Dr. B. N. Uprety and H. R. Mishra of the Office of National Parks and Conservation; Dr. Thomas Acker and Gabriel Campbell of the U. S. Educational Foundation in Kathmandu; and Dr. Daniel Taylor. Ram Shrestha, Rakesh Shrestha, R. B. Khadka, George Turner, F. M. Burhans, and R. T. Tashi all assisted with the fieldwork. George and Charlotte Whitesides participated in the Karnali-Bardia survey, and we are very grateful for their contributions.

REFERENCES

RICHIE, T.; SHRESTHA, R.; TEAS, J.; TAYLOR, H.; and SOUTHWICK, C.
1978. Rhesus monkeys at high altitudes in northwestern Nepal. Journ. Mammalogy, vol. 59, pp. 443-444.

SOUTHWICK, C. H.
1972. Aggression among nonhuman primates. Addison-Wesley Module in Anthropology, no. 23, pp. 1-23.

SOUTHWICK, C. H.; BEG, M. A.; and SIDDIQI, M. R.
1961a. A population survey of rhesus monkeys in villages, towns and temples of northern India. Ecology, vol. 42, pp. 538-547.

1961b. A population survey of rhesus monkeys in northern India: II. Transportation routes and forest areas. Ecology, vol. 42, pp. 698-710.

1965. Rhesus monkeys in north India. Pp. 111-159 *in* "Primate Behavior: Field Studies of Monkeys and Apes," Irven DeVore, ed. Holt, Rinehart and Winston, New York.

SOUTHWICK, C. H., and SIDDIQI, M. F.
1977.   Population dynamics of rhesus monkeys in northern India.   Pp. 339-362 *in* "Primate Conservation," H.S.H. Ranier and G. Bourne, eds. Academic Press, New York.
SOUTHWICK, C. H.; SIDDIQI, M. F.; FAROOQUI, M. Y.; and PAL, B. C.
1974.   Xenophobia among free-ranging rhesus groups in India.   Pp. 185-209 *in* "Primate Aggression, Territoriality, and Xenophobia," R. L. Hollaway, ed.   Academic Press, New York.
TAYLOR, H.
1976.   Rhesus monkeys of Kathmandu Valley.   Nepal Nature Conservation Society Newsletter, no. 33.
TAYLOR, H.; TEAS, J.; RICHIE, T.; SOUTHWICK, C.; and SHRESTHA, R.
1978.   Social interactions between adult male and infant rhesus monkeys in Nepal.   Primates: Journal of Primatology, vol. 19, pp. 343-351.
TEAS, J.
1975.   The rhesus monkey in Kathmandu, Nepal.   Nepal Nature Conservation Society Special Coronation Issue, no. 28, pp. 2-4.
1978.   Behavioral ecology of rhesus monkeys *(Macaca mulatta)* in Kathmandu, Nepal.   Ph.D. Thesis, The Johns Hopkins University, 131 pp. illus.
TEAS, J.; RICHIE, T.; TAYLOR, H.; and SOUTHWICK, C. H.
1980.   Population patterns and behavioral ecology of rhesus monkeys *(Macaca mulatta)* in Nepal.   Pp. 247-262 *in* "The Macaques; Studies in Ecology, Behavior and Evolution," D. G. Lindburg, ed.   Van Nostrand Reinhold, New York.
TEAS, J.; RICHIE, T.; TAYLOR, H.; FELDMAN, H. A.; and SOUTHWICK, C. H.
1980.   Aggressive behavior in free-ranging rhesus monkeys of Kathmandu, Nepal.   Anthropologia Contemp., vol. 3, no. 2, p. 283.

CHARLES H. SOUTHWICK
JANE TEAS
THOMAS RICHIE
HENRY TAYLOR

Explorations for Coral Reef Fishes in the Molucca Islands, Indonesia

Principal Investigator: Victor G. Springer, National Museum of Natural History, Smithsonian Institution, Washington, D. C.

Grant No. 1258:   In support of exploration for coral reef fishes in the Molucca Islands, Indonesia.

The principal investigator and his assistant, Martin F. Gomon, spent the period February 15–April 10, 1974, in Indonesia collecting fishes. Although the grant was made to collect fishes in the Moluccas, our Indonesian hosts, National Institute of Oceanology, altered our plans (to our pleasant surprise) to include collecting at a series of islands between Java and the Moluccas. These islands included: Pulau Seribu (off Djakarta), Karimundjawa, Bawean (both off north-central Java), Kabaena, Buton (both off southeast Sulawesi), Ambon, Banda, Ceram, and Saparaua (all in the Moluccas). The geographic extent of these islands covers approximately 1,500 miles of longitude. The result was that we traded the opportunity to sample a single locality (Ambon) thoroughly for the chance to obtain very important information on species composition and ranges of distribution of the fishes over much of the length of Indonesia. We obtained fewer species than we would have had we concentrated on a single locality, but the distributional data on those we got offset this fact.

We obtained over 500 species and over 13,000 specimens. A preliminary evaluation of some of these specimens provided the following results, which are indicative of the great importance of the collections.

A new species of the blenniid genus *Ecsenius* was obtained from localities over the entire distance covered by the trip, as was another species of *Ecsenius* previously known only from the Moluccas. The range of a third species of *Ecsenius* only provisionally believed to extend as far west as the Moluccas was collected in those islands. A series of specimens of a fourth species of *Ecsenius* previously known from the Solomon Islands and a single Moluccan specimen were collected. These specimens demonstrate that the Moluccan population is recognizably different from the Solomon Islands population.

631

A species of blenniid, *Meiacanthus smithi,* was recorded from outside the Indian Ocean for the first time, and the range of its closest relative, *Meiacanthus atrodorsalis* from the Pacific, was shown to break in the area east of where *M. smithi* was collected.

The range of the blenniid *Omobranchus elongatus* was extended significantly to the west.

Eighteen specimens of a species of jawfish of the genus *Stalix,* which genus was previously known from only five specimens belonging to three species, were collected. These specimens require revision of recently published conclusions concerning *Stalix,* and they will also allow specimens to be sacrificed for anatomical studies needed to delineate the relationships of the genus.

Specimens of a species of the anemone fish genus *Amphiprion* exhibiting an unusual color pattern were obtained. These made possible the synonymization of a previously recognized species (Allen and Springer, 1975).

The range of the flathead, *Platycephalus beauforti,* was extended significantly south.

The range of the gobiid *Eviota storthynx* was extended from the Philippine and Palau Islands to Pulau Seribu.

A new species of the gobiid genus *Cryptocentrus* was collected.

An undescribed species of the gobiid genus *Eviota,* previously known only from the Indian Ocean, was collected in the Java Sea. Two new species of *Eviota* were collected, so far known only from Indonesia, and ten other new species more wide ranging in the Indo-Pacific were taken. *Eviota nigriventris* and *E. lachdeberei,* originally described in 1933, were recollected at the type locality. In all, 24 species of *Eviota* were collected, thus providing important material for a revision of the genus now in progress by Dr. E. A. Lachner and S. J. Karnella.

We were unsuccessful on one of the goals of our trip: underwater photography. We had taken two air compressors to be used for diving on our trip. Dock hands irreparably damaged one of these on arrival in Indonesia and the other continuously malfunctioned on the trip in spite of numerous attempts at repair. We were on short air the whole trip and since our first priority was making collections we used all of our diving time collecting. There was no possibility to obtain another compressor as none was available in Indonesia and there was insufficient time to have another shipped to us.

All in all, the specimens obtained are tremendously important and will contribute to numerous studies now in progress and others contemplated for the future.

REFERENCES

ALLEN, GERALD R., and SPRINGER, VICTOR G.
1975.   *Amphiprion calliops* Schultz, a junior synonym of the red saddleback anemone fish *Amphiprion ephippium* (Bloch).   Tropical Fish Hobbyist, no. 23 (May), pp. 53-57.
MCKINNEY, JAMES F., and SPRINGER, VICTOR G.
1976.   Four new species of the fish genus *Ecsenius* with notes on other species of the genus (Blenniidae: Salariini).   Smithsonian Contr. Zool., no. 236, pp. 1-27.
SPRINGER, VICTOR G., and GOMON, MARTIN F.
1975.   Revision of the blenniid fish genus *Omobranchus* with descriptions of three new species and notes on other species of the tribe Omobranchini. Smithsonian Contr. Zool., no. 177, pp. 1-135.

VICTOR G. SPRINGER

Archeological Investigations of the Satingpra Civilization in Peninsular Thailand

Principal Investigator: Janice M. Stargardt, University of Cambridge, Cambridge, England.

Grant No. 1240:   To study the interaction of man and his environment in Isthmian Thailand, in the Protohistoric and Early Historic Period.

This grant enabled me to continue investigations, begun in 1970 and carried forward annually since that year, of a subpeninsula on the east coast of the isthmus of the Malay Peninsula. The subpeninsula has an area of 840 square kilometers and is situated in Songkhla Province, South Thailand. There is no name in Thai for this striking geological formation, which lies between the Gulf of Siam and the largest permanent lakes of Southeast Asia. For convenience, I had named it the Satingpra Peninsula, after the principal modern village there. The 1973/74 season revealed how appropriate this name was when I discovered an ancient city site buried under the modern village, and further work on the peninsula as a whole showed it to be the center of ancient civilization for that area.

The specific tasks set down for the season were (1) to extend surveys of the ancient hydraulic works and archeological sites of the Satingpra Peninsula, by a combination of *surface and aerial surveys* (the latter became possible for the first time in late 1973, as a result of a change in the policy toward security control over aerial survey); (2) to conduct *paleobotanical research,* which was included in the archeological project for the first time in that season and which included the washing of excavated layers and canal sediments to obtain ancient seed and organic materials and also the systematic coring of the ancient canals, reservoirs, and the lake beds for pollen cores; (3) to make a survey of the modern economic plants of the region as a control on (2) and also to fill one of the many gaps in the scientific data on the southern Thai provinces; and (4) last, but certainly not least, to extend the archeological excavations themselves.

The 1973/74 Season:

As a result of the combined financial support of the National Geographic Society, the Royal Society, and the University of Cambridge, I was able to work simultaneously during this season on the several aspects enumerated above with a view to obtaining detailed information on the ancient environment and on how the ancient civilization of the peninsula had fitted into it. Had the environment been overwhelmingly favorable to its development or, on the contrary, had there been difficulties to be overcome?

Three staff groups were set up to deal with the specific tasks of the season: the survey group, handling surface and aerial surveys and scale drawings; the botanical group, for ancient and modern botanical studies; the archeological group, which was also involved in surveys as well as excavations. Each group drew upon the pool of skilled technicians at the Prince of Songkhla University and hired its labor from the village where it was based for that day. In this way the practical benefits from the expedition's work were spread over as many villages of the isthmus as possible and a very valuable attitude of goodwill was established. Security conditions on the Satingpra Peninsula in 1973/74 prevented us from living on-site, as had been our practice in previous seasons. We returned to the campus of the Prince of Songkhla University each evening. This had the advantage of allowing me to coordinate with each group leader in the evening (if it had not been done during the day), going over drawings and specimens in the laboratory, which was put at our disposal, in a way that would not have been possible in our village quarters after dark.

Events of the Season

Fieldwork was undertaken from January to the end of April 1974. The "little monsoon" of April/May caused road flooding and excavation problems. Consequently work ceased until July 1975. The most dramatic event of the season was undoubtedly the discovery of the ancient city of Satingpra. The work done in previous years, between 1970 and 1973, had shown that there was a correlation between ancient canal-building and the pattern of settlement. This was one reason for giving such emphasis to hydraulic surveys as they were likely to lead to further discoveries of archeological sites. While the flights for the aerial survey of Satingpra Peninsula were begun during the 1974 season, the results became available only later. Therefore, once more, all the survey work of the expedition had to be done on foot. As it is extremely difficult to distinguish the bed of an ancient canal within a landscape of dyked and ponded ricefields, it may be useful to set out the techniques I was obliged by events to develop. Once a shallow but defined depression had been sited,

---

FIG. 1. Archeological map of the Satingpra Peninsula, including ancient hydraulic works (based on Janice Stargardt's survey and excavation data).

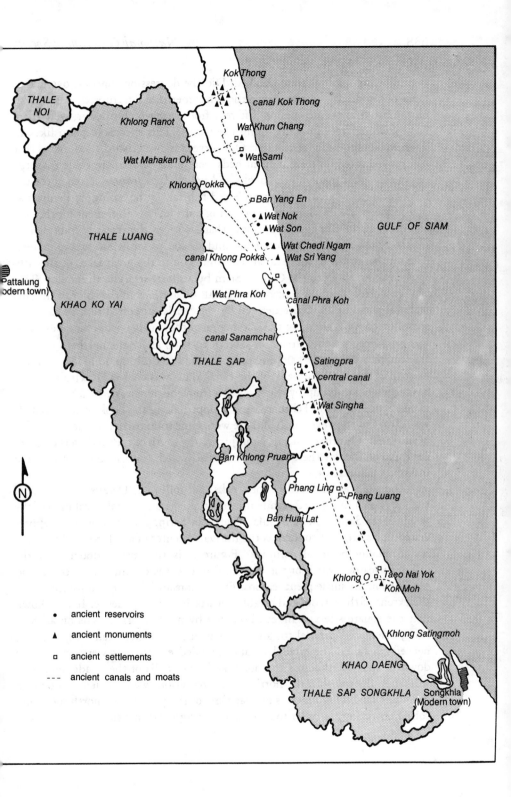

THALE
NOI

Khlong Ranot

Wat Mahakan Ok

Kok Thong

canal Kok Thong

Wat Khun Chang

Wat Sami

Khlong Pokka

THALE LUANG

Ban Yang En

▲ Wat Nok
▲ Wat Son

▲ Wat Chedi Ngam
canal Khlong Pokka   ▲ Wat Sri Yang

GULF OF SIAM

Pattalung
(modern town)

KHAO KO YAI

Wat Phra Koh

canal Phra Koh

canal Sanamchai

THALE SAP

Satingpra

central canal

Wat Singha

Ban Khlong Pruan

Phang Ling

Phang Luang

Ban Huai Lat

Khlong O

Taeo Nai Yok
▲ Kok Moh

Khlong Satingmoh

N

• ancient reservoirs

▲ ancient monuments

□ ancient settlements

--- ancient canals and moats

KHAO DAENG

THALE SAP SONGKHLA   Songkhla
(Modern town)

the following features were checked: Did the depression continue over a distance of hundreds of meters, even though sometimes interrupted; was the soil on the banks of the depression different from that which filled it; were there *Nipa fruticans* trees growing along the banks? This species of palm likes to grow with its roots in fresh water. Our surveys showed that the sediments that had moved into the ancient canal beds were much more permeable than the heavy clays that made up the banks and fields. *Nipa fruticans* often chose the banks of former canals as their preferred habitat on the Satingpra Peninsula.

It was while checking and correcting our previous alignment for the central canal of the Satingpra Peninsula that I noticed the traces of four ancient canals dug so as to form a square around an area of some 900 square meters. The southernmost of these canals continued on to the great lakes of the isthmus, linking them to the Gulf of Siam by a short, straight alignment. This was the correct course of the central canal. Gradations in the color of the surface soil within this square defined by the canals suggested to me that there were buried walls flanking the inner edge of the canals on all four sides. This was reinforced by the pattern of sand deposition along the northern canal of the square, where a low, sloping bank of sand had built up quite locally along the top of the southern bank of the canal. This was consistent with the sand having been picked up by the monsoon from the northeast, which blows between September and February, and dropped along the bank of the canal. It would do this, however, only if there were some solid barrier on the inner edge of the canal. Our first test pit, sunk just to the south of the sand on the northern canal on the day these features were discovered, confirmed the presence of massive brick walls.

The site was surveyed in the weeks that followed. Details of the citadel site are shown in figure 2, while figure 1 presents an archeological map of the whole of the Satingpra Peninsula. There, the Satingpra city site can be appreciated in its original context as the unrivaled center of an elaborate hydraulic and economic/political complex. Figure 2 is the survey drawing of the 1973/74 season; much of the data in figure 1 was obtained or checked and modified in the subsequent seasons. Excavations in 1974 were designed to test the extent of the citadel and establish a stratigraphic sequence. It was shown that the square site was indeed bounded by massive brick walls on all four sides, orientated parallel to, and just within, the ancient canal depressions, henceforth called the citadel moats. Detailed excavations were undertaken down to sterile soil across the north and west walls of the citadel and on a workshop floor within the north wall. Excavations were carried on down to the water table (1.40 meters at that time of the year) in the north moat and coring thereafter, in order to establish the original dimensions of the moat.

The Stratigraphy of the Citadel

Five productive layers were established in the sections of all trenches within the heavily fortified area of the citadel at Satingpra. The basic, sterile stratum was yellow sand belonging to an ancient beach ridge. Settlement began on this stratum, and it would appear, from the evidence of frequent flooding and environmental instability, that this early phase of settlement predated the digging of the central canal, the moats, and the construction of the walls of the citadel, all of which acted to stabilize the environment of this inner area. Subsequent layers comprised humus, clay, and fresh-water sediments in various mixtures and colors. Archeological debris from the period of ancient civilization were found in layers I, II, III, IV (numbered from the bottom). The greatest concentration, and at the same time objects of the finest quality and value, were in layers II and III.

The stratigraphic evidence of the interior of the citadel, together with the findings of the excavations across the walls, resulted in the definition of three main phases in the life of the city of Satingpra. Preliminary, but specific, chronological associations for these phases are provided by the datable Chinese trade ceramics associated with the layers of each phase.

Preliminary Chronology of Satingpra Citadel

The preliminary chronology indicates three phases: Phase I (Layer I), 7th to 9th century A.D.; Phase II (Layers II and III), 10th to late 13th century A.D.; and Phase III (Layer IV) late 13th to mid-14th century A.D. These phases coincided with three major assaults on the walls of the citadel. After the first two, extensive repairs were carried out; the third marked the end of ancient civilization at the site.

In the first phase, many sherds originating in pre-Angkorian Cambodia were found that could be related to dated sites in the Mekong Valley. These give us a provisional threshold of the participation of Satingpra in long-distance maritime trade from the first quarter of the 7th century. It must be emphasized that this date, both for the Cambodian site (Sambor Prei Kuk) and for Satingpra, is a minimum age rather than a maximum one for the sherd type may go back to an earlier horizon still. In this connection, the evidence provided by iconographic analysis shows that a major stone statue of Viṣṇu, found by chance at Satingpra many years ago, goes back to the 6th century A.D. (O'Connor, 1972, p. 46). To the first phase of the citadel also belong nu-

---

FIG. 2.   The Satingpra Citadel; Survey and Excavations 1974 (on pp. 640-641).

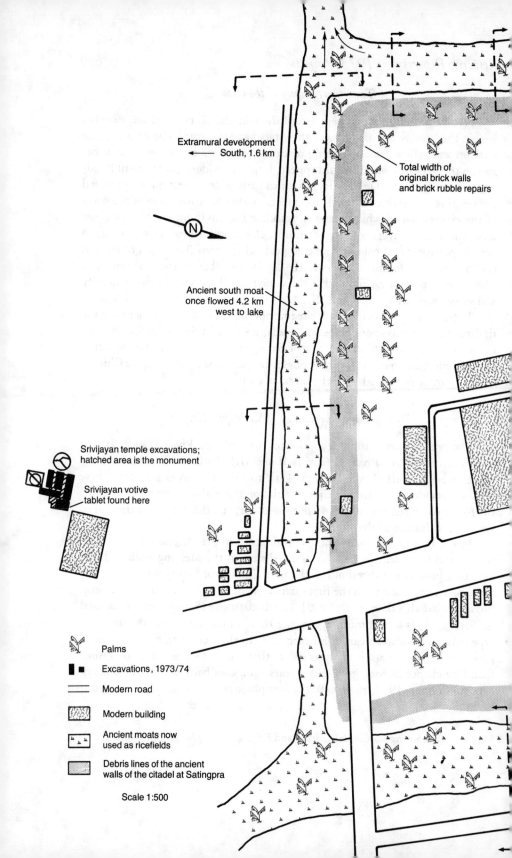

Extramural development
◄—— South, 1.6 km

Total width of
original brick walls
and brick rubble repairs

Ancient south moat
once flowed 4.2 km
west to lake

Srivijayan temple excavations;
hatched area is the monument

Srivijayan votive
tablet found here

Palms

Excavations, 1973/74

Modern road

Modern building

Ancient moats now
used as ricefields

Debris lines of the ancient
walls of the citadel at Satingpra

Scale 1:500

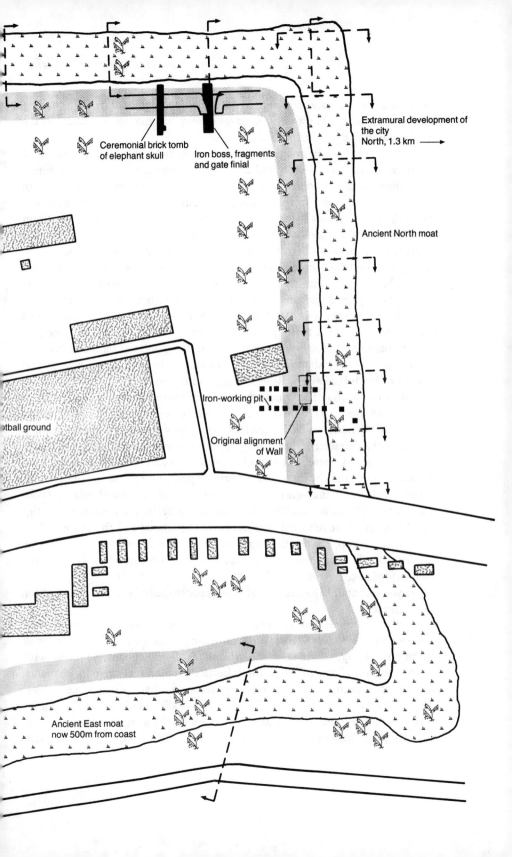

Ceremonial brick tomb
of elephant skull

Iron boss, fragments
and gate finial

Extramural development of
the city
North, 1.3 km ⟶

Ancient North moat

Iron-working pit

Original alignment
of Wall

otball ground

Ancient East moat
now 500m from coast

merous sherds of stoneware glazed in green, which originated in China during the T'ang Dynasty. These include wares of very fine quality not found at the lesser trading sites of Southeast Asia.

Phase II marked the apogee of the site. Both the density and the quality of the archeological debris increased dramatically during these layers. Whereas the Chinese trade ceramics were recorded in hundreds per square meter in phase I, they occurred in thousands per square meter in phase II. Figure 2 shows the selected areas that were excavated during the 1973/74 season. From these limited excavations a total of 20,000 fragments of Chinese ceramics was recovered, the bulk of them coming from the layers of phase II. The greater part by far of all the Chinese ceramics excavated were fine-quality bowls and small lidded boxes. A minor role, however, was taken by sherds of heavy amphorae, both glazed and unglazed. Side-by-side with the Chinese amphorae were found the sherds of Angkorian amphorae covered with a dark-brown glaze. This shows that Satingpra and Angkor were still part of the same network of maritime trade, reaching to the southern ports of China in the east and across to South India in the west. From there, the trade network stretched onward to reach the eastern Roman empire at Byzantium.

After the warfare that marked the end of phase II, the economic elan of that time disappeared. A lower level of intensity in foreign trade is reflected in the phase III deposits and a decline in the quality of goods imported, as well as the quantity, characterized this layer. Trade contact was still maintained with China during this phase, but the celadons of the Yüan period that occurred in this layer were sparse by comparison with the preceding phase and of moderate to poor quality. No blue-and-white wares were found in an archeological context at any of the numerous sites excavated on the Satingpra Peninsula (see fig. 1). This means that the final devastation of the citadel and the decline of its dependent sites took place before the trade in blue-and-white wares became established. I have, therefore, taken the mid-14th century as the latest possible terminal date for the citadel.

Layer V contains the debris and humus accumulated since the destruction of the citadel.

Carbon samples were excavated from three localities within the citadel. The lowest of these was a small brick tomb dug at the foot of the western wall of the citadel (fig. 2). It contained the skull of an elephant, together with charred tissue and sticks. Brick tomb burials are extremely rare in Thailand, and this appears to represent rites to provide a guardian spirit for the citadel. An iron-working hearth just within the north wall provided a small quantity of charcoal, while the third locality was again on the western side of the citadel, where an ancient gateway was uncovered. Small fragments of charred wood and numerous fragments of iron nails indicated the place where the former wooden gate had been burnt. A molded terra-cotta finial was also recovered from this locality and probably surmounted the gate originally. At the time of writing all these carbon samples are still awaiting testing in the Cambridge Radiocarbon Laboratory. Initially the chronology of the site depended on the stratigraphy and typology of objects rather than carbon dating.

Satingpra Citadel in Its Archeological Context

The sequence of archeological material recovered from the citadel remains the longest and richest of the entire Satingpra Peninsula. As such, it has provided a frame of reference for all the other sites excavated, all of which can be related to the phases established at the citadel. On the other hand, the work done since 1974 has changed the perspective considerably: I have been able to verify the fact that the urban area of Satingpra is much greater than that bounded by the four moats of the citadel. It is defined by the great reservoirs placed at each corner and is bisected by the central canal/south moat. This represents an urban area of 1,600 by 900 meters, in which the long axis runs from north to south, with an error of 13° to the west, (see fig. 3). Though of a homogeneous character with those of the citadel, the archeological deposits of the greater urban area are not as dense as those of the former. It therefore emerges as a heavily fortified treasury within the urban center. It is very likely that trade goods were concentrated here in such an exceptional manner because Satingpra was an active entrepôt as well as the center of a prosperous state.

From the central canal there radiated an extensive system of ancient canals serving each of the ancient sites of habitation, trade, and monumental development that I have located to date (see fig. 1). Each of these dependent sites was equipped with a varying number of reservoirs as well. From the size and number of the reservoirs, as well as from the archeological deposits, a great deal can be deduced about the relative size and importance of each site.

Hydraulic Surveying and the Satingpra Civilization

An extraordinary fact revealed by the work of the survey group during 1974 was the almost total absence of natural sources of fresh water on the eastern side of the Satingpra Peninsula, where all the ancient sites of civilization are concentrated. The official ordinance survey maps of the area show a very different picture. This is due to the fact that cropmarks of the ancient canals were picked up and recorded as contemporary rivers without a surface check.

Today, the Satingpra Peninsula is isolated, difficult of access. This explains
the absence of scientific data on the area. The survey team also collected soil
samples which, when studied in the laboratory at Cambridge, helped to explain why the natural drainage and distributive system was so inadequate (see
Stargardt, 1976a). In 1974, the results of our efforts to collect rainfall statistics over three years also became available. These showed that, contrary to data
of the geophysical maps, Satingpra is not in a high rainfall area. Its annual
rainfall is in the range of 1,500-2,000 millimeters. This is marginal to inadequate to the needs of rain-fed wet rice cultivation. We had already observed
that the modern farmers of the area have only a meager sufficiency in rice in
spite of the fact that the soils are very suitable. These data on the inadequacy of
the natural hydraulic conditions show why. They show also that the system of
ancient canals and reservoirs mentioned above was fundamental to the emergence and further growth of civilization on the peninsula. Work done since
1974, on the ancient ricefield system in relation to the reservoirs and canals,
has shown how, in these conditions, it was possible to develop a highly efficient wet rice agriculture and by that means to ensure the agricultural surpluses that were needed to support an urban concentration of people at
Satingpra as well as lesser concentrations at the dependent sites (see Stargardt,
1977).

    During the 1974 season the coring program in the beds of the central
canal and the two principal canals leading from it to the north and south, respectively, yielded data that enabled me to plot the periods of hydraulic maintenance and neglect in the ancient period. Not surprisingly, these related to
the phases already distinguished in the citadel but added a new form of evidence to that already gained from the land sites. It became apparent that the
hydraulic system, on which the settlements depended for so many things—
drinking water, irrigation, transport, trade, and administrative control—was
allowed to silt up throughout the entire third phase. There had been earlier
phases of neglect, but these had always been stopped and indeed to some extent reversed. After the attack that brought phase II to an end, the Satingpra
civilization was sufficiently resilient to repair its fortifications, but the restoration of its essential hydraulic basis was apparently beyond it.

    Between 1975 and 1977 this work has been extended to selected points in
the entire hydraulic system. As a result, 150 linear kilometers of ancient canals, serving 800 square kilometers, have now been surveyed. The area of civilization has been subdivided into 19 hydraulic sectors, each based on a site of
settlement with its agricultural lands and hydraulic works. Through the coring program data have been obtained that show the dimensions of each canal
and water tank during each of the three main phases of civilization.

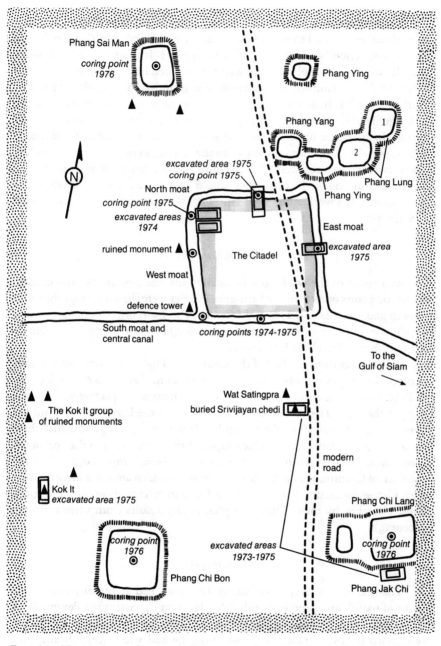

FIG. 3.   The ancient urban area of Satingpra, based on Stargardt's survey data, 1974-76   (⊙ = coring point).

On this basis I have been able to calculate the volume of water available from these sources and to relate it to the surface area under cultivation during the ancient period (see Stargardt, 1976a and n.d.). It emerges from this study that the volume of supplementary water introduced into the Satingpra Peninsula entirely by manmade means was very large indeed during phases I and II. During phase III, however, two trends become clear: that the canals and tanks no longer held enough water during the dry season to irrigate more than a tiny part of the total area under cultivation in each sector and that many of the canals, especially those most distant from the center, were no longer navigable. These two trends must reflect a declining yield from both agriculture and from maritime trade. In turn, they would have brought about a fall in the population and a weakening of all aspects of the material basis of civilization at Satingpra.

The Botanical Surveys

As a result of the work done by this group, the first lists of the modern economic plants of man in the Satingpra district were drawn up together with growth and use data and Thai and Latin names. Two collections of specimens were made, one to return to Cambridge for further study, the other to remain at the Prince of Songkhla University.

Pollen cores from the bed of the great lake, Thale Sap, were taken from a pontoon linking two boats. These were taken from three sites on the latitude of Pattalung, at distances of 30, 60, and 90 meters, respectively, from the edge of the lake. The Palaeobotany Laboratory of the University of Hull has undertaken the analysis of these samples. It is hoped in particular that these cores may throw some light on the origins of rice cultivation in the area of the great lakes. The first results, which have already been completed, do show the presence of Gramineae pollen grains of the size of cultivated rice in association with *Casuarina* grains, which the Hull Laboratory regards as an indicator of forest clearance by man. Thus, the preliminary results from these cores are encouraging.

Conclusion

The botanical surveys have shown that man had at his disposal a wide range of useful and sometimes valuable plants on the Satingpra Peninsula. A large number of the nonlocal plants appear to have been introduced in antiquity (Stargardt, 1977, table 2). In addition, he had wide ricelands and soils whose potential productivity under balanced hydraulic conditions was likely to be high (Stargardt, 1976b, table 1). In addition to these natural advantages, the lakes provided him with an inexhaustible supply of fish while the mountain ranges on the western edge of the lakes were, and are, clothed by the world's most complex primary forest. Satingpra is situated precisely where two zones of this forest meet and merge (Whitmore, 1975). From all these sources, the ancient inhabitants of the Satingpra Peninsula could exploit a wide variety of natural products of enormous importance, not only in the development of the local economy but also as elements in long-distance trade.

All these natural advantages were placed at risk, however, by the unfavorable hydraulic conditions of the peninsula. Thus the Satingpra Peninsula, far from being an area overwhelmingly favorable to the development of civilization, in fact posed serious obstacles to the growth of large and complex societies. These obstacles could be overcome only by the instrument of hydraulic works. It is no exaggeration to term the relationship between the ancient civilization and its hydraulic works as symbiotic; the truth of this can be seen both in their rise and in their decline.

Among its many interesting features, Satingpra is now the site of the Malay Peninsula with the most detailed data on its economic history over a period of some seven centuries. Culturally, it is no less interesting. Although this aspect has not been of primary concern in recording the work of the 1974 season, it is appropriate to note in concluding that its earliest religious materials belong to the Mon tradition of peninsular Thailand. These are succeeded, but never completely eclipsed, by religious art of Indonesian origins in the Śrivijayan style. Although such statuary has been found by chance in Sumatra, Java, the Malay Peninsula, and the southern Philippines, there has never been a firm archeological background for the material. Satingpra during its second phase has provided unique evidence of Śrivijayan objects, in situ, together with a mass of associated material, some of which is datable. In the field of the cultural evolution of Southeast Asia during the first 1,200 years of the present era, Satingpra promises to fill a number of lacunae and in turn to make it possible to provide a specific archeological context for material that is at present viewed merely as beautiful but isolated art objects.

REFERENCES

O'CONNOR, S. J.
  1972.   Hindu gods of Peninsular Siam, 76 pp.   Artibus Asiae, Ascona, Switzerland.
STARGARDT, JANICE M.
  1968.   Government and irrigation in Burma, a comparative survey.   Asian Studies, vol. 6, no. 3, pp. 358-371.

STARGARDT, JANICE M.—continued

1976a. Man's impact on the ancient environment of the Satingpra Peninsula, South Thailand: I, The natural environment and natural change. Journ. Biogeogr., vol. 3, pp. 211-228.

1976b. L'isthme de la péninsule Malaise, l'ancien dialogue entre l'homme et son environnement: Techniques agricoles et hydrauliques. Paper presented at 75th anniversary colloquy of École Française d'Extreme Orient, June 1976. (*In press* in Actes du Colloque.)

1977. Man's impact on the ancient environment of the Satingpra Peninsula, South Thailand, II: Ancient agriculture. Journ. Biogeogr., vol. 4, pp. 35-50.

n.d. Man's impact on the ancient environment of the Satingpra Peninsula, South Thailand, III: Ancient hydraulic works. Journ. Biogeogr. (forthcoming).

WHITMORE, TIMOTHY C.

1975. Tropical rain forests of the Far East, 282 pp., illus. Oxford University Press.

JANICE M. STARGARDT

The Aptian Fossil Locality of Gadoufaoua in the Republic of Niger

Principal Investigator: Philippe Taquet, Institut de Paléontologie, Paris, France.

Grant No. 1230: For a study of the dinosaur locality of Gadoufaoua, Niger Republic.

The remains of dinosaurs were discovered by the geologist H. Faure during the year 1954 in a region of the southern Sahara called Gadoufaoua (Gahdoo-fa-wa), situated about 170 kilometers east of the town of Agades. Beginning in 1963, geologists of the Atomic Energy Commission actively prospected in the area, and their work led to a delimitation of the fossil beds. At the same time it became apparent that this dinosaur locality was, with that of Tendaguru in Tanzania, one of the most important on the African continent. These geologists then invited the Paleontology Institute of the Natural History Museum of Paris to send someone to see for themselves, and in 1965 exploitation of the area's vertebrate fossils was begun.

The locality of Gadoufaoua is stratigraphically placed at the top of the "Continental Intercalaire," a term defined by the geologist C. Kilian in 1931 and comprising all the continental formations between the late marine Carboniferous and the late marine Cretaceous. In the Republic of Niger this continental series is particularly rich in vertebrate remains, and to date, during 6 expeditions to the region, 26 vertebrate fossil localities and 3 footprint, or trackway, localities have been discovered, distributed throughout 15 geologic horizons ranging in age from the late Permian to the late Cretaceous.

Gadoufaoua, which is one of these sites, is made up of sandstones, silts, and clays reaching a thickness of about 50 meters. During the course of the Tertiary epoch, the geologic beds in the area were lightly uplifted, a consequence of the rising of the Aïr Mountains, and they slope by several degrees to the east; this tectonic movement rejuvenated the topography, and erosion excavated a part of the fossiliferous beds. Moreover, the present action of sandstorms, which blow for months each year, blast away an additional part of the matrix and overburden, and also, unfortunately, dinosaur bones.

Completely unknown 14 years ago, the enormous dinosaur "cemetery" of Gadoufaoua has become one of the most important dinosaur sites in Africa, thanks to its size and the abundance and quality of its fauna. To date a total of

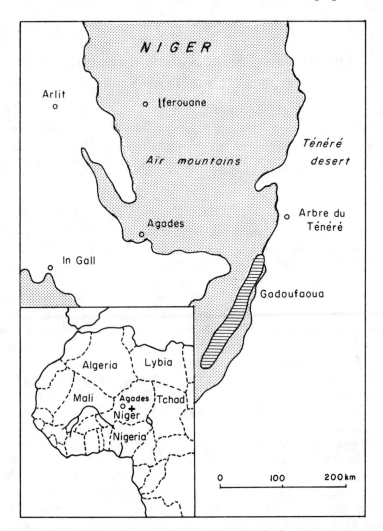

FIG. 1.   Map of West Africa showing position of Gadoufaoua locality in Niger.

25 tons of material has been collected. The site furnishing the fossils, a "locality" 93 miles long and averaging a mile wide, was the bed of an immense
swampy river area in the Aptian (early Cretaceous) period; the burying of the
cadavers in sandy sediments was relatively rapid, which explains their frequently excellent preservation. It should be added that early Cretaceous dino-

saurs are relatively poorly known; because of this, most of the specimens collected at Gadoufaoua represent rare species or forms that are completely new, and, owing to the conditions of preservation, we have the additional benefit of frequently finding complete skeletons.

The dinosaurs of Gadoufaoua consist of carnivorous bipeds (Theropoda), herbivorous quadrupeds (Sauropoda), and herbivorous bipeds (Ornithopoda). Among the carnivorous genera is a large member of the Spinosauridae, with impressively big claws and teeth that are genuine dagger blades. This genus (still undescribed) is very close to *Carcharodontosaurus,* a form known from elsewhere in the Sahara and so named because its teeth are reminiscent of those of the carcharodon shark. Another carnivore, the coelurid *Elaphosaurus iguidiensis,* is, in contrast, small and very slender. Its osteological characters seem indicative of a very quick and agile animal.

Together with the remains of these two biped predators, we find in the deposit a large number of skeletons and isolated bones of herbivorous dinosaurs, which must have been the prey of the carnivores cited above. Anatomically, some of them are quite similar to the North American *Diplodocus,* a heavy herbivorous quadruped that could grow to length of almost 70 feet; but its African homologue is extremely small by contrast with *Diplodocus.* A complete skeleton of this form was collected in 1970, and its body size is about that of a tapir. Perhaps this was a young animal?

The study of the skeleton should enable us to answer this question, but the fact remains that it is one of the smallest complete sauropods that has ever been found. In a realm where sizes are often enormous, this constitutes a new sort of record. Paradoxically, this specimen has been referred to the Titanosauridae.

Other herbivores are bipeds and members of the Ornithischia. This order of dinosaurs is the best represented in number of individuals, and probably also in number of species (at least 3), in the Gadoufaoua deposit. Two complete skeletons of iguanodontids were collected in 1966, one of which was described by Taquet (1976) and named *Ouranosaurus nigeriensis.* The latter is middle-sized by dinosaur standards and similar to the famous *Iguanodon mantelli* of Europe. It is distinguished from the latter by a certain number of characters, particularly in the skull and in the great length of the neural spines attached to the thoracic vertebrae.

But dinosaurs were not the sole inhabitants of the swamps and rivers of Niger during the Aptian. Particularly impressive were giant, long-snouted crocodilians with skulls up to 5 feet long and a total body length of about 36 feet. Named *Sarcosuchus imperator* by de Broin and Taquet (1966), these pholidosaurid mesosuchians were among the largest crocodiles ever to exist.

The remains of *Sarcosuchus* are frequent at Gadoufaoua, but smaller, short-snouted crocodiles, in fewer numbers, were also present. Recently, Buffetaut and Taquet (1977) have shown that the same giant genus, *Sarcosuchus,* occurs in the early Cretaceous of Brazil. The fact that this animal was exclusively nonmarine contributes to our certainty that the continental plates comprising Africa and South America had not yet completely separated during the early Cretaceous (see also Buffetaut and Taquet, 1979). This evidence of faunal continuity is shared by other groups, in particular, by ostracods and freshwater fish.

Actinopterygian fishes are represented at Gadoufaoua by numerous scales of *Lepidotes.* One nearly complete skeleton has been found, which suggests an individual close to 6 feet in length. A small picnodont also occurs. Among the sarcopterygians, the coelacanth *Mawsonia* is present in the form of a new species, *M. tegamensis* Wenz (1975), and two ceratodontid dipnoans, *Ceratodus africanus* and *C. tiguidiensis,* are known.

The vertebrate fauna is, for the present, completed by pelomedusid turtles, whose remains at Gadoufaoua are rather common; they were described by Mme. F. de Broin (1980), of our Institute. Skulls and limb bones have been collected, as well as carapaces, of at least two other species; these will also be studied by Mme. F. de Broin.

An effort was made also to recover Mesozoic mammalian remains. Eleven tons of fossil-rich sand were dry-screened and the 6 tons of concentrate shipped to Paris for sorting. Ensuing complications, however, resulted in a temporary postponement of the project. It is hoped that a mechanical method of separating the quartz sand from the fossil material will soon be made practical so that the microfauna of this time and place will become available for study.

The present grant permitted the collecting of 3 tons of undescribed fossil material, all of which has been transported to Paris for preparation and study. Included in the shipment was the skeleton of a sauropod dinosaur (presently being prepared), a skeleton of the giant crocodile *Sarcosuchus,* and a skeleton (unusually complete) of a new species of long-snouted crocodile.

The fossil bed at Gadoufaoua is far from being exhausted; material completing that already found, as well as (very probably) remains of new forms, awaits collecting by future expeditions. Until that moment, we find ourselves quite occupied by an impressive backlog of skeletons to prepare and matrix to process. It is a pleasure for us to acknowledge the part played by the National Geographic Society in this project.

In conclusion, it should be pointed out that the results of the research undertaken at Gadoufaoua are not all restricted to scientific studies. A region within the fossiliferous area that includes a number of dinosaur skeletons spectacularly exposed by the sand-blasting winds has been preserved intact and set aside for the creation of a national park or monument. And in the capital city of Niamey the type specimen of *Sarcosuchus*, as well as the first complete skeleton of the iguanodontid *Ouranosaurus*, is now on display in the National Museum of Niger. This sort of contribution to the education of the local people is extremely rare in Africa, and the attendance figures indicate that we are entitled to a certain satisfaction. The fossils of Gadoufaoua are broadening the horizons not only of the scientific world but also of a public little accustomed to the image of animals long extinct.

REFERENCES

BROIN, F. DE
  1980.   Les Tortues de Gadoufaoua (Aptien du Niger); aperçu sur la paléobiogéographie des Pelomedusidae (Pleurodira).   Mém. Soc. Géol. Fr., new ser., no. 139, pp. 39-46, illus.
BROIN, F. DE, and TAQUET, PHILIPPE
  1966.   Découverte d'un crocodilien nouveau dans le Crétacé inférieur du Sahara.   Compt. Rend. Acad. Sci. Paris, vol. 262, pp. 2326-2329, illus.
BUFFETAUT, E., and TAQUET, PHILIPPE
  1977.   The giant crocodilian *Sarcosuchus* in the early Cretaceous of Brazil and Niger.   Paleontology, vol. 20, no. 1, pp. 203-208, illus.
  1979.   An early Cretaceous terrestrial crocodilian and the opening of the South Atlantic.   Nature, vol. 280, no. 5722, pp. 486-487.
TAQUET, PHILIPPE
  1976.   Géologie et paléontologie du gisement de Gadoufaoua (Aptien du Niger).   Cahiers de Paléontologie, 191 pp., illus.
WENZ, S.
  1975.   Un nouveau Coelacanthidé du gisement du Crétacé inférieur du Niger: Remarques sur la fusion des os dermidues.   Pp. 175-190 *in* "Problèmes Actuels de Paléontologie-Evolution des Vertébrés." Colloque International, Centre National de la Recherche Scientifique, illus.

PHILIPPE TAQUET
DONALD E. RUSSELL

Competition between Mountain Bluebirds and Tree Swallows in Post-fire Areas of Yellowstone National Park

Principal Investigator: Dale L. Taylor, South Florida Research Center, Everglades
National Park, Homestead, Florida.

Grant No. 1160:   In support of a study of post-fire competition between hole-
nesting birds.

Two hole-nesting bird species, the mountain bluebird *(Sialia currucoides)* and the tree swallow *(Iridoprocne bicolor),* make up 30 percent or more of the breeding avifauna in the first 30 years of post-fire lodgepole pine *(Pinus contorta)* succession in Yellowstone National Park (Taylor, 1969). The two species are part of the "tree hole cycle" initiated by a forest fire.

The cycle occurs as follows: (1) A forest fire kills all the trees in a particular area, but most of the trees remain standing (snags);   (2) boring beetles and other insects attack the trees;   (3) woodpeckers concentrate in the burned area to feed on insects and raise their young, making nest holes in the snags; and   (4) tree swallows, mountain bluebirds, and a few other species use the woodpecker holes for nesting.

While studying post-fire succession in lodgepole pine forests of Yellowstone National Park, I observed a number of interspecific activities that indicated occurrence of nest-site competition between bluebirds and tree swallows. Because bluebirds and tree swallows are such an important part of the early successional avifauna and because there has been an apparent decline in mountain bluebird populations (Power, 1966), I studied possible competition between the two species.

Kendeigh (1974) defines competition as the active demand in excess of the immediate supply exerted by two or more organisms for a material or condition. In the present case, the demand for nest sites may exceed the available supply.

The purpose of the study was to measure populations of tree swallows and mountain bluebirds in burned areas, and to measure specific factors that might be involved in nest-site selection. My previous papers (Taylor, 1969, 1973, 1974, 1976, 1980) discuss in detail the history of forest fires in Yellowstone, history of the study areas, and successional changes of climate, soil, vegetation, birds, and mammals.

Power (1966) reported on the biology of the mountain bluebird in Montana. His study with artificial nest boxes was initiated as a result of his belief that the mountain bluebird population had been declining in Montana for some time. Miller (1970), however, found mountain bluebird populations had increased in his artificial nest-box study in Manitoba.

McLaren (1962) studied nest-site competition in a group of hole-nesting birds in British Columbia. His two-year study involved the analysis of 44 bluebird and 34 tree-swallow nests in the "flicker cycle." McLaren felt that competition for nest sites was probably absent before the addition of the European starling *(Sturnus vulgaris)* to the avifauna. The starling is absent from the Yellowstone study area.

Methods

Three areas selected for intensive study have been described in detail (Taylor, 1969, 1971). The areas were burned in 1954, 1960, and 1966, and are 18.6, 113.8, and 47.4 hectares in size. They are located on the Central Plateau, about the center of Yellowstone National Park, at 2,500 meters elevation. Most of the work was concentrated on the 1960 area because it was larger and more accessible.

Birds were censused by walking a predetermined strip transect and counting all birds within 150 feet (23 m) on either side of the strip (Kendeigh, 1944). Nest-site measurements follow McLaren (1962): *Diameter breast height* (dbh)—the diameter of any given tree as measured at a standard height of $4\frac{1}{2}$ feet (1.4 m) above ground level; *hole height*—height above ground of the bottom of the entrance of any given nest; *sill size*—thickness of wood remaining at the bottom of the entrance hole; *cavity*—horizontal distance from inside edge of the sill to the opposite wall of the cavity; *hole size*—horizontal and vertical distances measured at the opening; and *hole direction*—compass direction toward which entrance hole is oriented.

Nests were located by watching for activity suggesting nesting birds and nest holes. All nest sites were visited later to confirm nesting activity. The entire 114-hectare area was covered.

Bird Populations

In previous work (Taylor, 1969), I showed that forest canopy closure results in the reduction of breeding pairs of all nesting birds by 37 to 87 percent. The major element in this reduction is the elimination of mountain bluebirds and tree swallows. These two species make up 29 to 64 percent of the total avifauna, respectively. With canopy closure, nesting and feeding habitat is eliminated for the two species. This is shown by the dramatic drop from 72 breeding pairs per 100 acres (40.5 ha) 29 years post-fire to 0 pairs 57 years post-fire. Also, the hairy woodpecker *(Picoides villosus)*, another important member of early successional avifauna, is no longer present 57 years post-fire.

Populations fluctuated from 1967 to 1971 without any significant pattern; only the 1960 tract had a clear increase from 1971 to 1973 (table 1).

Nest-site Selection

ORIGIN OF NEST HOLES. Nest holes were made by hairy woodpeckers, Williamson's sapsuckers *(Sphyrapicus thyroideus)*, northern three-toed woodpeckers *(Picoides tridactylus)* and the common flicker *(Colaptes auratus)*. Five (9%) of the 55 nest holes examined were made by flickers and easily identified by their larger size. Other nest holes may have been made by the black-backed three-toed woodpecker *(Picoides arcticus)*, although this is not confirmed.

McLaren (1962) found that the flicker usually began excavation in locations where decay had occurred in sapwood, such as aspen with decayed

TABLE 1. Breeding Bird Pairs per 100 Acres (40.5 ha.) in Selected Areas of Yellowstone National Park (% = percent of total population)

Year of fire	Years post-fire	All species	Hairy woodpecker	Tree swallow No.	Tree swallow %	Mountain bluebird No.	Mountain bluebird %	Bluebird & tree swallow % of total
1966	5[b]	97	6	13	13	19	20	33
	7[c]	136	39	29	21	19	14	35
1960	7[a]	210	3	64	30	54	26	56
	11[b]	137	16	52	38	24	18	55
	13[c]	213	16	97	46	40	19	64
1954	13[a]	234	3	54	23	60	26	48
	17[b]	163	4	26	16	21	13	29
	19[c]	184	39	39	21	29	16	37
1942	25[a]	200	3	49	25	32	16	41
	29[b]	156	5	27	17	45	29	46
1910	57[a]	30	0	0	0	0	0	0

[a]1967 census.   [b]1971 census.   [c]1973 census.

TABLE 2. Nest-Site Measurements for Hole-nesting Birds

| Species | No. nests | Tree species[a] | | | | dbh (mm) | | height (m) | | Hole size (mm) | | | | | | | |
		Lp	Sp	F	U	av.	range	av.	range	horizontal av.	range	vertical av.	range	sill (mm) av.	range	cavity av.	range
Tree swallow	33	27	3	0	3	376	221-519	11.5	1.5-20.1	52.4	38-78	51.1	37-90	46.4	16-81	112.5	80-150
Bluebird	11	10	1	0	0	371	300-488	9.5	6.7-11.8	60	46-75	52	35-60	43	23-58	116	100-153
Hairy woodpecker	4	4	0	0	0	387	297-511	12.1	7.6-13.4	49	46-51[b]	48	46-49[b]	37	32-41[b]	167[b]	
Red shafted flicker	1	0	1	0	0	671		10.9		72		74		35		130	
Mountain chickadee	3	1	0	0	2	284		1.7		46		39		54		90	
White-breasted nuthatch	1	1	0	0	0	292.5		0.01		44		38		63		145	
Williamson's sapsucker	1	0	0	1	0	391		3.3		39		40		52		78	
Northern three-toed woodpecker	1	1	0	0	0	231		1.9		46		46		41		65	
TOTALS	55	44	5	1	5												

[a] LP = Lodgepole Pine (*Pinus contorta*); Sp = Spruce (*Picea engelmannii*); F= Subalpine Fir (*Abies lasiocarpa*); U = Unknown.
[b]

heartwood, thus providing softer wood with which to work. Most nests observed in this study were located in dead lodgepole pine trees which usually had sound heartwood (table 2). The curved bill of the flicker, primarily adapted for foraging, may be less suitable for excavating sound wood and perhaps explains why few flicker holes were found in the Yellowstone study.

The "flicker nest hole cycle," described for British Columbia by McLaren (1962), is equivalent to the "hairy woodpecker nest hole cycle" in Yellowstone National Park. Nest holes in Yellowstone would be smaller than those found in British Columbia, but they are large enough to accommodate the secondary nest-hole users which are smaller than hairy woodpeckers.

DURATION OF NEST HOLES. After a forest fire has occurred, snags remain for as long as 50 years (Taylor, 1969). Many snags fall by 25 years postfire, but some sturdy snags remain, supporting tree-hole-nesting populations. The rate at which snags topple depends upon soil moisture, wind, and root depth. The shallowly rooted lodgepole snags topple with great frequency in early spring when snow melt soaks the soil and high winds are frequent.

Mountain bluebirds fill holes with dried grass and some feathers. Tree swallows place mostly feathers in holes for nest material. Both activities eventually render holes unavailable for nesting use. Evidence from three nests indicated that nest holes may only be used two or three seasons by tree swallows and/or mountain bluebirds. Nest B7 had two bluebird nests, one made on top of the other, indicating hole use for two seasons. Nest B1 had a bluebird nest covered by a tree-swallow nest with four mummified young of fledgling size, and this, in turn, was covered by a bluebird nest that produced a successful brood in 1973. Hole 9, in the same tree as B1, had a bluebird nest covered by a tree-swallow nest containing four partially decayed young. Power (1966) observed that mountain bluebirds cleaned and repaired nests in artificial nest boxes in Montana. This datum differs from that of Miller (1970), who found that mountain bluebirds would not nest in a box holding an old clutch of eggs of another species.

TREE SPECIES. At least 80 percent of the nest holes were located in lodgepole pine snags (table 2). Considering that lodgepole pine snags were the most prevalent in the area, and that spruce and fir snags occurred only in low, wet areas, this is not surprising. A higher percentage of bluebird nests were located in lodgepole snags than were tree swallow nests but the difference was not significant. McLaren (1962) reported 90 percent of the nest holes of all species studied in British Columbia were in aspen and Douglas fir trees.

DIAMETER BREAST HEIGHT (DBH). Average dbh (in millimeters) for snags containing tree-swallow nests was 379.9 and for those containing blue-

TABLE 3. Directional Orientation of Nest-hole Openings

Species	N No. %	NE No. %	E No. %	SE No. %	S No. %	SW No. %	W No. %	NW No. %	Species total
Tree swallow	6 18	3 9	5 15	5 15	3 9	3 9	4 12	4 12	33
Bluebird	1 10	2 20	5 50	0 0	1 10	0 0	0 0	1 10	10
Hairy woodpecker	1	1	1	0	0	0	0	1	4
Red shafted flicker	0	0	0	0	0	0	0	1	1
Williamson's sapsucker	0	0	0	0	1	-	-	-	1
TOTALS	8 16	6 12	11 22	5 10	5 10	3 6	4 8	7 14	49

bird nests, 370.8. There was not a significant difference in dbh measurements of trees selected by the two species (t = 0.03; t $_{.05}$, 40 d.f. = 2.021).

HOLE HEIGHT. Nest holes were found from 1.2 to 20.1 meters above ground level (table 2). There was not a significant difference in tree-swallow and mountain-bluebird nest-hole height (t = 1.004; t $_{.05}$ 40 d.f. = 2.021).

These are quite different from conclusions of McLaren (1962) who found tree swallow and mountain bluebird nests in British Columbia to occur below 4 meters. This may have been due to (1) differences in the preferred nest height of the cavity excavating species in the two studies, and (2) differences between fire successional communities and the undisturbed forest communities studied by McLaren.

ENTRANCE SIZE. Entrance size would impose body size limitations on birds that could use nest holes. Because most nest holes apparently were made by hairy woodpeckers, holes would be expected to average approximately 50 millimeters in the horizontal and vertical dimensions (table 2). Horizontal and vertical measurements are within the general range expected (table 2). Some holes were slightly smaller than holes hairy woodpeckers make and may have been made by the Williamson's sapsucker, the northern three-toed woodpecker, or the black-backed three-toed woodpecker (Taylor, 1976). The sapsucker, a bird approximately the same size as the hairy woodpecker, apparently makes a smaller nest opening. Several observations of sapsuckers going in and out of their nests revealed the nest opening to be just large enough for their entrance and exit, and then only with wiggling side-to-side as they worked their way through the hole.

Bluebird nest holes showed an average size that was slightly larger on the horizontal than the tree-swallow nests (table 2). However, the difference was not significant (t = 1.6; t $_{.05}$, 25 d.f. = 2.060). Vertical size was also not significantly different (t = 0.089; t $_{.05}$, 25 d.f. = 2.060).

SILL SIZE. Sills are used for perching by both the mountain bluebird and tree swallow and could possibly be of significance in nest-site selection.

Sill sizes were of a greater range in thickness for tree swallows than for mountain bluebirds (table 2). However, average thickness was not significantly different between the two species (t = 0.549; t $_{.05}$, 25 d.f. = 2.060).

McLaren (1962) stated that starlings selected nests with thicker sills than did mountain bluebirds. He found sill sizes from 10 to 40 millimeters included 49.1 percent of all starling nests and 81.8 percent of all bluebird nests. The interval of 40 to 60 millimeters included an additional 37.6 percent of starling nests and only 9.2 percent of the bluebird nests. He suggested a study of bluebird nests in an area not occupied by starlings would be instructive. In this study, 50 percent of the sill sizes on mountain bluebird nests were 40 millimeters or less in thickness. Possibly starlings were selecting the thicker silled nests in British Columbia and forcing bluebirds to use nests with thinner sills.

CAVITY.   Size of cavity is an indication of space available to nesting birds. Miller (1970) reported mountain bluebirds preferred a deep nest cavity, although mountain bluebirds were observed to nest in shallow boxes on numerous occasions. There was no difference in cavity size in nests selected by tree swallows and mountain bluebirds in this study ($t = 0.368$; $t_{.05}$, 25 d.f.= 2.060).

HOLE DIRECTION.   The direction the nest hole faces may be of particular importance to certain species for taking advantage of warming sun or prevailing winds. However, nests showed no particular directional orientation (table 3). Bluebird nest holes may have been oriented toward the northeast or east more frequently than other directions; however, the low number of observations prevents definite conclusions. The results of no orientation are in agreement with McLaren (1962).

Rather than a directional orientation being important, the nest faced toward an open space of 12 to 20 feet in diameter or toward an edge, such as a meadow. McLaren (1962) attributed the orientation to open space to the flight pattern of the flicker. Since all woodpeckers have a wavy, galloping flight, the open space would be important to the hairy woodpecker in choosing the position to make a hole.

PERCH REQUIREMENTS.   While making observations at nest holes, I noted that the tree swallow would fly directly to the hole, calling as it approached, so that the mate would usually leave the nest. The bird would then light on the sill. If the mate failed to leave, the pair member would circle until it did so, or occasionally enter the nest hole with the mate. By contrast, after 21.5 hours of observation at seven mountain bluebird nests, I concluded that male bluebirds perched away from the nest more frequently than not before entering to feed the young ($t = 2.187$; $t_{.05}$, 12 d.f. = 2.179).

The general pattern of mountain bluebird feeding behavior is for the male to call as he approaches the nest. If the female is on the nest, she will emerge and fly away or go to the perch. The male perches, goes to the nest sill, enters the nest, feeds the young, then either perches or flies away.

Apparently, the perch is an important requirement in nest-site selection. Male mountain bluebirds arrived at least one week before female birds. Male birds were present upon my arrival May 31, but female bluebirds were not observed until June 8. The perch was much more important for the male than for the female. Power (1966) concluded that females make the choice of nest site. His conclusion was based on mateless males not centering activity on one nest site while mated males did center activity and began nest building. Miller (1970) stated that mountain bluebirds occupied nest boxes which did not afford a nearby perch more often than did eastern bluebirds. Miller noted mountain bluebirds were paired upon their arrival in Manitoba. Criddle (1927), however, reported that male mountain bluebirds preceded females by several days in Manitoba.

Mountain bluebird perches observed in this study were highly variable, ranging from a 1- × 12-inch branch below the nest to a 4- × 48-inch L-shaped branch located above the nest. One bird used a perch in a tree near the nest hole (about 4 feet away) and another used a protruding ledge just below the nest hole.

Discussion

The overlap of the measured nest-site parameters suggests competition does exist for nesting places in bluebirds and tree swallows. With the perch requirement, it appears the mountain bluebird is more exacting in its nest-site selection than the tree swallow. Since not all nests have the required perch, there are fewer available sites for mountain bluebirds than for tree swallows.

Tree swallows apparently nested wherever a nest hole was available. For example, swallows were observed nesting on the opposite side of a tree from a white breasted nuthatch, within 3 feet of a mountain bluebird nest, 1 to 2 feet below a great grey owl (*Strix nebulosa*) nest, and in the same tree, but a few feet below, a hairy woodpecker nest.

Apparently, one of the main problems affecting tree-swallow nesting was the extremely high population in relation to available nest sites (tables 1 and 2). Population estimates showed 97 tree swallows per 100 acres (40.5 ha), but only 11.4 nest holes per 100 acres occupied by tree swallows were found. Even when all available nest holes were considered, there were only about 20 nests per 100 acres. This amounts to a shortage of about 36 nests.

The excess tree-swallow population in relation to available nest sites was obvious at most nests. As many as twelve tree swallows flew around an active nest, trying to enter the hole, bumping one another off the sill, and in general being aggressive. Some members of what appeared to be the excess population had light-colored backs, suggesting they were young birds. They may have been young birds raised at a much lower elevation that after fledging moved up to the 2,500-meter elevation where the nesting season was much later, or they may have been birds reared in earlier years simply unable to find nest sites.

The continued disruption undoubtedly affected nesting success. Swallows that apparently were mates would block the nest entrance with their backs or heads, preventing extra birds from entering the nest hole. Excess birds would be present for several minutes, leave for a few minutes and return to attempt to enter the nest. Only those nests that were relatively isolated were free from continual harassment.

Tree swallows dispossessed mountain bluebirds from at least three nests. Nest 4 was occupied by mountain bluebirds when five tree swallows began harassment by flying around the nest, perching at the sill, and flying toward and after the bluebirds. When the bluebirds would leave the nest, tree swallows would move in. One would block the entrance as described above and prevent the bluebirds from returning to their nest. After several hours, the bluebird pair left. Bluebirds were observed a week later at nest 4, but they stayed only a few minutes. Similar activity occurred at nest B3, also an unsuccessful bluebird nesting attempt. The bluebird pair driven from hole 22 was not known to occupy another nest site. Power (1966) stated no bluebird was ever defeated by a tree swallow during his study of nest boxes. Miller (1970) found competition between mountain bluebirds and tree swallows, but earlier arrival and nest selection by mountain bluebirds was thought to reduce competition. When individual birds are in combat, the larger bluebird has an advantage, but when large numbers of swallows continually harass the bluebird pair, as in this study, bluebirds are often defeated.

The mountain bluebird population of 40 pairs per 100 acres (40.5 ha) was much higher than the number of nest sites found. Few nest holes were actually available. Several pairs of mountain bluebirds were followed for over an hour each, and neither of the pair entered a nest hole. No nests were ever located for at least six pairs of bluebirds known to be present. Other birds, apparently unpaired, were present throughout the summer.

The problem seems to be that both tree swallows and mountain bluebirds lack enough suitable nesting sites. Power (1966) concluded that the alleged decline of mountain bluebird populations could possibly have been due to its overly specialized nesting requirements. Two reasons stand out as to why nesting sites may have been in short supply: (1) The number of acres burned by forest fires in the past few years has declined (Taylor, 1974), and with fewer acres burned, fewer snags are available for nest sites, and as succession occurs, older snags fall, also reducing potential nest sites. (2) Replacement of wooden fence posts with steel ones outside Yellowstone National Park may have been important in causing the bluebird population decline; and Miller (1970) noted frequent replacement of telephone poles and fence posts, often holding cavities, eliminated a vital source of nest sites in Manitoba.

Artificial nest boxes have been used successfully for rearing mountain bluebirds (Power, 1966; Miller, 1970). A situation exists in Yellowstone National Park where, rather than nest boxes, a retaining wall with holes of the appropriate size is present at the Grant Village marina on Yellowstone Lake. Even though not all holes (several hundred in all) are suitable for nesting, 10 tree swallow nests, 1 mountain bluebird nest, and 1 violet-green swallow nest were present along the boat dock. Additional nests were present in an area over water. Artificial nesting sites have little place in a national park where the emphasis and purpose of the park is to maintain a natural environment. As an alternative, Balda (1975) stresses the need to leave naturally occurring snags standing in managed forests.

Recently, the National Park Service management policy was changed from total fire suppression to one allowing use of fire to achieve approved vegetation and/or wildlife management objectives (Kilgore, 1974). Certain forest fires, allowed to burn according to prescription, will create a mosaic of habitat that includes niches suitable for mountain bluebirds, tree swallows, woodpeckers, and other bird species.

Summary

Competition between secondary tree-cavity-nesting mountain bluebirds and tree swallows was studied in post-fire lodgepole pine areas of Yellowstone National Park. The two species make up 29 to 64 percent of the total avifauna until forest canopy closes about 57 years post-fire, when fire-killed snags used as nest sites have fallen. Lodgepole pine snags contained 80 percent of the nest holes. Most nest holes were excavated by hairy woodpeckers, although the common flicker, the northern three-toed and the black-backed three-toed woodpeckers, and Williamson sapsucker excavated cavities possibly used by the two species.

No differences between the two species' nesting requirements could be detected in the following parameters: diameter breast height of nest trees, hole height, hole entrance, sill size, cavity size, and direction of hole orientation. The bluebird was more exacting than the tree swallow in nest selection by requiring a perch used by the male bird before entering the hole to feed the young.

Population estimates of 97 pairs of tree swallows per 100 acres were much higher than the 11.4 nest holes per 100 acres occupied by tree swallows. Bluebird populations of 40 pairs per 100 acres were also much greater than the number of nests found. Large numbers of tree swallows without nest sites continually harassed other tree swallows and mountain bluebirds, dispossessing bluebirds from at least three nests. Lack of suitable nest sites apparently has contributed to a decline in mountain bluebird populations. Fewer acres have been burned through efficient fire control, and as a result of this, availability of fire-killed snags as nesting sites has decreased. Recent changes in National Park Service management policy from total fire suppression to one allowing use of fire for wildlife and/or vegetation management objectives, may result in increased habitat for secondary cavity-nesting species.

Acknowledgments

I thank the National Geographic Society for financial support during the summer months of 1971 and 1973. Thane, Todd, and Kevin Taylor assisted with fieldwork. William B. Robertson, Jr., reviewed the manuscript. Biostatisticians Charles Hilsenbeck and Alan Herndon gave advice on statistical procedures.

REFERENCES

BALDA, RUSSEL P.
  1975.   Vegetation structure and breeding bird diversity. Symposium on Management of Forest and Range Habitats for Nongame Birds, Tucson, Arizona.   U. S. Dept. of Agriculture, Forest Service General Techn. Rept. WO-1, pp. 59-80.
CRIDDLE, N.
  1927.   Habits of mountain bluebird in Manitoba.   Canadian Field Nat., vol. 41, pp. 40-44.
HOUSTON, D. B.
  1973.   Wildfires in northern Yellowstone National Park.   Ecology, vol. 54, no. 5, pp. 1111-1117.
KENDEIGH, S. C.
  1944.   Measurement of bird populations.   Ecol. Monogr., vol. 14, pp. 67-106.
  1974.   Ecology with special reference to animals and man, 474 pp.   Prentice-Hall, Inc., Englewood Cliffs, N.J.
KILGORE, BRUCE M.
  1974.   Fire management in the National Park: An overview.   Tall Timbers Fire Ecology Conference, No. 14, pp. 45-57. Tall Timbers Research Station, Tallahassee, Fla.
McLAREN, W. D.
  1962.   A preliminary study of nest site competition in a group of hole nesting birds.   M.S. Thesis. University of British Columbia, Vancouver.
MILLER, WAYNE
  1970.   Factors influencing the status of eastern and mountain bluebirds in southwestern Manitoba.   The Blue Jay, vol. 28, no. 1, pp. 38-46.

POWER. H. W.
  1966. Biology of the mountain bluebird in Montana.   The Condor, vol. 68, pp. 351-371.
TAYLOR, D. L.
  1969. Biotic succession of lodgepole pine forests of fire origin in Yellowstone National Park. Ph.D. Dissertation. University of Wyoming, Laramie.
  1973. Some ecological implications of forest fire control in Yellowstone National Park, Wyoming.   Ecology, vol. 54, no. 6, pp. 1394-1396.
  1974. Forest fires in Yellowstone National Park.   Journ. Forest History, vol. 18, pp. 68-77.
  1979. Forest fires and the tree-hole nesting cycle in Grand Teton and Yellowstone National Parks.   First Conference on Scientific Research in National Parks, New Orleans, La.   U. S. Department of the Interior, National Park Service Transactions and Proceedings Series, no. 5 (1976), vol. 1, pp. 509-511.
  1980. Biotic succession of lodgepole-pine forests of fire origin in Yellowstone National Park.   Nat. Geogr. Soc. Research Reports, vol. 12, 1971 Projects, pp. 693-702.

DALE L. TAYLOR

Field Collection and Study of Old World (Indo-Pacific) Mangroves

Principal Investigator: Philip B. Tomlinson, Harvard Forest, Petersham, Massachusetts.

Grant Nos. 1243, 1572. For collecting and study of Old World mangrove species.[1]

General Outline and Research Objectives

Estuaries and sheltered intertidal areas in the Tropics develop a characteristic forest vegetation—mangrove—for which there is no Temperate equivalent. The word "mangal" has been coined by ecologists to distinguish the vegetation as a whole from individual mangrove plants. Mangal is highly productive but loses most of its biomass to marine food chains and is appreciated as a major supplier of nutrients to coastal marine communities. Mangroves are also commercially valuable because they form a protective coastal interface but are exploited for timber, pulpwood, cellulose, charcoal, and minor products, often without concern for ecological consequences. This ecological and economic impact has stimulated a wealth of interdisciplinary study in recent decades.

Botanical interest in mangrove plants has always been high because of their numerous biological specializations: their tolerance to sea water, pronounced tendency to vivipary, xeromorphy, and elaborated above-ground root systems, the last usually interpreted as aerating organs since tidally inundated fine sediments are anaerobic. Floristically, in comparison with other tropical communities they are species-poor and by and large are well circumscribed ecologically, providing a unit easy for study. The *alpha*-taxonomy of mangrove species is primarily the result of herbarium study and would appear

---
[1] Grateful acknowledgment for collaborative support in this study is made to John S. Womersley, of the Department of Forests, Lae, Papua, New Guinea, and Dr. John S. Bunt, of the Australian Institute of Marine Sciences, Townsville, Queensland, Australia. Further support in June-July 1977, was made possible by a grant (INT 76-24479) from the Office of International Programs (United States-Australia Scientific Collaborative Program), National Science Foundation, Washington, D. C. Dr. Richard B. Primack, Department of Biology, Boston University, participated in this later phase.

to be stable but recent fieldwork reported here shows that there is room for improvement. There has been little previous comparative fieldwork at a population level.

The main facts of mangrove phytogeography are well established. There is a clear circumscription between an Atlantic ("New World") group—essentially the Caribbean and West Africa—and an Indo-Pacific ("Old World") group—East Africa to the western Pacific. The former is floristically poor, including about 10 species in four genera, the latter much richer with about 50 species and many genera. Only two woody genera are pan-tropical, *Avicennia* and *Rhizophora,* but the distribution of their constituent species corresponds almost exactly to over-all mangrove phytogeography. The consequence is that one can gain only limited appreciation of mangroves by studying the Atlantic group, and I wished to broaden my knowledge of mangroves obtained from their study in South Florida (where there are only three species) by working with the Indo-Pacific flora. The primary general objectives were to examine whole plant morphology with living specimens at hand and collect material to be used for morphological and anatomical study and for preparation of diagnostically informative drawings (fig. 1). Detailed observations were made on floral biology in relation to breeding mechanisms, since this topic has been neglected (cf. Gehrmann, 1911; Porsch, 1924). In contrast, seed and seedling morphology in relation to dispersal and establishment has been relatively well studied.

Mangal is an unusual vegetation type for the wet lowland tropics because there is frequent single-species dominance; populations are typically "linear" and discontinuous, with many species extending over long distances (e.g., *Rhizophora mucronata* from East Africa to the Solomon Islands). Interspecific barriers and isolation mechanisms in relation to gene flow are therefore likely to be distinctive, but their evolutionary interpretation obviously depends on a knowledge of breeding mechanism.

Travel

The present grants enabled me to make two separate visits to the Western Pacific, the first (1974) concentrating on New Guinea (area of Port Moresby, Lae, and Bougainville), the second (1976) in Queensland (Hinchinbrook Island, near Townsville). The further visit in 1977, supported by a grant from the National Science Foundation (NSF), restricted to Queensland, consolidated much of the earlier information. Most time was spent in the field but travel permitted herbarium study in a number of institutions, since this aspect of investigation in any wide-ranging study cannot be neglected. On the first visit,

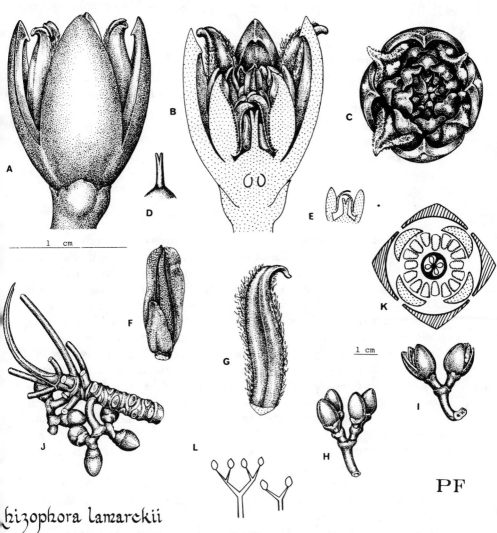

Ŗizopĥora lamarckii

FIG. 1.   Flower and inflorescence morphology of *Rhizophora lamarckii* (P. B. Tomlinson, Barune, Port Moresby, Papua New Guinea): A, flower from side; B, flower in longitudinal section; C, flower from above; D, style and stigma; E, relation between style and dehisced stamen; F, dehisced stamen; G, petal; H, 4-flowered inflorescence; I, 2-flowered inflorescence; J, shoot with leaf blades removed to show inflorescence within or just below leafy crown; K, floral diagram; L, diagram of inflorescence. (A–G, same magnification; H–J, same magnification). This species, previously thought to be endemic to New Caledonia, has now been shown to have a wider, scattered distribution elsewhere and to be a hybrid. (Drawn by Priscilla Fawcett, botanical illustrator, Fairchild Tropical Garden.) This is an example of the kind of illustration produced from material assembled during the expeditions.

I attended en route an International Symposium on the Biology and Management of Mangroves in Honolulu. The opportunity to make three separate visits has been highly beneficial; the first proved useful in orientation and as a general survey, followed by a period of assessment before the second visit, which dealt with more specific problems, the third at a different season broadened the range of examples which could be studied. Special attention was given to *Rhizophora* because of its abundance and the early demonstration of its complexities. Citations of published research is given later.

Summary of Scientific Results

I have shown that mangrove species have a diversity of mechanisms for transferring pollen from one flower to another, largely mediated by a wide variety of animals, i.e., bats, birds, and insects (in particular instances butterflies, moths, flies, and bees). On the other hand, the genus *Rhizophora,* which is the most common constituent of mangroves in both hemispheres, is wind pollinated, with some evidence that this mechanism is of recent derivation. In some instances the floral mechanism is quite elaborate, as in *Bruguiera* and *Ceriops* (which have an explosive mechanism for pollen release). However, the pollination mechanism tends to be suited to rather generalized flower visitors.

Although the survey is very incomplete there is evidence for devices which promote outbreeding (heterostyly, protandry, protogyny) in sufficient examples to suggest that outcrossing is a major genetic mechanism in mangrove species.

It is tempting to ascribe the obvious success of *Rhizophora* species in mangrove communities, at least in part, to their unique wind-pollination mechanism. Further peculiarities of *Rhizophora* which I have revealed are the distinctive F_1 hybrid stands in several parts of the South Pacific, involving three distinct species. This, together with a similar report involving further species in the Atlantic species, raises interesting questions about normal barriers to interspecific hybridization in this important genus. The ability of these F_1 populations to form a significant component of the mangrove community while remaining sterile is of major ecological importance.

The floral biology of the tribe Rhizophoreae (Rhizophoraceae) has been examined in the greatest detail, resulting in the demonstration of a complex partitioning of the pollinator resource. This partitioning depends on elaboration of a common floral plan. This partitioning of pollinator resource seems characteristic of mangroves generally, with *Rhizophora* "escaping" the constraints by adopting wind pollination.

The study, although preliminary, has provided valuable insights into an important aspect of the biology of a tropical vegetation type.

General Results

From table 1, obligate outcrossing, which occurs in dioecious species, is known in only 4 out of 54 species (7%). The relatively high incidence of dioecy in the Atlantic mangroves, 2 out of 5 genera (40%) and 2 out of 9 species (22%) is simply a reflection of the small sample size and should not be regarded as phytogeographically significant.

Mechanisms which may promote outcrossing are known in a small number of examples. Monoecism is known in 4 species (7%), all of them Indo-Pacific. In *Nypa*, since this condition is associated with pronounced protogyny, outbreeding is strongly promoted. Information is lacking for *Xylocarpus* and *Heritiera*. Heterostyly is known in *Pemphis* which is also known to be self-incompatible (Gill and Kyauka, 1977). Protandry, a form of dichogamy, is known in *Avicennia* and *Scyphiphora*. Precocious dehiscence of anthers which may be associated with protandry in Rhizophoraceae is discussed in Tomlinson et al., (1979). Protandry has been recorded in *Lumnitzera* (Tomlinson et al., 1978). Protogyny is known in *Nypa*, as mentioned above. The record of protogyny in *Avicennia germinans* by Tomlinson (1974) is probably incorrect, since the genus seems to be protandrous. Further evidence for a high degree of outcrossing comes from the observation that most mangrove species are dependent on animals for pollen vectors, the flower often being elaborately specialized (see below).

TABLE 1. Summary Distribution of Flower Types in Mangrove Species

[Totals for genera are not cumulative, because *Avicennia* and *Rhizophora*, being pan-tropical, appear twice; totals for species are made cumulative, since the slight overlap between the two groups in species of *Rhizophora* is ignored.]

Sex distribution	All		Indo-Pacific Group		Atlantic Group	
	Genera	*Species*	*Genera*	*Species*	*Genera*	*Species*
Perfect	18	46	17	39	3	7
Monoecious	3	4	3	4	-	-
Dioecious	4	4	2	2	2	2
TOTAL	25	54	22	45	5	9

However, the real measure of degree of outcrossing must come from a study of the extent of self-incompatability. In the present study, visits have been too short to permit the necessary artificial pollination, bagging, and emasculation techniques which are needed to provide unequivocable evidence for outcrossing. A more extended visit would be needed to carry out these experiments which could be done collaboratively. Information from types of pollen vector and other circumstantial evidence by itself is inconclusive, but there is every indication that mangroves are outbreeders, as the high dependence on animal visitors for pollen movement, which I have observed in all genera except *Rhizophora,* shows.

Indirect evidence of pollen vectors provided by animals is found in mangrove species that have large, showy, scented, nectariferous or otherwise attractive flowers indicative of animal pollination. The more spectacular include *Cerbera, Dolichandrone,* and *Pelliciera. Aegialitis* has very large pollen grains which could not be transported by wind. Pollen in *Nypa* and *Excoecaria* is sticky, requiring an animal vector. In addition, the following animal visitors have been observed during the present study or are recorded in the literature: Birds, in large-flowered *Bruguiera* species and *Lumnitzera littorea;* bats, in *Sonneratia* species; butterflies, in small-flowered *Bruguiera* species; moths, in *Ceriops tagal;* bees, in a diversity of species, e.g., *Excoecaria, Avicennia, Kandelia;* and flies, in *Nypa.*

The pollination mechanisms may be very elaborate, as in certain Rhizophoraceae, and may be related to specialist pollinators. Many mangroves seem rather nonspecific in their *type* of flower visitor, but are dependent on visitors of a restricted *size.*

In contrast to this diversity of animal visitors, there is strong circumstantial evidence that *Rhizophora* is exceptional among mangroves in being wind pollinated. Comparative floral morphology, pollen-ovule ratios and floral function provide the evidence. There is no correlation between dioecism or monoecism and wind pollination. *Excoecaria* is dioecious, but has sticky pollen, abundant nectar, and is visited by bees. *Nypa* is monoecious but has sticky pollen, is protogynous, and is visited by drosophilid flies and small bees (Uhl and Moore, 1977). *Laguncularia* is dioecious, but nectariferous, and is actively visited by bees.

Wind pollination may occur in *Conocarpus,* a dioecious member of the Atlantic group, but this species is not restricted to mangrove communities and could be excluded from the above table 1.

The diversity of flower visitors in mangroves suggests a high degree of resource partitioning, such that competition among mangroves for the favors of flower visitors is minimized. This may be important where pollination is expensive by virture of the amount of nectar produced. Thus there is diversification between night- and day-time visitors (bats, moths versus birds and day-flying insects). There may be diversification among closely related taxa. *Lumnitzera littorea* is bird pollinated; *Lumnitzera racemosa* is insect pollinated. The best example is provided by the mangrove Rhizophoraceae (tribe Rhizophoreae) where there is a basically similar floral plan, but a diversity of flower visitors, with each plant species designed to accommodate a particular kind or range of flower visitor—birds, butterflies, bees, moths. Many simple morphological features seem to be correlated with the kind of flower visitor, e.g., size of flower, type of inflorescence, flower orientation at time of anthesis. Floral mechanism in *Bruguiera* and *Ceriops* involves a distinctive explosive method of pollen release and yet this is modified to suit the size and feeding habit of the visitor.

In this context, *Rhizophora* in its wind pollination has "escaped" the constraints which might be put upon it by competition for pollinators.

The mutualistic relation between mangroves and animals is well exemplified in bird-pollinated species in Queensland where there is an extended dry season. Australia is well known as a center of concentration for nectariferous birds. However, in the Queensland dry season, terrestrial communities may be deficient as a nectar source, in the absence of frequent flowering. *Bruguiera* species then become an important and even exclusive nectar source for birds; it may be assumed that climatic seasonality does not influence flowering in this species, although it certainly does for other mangrove species in the area.

Rather more specialized biological interactions between birds and mangroves have been shown for *Rhizophora* species in Queensland, since birds feed on sugary secretions from the stipules or *R. stylosa*, the birds also eating insects during this process and so reducing insect predation of plants (Primack and Tomlinson, 1978). However, one notes no precise or obligate flower-pollinator relationship such that the range of vector and plant is precisely correlated. Even when the floral mechanism is precise, it can still accommodate a diversity of visitors.

Where closely related taxa are sympatric in mangrove communities, the normal isolating mechanisms can break down and hybrid swarms can be generated. Examples are known in *Sonneratia*, where information is well documented (e.g., Muller and Hou-Liu, 1966); in *Lumnitzera*, where, however, hybrids have been reported only once (Tomlinson et al., 1978); and in *Rhizophora*. Two forms of *Rhizophora* originally described as distinct species have been shown, on the basis of strong circumstantial evidence, to be hybrids, i.e., *R.* × *harrisonii* (Breteler, 1969, 1977) and *R.* × *lamarckii* (Tomlinson and Womersley, 1976; Tomlinson, 1978). A third form, originally recognized by Guppy (1906) in Fiji as a hybrid has now been shown by me to occur in New Caledonia and I have given it a formal name (*R.* × *selala*, Tomlinson,

1978). These hybrid populations are particularly intriguing because they indicate that the normal isolating mechanism between sympatric species can break down under unknown circumstances, and produce sterile hybrids which may persist without back-crossing to the parental types.

Field study has demonstrated deficiency in our present understanding of species even in a genus as common as *Rhizophora*. Where species are very similar and not easily distinguished on the basis of herbarium specimens, this has also led to misunderstanding about the limits of distribution of wide-ranging species. Greater precision in taxonomy is beginning to clarify distributional ranges (e.g., Tomlinson, 1978). This information is necessary to an understanding of evolutionary processes in mangroves.

Other taxa where field familiarity demonstrates error in taxonomic understanding or morphological description include *Acrostichum* (Adams and Tomlinson, 1929) and *Lumnitzera* (Tomlinson et al., 1978). The genus *Avicennia* is not well described at the taxonomic level. Preliminary observation of field populations suggests that reliable characters do occur but have been overlooked in the exclusive study of herbarium specimens.

The above conclusions are obviously tentative. They need to be substantiated by examination of the behavior of species throughout their ranges, a difficult task in view of the wide range of most mangroves. However, observations have been published in a tentative manner in the hope that they will provide guidelines for investigators in different parts of the world.

Much more precise information is needed about the extent of self-incompatability, floral biology in relation to outbreeding mechanism and the efficiency of pollination processes. *Rhizophora,* the most abundant mangrove genus, presents particular problems. Information such as that provided by chemical analysis is needed to distinguish taxa other than by the often obscure morphological characters which are presently used and to determine the nature of the specific isolating mechanism which seems to break down periodically with peculiar demographic results.

The value of the present survey is that it provides a realistic foundation on which a more precise understanding of the biology of mangroves can be used.

REFERENCES

(a) *General*

ADAMS, D. C., and TOMLINSON, P. B.
  1979.   *Acrostichum* in Florida and Tropical America.   American Fern Journal, vol. 69, pp. 42-46.
BRETELER, F. J.
  1969.   The Atlantic species of *Rhizophora*.   Acta. Bot. Neerl., vol. 18, pp. 434-441.

1977. America's Pacific species *Rhizophora.* Acta Bot. Neerl., vol. 26, pp. 225-230.

GERHMANN, K.
1911. Zur Blutenbiologie der Rhizophoraceae. Ber. Deutsch. Bot. Ges., vol. 29, pp. 308-318.

GILL, L. S., and KYAUKA, P. S.
1977. Heterostyly in *Pemphis acidula* Forst. (Lythraceae) in Tanzania. Adansonia, vol. 17, pp. 139-146.

GUPPY, H. B.
1906. Observations of a naturalist in the Pacific between 1896 and 1899. Vol. II. Plant dispersal, 627 pp. Macmillan, London.

MULLER, J., and HOU-LIU, S. Y.
1966. Hybrids and chromosomes in the genus *Sonneratia* (Sonneratiaceae). Blumea, vol. 14, pp. 337-343.

PORSCH, O.
1924. Vogel Blumenstudium I. Jahrb. Wiss. Bot., vol. 63, pp. 553-706.

TOMLINSON, P. B.
1974. Breeding mechanism in trees native to tropical Florida—a morphological assessment. Journ. Arnold Arbor., vol. 55, pp. 209-290.

ULH, N. W., and MOORE, H. E.
1977. Correlations of inflorescence, flower structure, and floral anatomy with pollination in some palms. Biotropica, vol. 9, pp. 170-190.

(b) *By the principal investigator, mainly arising out of this survey.*

PRIMACK, R. B., and TOMLINSON, P. B.
1978. Sugar secretions from the buds of *Rhizophora.* Biotropica, vol. 10, p. 74.
1980. Variation in tropical forest breeding systems. Biotropica, vol. 12, no. 3, pp. 229-231.

TOMLINSON, P. B.
1978. *Rhizophora* in Australasia: Some clarification of taxonomy and distribution. Journ. Arnold Arbor. vol. 59, pp. 156-169.

TOMLINSON, P. B.; BUNT, J. S.; PRIMACK, R. B.; and DUKE, N. C.
1978. *Lumnitzera rosea* (Gaud.) Presl. (Combretaceae)—its status and floral morphology. Journ. Arnold Arbor., vol. 59, pp. 342-351.

TOMLINSON, P. B.; PRIMACK, R. B.; and BUNT, J. S.
1979. Preliminary observations on floral biology in mangrove Rhizophoraceae. Biotropica, vol. 11, no. 4, pp. 256-277, illus.

TOMLINSON, P. B., and WHEAT, D. W.
1979. Bijugate phyllotaxis in Rhizophoreae (Rhizophoraceae). Bot. Journ. Linn. Soc., vol. 78, pp. 317-321.

TOMLINSON, P. B., and WOMERSLEY, J. S.
1976. A species of *Rhizophora* new to New Guinea and Queensland with notes relevant to the genus. Contrib. Herb. Austr., vol. 19, pp. 1-10.

PHILIP B. TOMLINSON

The Mammals of the Chaco of Paraguay

Principal Investigator: Ralph M. Wetzel, University of Connecticut, Storrs, Connecticut.

Grant Nos. 1202, For studies of mammals of the Chaco Boreal, Paraguay.
1475, 1631, 1771.

At the beginning of our studies the mammals of Paraguay were known chiefly from the classic reports of Azara (1801, 1809) and of Rengger (1830). Although Bertoni (1914, 1939) listed a number of vertebrates and Podtiaguin (1944) later did the same for the bats of Paraguay, both reports were relatively parochial and incomplete. Reports of mammalian specimens from Paraguay are scattered also through the literature of mammalogy, including Thomas (1901, 1921), Allen (1916), Sherman (1955), and, for the expeditions of Krieg (1931), through the upper La Plata drainage, in Krumbiegel (1940-1942) and Schwangart (1941). In summary, the mammals of Paraguay, particularly of the more deserted western two-thirds of that nation—the Chaco—were less well known than in many parts of the Amazonian basin. And few specimens of mammals from Paraguay were available in the museums of the world for systematic zoogeographic analysis. It was for these reasons and the spirit of adventure that support for field research in Paraguay was sought from the National Geographic Society.

Our study has had two approaches, both necessarily opportunistic and conceptually simplistic because of the limited knowledge of the fauna: (1) Inventory and (2) autecology of the species found: In short, a fishing trip to find what is there, what it is like, and what it does. An additional goal has been the accumulation of research study material that will form the basis for reference by our group and by scientists elsewhere for a number of years.

Financial aid from the Society in 1973, 1975, 1976, and 1977, as well as support from the University of Connecticut Research Foundation, the Carnegie Museum of Natural History, the National Science Foundation, and the World Wildlife Fund, permitted a continuation of my fieldwork of 1972 for six additional seasons, from 1973 through 1978. The field season was winter to early spring, roughly June to September, because of the relative ease of travel on the dirt roads of the Chaco during the dry season and because of the academic year in the United States. In 1973 and 1976 the field parties stayed in the Chaco through October. Although the restriction of our field periods introduces a seasonal bias, our observations and collections in Paraguay have been at the two most critical times in the year for most species—at population lows in late winter and during the breeding and reproductive season in spring. Despite Paraguay's being in semitropical latitudes, we have found that the reproductive cycles of most of the species are adjusted to the seasonal rainfall and temperature cycle, as did Myers (1977a) for certain of the bats.

The participating personnel whose field expenses were partially or entirely paid by grant money from the Society were as follows: *Senior personnel*—Dr. Robert L. Martin, University of Maine at Farmington, 1973, 1974, 1975; Dr. Philip Myers, University of Michigan, 1976; Dr. James Talbot[1], Instituto de Ciencias Basicas, Universidad de Asunción, 1976; Dr. Lyle K. Sowls, University of Arizona, 1976; Robert E. Dubos, University of Connecticut, 1975; and myself, 1973, 1974, 1975, and 1976. *Graduate students*—University of Connecticut, Johnny Wayne Lovett, 1973; Karen L. Anderson, 1977; Philip N. Brandt, 1975, 1976, 1977; and John J. Mayer II, 1975, 1976, 1977. *Field assistants*—Philip Hazelton, Whitehorse, Yukon, 1973, 1975, 1976; Juan Balbuena, Asunción, 1974; José González, Luque, 1973, 1974. *Peace Corps of Paraguay*—Juan Guerrero Cruz, 1975; Tom Nelson, 1976, 1977.

The problems of study in the Chaco have been many and include: *Vehicles*—difficult and expensive to rent and maintain; *logistics*—solved by carrying large drums of water and gasoline into the field and camping or staying with land owners or at military outposts; *local irritations*—caused by spines of shrubs, trees, and cacti, by numerous ticks, by hordes of carrion flies attracted to dissections, and clouds of small wasps attracted to moisture of eyes, ears, and noses during the dry season. On cloudy days, getting lost in the flat, monotonous landscape is, perhaps, the major danger of the Chaco.

However, the results of these studies have been encouraging. Although the greater part of the analysis of already accumulated data is still before us, certain of the findings have already been reported. Two papers (Wetzel and Lovett, 1974; Myers and Wetzel, 1979) contained a number of new records of mammalian species for Paraguay, with distributional and taxonomic changes from those used in Cabrera's (1958, 1961) catalogue of South American mammals. Scott and Lovett (1975) listed the reptiles and amphibians collected in the Chaco during our first two years. And the first comprehensive reviews or revisions of the following Neotropical taxa were made possible by the Society's support of both fieldwork and travel to repositories of specimens in South America and Europe: The tree sloths, *Bradypus* and *Choloepus* (Wetzel and

---

[1] Currently (1981) at National Research Council, Washington, D. C.

Kock, 1973; Wetzel, 1974; Wetzel and Avila-Pires, 1980); the lesser ant-eater, *Tamandua* (Wetzel, 1975); the long-nosed armadillos, *Dasypus* (Wetzel and Mondolfi, 1979); the naked-tailed armadillos, *Cabassous* (Wetzel, 1980); and the Xenarthra, Edentata (Wetzel, in press).

As I had hoped in my original plans for research in Paraguay, new animals have been discovered. One represents the first addition of a large mammal since the okapi was discovered early in this century. This was a new peccary, family Tayassuidae, which we found to belong to a genus thought to be extinct since the middle Pleistocene (Wetzel, Dubos, Martin, and Myers, 1975; Wetzel and Crespo, 1976; Wetzel, 1977a, 1977b, 1981). The Chacoan peccary, or tagua, *Catagonus wagneri* (Rusconi), is an evolutionary product from the semiarid thorn forests and thorn steppes of the Gran Chaco. Because it is restricted to this relatively small pocket and because the habitat is being rapidly replaced by pasture for beef cattle, I have recommended that the tagua be classified as "vulnerable" in my submission to the Red Data Book, vol. 1, IUCN (Wetzel, 1978). In the meantime two graduate students at the University of Connecticut, Philip N. Brandt, and John J. Mayer II, have been studying the behavior, ecology, and natural history of the tagua (Brandt and Mayer, 1978, and Mayer and Brandt, 1978).

The support of the Society is also acknowledged in reports of three other new mammals. Wetzel (1980) described a new naked-tailed armadillo, *Cabassous chacoensis*, collected on the trip of 1974. Myers (1977b), who was aided by specimens in our collection which formed his paratype series, reported on a new species of native rat, genus *Graomys*, from the Chaco. And Pine and Wetzel (1976) described a new subspecies of a rare mouse, *Pseudorymomys wavrini*, from Bolivia as the result of our accumulating a comparative series from near the type locality of the species in the Chaco of Paraguay.

Another addition to the South American fauna resulting from the Society's support of our fieldwork is a new genus and two species of geckos (Smith, Martin, and Swain, 1977). This was triggered by Dr. Martin's collection, in our 1975 expedition, of a specimen later designated as the holotype of one of the new species. The authors found that the new genus, *Vanzoia*, shares characters with both the African and South American geckos and may, therefore, provide additional evidence of continental drift.

The collection of both internal and external parasites provides valuable information on the food web in the Chacoan environment. Additionally, knowledge of the ectoparasites is essential for an understanding of the arthropod-borne disease vectors. Reports on the parasites found to be new in our collections from Paraguay are just beginning to be made. Fischtal and Martin (1977) reported a fluke (Trematoda) from a puma, *Felis concolor*. Schmidt

(1977) described a new spiny-headed worm (Acanthocephala), naming it in honor of its collector, Dr. R. L. Martin. Fischtal and Martin (1978) described a new trematode in the fishing bat, *Noctilio leporinus.* Seesee et al. (in press) report numerous new host and geographic records in their survey of parasites collected by R. L. Martin from the Carnivora of the Chaco.

Additional reports on Paraguayan animals, based upon work supported by the Society, are in varied stages of progress. In manuscript are publications by Martin and Smith (additional records of lizards from the Gran Chaco of Paraguay), Schmidt and Martin (tapeworms of the Chaco Boreal, Paraguay), and Wetzel (revision of the euphroctine armadillos, genus *Cabassous*).

Future work on the mammals of Paraguay will make use of the start given by the National Geographic Society. This start includes much of the equipment needed to continue the study; a data base of field observations; a collection of unique parasites and soft tissues; a collection at the University of Connecticut of terrestrial vertebrates from Paraguay, including 1,664 mammals, 288 reptiles and amphibians, and 164 birds; 3 manuscripts in progress and 23 published or in press; and the field research of 4 graduate students.

REFERENCES

ALLEN, JOEL A.
   1916.   Mammals collected on the Roosevelt Brazilian Expedition, with field notes by Leo E. Miller.   Bull. Amer. Mus. Nat. Hist., vol. 35, pp. 559-610.
AZARA, FELIX DE
   1801.   Essais sur l'histoire naturelle des quadrupèdes de la Province du Paraguay, 2 vols.   Paris.
   1809.   Voyages dans l'Amérique méridionale, vol. 1, chap. 9.   Paris.
BERTONI, A. DE W.
   1914.   Fauna Paraguaya. Catálogos sistemáticos de los vertebrados del Paraguay . . .   Descr. Fís. y Econ. Paraguay, vol. 59, pp. 1-83.
   1939.   Catálogos sistemáticos de los vertebrados del Paraguay, vol. 4, pp. 3-59.
BRANDT, PHILIP N., and MAYER, JOHN J.
   1978.   Winter food habits and behavior of *Catagonus wagneri,* a new species of peccary.   58th Annual meeting, American Society of Mammalogists, Athens, Ga.
CABRERA, ÁNGEL
   1958,   Catálogo de los mamíferos de America del Sur.   Rev. Mus. Argentino
   1961.   Cienc. Nat "Bernardino Rivadavia," Zool., vol. 4, no. 1 (1957), pp. 1-307; no. 2 (1960), pp. 309-732.
FISCHTAL, JACOB H., and MARTIN, ROBERT L.
   1977.   *Alaria (Alaria) marcianae* from a mountain lion, *Felis concolor acrocodia* Goldman, from Paraguay.   Journ. Parasit., vol. 63, no. 2, p. 202.
   1978.   *Postorchigenes paraguensis* sp. n. (Pleurogenidae), a digenetic trematode from the large fishing bat, *Noctilio leporinus rufescens* Olfers, from Paraguay.   Acta Parasitol. Polonica, vol. 25, pp. 217-221.

KRIEG, H.
1931.   Geographische Übersicht und illustrieter Routenbericht, 95 pp., illus. Streker und Schroder, Stuttgart.

KRUMBIEGEL, INGO
1940-42.   Die Säugetiere der Südamerika-Expeditionen Prof. Dr. Kriegs. Zool. Anz., vol. 131-139 (17 papers).

MAYER, JOHN J., and BRANDT, PHILIP N.
1978.   Pelage description and reproductive data on the Chacoan peccary *Catagonus wagneri*. 58th Annual Meeting, American Society of Mammalogists, Athens, Georgia.

MYERS, PHILIP
1977a.   Patterns of reproduction of four species of vespertilionid bats in Paraguay. Univ. California Publ. Zool., vol. 107, pp. 1-41, illus.
1977b.   A new phyllotine rodent (genus *Graomys*) from Paraguay. Occ. Pap. Mus. Zool. Univ. Michigan, no. 676, 7 pp.

MYERS, PHILIP, and WETZEL, RALPH M.
1979.   New records of mammals from Paraguay. Journ. Mamm., vol. 60, pp. 638-641.

PINE, R. H., and WETZEL, RALPH M.
1976.   A new subspecies of *Pseudoryzomys wavrini* (Mammalia: Rodentia: Muridae: Cricetinae) from Bolivia. Mammalia, vol. 39, no. 4 (1975), pp. 649-655.

PODTIAGUIN, B.
1944.   Contribuciones al conocimiento de los murcielages del Paraguay, Rev. Soc. Cient. Paraguay, vol. 6, pp. 25-62.

RENGGER, JOHANN R.
1830.   Naturgeschichte der Saeugethiere von Paraguay, 394 pp.   Schweighauserchen Buchhandlung, Basel.

SCHMIDT, GERALD D.
1977.   *Oncicola martini* sp. n., and other Archiacanthocephala of the Chaco Boreal, Paraguay. Journ. Parasit., vol. 63, no. 3, pp. 508-510, illus.

SCHWANGART, F.
1941.   Südamerikanische Bush-, Berg-, und Steppenkatzen. Abh. Bay. Akad. Wiss. Munich, neue Folge, vol. 49, pp. 1-44, illus.

SEESEE, FLOYD M.; WORLEY, DAVID E.; and MARTIN, ROBERT L.
_____.   A survey of nematode parasites from carnivores of the Chaco Boreal, Paraguay. Proc. Worldwide Furbearers Conference, Lynchburg, Maryland, 1980. (In press.)

SCOTT, NORMAN J., and LOVETT, JOHNNY WAYNE
1975.   A collection of reptiles and amphibians from the Chaco of Paraguay. Occ. Pap. Univ. Connecticut (biol. sci. ser.), vol. 2, no. 16, pp. 257-266.

SHERMAN, H. B.
1955.   A record of *Lasiurus* and of *Vampyrops* from Paraguay. Journ. Mamm., vol. 36, p. 130.

SMITH, HOBART M.; MARTIN, ROBERT L.; and SWAIN, TOM A.
1977.   A new genus and two new species of South American geckos (Reptilia: Lacertilia). Pap. Avul. Zool., São Paulo, vol. 30, no. 14, pp. 195-213.

THOMAS, OLDFIELD
1901. On a collection of bats from Paraguay. Ann. Mag. Nat. Hist., ser. 7, vol. 8, pp. 435-443.
1921. Two new Muridae discovered in Paraguay by the Marquis de Wavrin. Ann. Mag. Nat. Hist., ser. 8, vol. 7, pp. 177-179.
WETZEL, RALPH M.
1974. A review of the Recent species of *Bradypus* and *Choloepus*. Vol. 2, pp. 294-295 *in* "Transactions, 1st International Theriological Congress," A. V. Yablokov, ed. Moscow.
1975. The species of *Tamandua* Gray (Edentata, Myrmecophagidae. Proc. Biol. Soc. Washington, vol. 88, pp. 95-112.
1977a. The extinction of peccaries and a new case of survival. Ann. New York Acad. Sci., vol. 288, pp. 538-544, illus.
1977b. The Chacoan peccary, *Catagonus wagneri* (Rusconi). Bull. Carnegie Mus. Nat. Hist., no. 3, 36 pp.
1978. Chacoan peccary or tagua, *Catagonus wagneri*. Red Data Book, vol. 1, pp. 1921-1921a. International Union for the Conservation of Nature.
1980. Revision of the naked-tailed armadillos, genus *Cabassous* McMurtrie. Ann. Carnegie Mus., vol. 49, art. 20, pp. 323-357.
1981. The hidden Chacoan peccary. Carnegie Mag., vol. 55, art. 2, pp. 24-32.
——. The taxonomy and distribution of armadillos, Dasypodidae. The identification of Recent Xenarthra (Edentata). Chapters *in* "Evolution and Ecology of Sloths, Armadillos and Anteaters," G. Gene Montgomery, ed. Smithsonian Institution Press. (In press.)
WETZEL, RALPH M., and AVILA-PIRES, FERNANDO DIAS DE
1980. Identification and distribution of the Recent sloths of Brazil (Edentata). Rev. Brasil. Biol., vol. 40, no. 4, pp. 831-836.
WETZEL, RALPH M., and CRESPO, JORGE A.
1976. Existencia de una tercera especie de pecari, fam. Tayassuidae, Mammalia, en Argentina. Rev. Mus. Argentino Cienc. Nat. "Bernardino Rivadavia," Zool., vol. 12 no. 3 (1975), pp. 25-26.
WETZEL, RALPH M.; DUBOS, ROBERT E.; MARTIN, ROBERT L.; and MYERS, PHILIP
1975. *Catagonus*, an "extinct" peccary, alive in Paraguay. Science, vol. 189, pp. 379-381.
WETZEL, RALPH M., and KOCK, DIETER
1973. The identity of *Bradypus variegatus* Schinz (Mammalia, Edentata). Proc. Biol. Soc. Washington, vol. 86, no. 3, pp. 25-34.
WETZEL, RALPH M., and LOVETT, JOHNNY WAYNE
1974. A collection of mammals from the Chaco of Paraguay. Occ. Pap. Univ. Connecticut (biol. sci. ser.), vol. 2, no. 13, pp. 203-216.
WETZEL, RALPH M., and MONDOLFI, EDGARDO
1979. The subgenera and species of long-nosed armadillos Genus *Dasypus* L. Pp. 43-63 *in* "Vertebrate Ecology in the Northern Neotropics," John F. Eisenberg, ed. Smithsonian Institution Press, Washington, D. C.

RALPH M. WETZEL

Religion, Social Organization, and Socioeconomic Change Among the Kenyah Dayak of Sarawak, Malaysia

Principal Investigator:　　Herbert L. Whittier, Department of International Studies and Programs, Michigan State University, serving in Indonesia as Associate Director of the MUCIA-AID-Indonesia Higher Education Development Projects.

Grant No. 1226:　　In support of the study of religion and social organization of the Kenyah Dayak of Sarawak, Malaysia.

From October 1973 through March 1975, I carried out ethnographic research among the Kenyah Dayak of central Borneo with financial support from the National Geographic Society's Committee for Research and Exploration. I was accompanied by my wife, Dr. Patricia Whittier, who was conducting her own research under a Fulbright grant.

Today, the majority of Kenyah live peaceful, somewhat isolated lives as swidden rice agriculturalists in the mountains of central Borneo (Sarawak, Malaysia, and Kalimantan, Indonesia). The Kenyah population numbers about 40,000, with 8,000 in Sarawak and 32,000 in Kalimantan; this population comprises about 110 villages. The Kenyah have maintained their traditional longhouse dwellings and, to a great extent, their traditional social and economic lives but the forces of national development and modernization have not passed them by.

On the most general level, the results of the research were to add both breadth and depth to the ethnography of the Kenyah. Specifically, several focal points were addressed: (1) the balance of the swidden system in the absence of rapid population growth, (2) Kenyah religion and its relation to social stratification, (3) religion and social change, (4) the potential for land tenure shifts, and (5) trends in the changing economy.

The present research is a continuation of an ongoing study of the Kenyah people. In 1970-1971, with the support of a grant from the National Institutes of Health, I conducted ethnographic research among the Kenyah of East Kalimantan, Indonesia, in the Christian villages of Long Nawang and Mara Satu (a migrant village from Long Nawang). The village in which I worked in

1973-1975 (Long Moh in Sarawak) has a common origin with the village of Long Nawang. According to Kenyah oral histories, the villages that are now Long Moh and Long Nawang were one village in the Iwan River area of East Kalimantan until about 200 years ago, when one group began moving into Sarawak and the other up the Kayan River in Kalimantan.[1]

Although it is not elaborated upon in this report, the two research sites were chosen specifically because there were some differences in their responses to the changing world around them, and a series of factors made these two areas an ideal laboratory for examining socioeconomic and cultural change through a method of controlled comparison. For the two areas the differing or control factors include: (1) the two groups, separated only eight generations, have been under different colonial administrations, the British in Sarawak and the Dutch in Kalimantan; (2) they have been exposed to different missionary groups with different philosophies and attitudes toward them, i.e., fundamentalist Protestants and Roman Catholics; (3) they have been in quite different power positions vis-a-vis other groups in their respective areas; (4) they are now under different national governments (Malaysia and Indonesia) with different attitudes and policies toward ethnic minorities; and (5) they inhabit significantly different ecological niches. These circumstances, a set of controllable variables, provided an excellent field for the study of the differential impacts of external forces on small ethnic minorities and the kinds of changes that take place under these differential influences. A full analysis of the results of this comparative study is in process and should be published in 1982. For brevity here in this current report, I have chosen to focus more on some general aspects of change common to both areas.

To carry out our research, my wife and I lived in the village of Long Moh (population 767) for 17 months, participating in most aspects of village life; our first son was born during this time. This "participant-observation" is the primary research method of anthropologists working in small-scale societies. Participant-observation was supplemented by structured interviews on specific topics, informal interviews, the collection of genealogies and oral histories, and a complete mapping of the village and ricefield areas. The tape recorder was used to record rituals, music and song, and linguistic data; extensive photography documented all aspects of village life and death.

One of the purposes of the extensive oral histories compiled was to trace the migration patterns of the Lepo Tau Kenyah over the past several hundred

[1] Public Health Service Research Fellowship 5 F01 MH43246-03 (CUAN) and Field Research Training Grant 1 T01 MH11023-01. Research in Indonesia was sponsored by the Lembaga Ilmu Pengetahuan Indonesia, Jakarta. Research in Sarawak, Malaysia, was sponsored by The Sarawak Museum, Kuching.

years. The evidence of these histories is that the exhaustion of swidden lands is not, as is commonly supposed, a primary impetus to migration for the Kenyah. There are two pieces of evidence supporting this. First, the Kenyah themselves do not state exhaustion of swidden lands as a motive for migration. In the days of headhunting and warfare, safety and political alliance and protection were the more often stated motives. In the modern era, desire to be closer to government centers, markets, medical care, and schooling may motivate migration, often encouraged by the government. Second, a study of the patterns of migration shows that a group often settles in an area previously abandoned by another group. Assuming that no group would move into an area of exhausted swidden lands, this is secondary evidence that migration for the Kenyah is based primarily on other factors.

One of the major focuses of the research was the Kenyah religious system and its relationship to social class and other aspects of social organization. The village of Long Moh was specifically selected because it is the last non-Christian Kenyah village. Even there, most people are adherents of the Bungan Cult, a somewhat streamlined form of traditional Kenyah religion. Only one family remained following the "old religion" during the research period. The Bungan Cult, however, has eliminated only some aspects of the older form and is new enough that most people remember the now-unused elements (e.g., bird augury) very clearly. Thus, it is still possible to gather a fairly complete picture of traditional Kenyah religion from a combination of observation and interview. The study of religion also incorporated religious change as part of the general forces of social change.

Particular attention was paid to the relationship of religion to the class system of the Kenyah. The Kenyah are one of several groups in Borneo to have such systems of social organization; a primary question is how low-energy societies, based on swidden farming and on hunting and gathering, can support systems of social stratification. Social stratification is generally considered to be a function of socioeconomic factors, of differential access to concrete means of production. For the Kenyah, religion supports the system of stratification by providing differential access to the supernatural. There is no priestly class nor are there full-time religious practitioners, but the system is interpreted and controlled by the aristocratic elders. This includes the all-important rituals involved with every stage of the planting and growing of rice and with the general level of village well-being. Commoners are, thus, dependent on the knowledge and help of the aristocrats in the production of their primary staple food as well as for general good fortune. Aristocrats are necessary to maintain *adat*, a central concept in many insular Southeast Asian societies; this research contributed to a deepening of the understanding of the *adat* concept (see

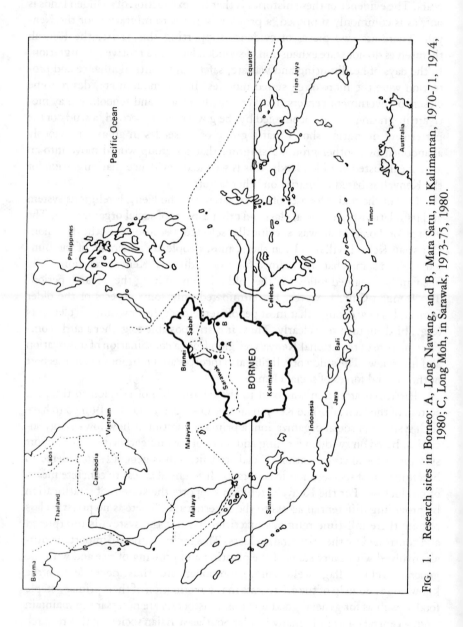

FIG. 1.   Research sites in Borneo: A, Long Nawang, and B, Mara Satu, in Kalimantan, 1970-71, 1974, 1980; C, Long Moh, in Sarawak, 1973-75, 1980.

Whittier, 1978a). *Adat* has frequently been defined as simply "customary law" and/or "customary behavior." In some senses, such a translation is accurate enough, but in its fullest sense, *adat* is ". . . the entire cosmos and the behavior within this ordered cosmos." (Whittier, 1978b). Improper or inappropriate behavior in one corner of the cosmos can trigger unfortunate results in another. The consequences may befall not only the perpetrator of the impropriety but others as well. Thus, it is up to the aristocrats, their position ordered by *adat,* to keep the cosmos in balance by interpreting misfortune and seeing that the appropriate rituals are performed to correct it and, if possible, prevent its recurrence.

This need for aristocrats is reflected in the dynamics of village schism; a new village cannot form without aristocrats. During the research, one group of families who made their rice fields together in a particular area began spending more and more time in the *lubong petok* (a smaller longhouse away from the village proper in the field area). The heads of several of these families said to the researcher that they would like to hive off into a separate village. They were numerous enough under government regulations to do so, but the one aristocrat family in the group refused to go along with the separation. Without them, it was impossible to form a new village since the village is a ritual unit with aristocrats responsible for seeing that everything is done to maintain or restore the natural balance of the cosmos and, consequently, the well-being of the village and its people.

Given these factors, i.e., the nature of the village as a ritual unit and the position of the aristocrats in maintaining the system, the adoption of Christianity would be expected to bring about social changes. Despite the views of some Christian missionaries that Christianity can simply replace the traditional religious system, leaving other aspects of society untouched, a careful examination of the articulation of religion and social organization shows this to be impossible. "Religion" in this case is not merely a set of beliefs about the supernatural but a total view of the construction of the universe, the behavior of its components, and the allocation of responsibility for that behavior. In addition, Christianity, as well as bringing its own load of cultural baggage, is attended by other forces of "modernization."

One inescapable conclusion is that the force of the village as a ritual unit is lessened by the advent of Christianity. In the traditional Kenyah belief system, certain kinds of behavior on the part of an individual could threaten the welfare of the entire village. The individual was obligated to right his wrong not only for his sake but for the good of all, and others would see to it that he did so. The Christian concept of wrong (sin) puts every individual responsible for his own acts personally to the deity rather than to society; crimes against society are the province of law.

Christianity also does not recognize the superiority (or, theoretically does not) of any one group (i.e., aristocrats) in proper behavior and relationship to the supernatural; all are equal. In the early days of conversion, leadership positions in the local churches tended to be held by aristocrats, but that is changing as it becomes clear that the rewards of church leadership in this situation are strictly spiritual. Political leadership, however, is still primarily in the hands of the aristocrats, thus creating a division between the spheres of religion and politics.

It would be misleading to give the impression that Christianity is the only, or even the primary, basis of change. Education is another major force. Primary schooling is now available to all Kenyah children; more and more children are also attending secondary school at government schools in the downriver towns. Those who manage to complete secondary school—a very small but growing minority—rarely return permanently to their villages but find employment downriver or in other areas, frequently as school teachers or government clerks. They return to their villages on periodic holidays, bringing money and goods for their families. An interesting question for future research is the extent to which a remittance economy will develop from this situation.

These educated town-dwellers also provide a focus for their families and fellow villagers in downriver towns and settlements. People traveling downriver for medical attention, bringing produce from the forest to trade, seeking temporary wage labor, or on shopping trips expect to receive hospitality in their homes. They may even expect the townsman to pay their medical expenses. With these focal points of their own fellow villagers or fellow Kenyah in the towns, the Kenyah visiting towns and bazaars for trading are changing their relationships with Chinese shopkeepers and middlemen. They are no longer tied into permanent relationships with one shop; they compare prices before selling their products or buying goods. Thus, when a Kenyah trades in town, he is no longer necessarily the client of a particular patron but, on the other hand, he also no longer has a particular patron who can be relied on to buy his goods, supply him credit, or employ him as temporary labor.

In addition to the educated, permanent migrants, there are other villagers who travel downriver to work for wages on a temporary basis, mostly in the timber and quarrying industries. They, too, bring home town goods, including sewing machines and outboard engines as well as salt, sugar, cloth, kerosene, and a variety of other goods. With these inputs, the value of cash and prestige goods in the village economy is increasing.

With government encouragement, the planting of cash crops is also increasing. These are primarily such items as rubber, cloves, cocoa, and pepper. Aside from bringing cash into the village economy, these cash crops are producing an as-yet unresolved problem in land tenure. Land tenure in this swidden agriculture society has traditionally been usufructuary, with rights to a particular plot initially gained by cutting virgin forest. The rights of this "first-cutter" are vested in his household and are passed down through the household; in any given year the household head supervises the distribution of plots among those holding various degrees of rights. Rights to land may go beyond the household in that an individual who leaves his/her natal household to reside in that of her/his spouse retains secondary rights to the land of his/her natal household. Even other villagers may use the land on a temporary basis with the permission of those who have primary and secondary rights to it. The cash crops mentioned above are all permanent crops in that land planted in them is permanently removed from the swidden system, thus decreasing the amount of swidden land available. In addition, when land is planted in cash crops under government programs, a formal title to the land is granted to the planter, removing that land from the traditional tenure system. This phenomenon is fairly new, and the few questions of inheritance that have arisen thus far have been dealt with on an ad hoc basis.

The traditional Kenyah land tenure system allows for the continual redistribution of swidden land based on the needs of each household in any given year; no household is ever without access to land. All adult members of the household have equal rights to the household's land but households claim only use rights. If cash crop land becomes owned outright with government supervision over title deeds, a new system of land inheritance will have to evolve as well as a mechanism for settling land disputes.

The removal of land from the swidden system in favor of cash crops has several implications. At this point, the land nearer the village and the better land tends to be used. Traditionally, swidden plots near the village were reserved for the older members of the household, sparing them the journey to more distant areas while allowing them to remain economically active. If the lands near the village are occupied by cash crops, it is possible that older people, no longer able to produce their own subsistence, could become dependents in the households of their children. This could produce a change in the traditional high status of the elderly.

It is possible for the Kenyah to devote so much land to cash crops that they are no longer able to produce their own basic subsistence and are, thus, totally dependent on the market economy, but it is unlikely in the near future. At least at present, they have had too much experience with the extreme fluctuations in market prices for cash crops to allow themselves to become completely dependent on them.

Through cash crops, increasing opportunities for wage labor, and increasing numbers of younger people permanently employed in salaried positions, the Kenyah are moving slowly into a market economy. They are still not dependent on the market and still produce and gather their own basic subsistence. It would be interesting at this point (1980) to conduct a detailed economic study to determine to what extent this process has proceeded. The Kenyah had never thought of themselves or described themselves as "poor" but, during the researcher's brief visit to Long Moh in 1980, they had begun to do so. This is a reflection of increasing involvement in a cash economy in which the concepts "rich" and "poor" are directly related to the amount of cash, or goods obtainable with cash, one has.

It is impossible, or at the very least misleading, to study the Kenyah today without studying social and economic change. Economic changes that are still in their beginning phases (e.g., cash crops, young employed outside the village) are too new to predict their consequences in other aspects of social life. It would seem, however, that these economic forces, in conjunction with the change in the religious system, would be likely to produce, among other things, a realignment of the traditional system of social stratification. This would tend toward stratification based on wealth and control of productive resources (i.e., land) rather than on control of knowledge. A potential question for future research on Kenyah social life might be the changing base of social stratification.

REFERENCES

(These publications are based on the research described in this report and on other relevant research.)

WHITTIER, HERBERT L.
1970. The Punan of East Kalimantan. Research note in the Borneo Research Bull., vol. 2, no. 1, June.
1973a. Social organization and symbols of social differentiation: An ethnographic study of the Kenyah Dayak of East Kalimantan (Borneo). Ph.D. dissertation, Department of Anthropology, Michigan State University.
1973b. A data source from Kalimantan—APDN Skripsi. Borneo Research Bull., vol. 5, no. 2, pp. 49-57.
1974a. The meaning of the terms long, uma', and lepo among the Kenyah. Borneo Research Bull., vol. 6, no. 2, pp.3-4.
1974b. The distribution of Punan in East Kalimantan. Borneo Research Bull., vol. 6, no. 2, pp. 42-48.

1975.   Film review. The Dayak people of Borneo, by Georges Bourdelon. Amer. Anthrop., vol. 78, no. 3, p. 723.

1976.   Singing one's way to structure: Bali Dayung, the Kenyah structural mechanic.   Paper delivered in Symposium: Contributions to the Study of a Changing Social Environment. Richard Fidler, organizer. American Anthropological Association Annual Meeting, Washington, D. C., November, 1976.

1977.   Changing concepts of adat and cosmology among the Kenyah Dayak of Borneo: The shaman as a structural mechanic.   Paper presented at the 26th Annual Meeting of the Midwest Conference on Asian Affairs. Northern Illinois University. October, 1977.

1978a.   The Kenyah. Pp. 134-181 *in* "Essays on Borneo Societies," Victor King, ed.   University of Hull Monographs on Southeast Asia, no. 7. Oxford University Press.

1978b.   Concepts of adat and cosmology among the Kenyah Dayak of Borneo: Coping with the changing socio-cultural milieu.   Sarawak Mus. Journ., vol. 26, no. 47, pp. 103-113.

WHITTIER, HERBERT L., and WHITTIER, PATRICIA R.

1974a.   The Apo Kayan area of East Kalimantan.   Sarawak Mus. Journ., vol. 12, no. 43, pp. 5-15.

1974b.   Some Apo Kayan megaliths.   Sarawak Mus. Journ., vol. 12, no. 43, pp. 369-381.

HERBERT L. WHITTIER

Biologic and Geologic Relationships of Small Fossil Mammals in Austria, with Special Attention to Those from Kohfidisch

Principal Investigator: Robert W. Wilson, Professor Emeritus, South Dakota School of Mines, and Associate, Museum of Natural History, The University of Kansas, Lawrence, Kansas.

Grant Nos. 1157,   For continuation of a long-term study of small fossil mam-
1333[1]and 1857.   mals of Austria.

Introduction

Eastern Austria, and especially the Vienna Basin, is a classic area for Miocene-Pliocene stratigraphy. The Vienna Basin was mentioned in Lyell's original description of the Miocene, and D'Orbigny did classical foraminiferal studies of the collections from this area. Also, the Vindobonian, Sarmatian, and Pannonian stages were established here. Although these three stages are hardly definable outside the local area, and it is easy to exaggerate their practical importance as a stratigraphic standard, they do have interculated marine and nonmarine faunas. Moreover, several fissure accumulations carry vertebrate faunas that may be biologically compared to those from bedded sequences. At several localities micromammalian faunas (Insectivora, Chiroptera, Lagomorpha, Rodentia) are abundant, sometimes from fissures and sometimes from bedded deposits. These faunas do have the potential of accurate correlations with each other and with other faunas in central and southern Europe.[2]

Because a number of the Tertiary genera of rodents and insectivores seem to be found in North America as well as Europe, I have been interested in the European mammalian faunas for some time (Wilson, 1960, 1968). In 1967-68, I was in Vienna as a Fulbright Research Scholar. During part of that time,

---

[1] In 1974 Dr. Wilson was the recipient of the Arnold Guyot Memorial Award of the National Geographic Society, "in recognition of a lifetime of outstanding contributions to the sciences of geology and paleontology."—Ed.

[2] The Lyellian terms Miocene and Pliocene have almost ceased to have meaning in biostratigraphical discussions relating to fossil mammals. Approximate equivalents to the terms employed herein are given in figure 1.

I worked with Professor Friedrich Bachmayer, recently retired Director of the Natural History Museum of Vienna, collaborating in the study of a rich fissure fauna from Kohfidisch, a locality which lies 115 kilometers south of Vienna in the Burgenland. This fauna contains the richest "early Pliocene" microfauna in Austria, and we were able to complete a preliminary account of it (Bachmayer and Wilson, 1970). In the late spring of 1973, through joint support from the Natural History Museum of Vienna and the National Geographic Society, we were able to continue our work on additional materials from Kohfidisch, and again in the late spring and early summer of 1976, and the springs of 1978 and 1979. A second contribution was issued by us in 1978, and a third in 1980.

Kohfidisch is a fissure deposit and as such lacks real stratigraphic control. Such geologic data as bears on the age has been given by Bachmayer and Zapfe (1969). However, two vertebrate faunas in the Vienna Basin contain small mammals and are under strict stratigraphic control, and thus permit biologic comparison with the Kohfidisch fauna. One is the Vösendorf fauna (Papp and Thenius, 1954) coming from the neotype locality of the Pannonian, and the other is the Eichkogel fauna (see especially Daxner-Höck and Rabeder below), formerly placed as late Pannonian, but now as Pontian *(s.s.)*. Eichkogel overlies the zone containing the Vösendorf fauna. As will be discussed later, the Kohfidisch fauna seems to be intermediate in age. Additionally, important new faunas, related in time to Kohfidisch, are being discovered and described throughout the Mediterranean and middle European area, as detailed by researchers from Austria, Czechoslovakia, France, Germany, Hungary, the Netherlands, and Spain. The present report is a summary of some Austrian localities, especially Kohfidisch, and their relationships to some of these other areas.

Faunal Comparisons of Kohfidisch and Eichkogel

Bachmayer and Wilson compared Kohfidisch and Eichkogel in 1970, but only limited comparisons could be made at that time. Although work on both the Kohfidisch and Eichkogel faunas continues, a much more detailed comparison can now be made. The Eichkogel list that follows has been compiled from Daxner-Höck (1970, 1972a, 1972b, 1975, 1977), Rabeder (1970, 1973a and b), and from Daxner-Höck and Rabeder (1970).

KOHFIDISCH	EICHKOGEL
Family Erinaceidae	
Galerix cf. *G. moedlingensis*	*Galerix moedlingensis*

Galerix zapfei
Lanthanotherium sp.   *Lanthanotherium* cf. *sanmigueli*
Erinaceus? sp.

Family Soricidae
  Petenyia dubia   *Petenyia hungarica*
  Petenyiella? *repenningi*   *Petenyiella* cf. *pannonica*
  Anourosorex kormosi   *Anourosorex* sp.
  Neomyine? sp.   *Sorex* spp.
                              Limnoecus? sp.

Family Talpidae
  Desmana pontica?   *Desmana* cf. *kormosi*
  Cf. *Desmanella crusafonti*   desmanine spp.
  Talpa gilothi (see Storch, 1978)   various remains of talpids

Family Megadermidae
  Megaderma vireti   undetermined fragments of
                              Chiroptera

Family Rhinolophidae
  Rhinolophus delphinensis
  Rhinolophus grivensis

Family Vespertilionidae
  Myotis nr. *M. boyeri*
  Plecotus (Paraplecotus) sp.
  Cf. *Myotis* sp.

Family Ochotonidae
  Prolagus cf. *P. oeningensis*   no lagomorphs

Family Sciuridae
  Spermophilinus cf. *S. bredai*   *Spermophilinus bredai-*
                              turolensis complex
  Pliopetaurista cf. *P. bressana*   *Pliopetaurista bressana*
                              Pliopetes cf. *hungarica*
                              Blackia miocoenica

Family Castoridae
  Cf. *Chalicomys jaegeri*   castorid sp. (one tooth, oral
                              communication, Höck, 1978)

Family Gliridae
  Muscardinus austriacus   *Muscardinus pliocoenicus*
  Cf. *Myomimus dehmi*   *Myomimus* sp.
  Cf. *Myomimus multicristatus*   *Vasseuromys* sp. (according to
    (= *Vasseuromys?*)   oral communication, 1978)

Family Gliridae (continued)
  Paraglirulus cf. *P. lissiensis*   *Glirulus* sp.
  Graphiurops austriacus   graphiurid sp.

Family Zapodidae
  Protozapus intermedius   *Protozapus intermedius*

Family Eomyidae
  Keramidomys sp.   *Keramidomys* aff. *mohleri*
  Leptodontomys sp.

Family Cricetidae
  Kowalskia fahlbuschi   *Kowalskia* cf. *fahlbuschi*
                                                      Collimys primus
  Epimeriones cf. *E. austriacus*   *Epimeriones austriacus*
  Promimomys (*Prosomys*) sp.   none
  Prospalax petteri   *Prospalax priscus*
                                                      spalacid indet.

Family Muridae
  Progonomys woelferi   *?Progonomys woelferi* (one
                                                      tooth)
  Parapodemus lugdunensis   *Parapodemus lugdunensis*

Family Hystricidae
  Hystrix cf. *H. suevica*   none

Comparison of Kohfidisch and Eichkogel shows a total of 30 determined genera at Kohfidisch, and 24 determined genera at Eichkogel. Seventeen genera are in common. Bats at the Eichkogel locality have not been determined, and no lagomorphs are present. If Eichkogel records are omitted which are not from the quarry where all recent material has been obtained, the faunas have an approximate resemblance, according to the Simpson coefficient of faunal resemblance, of 70 percent. This correspondence seems surprising in view of the modes of occurrence, the one from fissures, the other from normal, stratified sediments. At a specific level, the correspondence is much less. These specific distinctions are perhaps owing principally to differences in nomenclatural treatment and time rather than to local differences in environment.

The Pannon stage of the Vienna Basin has been divided into eight zones (A through H) by A. Papp (1948) on the basis of its invertebrate content. Zones A through D are referred to as lower, Zone E as middle, and Zones F through H as upper Pannon. The Eichkogel material comes from Zone H of the Pannon sequence of the Vienna Basin. Geologically, the Kohfidisch fissures offer evidence that the filling occurred in Pannon F time (Bachmayer and

Zapfe, 1969). Faunally there is some evidence as well, as outlined below, that Kohfidisch is older. Both faunas can be considered as late Pannonian, but they also have been referred to the restricted Pontian (see Daxner-Höck, 1975, p. 69).

The chief distinctions between these two faunas are: (1) Absence of lagomorphs, microtines, and porcupines at Eichkogel; (2) greater diversity at Eichkogel in some groups of small mammals as, for example, in the sciurids and shrews; (3) some specific differences when genera are in common, for example, in species of *Prospalax, Desmana,* and *Petenyia;* and (4) near absence of *Progonomys* in the Eichkogel fauna.

In regard to (1), lagomorphs and porcupines appear earlier and survive later than the time of either fauna. The Kohfidisch microtine is represented only by a single specimen, and, if that rare, could be missing for that reason from Eichkogel. Further, in faunal sequences from other European regions, the microtines are distinctly later in their first appearance than the Austrian faunas appear to be, and for that reason the occurrence may be suspect.

The second difference may be due to a wider source area at Eichkogel, differences in screen size used in washing, or a more refined taxonomy. It does not point to an age difference.

The third difference is much more critical and difficult to evaluate. It concerns species from Eichkogel that have not been studied in detail, are fragmentary compared to Kohfidisch, and were determined before the Kohfidisch work was available to Daxner-Höck and Rabeder. Also there may be a choice of specific names because of poor type specimens, giving rise to different names whether the species are taxonomically the same or not. In the instance of *Prospalax priscus* versus *P. petteri,* the former species is generally a geologically later one and, if both determinations are valid, the distinction may have temporal significance.

The final difference, near absence of *Progonomys* (one specimen?) at Eichkogel, seems to be the most valid evidence for an age difference. Murines are common at both localities, but *Parapodemus* is less common than *Progonomys* at Kohfidisch (one-third as abundant numerically). Generally, the two genera do not occur together, and *Parapodemus* is known to survive after *Progonomys* becomes extinct. On this basis, the Kohfidisch fauna seems somewhat older than that at Eichkogel.

Other Faunal Comparisons

The lowest *Hipparion*-bearing beds of the Pannon stage occur in Zone C at Gaiselberg bei Zistersdorf. The mammalian fauna from this locality does not contain small mammals. Its earlier and Vallesian age in comparison with Kohfidisch, however, is confirmed by the coexistence in it of *Hipparion* and *Anchitherium*. The Gaiselberg fauna has been described by Zapfe (1949).

The Vösendorf micromammal fauna is scanty. Based on the literature (Papp and Thenius, 1954; Daxner-Höck, 1972b) the following species may be listed:

Galerix voesendorfenis	*Megacricetodon (Mesocricetodon) minutus*
Trimylus sansanensis	*Cricetodon* n. sp. (aff. *gregarius*)
Talpid, indet.	*Kowalskia* sp.
Monosaulax minutus	*?Anomalomys* sp.

The principal faunal item pointing to an age for this fauna older than Kohfidisch is negative, that is the absence of murids. Perhaps the greater variety of cricetids also suggests the same age difference. However, *Cricetodon* n. sp. (aff. *gregarius*) has been called *Megacricetodon* aff. *minor* (see Freudenthal and Sondaar, 1964), and Mein and Freudenthal (1971) would presumably regard all Vösendorf cricetids save *Kowalskia* as *Megacricetodon*. The absence of *Megacricetodon* at Eichkogel and Kohfidisch suggests a slightly older stage at Vösendorf, in agreement with the geologic situation. The presence of *Anomalomys* also suggests an older age except that this identification seemingly is based on a toothless palatal fragment. On the other hand, the presence of *Hipparion* and the absence of *Anchitherium* might be taken to indicate an equivalent age. Nevertheless, the sum of the evidence points to an age for Kohfidisch intermediate between that of Vösendorf and Eichkogel.

According to A. Papp, the Götzendorf fauna, from the eastern part of the Vienna Basin, comes from a freshwater sandstone of Pannon F age. This position indicates an age intermediate between Vösendorf and Eichkogel, and should be equivalent in age to that postulated for Kohfidisch. The fauna, however, represents a considerably different biotope, and is rather strictly a stream and stream border fauna. Much of the material consists of single teeth. A tentative faunal list follows:

desmanine sp.	*"Steneofiber" minutus*
talpid sp. or spp.	castorid sp. (?Cf. *Chalicomys jaegeri*
soricid spp.	from Kohfidisch)
?Plesiodimylus chantrei	*Democricetodon* sp.
Prolagus cf. *P. oeningensis*	Cf. *Microcricetus* sp.
Spermophilus cf. *S. bredai*	anomalomyine sp.

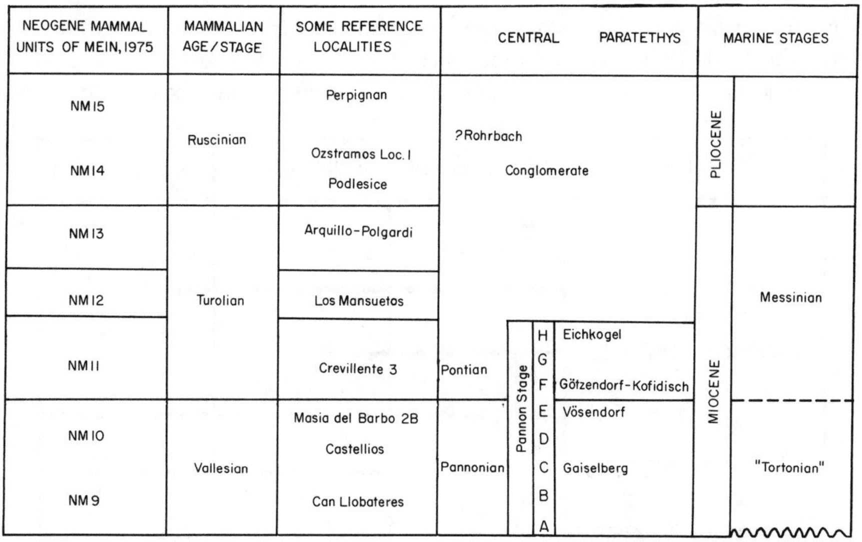

NEOGENE MAMMAL UNITS OF MEIN,1975	MAMMALIAN AGE/STAGE	SOME REFERENCE LOCALITIES	CENTRAL PARATETHYS				MARINE STAGES
NM 15	Ruscinian	Perpignan	?Rohrbach			PLIOCENE	
NM 14		Ozstramos Loc. I / Podlesice	Conglomerate				
NM 13		Arquillo–Polgardi					
NM 12	Turolian	Los Mansuetos					Messinian
NM 11		Crevillente 3	Pontian	H	Eichkogel	MIOCENE	
				G			
				F	Götzendorf–Kofidisch		
NM 10	Vallesian	Masia del Barbo 2B		E	Vösendorf		
		Castellios		D			"Tortonian"
			Pannonian	C	Gaiselberg		
NM 9		Can Llobateres		B			
				A			

FIG. 1.   Biostratigraphic relationships of Vienna Basin and Kohfidisch faunas.

Perhaps because of its stream border character, some elements of Götzendorf suggest an older age than Kohfidisch, as well as does the absence of murines. If Götzendorf is of the same age as Kohfidisch, then there is a striking difference in fauna not found in comparing Eichkogel and Kohfidisch. There is in common with Kohfidisch only cf. *Chalicomys jaegeri, Prolagus* cf. *P. oeningensis, Spermophilus* cf. *S. bredai,* and perhaps some of the talpids, all species with long ranges. Absent from Götzendorf is the relatively common Kohfidisch genus *Kowalskia,* and all representatives of the Murinae and Gliridae. Absence of the Murinae is especially striking in view of the supposed age of Götzendorf.

The Rohrbach Conglomerate is exposed on the southern edge of the Vienna Basin. It has been regarded as the youngest pre-Pleistocene formation in the area. Unfortunately, only mammal tracks of various sized carnivores and pecorans and leaf impressions have been recovered from it. Küpper, Papp, and Thenius (1952) have suggested that this conglomerate may be of Astian-Plaisancian age.

The relation of the Kohfidisch fauna to that of Polgardi (Hungary) has already been discussed (Bachmayer and Wilson, 1970, p. 539) almost as fully as can be with profit. It might be noted, however, that *Parapodemus schaubi* is probably a synonym of *P. gaudryi,* but in either case the species is advanced over *P. lugdunensis*. Also, small and large species of *Hystrix* seem known back into the "early Pliocene," nullifying size of porcupines as significant in age determinations (Jánossy, 1972). Probably the consensus would be that Polgardi

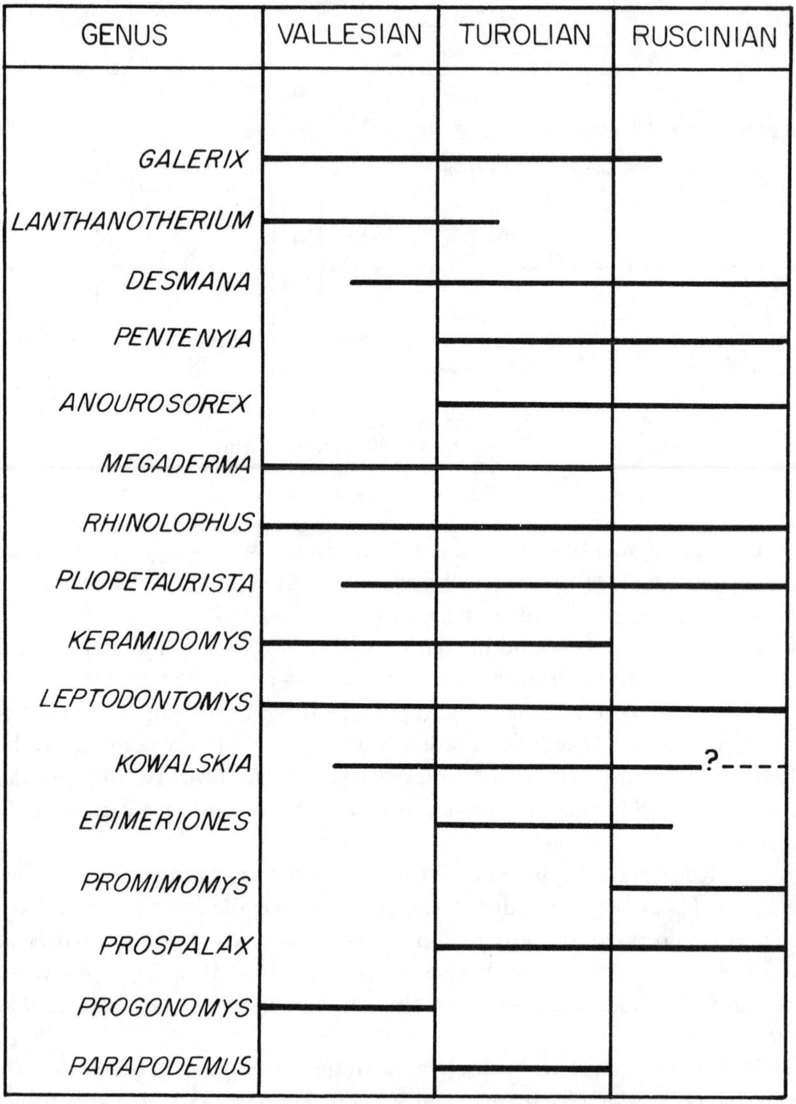

GENUS	VALLESIAN	TUROLIAN	RUSCINIAN
GALERIX			
LANTHANOTHERIUM			
DESMANA			
PENTENYIA			
ANOUROSOREX			
MEGADERMA			
RHINOLOPHUS			
PLIOPETAURISTA			
KERAMIDOMYS			
LEPTODONTOMYS			
KOWALSKIA			?
EPIMERIONES			
PROMIMOMYS			
PROSPALAX			
PROGONOMYS			
PARAPODEMUS			

FIG. 2.   Temporal distribution of some Kohfidisch genera exclusive of Kohfidisch occurrence.

is distinctly younger than Kohfidisch rather than slightly younger as suggested by Bachmayer and Wilson in 1970.

The fissure fauna of Osztramos Locality 1 in northeast Hungary has been designated as middle Pliocene by Jánossy (1972).[3] The pertinent fauna given by Jánossy follows:

Talpa aff. *csornatana*	*Muscardinus* aff. *pliocoenicus*
Talpa aff. *fossilis*	*Muscardinus* sp.
"*Desmana,*" 2 spp.	*Glirulus (Aphidyromys) pusillus*
?Episoriculus group	*Sminthozapus janossyi*
Petenyia cf. *hungarica*	*Prospalax kretzoii*
Petenyia sp.	*Apodemus* aff. *dominans*
Amblycoptus topali	*Rotundomys (Kowalskia) polonica*
?Sorex sp.	*Rotundomys (Kowalskia) magna*
Chiroptera (includes *Rhinolophus,*	*Rotundomys* sp.
2 spp.)	
Leptodontomys bodvanus	*Meriones* sp. ?
Sciurus sp.	*Baranomys kowalskii progressus*
Sciurus aff. *warthae*	*Polonomys* sp.
Pliopetes sp.	leporid indet. (*Hypolagus?*)
Glis minor	ochotonid indet.

Jánossy thinks that in the above fauna, forest elements are dominant over steppe. The reverse seems true at Kohfidisch. Differences in the faunal lists may in part reflect this. The most pertinent items pointing to later age for the Osztramos fauna are *Amblycoptus topali, Sminthozapus, Apodemus,* and some kind of true leporid. *A. topali* is advanced over *A. oligodon* (Polgardi), and the latter over *Anourosorex kormosi* of Kohfidisch. The Recent *Anourosorex squamipes* is, however, also more primitive than species of *Amblycoptus* in the presence of the third molar. *Sminthozapus* and *Protozapus* presumably occupied similar environments, with the former genus slightly more advanced. Again, however, A. van de Weerd (1976) thinks that *Protozapus* is a synonym of the living *Eozapus* of China. If certain species of *Progonomys, Parapodemus,* and *Apodemus* form a continuous line as most workers think, this is clear evidence of a considerably earlier age for Kohfidisch. Leporids are invaders from outside Europe. In the North American Miocene, the abundance of true leporids versus

---

[3] Perhaps it should be pointed out that the Province of Burgenland, in which the Kohfidisch fissures lie, was part of Hungary until the dissolution of the old Austro-Hungarian empire (Kohfidisch has the Hungarian name of Gyepüfüses). Thus Kohfidisch should be more or less readily fitted into the Hungarian sequence, although in practice this seems difficult.

the abundance of ochotonids is a matter frequently of flood plain deposits (inhabitants of more open country) versus stream deposits (inhabitants of stream borders) and suggests that if leporids had already arrived in the area of Kohfidisch they should be represented in this steppe-dominated fauna. Lastly, if Osztramos is a forest-dominated fauna, then the absence of such Miocene relicts as *Galerix* indicates that these genera were finally being eliminated even under woodland conditions, and hence that the Hungarian fauna is later than Kohfidisch.

In 1969, Kretzoi reviewed the Pliocene and Quaternary terrestrial stratigraphy of Hungary, and placed the abundant individual fossil faunas in a series of faunal waves—ten waves in all for his Pliocene. Several non-Hungarian faunas, for example the principal east Austrian faunas, were included. In this review, Kretzoi placed Kohfidisch too low in his sequence, but as of the date of Kretzoi's paper, the Kohfidisch fauna was almost completely unpublished. It would be interesting to attempt to correlate Kretzoi's faunal waves with the mammalian age-stage units now being proposed by other European workers (see especially Fahlbusch, 1976, for background), but it is in fact difficult even to fit Eichkogel and Kohfidisch into the Hungarian sequence. Perhaps Kohfidisch falls somewhere in the fifth or sixth Pliocene faunal wave, but no later than the seventh.

If evaluating faunal distinctions in geographically close areas is difficult, it obviously becomes even more hazardous for areas as distant from each other as eastern Austria on the one hand, and France and Spain on the other. Nevertheless, as indicated earlier, attempts are now being made, and I shall make my own attempt to place Kohfidisch in the framework proposed by Mein (1975), the International Symposium on mammalian stratigraphy of the European Tertiary (Fahlbusch, 1976), and the Dutch workers at Utrecht and Leiden (see fig. 1).

First of all, though, I would like to summarize the faunal characteristics of the small fossil mammals from Kohfidisch.

Chief Faunal Characteristics of the Small Mammals of Kohfidisch

Assuming that accumulation of the Kohfidisch fauna represents only a short time span, there is a peculiar mixture of Vallesian and Turolian[4]

---

[4] Vallesian and Turolian are age terms proposed by Crusafont-Pairó (1951, 1965), which have gained almost complete acceptance. Vallesian is equivalent to the Meotian (upper Sarmatian of the Black Sea area) and lower Pontian of older authors. Turolian is equivalent to the Pikermian and also to the restricted Pontian in the more recent literature.

elements as forms from these stages are known from outside eastern Austria, and especially from France and Spain (fig. 2).

Vallesian age is suggested by the following: (1) Abundant *Progonomys*, (2) cf. *Chalicomys jaegeri* rather than *Dipoides problematicus*, (3) relatively primitive dormice except for *Muscardinus*, (4) no leporids, (5) mostly warmth-loving bats, and (6) species allied to Vallesian forms such as *Lanthanotherium sanmigueli* and *Pliopetaurista bressana*.

A younger age than Vallesian is suggested by the following: (1) Presence of *Kowalskia*, *Parapodemus*, *Epimeriones*, *Promimomys (Prosomys)*, *Protozapus*, *Prospalax*, and (2) cricetines rather than cricetodontines in the cricetid fauna.

If reliance is better placed on newcomers to the fauna, then the fauna is to be considered Turolian. If Turolian, the presence of abundant *Progonomys*, *Kowalskia* rather than *Cricetus kormosi*, *Prospalax petteri* rather than *P. priscus*, *Anourosorex* rather than *Amblycoptus*, the absence of leporids and *Dipoides*, and *Parapodemus lugdunensis* as the most advanced murine, all suggest a lower Turolian, perhaps even a basal Turolian, age. The chief anomalous rodents are *Epimeriones* and *Prosomys*, otherwise known only from somewhat to considerably later faunas in eastern Europe. The presence of these two genera at Kohfidisch can be explained in several different ways, one of which simply accepts the occurrence as the earliest European records of these genera. All in all, an assignment to Zone 11 of the Mein scheme (1975) is quite feasible.

General Correlations

De Bruijn, Mein, Montenat, and van de Weerd (1975) have made an attempt to correlate certain rodent faunas from Spain with marine sections of the late Miocene at Crevillente. Here they find *Parapodemus lugdunensis* and *Kowalskia fahlbuschi* in Crevillente faunas 1, 2, and 3. The Spanish levels are regarded by them as nearly on the boundary of the Turolian and Vallesian, but within the Turolian as early Turolian. However, in a paper by Benda and Meulenkamp (1972) a chart was presented (composed by 15 specialists) in which Kohfidisch and Eichkogel are equated with the type Turolian (Los Mansuetos) and placed well above Crevillente. In terms of the marine sequence, Crevillente 1, 2, and 3 are placed in the late Tortonian and pre-Messinian, and in the lower part of Zone 16 of Blow. Kastellios Hill on the island of Crete is regarded in their paper as Vallesian. This important locality has both foraminifera and species of *Progonomys*, *P.* cf. *woelferi* and *P. cathali*, in near association (de Bruijn, Sondaar, and Zachariasse, 1971). Correlation of the foraminifera is made with the basal part of Zone 16 of Blow, and hence of the small mammal fauna also. That Kohfidisch fits into some part of the marine Messinian, however, rather than late Tortonian seems as still possible to me (but see Van Couvering and Berggren, 1977, p. 304, in which the view is expressed that the Turolian and Messinian do not overlap in time).

What may be the equivalent of Kohfidisch and other related faunas of Europe to the well-known mammalian sequence in North America? Repenning (1967) in a well-reasoned paper on Palearctic-Nearctic mammalian dispersal in the Late Cenozoic has suggested that correlation of the Pannonian with the Hemphillian is one of the strongest in the Tertiary. Repenning here uses the term Pannonian to cover older terms such as *Hipparion fauna* or "Pontian." Essentially the same correlation was made earlier by Guy Pilgrim (1940), and R. A. Stirton (1951). The rodent fauna of Kohfidisch does not offer much evidence in regard to correlation except *Promimomys (Prosomys)* which is a Hemphillian genus in North America. Aside from small mammals, from what I have seen of European *Hipparion,* this horse is in a stage of evolution no earlier than late Clarendonian. Finally, it would seem that if the late Pannonian (faunas of Zones F-H) is equivalent to the restricted Pontian, then Kohfidisch and Eichkogel are as late in time as almost anything in the Hemphillian.

REFERENCES

BACHMAYER, F., and WILSON, R. W.
1970. Small mammals (Insectivora, Chiroptera, Lagomorpha, Rodentia) from the Kohfidisch fissures of Burgenland, Austria. Ann. Naturhist. Mus. Wien, vol. 74, pp. 533-587, Vienna.
1978. A second contribution to the small mammal fauna of Kohfidisch, Austria. Ann. Naturhist. Mus. Wien, vol. 81, pp. 129-161, Vienna.
1980. A third contribution to the fossil small mammal fauna of Kohfidisch (Burgenland), Austria. Ann. Naturhist. Mus. Wien, vol. 83, pp. 351-386.
BACHMAYER, F., and ZAPFE, H.
1969. Die Fauna der altpliozänen Höhlen- und Spaltenfüllungen bei Kohfidisch, Burgenland (Österreich). Ann. Naturhist. Mus. Wien, vol. 73, pp. 123-139, Vienna.
BENDA, L., and MEULENKAMP, J. E.
1972. Discussion on biostratigraphic relations in the Eastern Mediterranean Neogene. Zeit. Deutsch. Geol. Ges., vol. 123, pp. 559-564, Hannover.
BRUIJN, H. DE; MEIN, P.; MONTENAT, C.; and VAN DE WEERD, A.
1975. Correlations entre les gisements de rongeurs et les formations marines du Miocene terminal d'Espagne Meridionale I (Provinces d'Alicante et de Murcia). Kon. Nederl. Akad. Wetenschappen, Proc., Ser. B, vol. 78, no. 4, pp. 1-32, Amsterdam.

BRUIJN, H. DE; SONDAAR, P. Y.; ZACHARIASSE, W. J.
1971.   Mammalia and Foraminifera from the Neogene of Kastellios Hill (Crete), a correlation of continental and marine biozones.   Kon. Nederl. Akad. Wetenschappen, Proc., Ser. B, vol. 74, no. 5, pp. 1-22, Amsterdam.
CRUSAFONT-PAIRO, M.
1951.   El sistema Miocénico en la depresión Española del Vallés-Penedes. Proc. Inter. Geolog. Congress, Great Britain 1948, vol. 11, pp. 33-42, London.
1965.   Observations à un travail de M. Freudenthal et P. Y. Sondaar sur les nouveaux gisements à *Hipparion* d'Espagne.   Kon. Nederl. Akad. Wetenschappen, Proc., Ser. B, vol. 68, pp. 121-126, Amsterdam.
DAXNER-HÖCK, G.
1970.   Die Wirbeltierfauna aus dem Alt-Pliozän (O-Pannon) vom Eichkogel bei Mödling (N.Ö.), III, Rodentia.   Ann. Naturhist. Mus. Wien, vol. 74, pp. 597-605, Vienna.
1972a.   Die Wirbeltierfauna aus dem Alt-Pliozän (Pont) vom Eichkogel bei Mödling (Niederösterreich). IV. Gerbillinae (Rodentia, Mammalia). Ann. Naturhist. Mus. Wien, vol. 76, pp. 143-160, Vienna.
1972b.   Cricetinae aus dem Alt-Pliozän vom Eichkogel bei Mödling (Niederösterreich) und von Vösendorf bei Wien.   Paläont. Zeit., vol. 46, nos. 3/4, pp. 133-150, Stuttgart.
1975.   Sciuridae aus dem Jungtertiär von Österreich.   Paläont. Zeit., vol. 49, nos. 1/2, pp. 56-74, Stuttgart.
1977.   Muridae, Zapodidae und Eomyidae (Rodentia, Mammalia) des Eichkogels bei Mödling (Niederösterreich).   Paläont. Zeit., vol. 51, nos. 1/2, pp. 19-31, Stuttgart.
DAXNER-HÖCK, G., and RABEDER, G.
1970.   Vorläufige Ergebnisse der paläontologischen Grabung 1968 im Altpliozän (O-Pannon) des Eichkogels (N.Ö.).   Anz. Österr. Akad. Wiss., math.-naturw. Klasse, Jahrg. 1970, no. 2, pp. 47-50, Vienna.
FAHLBUSCH, V.
1976.   Report on the International Symposium on mammalian stratigraphy of the European Tertiary.   Newsl. Stratigr., vol. 5, no. 2/3, pp. 160-167, Berlin. Stuttgart.
FREUDENTHAL, M., and SONDAAR, P. Y.
1964.   Les faunes a Hipparion des environs de Daroca (Espagne) et leur valeur pour la stratigraphie du Neogene de l' Europe.   Kon. Nederl. Akad. Wetenschappen, Proc., Ser. B, vol. 67, no. 5, pp. 473-490, Amsterdam.
JÁNOSSY, D.
1972.   Middle Pliocene microvertebrate fauna from the Osztramos Loc. 1 (Northern Hungary).   Ann. Hist.-Nat. Mus., Natl. Hungarica, vol. 64, pp. 27-52, Budapest.
KRETZOI, M.
1969.   Sketch of the Late Cenozoic (Pliocene and Quaternary) terrestrial stratigraphy of Hungary.   Földr. Közlem, vol. 3, pp. 179-204, Budapest.

KÜPPER, H.; PAPP, A.; THENIUS, E.
1952. Über die stratigraphische Stellung des Rohrbacher Konglomerates. Sitz.-Ber. Österr. Akad. Wiss., math.-naturw. Klasse, vol. 161, pp. 441-453, Vienna.

MEIN, P.
1975. Résultats du Groupe de Travail des Vertébrés. Report on activity of the Committee on Mediterranean Neogene Stratigraphy, Working Groups (1971-1975), pp. 78-81, Bratislava.

MEIN, P., and FREUDENTHAL, M.
1971. Une nouvelle classification des Cricetidae (Mammalia, Rodentia) du Tertiaire de l'Europe. Scripta Geologica, vol. 2, pp. 1-37, Leiden.

PAPP, A.
1948. Fauna und Gliederung der Congerienschichten des Pannons im Wiener Becken. Anz. Österr. Akad. Wiss., math.-naturw. Klasse, Jahrg. 1948, no. 11, pp. 123-134, Vienna.

PAPP, A., and THENIUS, E.
1954. Vösendorf—Ein Lebensbild aus dem Pannon des Wiener Beckens. Mitt. Geol. Ges. Wien, vol. 46, pp. 1-109, Vienna.

PILGRIM, G. E.
1940. The application of the European time scale to the Upper Tertiary of North America. Geol. Mag., vol. 77, pp. 1-27, Hertford.

RABEDER, G.
1970. Die Wirbeltierfauna aus dem Alt-Pliozän (O-Pannon) vom Eichkogel bei Mödling (N.Ö.). I. Allgemeines—II. Insectivora. Ann. Naturh. Mus. Wien, vol. 74, pp. 589-595, Vienna.

1973a. *Galerix* und *Lanthanotherium* (Erinaceidae, Insectivora) aus dem Pannon des Wiener Beckens. Neues Jahrb. Geol. Paläont. Monatsh., Jahrg. 1973, vol. 7, pp. 429-446, Stuttgart.

1973b. Plecotus (Paraplecotus) aus dem O-Miozän von Kohfidisch (Burgenland). Part B in Myotis, Mittellungsblatt für Fledermauskundler, vol. 11, pp. 15-17, Bonn.

REPENNING, C. A.
1967. Palearctic-Nearctic mammalian dispersal in the Late Cenozoic. Pp. 288-311 *in* "The Bering Land Bridge." Stanford University Press, Stanford.

STIRTON, R. A.
1951. Principles in correlation and their application to Later Cenozoic Holarctic continental mammalian faunas. Rept. Inter Geol. Congress, Great Britain 1948, vol. 11, pp. 74-84, London.

STORCH, G.
1978. Die turolische Wirbeltierfauna von Dorn-Dürkheim, Rheinhessen (SW-Deutschland). 2. Mammalia: Insectivora. Senckenbergiana Lethaea, vol. 58, no. 6, pp. 421-449, Frankfurt am Main.

THENIUS, E.
1967. Säugetierfährten aus dem Rohrbacher Konglomerat (Pliozän) von Niederösterreich. Ann. Naturhist. Mus. Wien, vol. 71, pp. 363-379, Vienna.

VAN COUVERING, J. A., and BERGGREN, W. A.
  1977.   Biostratigraphical basis of the Neogene time scale. Pp. 283-306 *in* "Concepts and Methods of Biostratigraphy," E. G. Kauffman and J. E. Hazel, eds., xiv+658 pp. Dowden, Hutchinson and Ross, Stroudsburg.
WEERD, A. VAN DE
  1976.   Rodent faunas of the Mio-Pliocene continental sediments of the Teruel-Alfambra Region, Spain. Utrecht Micropaleont. Bulletins, Spec. Publ., vol. 2, pp. 1-218, Meppel.
WILSON, R. W.
  1960.   Early Miocene rodents and insectivores from northeastern Colorado. Univ. Kansas Publ., Palaeontol. Contr., Vertebrata, Art. 7, pp. 1-92, Lawrence.
  1968.   Insectivores, rodents and intercontinental correlation of the Miocene. Proc. Inter. Geolog. Congress, Czechoslovakia 1968, vol. 10, pp. 19-25, Prague.
ZAPFE, H.
  1949.   Die Säugetierfauna aus dem Unterpliozän von Gaiselberg bei Zistersdorf in Niederösterreich. Jahrb. Geol. Bundesanstalt, 1948, pp. 83-97, Vienna.

ROBERT W. WILSON

Spatial Patterning in a Hunting and Gathering Society

Principal Investigator:	John E. Yellen, Program Director for Anthropology, National Science Foundation, Washington, D. C.
Grant No. 1234:	For an ethno-archeological investigation in Western Ngamiland, Botswana.

Research Goals

In recent years two major trends have characterized developments in human prehistory. Beginning in the mid 1960's archeologists shifted their focus from an almost exclusive emphasis on culture history—the definition of prehistoric cultural units and their distribution in time and space—and focused more on the reconstruction of the ways in which such units functioned. Many of the most widely cited publications of this period deal either with the internal structure of prehistoric units (Longacre, 1964; Hill, 1968) or with the interactions between such societies and the natural environment in which they functioned. A parallel emphasis can be observed in paleoanthropology of the mid to late 1970's, with less attention paid to hominid taxonomic questions per se and greater concern for functional and ecological interpretations that examine the ways in which species adapted to and utilized their particular environmental niches. A second trend, closely related to the first, is the increased emphasis on questions of *process,* both cultural and biological, which underlie both short- and long-term change. Such debates as the relevance of sociobiology to the understanding of human evolution (Wilson, 1978), or the role of trade in the emergence of complex stratified societies, evidence such concerns.

What archeologists and paleoanthropologists have come to realize is that to understand how change and development occur, it is necessary to be able to reconstruct specific aspects of human behavior. One must be able to answer such questions as: When did hominids first utilize a home base? When did the nuclear family first appear? How far back can the antecedents of such universal human behaviors as language be traced? As such problems come to the fore, one also comes to realize how scanty the archeological record is, and how difficult its interpretation can be. One approach to attempt to "flesh out" this record is through the study of extant societies and the development of "ethnoarcheology"—the study of living peoples from an archeological perspective—as a distinct archeological subdiscipline can also be traced to the mid 1960's with Richard Gould's pioneering work among the Western Desert Aborigines of Australia (Gould, 1969). Similar research aimed at elucidating mankind's paleolithic past was also conducted by Lewis Binford in the late 1960's and early 1970's, and my own research has followed in that tradition.

There are two main ways in which the ethnographic present can be used to elucidate the archeological past, and I have incorporated both of these approaches in my work. First, carefully selected modern societies can provide, one hopes, some insight into how their prehistoric analogs may have functioned. My studies have focused on the Bushman, or San, hunters and gatherers on the northern fringe of the Kalahari desert in Botswana. It is clear that the San, at least as they were in the late 1960's, represented a special form of hunting and gathering society, one whose adaptation to a specific set of environmental conditions was, in some ways, unique. Therefore they cannot serve as a general model for Paleolithic hunters and gatherers. On the other hand, a hunting and gathering mode of subsistence employing a simple technology must, by necessity, impose severe constraints and limitations on any group which follows this way of life. One may argue that at least the study of one particular modern example can provide information useful in establishing boundaries and discovering what may be more or less reasonable long-run options.

Secondly, the controlled context provided by the ethnographic present offers the archeologist an ideal situation to test a wide range of analytic procedures and techniques. For example, confronted with an excavated paleolithic "living floor"—most often a jumble of bone and stone debris—it is quite difficult to draw the most basic social interpretations from it. How long, for example, might such a site have been occupied? How many people might have been responsible for these remains? How did the inhabitants group themselves? Were they formed into nuclear families? Working in the ethnographic present, one can observe the "answers" directly, gather the comparable "archeological data," and then examine the fit between the two. For example, one can observe how site characteristics vary in relation to the number of occupants and length of occupation. One can also use such a controlled situation to develop and test, in a fairly rigorous context, statistical techniques which permit one to move from data to the conclusions derived therefrom.

The Dobe Sample

Although the situation is now dramatically changed, in the late 1960's a number of San groups (referred to as !Kung or zu/wasi) in the northwestern parts of Botswana and adjacent Namibia still followed a more-or-less traditional hunting and gathering way of life. One such group, which centered around the Dobe waterhole (19°37'S., 21°2'E.), has been studied from a wide range of anthropological perspectives, beginning in the early 1960's (Lee and DeVore, 1976). Although the Dobe San had been in contact with Bantu pastoralists for several decades, and many of the men had worked for the Bantu at one time or another, in 1968, when my own field research began, the Dobe group was still meeting essentially all its subsistence needs with hunted and gathered resources.

This northern Kalahari region is properly classed as semiarid, and rainfall varies significantly from year to year, both in amount and in temporal and geographic distribution. This area is termed a "thirstland," for while rainfall is high enough to support a fairly rich vegetation, water sinks rapidly into the sandy soil and is available year round only in a very few places. Longitudinal, or "alab," dunes which are now stable characterize the region, and vegetation associations are closely correlated with their location in relation to dune crests. Because of this varied topography, a surprisingly large number of plant species are packed within a limited area. The mongongo, *Ricinodendron rautanenii,* is the most important of the 80-plus plant species that provide food for the San. Common game animals include giraffe, kudu, eland, warthog, wildebeest, and gemsbok, as well as a number of smaller species important for San subsistence. From the San's perspective, water is the basic limiting resource, and the yearly subsistence round is based largely on changes of water distribution. During the dry season, groups congregate around permanent water sources and with the onset of the rains they disperse to widely scattered ephemeral pans which hold water for varying periods. This strategy permits them to utilize resources in areas uninhabitable for large portions of the year.

From January through July 1968—this includes most of the rainy season and the winter—I followed the movements of a San group which spent the dry season at the Dobe waterhole. The core of the group consisted of three adult brothers, the wives and children of two of them, and their parents. The group varied in size over this period but the core remained fairly constant. Over this interval, the group made a number of extended trips of varying length from Dobe to hunt and gather in the hinterland north and west of the waterhole. During these extended periods they subsisted solely on hunted and gathered foods obtained through traditional methods. I was resident at Dobe throughout this time and attempted to maintain daily records on the group's movement. I accomplished this through both participant observation and detailed interviewing to reconstruct events during the periods when I was not present. Over this period the group moved camp 38 times. The data I collected focused specifically on areas of general interest to the archeologist. Detailed records of hunting trips were obtained. I noted when and where camp shifts were made and tried to determine the reasons for these moves. I visited most of these camps and made detailed maps of 15 of them. These maps included the position of all huts, hearths, and other cultural features as well as the location, to the nearest centimeter, of each bone and other object. The faunal materials were then numbered, collected, and analyzed. Detailed information was obtained for each camp: the number of days occupied, people present, activities carried out both in the camp and away from it, the reason people moved there, and why they left.

The generous support of the National Geographic Society permitted the subsequent analysis of this data over a year's period at the Smithsonian Institution. The major conclusions are presented in my analysis (Yellen, 1977). In general, it focuses on the distribution of individuals and activities over space and time. A series of analytic levels may be distinguished. The first involves the long-term movement of individuals over many years into and out of the Dobe region; this work reveals, I believe, the long-term adaptive strategy of the San to the unpredictable northern Kalahari environment. Second, I used the 1968 Dobe sample to examine movement from camp to camp. Such data not only permit an understanding of short-term subsistence strategy, but also allow one to examine variability between camps. It provides a controlled analog to study what archeologists term "intersite variation." Finally, I analyzed both quantitatively and qualitatively spatial patterning within campsites; and this phase of the research has, I hope, provided techniques to help in the interpretation of archeological "living floors." The major conclusions, grouped under these headings, are discussed below.

Long Term Spatial Adaptation

A central question in hunter and gatherer research concerns the extent to which such societies are organized into tightly defined "bands" which are associated with clearly demarcated core areas, or territories. Analysis of the Dobe data yields interesting insights. From one perspective, bands and territories do exist. When one examines the size and range of the Dobe group from data collected between 1963 and 1968, two consistencies are apparent. First, the number of individuals in the Dobe group remained almost constant, and this implies the existence of a tight constraint on group size. Second, the yearly movement of the group over the landscape is highly patterned, and on the basis of such empirical observation it is possible to define a "territory" that includes the area around the Dobe waterhole, plus a large hinterland to the north and west that is exploited during the rainy and winter seasons. These two regularities, however, tend to conceal the dynamic nature of the social group. While group *size* remains fairly constant, group *membership* undergoes radical change. Although the core of the group remained the same, between the early and late 1960's there was a membership turnover of approximately 50 percent. Interviews show that many "group members" see and describe themselves as "outsiders" whose territories lie elsewhere, even though their association with Dobe may extend back for many years. The conclusion that I draw from this unexpected observation is that such a system serves a dual purpose. Over the short run, it provides a predictable way to map people onto the landscape in, presumably, a reasonable relationship to the available resources. A relatively high degree of individual and family mobility, on the other hand, may prove highly adaptive over the long run. Given the very unpredictable and variable rainfall pattern, productivity may vary dramatically from area to area, and year to year. People establish ties through marriage and trading relationships in a number of areas; and they make use of these ties, as is evidenced in frequent shifts in residence. This mechanism provides a relatively easy way for population redistribution in response to areal fluctuations in productivity.

During the Neolithic and later periods of human prehistory, it is clear that trade played an important role in shaping societal development, and prehistorians have speculated on its importance during the Paleolithic. While this same mechanism might have been employed, the Dobe data suggest the possibility that extended, long distance networks may have been maintained more through the movement of people themselves than through the exchange of goods.

Intersite Patterning

Archeologists use settlement patterns, reconstructed from site distributions, to determine how particular prehistoric groups utilized their environment. Therefore, I tried to understand why the San placed their rainy and winter season camps where they did, and how they decided when and where to move. The main conclusion emerging from this study is that during those periods of the year when water is not a severely limiting factor, the tie between human and resource distribution is not a very tight one and is certainly much looser than archeologists would like. With a wide variety of relatively abundant resources, the principle of "least effort" did not come strictly into play, and the Dobe group would abandon a campsite while resources were still abundant and easy to come by in the immediate area. What the San themselves say, and what analysis of data tends to confirm, is that a relatively high priority is set on "variety," and that individuals get tired of eating the same foods day after day. Moves were often made because people wanted to obtain a particular resource—a special kind of fruit or honey for example—and they would go to considerable effort to obtain it. The archeological implication of this is that it is difficult to predict in detail how a prehistoric group might have utilized a particular reconstructed environment.

A second question I posed concerned intercamp variability: How "typical" might any camp be and how validly might a single site, or a limited number of sites, serve as a basis for broader generalization? Given the restricted nature of their data, archeologists must, of necessity, make generalizations of this type. But the question is, how likely are these generalizations to be accurate. I considered two related aspects of this question: First, what is the nature and degree of variability from camp to camp? And second, to what extent could this variability be viewed as "random"? Analysis revealed that it was useful to draw a basic distinction between subsistence and manufacturing activities. Subsistence activities were highly patterned and a good fit existed between the foods available in the immediate environment, the foods actually consumed in camp, and the physical remains of these species found in the site after it was abandoned. From this perspective, variations observed between camps made sense and reflected an important cultural pattern. On the other hand, no neat fit existed for manufacturing activities. Most such undertakings—the production of ostrich egg-shell beads, arrows, digging sticks, etc.—were relatively rare events which took place only a limited number of times each year. Since the materials required for the manufacture of most San goods are relatively light and compact, they were carried around for a considerable period of time and worked on at a number of locations. Therefore it is almost impossible to predict what manufacturing activity will be conducted at a particular site. There may be no overlap in such activities from one site to the next and it is not possible to draw meaningful conclusions from an analysis of observed variability. Since the likelihood that any particular manufacturing activity will occur is time dependent, sites occupied for longer periods of time by greater numbers of people tend to exhibit more "representative" ranges of such activities. Likewise differences between short-term occupation sites are often extremely large.

Intracamp Patterning

Direct observation indicates that the !Kung group themselves in nuclear families and that older unmarried children share a hut with members of the same sex. Families tend to set their huts, with hearths in front, in a circular arrangement, leaving an open space in the center of the camp. A wide range of actions—food preparation, eating, tool making, sitting and sleeping—is viewed as family activities and takes place around the family hearth. Activities which take up a lot of space or are extremely messy—skin-drying or pit-roasting for example—are relegated to areas immediately outside the hut circle. During parts of the day when shade is not available within the hut circle, groups of individuals will move to shady areas behind the huts. These rather straightforward observations have, I believe, considerable archeological significance. Perhaps the most important is that activities per se are not strictly segregated and the common archeological assumption about activity areas, namely that people usually distinguish activities task by task and specifically assign areas to each, is not necessarily correct. In the !Kung case, it is usually the social nature of the task, rather than the task itself which determines where it will be carried out. Associations of different kinds of remains in an abandoned campsite usually reflect the fact that all occur in the same social context and not that they are part of a single goal-directed task. While this makes it extremely difficult to reconstruct specific activities on the basis of co-variance of material remains, it does open up another possibility. It suggests that archeological remains permit one to reconstruct social organization directly, even if the particular activities which occurred are unknown.

A second conclusion of potential archeological significance to emerge from this study involves the relationships between the distribution of debris in a camp, the number of people who occupied it, and the length of time they were present. Absolute amount of debris is clearly related both to the number of inhabitants and to the length of occupation. But I wanted to find out whether it would be possible to factor out the relative effect of each independent variable. Analysis has shown that from material remains it is possible to estimate with reasonable accuracy both the number of inhabitants and length of occupation. Because special activities, which in sum are time dependent, take place in the outer part of the circle (outside the huts) the relative size of this area correlates directly with the length of occupation. By contrast, the hut circle area relates directly to the number of occupants, and in Yellen (1977) I develop regression equations which permit the prediction of both independent variables. The major points discussed in this research report are presented in greater detail in this book.

Acknowledgments

I gratefully acknowledge the support of the National Geographic Society. The field portion of this research was supported by the National Institute of

Mental Health and the Wenner Gren Foundation. While I analyzed the data, I was a postdoctoral fellow (without stipend) at the Smithsonian Institution.

REFERENCES

GOULD, R. A.
  1969.   Subsistence behavior among the Western Desert aborigines of Australia. Oceania, vol. 39, no. 4, pp. 253-274.
HILL, J. N.
  1968.   Broken K Pueblo: Patterns of form and function. Pp. 103-142 *in* "New Perspectives in Archaeology," S. R. Binford and L. R. Binford, eds. Aldine Press, Chicago.
LONGACRE, W. A.
  1964.   Archaeology as anthropology. Science, vol. 144 (no. 3625), pp. 1454-1455.
LEE, R. B., and DeVORE, I.
  1976.   Kalahari hunter-gatherers: Studies of the !Kung San and their neighbors, 408 pp. Harvard University, Press, Cambridge, Mass.
WILSON, E. O.
  1978.   On human nature, 260 pp. Harvard University Press, Cambridge, Mass.
YELLEN, J. E.
  1977.   Archaeological approaches to the present, 257 pp. New York Academic Press.

JOHN E. YELLEN

APPENDIX

List of Grants for Research and Exploration Made by the National Geographic Society in 1980

2131: To Dr. Anta Montet-White, University of Kansas, Lawrence, Kansas, for a study of the Paleolithic of the Ukrina Valley, Yugoslavia.

2132: To Dr. Morgan Ray Crook, Jr., West Georgia College, Carrollton, Georgia, for basic research at the Bourbon Field Site.

2133: To Dr. Robert Ornduff, University of California, Berkeley, California, for a plant collecting expedition to the People's Republic of China.

2134: To Dr. Robert Palmquist, Iowa State University, Ames, Iowa, for a study of landslide history in the Gros Ventre Mountains, Wyoming.

2135: To Dr. Kathleen Crane, Lamont-Doherty Geological Observatory, Palisades, New York, to use remote sensing for geothermal activity in the East African Rift.

2136: To Dr. John B. Heppner, Smithsonian Institution, Washington, D. C., for biological and ecological studies of Atychia moths in the Balkans.

2137: To Dr. Hannon B. Graves, Pennsylvania State University, University Park, Pennsylvania, to study mating and parent-offspring behavior of crested tinamou.

2138: To Dr. Mary D. Leakey, Nairobi, Kenya, for a detailed study of Laetoli Hominid tracks, preparation of report, study of fossil termitaries.

2139: To Dr. Donald Messerschmidt, Washington State University, Pullman, Washington, to study the cultural symbolism of the Hindu pilgrimage to Muktinath, Nepal.

2140: To Dr. Jane C. Goodale, Bryn Mawr College, Bryn Mawr, Pennsylvania, for a restudy of the change and continuity in Tiwi culture.

2141: To Dr. Patrick E. McGovern, University of Pennsylvania, Philadelphia, Pennsylvania, to test soundings of magnetometer and resistivity anomalies in the Baqcah Valley project.

2142: To Dr. Peter S. Wells, Harvard University, Cambridge, Massachusetts, for excavation and analysis of Early Iron Age settlement of Hascherkeller.

2143: To Mr. J. N. Postgate, Cambridge, United Kingdom, for a British archeological expedition to Iraq to study excavations at Abu Salabikh.

2144: To Dr. Barbara L. Drinkwater, University of California, Santa Barbara, California, to study women's physiological responses to hypoxia and cold at altitude.

2145: To Dr. Ian D. Hume, University of New England, Armidale, N.S.W., Australia, to study the utilization of eucalyptus foliage by arboreal marsupials.

2146: To Dr. James J. Childress, University of California, Santa Barbara, California, for the capture and live recovery of deep-sea crustaceans for physiological studies.

2147: To Dr. John B. West, University of California, San Diego, California, to study the biological effects of hypoxia of extreme altitudes on man.

2148: To Dr. Patricia D. Moehlman, University of Wisconsin, Madison, Wisconsin, for a survey of feral ass distribution and ecological impact on the Galápagos Islands.

2149: To Dr. Andrew S. Goudie, School of Geography, Oxford, United Kingdom, to study the geomorphology of the Baltit area of the Karakoram Mountains in Pakistan.

2150: To Dr. Russell G. Gastil, San Diego State University, San Diego, California, to study strontium and lead isotopes for correlating metamorphosed carbonate formations.

2151: To Dr. Kubet E. Luchterhand, Roosevelt University, Chicago, Illinois, for a paleontological investigation of the La Venta formation in Colombia.

2152: To Dr. John G. Robinson, Smithsonian Institution, Washington, D. C., to study the influences of neighboring groups on ranging in *Cebus nigrivittatus*.

2153: To Dr. Alison S. Brooks, George Washington University, Washington, D. C., for a survey of Toromoja, a potential Early Man site.

2154: To Dr. Marvin J. Allison, Virginia Commonwealth University, Richmond, Virginia, to study Pre-Columbian disease.

2155: To Mr. Richard E. Leakey, National Museum of Kenya, Nairobi, Kenya, for paleontological research in Plio-Pleistocene sediments of Lake Turkana Basin.

2156: To Dr. Norman Hammond, Rutgers University, New Brunswick, New Jersey, for the archeological excavation of the Cuello site.

2157: To Ms. Paula Wapnish-Hesse, Smithsonian Institution, Washington, D. C., to study taphonomy and paleoeconomy in historic archeology in the archeozoology project at Tell Jemmeh.

2158: To Dr. H. Arthur Bankoff, Brooklyn College, Brooklyn, New York, to study the ecology and culture change in the later prehistory of the Morava Valley, Yugoslavia.

2159: To Mr. Bruce M. Beehler, Smithsonian Institution, Washington, D. C., to study the comparative socioecology of birds of paradise.

2160: To Mr. Ricardo Praderi, Museum of Natural History, Montevideo, Uruguay, for the research and conservation of dolphins incidentally caught in Uruguay.

2161: To Dr. Duncan M. Porter, Virginia Polytechnic Institute, Blacksburg, Virginia, to study the botany of the *Beagle* voyage.

2162: To Dr. John M. Melack, University of California, Santa Barbara, California, to study the ecology of Mono Lake, California.

2163: To Dr. Bernard Q. Nietschmann, University of California, Berkeley, California, to study traditional knowledge of marine environments and biota in the Torres Strait, Australia.

2164: To Dr. Mario C. Barberena, Federal University of Rio Grande do Sul, Brazil, to study the upper Permian and Triassic Tetrapods of southern Brazil.

2165: To Dr. Karel L. Rogers, Adams State College, Alamosa, Colorado, to make paleontological investigations of the Alamosa formation.

2166: To Dr. M. Philip Kahl, Sedona, Arizona, to study the reproductive biology and behavior of African spoonbills.

2167: To Dr. Zuleyma T. Halpin, University of Missouri, St. Louis, Missouri, to study behavioral correlates of dispersal in the black-tailed prairie dog.

2168: To Dr. Melvyn C. Goldstein, Case Western Reserve University, Cleveland, Ohio, for a social, ecological, and demographic study of Buddhist monasticism.

2169: To Dr. Andrew G. Sherratt, Ashmolean Museum, Oxford, United Kingdom, to study prehistoric settlement history of the Great Hungarian Plain.

2170: To Dr. Richard F. Townsend, Somerville, Massachusetts, to decipher the ancient capital of Xochicalco in highland Mexico.

2171: To Dr. William H. Isbell, State University of New York, Bingham, New York, for an archeological exploration of a Tiahuanacoid Temple at Huari, Peru.

2172: To Dr. Eric M. Meyers, Duke University, Durham, North Carolina, for excavations at En-Nabratein and its regional context.

2173: To Dr. William M. Hurley and Dr. Peter Bleed, University of Toronto, Toronto, Canada, to study the social dynamics and subsistence strategies of the Yagi site in Japan.

2174: To Dr. Tom Gehrels, Lunar and Planetary Laboratory, The University of Arizona, Tucson, Arizona, for a study of asteroid topography.

2175: To Dr. Joseph R. Jehl, Jr., Hubbs/Sea World Research Institute, San Diego, California, to study the importance of Mono Lake, California, to migrating Wilson's phalaropes.

2176: To Dr. Ralph P. Collins, University of Connecticut, Storrs, Connecticut, for a study of the beach heather community.

2177: To Dr. Richard L. Hay, University of California, Berkeley, California, to study the geology of the Laetoli area in northern Tanzania.

2178: To Dr. Robert M. West, Milwaukee Public Museum, Milwaukee, Wisconsin, for the study of magnetostratigraphy, eureka sound formation in the Canadian arctic: lithostratigraphic, biostratigraphic, paleoclimatic correlations.

2179: To Dr. Richard H. Tedford, American Museum of Natural History, New York, New York, to study stratigraphy and vertebrate paleontology in Eastern Lake Eyre Basin, South Australia.

2180: To Dr. Edward H. Miller, British Columbia Provincial Museum, Victoria, British Columbia, to study the female-calf bond in the walrus.

2181: To Dr. Lisbeth Francis, Bates College, Lewiston, Maine, to study the ecology and evolution of aggression among sea anemones (actiniidae).

2182: To Dr. Thomas H. Rich, National Museum of Victoria, Victoria, Australia, to search for Gondwana Cretaceous mammals and birds.

2183: To Dr. Lawrence G. Straus, University of New Mexico, Albuquerque, New Mexico, for a preliminary archeological survey in the Chalosse district of southwestern France.

2184: To Dr. Richard M. Gramly, Maine State Museum, Augusta, Maine, for an archeological investigation of the Vail Paleo-Indian site in Oxford County, Maine.

2185: To Dr. J. M. Adovasio, University of Pittsburgh, Pittsburgh, Pennsylvania, to study the archeology and geomorphology of Rocky Dell Rockshelter in Allegheny County, Pennsylvania.

2186: To Dr. Peter I. Kuniholm, Cornell University, Ithaca, New York, for a study of tree-ring chronologies for the Aegean and adjacent areas.

2187: To Dr. George F. Bass, Institute of Nautical Archaeology, College Station, Texas, for a survey of ancient shipwrecks in Greece and Turkey.
2188: To Dr. Kenan T. Erim, New York University, New York, New York, for study, research, and restoration activities at Aphrodisias.
2189: To Dr. E. James Dixon, University of Alaska, Fairbanks, Alaska, for an archeological survey and testing of cave deposits and alluvial sediments along the Porcupine River, Alaska.
2190: To Dr. Dennis J. Stanford, Smithsonian Institution, Washington, D. C., for the Lamb Springs Early Man project.
2191: To Dr. David C. Oren, Harvard University, Cambridge, Massachusetts, to study species area requirements in a patchy habitat in Amazonian Brazil.
2192: To Dr. Robert E. Ricklefs, University of Pennsylvania, Philadelphia, Pennsylvania, for the study of energetics, reproduction, and population biology of Christmas Island seabirds.
2193: To Dr. John M. Bird, Cornell University, Ithaca, New York, to study the native iron of Disko Island, western Greenland.
2194: To Dr. J. Alan Holman, Michigan State University, East Lansing, Michigan, for a comparative study of Pleistocene fissure-fills in Ladds Quarry, Georgia.
2195: To Dr. Harry L. Fierstine, California Polytechnic State University, San Luis Obispo, California, for the collection of a fossil billfish from the Philippines.
2196, 2272: To Dr. Sankar Chatterjee, Texas Tech University, Lubbock, Texas, for the exploration of Triassic vertebrates in west Texas.
2197: To Dr. Joseph R. Thomasson, Black Hills State College, Spearfish, South Dakota, for the study of fossil plants from Antelope and Garden counties, Nebraska.
2198: To Dr. Charles J. Cole, American Museum of Natural History, New York, New York, to study unisexual clones of the shiny lizard in Surinam.
2199: To Dr. Dietland Muller-Schwarze, State University of New York, Syracuse, New York, to study the behavioral ecology of Labrador caribou.
2200: To Dr. Stewart M. Evans, The University of Newcastle Upon Tyne, Newcastle Upon Tyne, England, for an expedition to Dinder Park and Lake Kundi in Sudan.
2201: To Dr. Gary F. McCracken, University of Tennessee, Knoxville, Tennessee, to study mating systems and kinship in neotropical bats in Trinidad.
2202: To Dr. George B. Schaller, New York Zoological Society, Bronx Park, New York, to study the ecology and behavior of jaguar in Brazil.
2203: To Dr. Frank McKinney, University of Minnesota, Minneapolis, Minnesota, to study the social systems of Australian dabbling ducks.
2204: To Mr. Peter Klimley, Scripps Institution of Oceanography, La Jolla, California, and Dr. Donald R. Nelson, California State University, Long Beach, California, to study schooling and associated behaviors in scalloped hammerhead sharks.
2206: To Dr. Katharine Milton, Cornell University, Ithaca, New York, to study mutualistic relationships between the Tukanoan fishing and Maduan hunting tribes of Amazonia.
2207: To Dr. Cesar A. Fonseca, University of San Marcos, Lima, Peru, to study the subsistence economy of Quechua communities of north Peruvian Andes.

2208: To Dr. Robert M. Laughlin, Smithsonian Institution, Washington, D. C., to study the botany of highland Mayan farmers in Mexico.

2209: To Dr. Christy G. Turner II, Arizona State University, Tempe, Arizona, to trace the origin of the first Americans through dental evidence.

2210: To Dr. Robert J. Braidwood, University of Chicago, Chicago, Illinois, for the continued excavation of an early village site in southeastern Turkey.

2211: To Dr. Gerald L. Kooyman, Scripps Institution of Oceanography, La Jolla, California, to study the feeding behavior of Galápagos Island fur seals and sea lions.

2212: To Mr. James L. B. Mallet, University of Texas, Austin, Texas, to study gregarious roosting in Heliconius butterflies.

2213: To Dr. Gerald Fish, Virginia Polytechnic Institute, Blacksburg, Virginia, to study traditional water-harvesting systems of northwest Mexico.

2214: To Dr. Michael D. Sabath, Griffith University, Brisbane, Australia, to study the evolutionary response of the marine toad, Bufo Marinus.

2215: To Dr. Robert B. Payne, University of Michigan, Ann Arbor, Michigan, for studies in song mimicry and brood parasitism in Cameroon finches.

2216: To Dr. James E. Lloyd, University of Florida, Gainesville, Florida, to study sexual selection and mate competition in synchronizing, Thailand *Pteroptyx* fireflies.

2217: To Dr. Dagmar I. Werner, Max-Planck Institut, Seewelsen, West Germany, for a natural history and conservation survey of Galápagos Island iguanas.

2218: To Dr. Krzysztof M. Serkowski, University of Arizona, Tucson, Arizona, to search for other planetary systems in the universe.

2219: To Dr. Judith W. McIntyre, Utica College of Syracuse University, Utica, New York, to study the vocal behavior of common loons.

2220: To Dr. Donald W. Thomas, University of Aberdeen, Aberdeen, United Kingdom, to study the ecology of an African savannah fruit bat community.

2221: To Dr. Eldon E. Ball, Australia National University, Canberra City, Australia, to study island colonization in New Guinea.

2222: To Dr. Jacob G. Sivak, University of Waterloo, Waterloo, Ontario, Canada, to study photorefraction and penguin vision.

2223: To Dr. Alister G. MacDonald, Aberdeen University, Aberdeen, Scotland, to study the pressure-tolerance of deep sea animals.

2224: To Dr. Bernice M. Wenzel, University of California, Los Angeles, California, to study olfactory behavior and neurophysiology in Procellariiform birds.

2225: To Dr. Louise H. Emmons, Smithsonian Institution, Washington, D. C., to study fruit and vertebrate frugivore interaction in equatorial rainforests.

2226: To Dr. William A. Clemens, University of California, Berkeley, California, to study vertebrate paleontology of the Judith River Formation in Montana.

2227: To Dr. Everett H. Lindsay, University of Arizona, Tucson, Arizona, to study European Late Cenozoic biochronology and the magnetic polarity time scale.

2228: To Dr. Larry D. Martin, University of Kansas, Lawrence, Kansas, to study cranial anatomy, brain size, and flight capabilities of the earliest birds.

2229: To Mr. David E. Crockett, Northland, New Zealand, for the Chatham Island Taiko expedition.

2230: To Dr. Joan C. Dobbs, University of the Witwatersrand, Johannnesburg, South Africa, to study human interaction in the survival of the Cape Vulture.

2231: To Mr. Paul M. Taylor, Yale University, New Haven, to examine the ethnobiology of the highland Tugutil in Indonesia.

2232: To Dr. Donald C. Johanson, The Cleveland Museum of Natural History, Cleveland, Ohio, for paleoanthropological investigations in the Hadar Region and the Middle Awash Valley of Ethiopia.

2233: To Mr. P. Pedro I. Porras G., La Pontificia Universidad Catolica del Ecuador, Quito, Ecuador, for archeological investigations at Sangay: A site in the Morona-Santiago Province of Ecuador.

2234: To Dr. Russel W. Graham, Illinois State Museum, Springfield, Illinois, to study Clovis adaptations in the Midwest at Kimmswick.

2235: To Dr. Trude Dothan, The Hebrew University, Jerusalem, Israel, for the Deir el-Balah Regional Project.

2236: To Dr. Stanley A. Temply, University of Wisconsin, Madison, Wisconsin, to examine how polymorphism and feeding ecology are related in the hook-billed kite.

2237: To Dr. Nancy C. Garwood, Loyola University of Chicago, Chicago, Illinois, to study earthquake-caused landslides in Panama and the recovery of vegetation.

2238: To Dr. William L. Graf, Arizona State University, Tempe, Arizona, to transport and store natural mercury in stream sediments of the Southern Colorado Plateau.

2239: To Dr. Stefan L. Hastenrath, University of Wisconsin, Madison, Wisconsin, for a field program on Lewis Glacier, Mt. Kenya.

2240: To Dr. Jens Munthe, Faculty of Natural Sciences and Mathematics, Stockton State College, Pomona, New Jersey, for a study of vertebrate paleontology and stratigraphy of Cenozoic deposits in Nepal.

2241: To Dr. Laurence M. Cook, University of Manchester, Manchester, England, to study the evolution of endemic fauna of Madeira and Deserta Islands.

2242: To Dr. John G. Frazier, Smithsonian Institution, Washington, D. C., to study the population ecology of the Olive Ridley sea turtle.

2243: To Dr. James J. Hebrard, University of Nairobi, Nairobi, Kenya, to study ecological niches and geographic distribution of ten species of chamaeleons in Kenya.

2244: To Dr. Wolfgang M. Schleidt, University of Maryland, College Park, Maryland, for a cross-cultural comparison of facial expression patterns.

2245: To Dr. Paul E. Bugos, Jr., Santa Cruz, Bolivia, to study the cultural ecology of the Ayoreo Indians of southeastern Bolivia.

2246: To Mr. Theodore A. Wertime, Smithsonian Institution, Washington, D. C., for the study of early hydraulic cement in Greece and Cyprus.

2247: To Dr. Naguib Kanawati, Macquarie University, North Hyde, Australia, for excavations at Akhmim, Upper Egypt.

2248: To Dr. Arthur D. Cohen, University of South Carolina, Columbia, South Carolina, to study the paleoecology and palynology of Little Salt Spring Paleo-Indian archeological site in Florida.

2249: To Dr. Jared M. Diamond, University of California, Los Angeles, California, to study the birds of remote mountain ranges of west Irian.

2250: To Dr. Kendall W. Corbin, University of Minnesota, Minneapolis, Minnesota, to study genetic variation in the rufous-collared sparrow.

2251: To Dr. Robert R. Compton, Stanford University, Stanford, California, to study the geology and botany of the Windward coast of Molokai, Hawaii.
2252: To Dr. Ralph E. Eshelman, Calvert Marine Museum, Solomons, Maryland, to study Tobagan recent mammals, fossil vertebrates, and their zoogeographical implications.
2253: To Dr. Rolf O. Peterson, Department of Biological Sciences, Michigan Technological University, Houghton, Michigan, for a study of wolf-moose ecology in an island ecosystem.
2254: To Dr. Francine G. P. Patterson, Stanford University, Stanford, California, to study the linguistic and cognitive abilities of the lowland gorilla.
2255: To Dr. Bruno Frøhlich, Smithsonian Institution, Washington, D. C., to study the skeletal biology of Near Eastern human populations in the Early Bronze Age.
2256: To Dr. George W. Gill, University of Wyoming, Laramie, Wyoming, for the excavation and analysis of prehistoric human skeletons on Easter Island.
2257: To Dr. Barbara Voorhies, University of California, Santa Barbara, California, to study ancient economic history in coastal Chiapas, Mexico.
2258: To Dr. C. Vance Haynes, Department of Anthropology, The University of Arizona, Tucson, Arizona, Pluvial Lake Studies, Western Desert, Egypt and Sudan.
2259: To Dr. Michael E. Brookfield, University of Guelph, Guelph, Ontario, Canada, for radiometric dating of rocks north of the Indus Suture Zone.
2260: To Dr. Joseph R. Curray, Scripps Institution of Oceanography, La Jolla, California, to study the bathymetry and physiography of the northeastern Indian Ocean.
2261: To Dr. James D. McCleave, University of Maine, Orono, Maine, to find the true breeding area of the American eel.
2262: To Dr. Michael L. Lay, Rutgers University, New Brunswick, New Jersey, to study thermoregulation and flight energetics of Euglossine bees.
2263: To Dr. Arthur M. Shapiro, University of California, Davis, California, to study the biogeography of the Argentine *Tatochila sterodice* species-group.
2264: To Dr. Robert S. Kennedy, to study population dynamics and breeding biology of the Philippine eagle.
2265: To Dr. Merlin D. Tuttle, Milwaukee Public Museum, Milwaukee, Wisconsin, to study the use of acoustical mimicry by frogs to evade bat predation.
2266: To Dr. Victor H. Hutchison, University of Oklahoma, Norman, Oklahoma, to study physiological ecology of West African amphibians.
2267: To Dr. Paul K. Anderson, University of Calgary, Calgary, Alberta, Canada, to study the dugongs of Shark Bay, western Australia.
2268: To Dr. Harold E. Edgerton, M.I.T., Cambridge, Massachusetts, for the development of underwater instrumentation for geology, archeology, and biology.
2269: To Dr. Barry C. Bishop, National Geographic Society, Washington, D. C., for the publication of Ph.D. dissertation on Karnali under stress: Livelihood strategies and seasonal rhythms in a changing Nepal.
2270: To Dr. Bobb Schaeffer, American Museum of Natural History, New York, New York, to study Jurassic Actinopterygian fishes from the western United States.

2271: To Dr. Storrs L. Olson, National Museum of Natural History, Washington, D. C., to study paleobiology of the Bahamas, i.e., vertebrates of San Salvador.

2273: To Mr. Steven L. Swartz, University of California, Santa Cruz, California, for demographic studies of gray whales.

2274: To Dr. Gary L. Nuechterlein, University of Michigan, Ann Arbor, Michigan, to study behavior and nesting ecology of the hooded grebe.

2275: To Dr. Bruce J. Turner, Virginia Polytechnic Institute, Blacksburg, Virginia, to study evolutionary genetics of a unisexual fish, *Poecilia formosa*.

2276: To Dr. Berta G. Ribeiro, Rio de Janeiro, Brazil, to study the technology and ergology of Brazilian Indian fabrics.

2277: To Dr. Joseph W. Ball, San Diego State University, San Diego, California, to study classic Maya settlement organization and internal function.

2278: To Mr. Kent H. Redfor, Harvard University, Cambridge, Massachusetts, to study the feeding biology of the giant anteater.

2279: To Dr. Lyle K. Sowls, University of Arizona, Tucson, Arizona, to study the behavior and ecology of the Chacoan peccary *Catagonus wagneri*.

2280: To Dr. Roger S. Payne, Lincoln, Massachusetts, to study migration, behavior, and songs of North Pacific humpback whales.

2281: To Dr. Robert H. Smith, College of Wooster, Wooster, Ohio, for the third season of archeological investigations at Pella, Jordan.

2282: To Dr. Richard A. Matzner, University of Texas, Austin, Texas, to study the structure of the early universe.

2283: To Dr. Wallace L. W. Sargent, California Institute of Technology, Pasadena, California, for new sky surveys with the Palomar 48-inch Schmidt telescope.

2285: To Mr. Kurt M. Fristrup, Harvard University, Cambridge, Massachusetts, to study the lek mating system of the cock-of-the-rock.

2286: To Mr. Laurence G. Frank, University of California, Berkeley, California, to study social behavior of the spotted hyena.

2287: To Ms. Margaret B. Shepard, Cornell University, Ithaca, New York, to study feeding ecology and social behavior of the Stewart Island kakapo.

Index

727

of the splashing characid in Guyana, field observations of, 381
Eutsler, Robert L., 211, 224

Faas, Richard W., 225, 233
Fishes. *See* Ichthyology.
Ford, Derek C., 235, 242
Fossey, Dian, 243, 258
Fossils:
African, dating of, 23
Cenozoic biota in the eastern Arctic, 143
Cretaceous vertebrates in north-central Texas, recovery and study of, 617
dinosaur locality of Gadoufaoua, in Niger, study of, 649
extinct mammalian Order Desmostylia, study of, 549
microvertebrate faunas in South Dakota, 289
salamanders and frogs, 191
search for in New Zealand and Australia, 557
small mammals of Austria, biologic and geologic relationships of, 695
terrestrial avian, from Mesozoic strata, Baja California, 487
vertebrates from deposits at Lake Bonneville, Utah, 473
Freeman, Hugh Avery, 259, 260
Frost, Honor E., 261, 267
Fulani of subsahara Africa, the, 425

Galápagos Islands, genetic analysis of evolutionary patterns in finches, 65
Garífuna, search for the, 129
Geography, cultural:
colonial impact on the Kamba system of survival: a regional perspective on an economic system in change in Kenya, 601

of the Garífuna, beachfolk of the Bay of Honduras, 129
Geography, physical, exploration of ice caves in the Canadian Cordillera, 235
Geological oceanography, bioturbation of carbonate reef sands, 479
Geology:
Central Arizona Ecotone Project, 293, 296
exploration of ice caves in the Canadian Cordillera, 235
investigation of ridge off Cape Hatteras, 157
Lubbock Lake site, Texas, investigations, 57
marine, 157
marine, interrelationships between internal sediments and submarine lithification, 211
mineralogy and distribution of clay sediments, Turnagain Arm, Alaska, 505
of Marble Canyon Quadrangle, Death Valley, California, 369
Geology. *See also* Sedimentology.
Georgia, King site, Floyd County, archeological investigations at, 303
Gillis, William T., 269
Goldblatt, Peter, 273, 276
Golubic, Stjepko, 277, 286
Gould, Frank W., 287
Greece, Halieis in the Argolid, excavation of the submerged sanctuary of Apollo at, 363
Green, Morton, 289, 292
Gumerman, George J., 293, 302
Guyana, behavior studies of the splashing characid in, 381

Hally, David J., 303, 309
Hardy, John William, 311, 314
Haring, Kirsten Johnson, 315
Hart, Benjamin L., 425, 430